SET THEORY

STUDIES IN LOGIC

AND

THE FOUNDATIONS OF MATHEMATICS

NORTH-HOLLAND PUBLISHING COMPANY
AMSTERDAM

SET THEORY

K. KURATOWSKI

and

A. MOSTOWSKI

Members of the Polish Academy of Sciences

1968

PWN — POLISH SCIENTIFIC PUBLISHERS — WARSZAWA

NORTH - HOLLAND PUBLISHING COMPANY — AMSTERDAM

This book is a translation of the original Polish "*Teoria mnogości*" published by PWN—Polish Scientific Publishers, 1966 in the series "Monografie Matematyczne" edited by the Polish Academy of Sciences.

Translated from the Polish by
M. Mączyński

The English edition of this book has been published jointly by PWN and
NORTH - HOLLAND PUBLISHING COMPANY

Library of Congress Catalogue Card Number 67-21972.

PRINTED IN POLAND

PREFACE

The creation of set theory can be traced back to the work of XIX century mathematicians who tried to find a firm foundation for calculus. While the early contributors to the subject (Bolzano, Du Bois Reymond, Dedekind) were concerned with sets of numbers or of functions, the proper founder of set theory, Georg Cantor, made a decisive step and started an investigation of sets with arbitrary elements. The series of articles published by him in the years 1871–1883 contains an almost modern exposition of the theory of cardinals and of ordered and well-ordered sets. That the step toward generalizations which Cantor made was a difficult one was witnessed by various contradictions (antinomies of set theory) discovered in set theory by various authors around 1900. The crisis created by these antinomies was overcome by Zermelo who formulated in 1904–1908 the first system of axioms of set theory. His axioms were sufficient to obtain all mathematically important results of set theory and at the same time did not allow the reconstruction of any known antinomy. Close ties between set theory and philosophy of mathematics date back to discussions concerning the nature of antinomies and the axiomatization of set theory. The fundamental problems of philosophy of mathematics such as the meaning of existence in mathematics, axiomatics versus description of reality, the need of consistency proofs and means admissible in such proofs were never better illustrated than in these discussions.

After an initial period of distrust the newly created set theory made a triumphal inroad in all fields of mathematics. Its influence on mathematics of the present century is clearly visible in the choice of modern problems and in the way these problems are solved. Applications of set theory are thus immense. But set theory developed also problems of its own. These problems and their solutions represent what is known as abstract set theory. Its achievements are rather modest in comparison to the applications of set theoretical methods in other branches of mathematics, some of which owe their very existence to set theory. Still, abstract set theory is a well-established part of mathematics and the knowledge of its basic notions is required from every mathematician.

Last years saw a stormy advance in foundations of set theory. After breaking through discoveries of Gödel in 1940 who showed relative consistency of various set-theoretical hypotheses the recent works of Cohen allowed him and his successors to solve most problems of independence of these hypotheses while at the same time the works of Tarsk showed how deeply can we delve in the domain of inaccessible cardinals whose magnitude surpasses all imagination. These recent works will certainly influence the future thinking on the philosophical foundations of mathematics.

The present book arose from a mimeographed text of Kuratowski from 1921 and from an enlarged edition prepared jointly by the two authors in 1951. As a glance on the list of contents will show, we intended to present the basic results of abstract set theory in the traditional order which goes back still to Cantor: algebra of sets, theory of cardinals, ordering and well-ordering of sets. We lay more stress on applications than it is usually done in texts of abstract set theory. The main field in which we illustrate set-theoretical methods is general topology. We also included a chapter on Borel, analytical and projective sets. The exposition is based on axioms which are essentially the ones of Zermelo–Fraenkel. We tried to present the proofs of all theorems even of the very trivial ones in such a way that the reader feels convinced that they are entirely based on the axioms. This accounts for some pedantry in notation and in the actual writing of several formulae which could be dispensed with if we did not wish to put the finger on axioms which we use in proofs. In some examples we use notions which are commonly known but which were not defined in our book by means of the primitive terms of our system. These examples are marked by the sign #.

In order to illustrate the role of the axiom of choice we marked by a small circle ° all theorems in which this axiom is used. There is in the book a brief account of the continuum hypothesis and a chapter on inaccessible cardinals. These topics deserve a more thorough presentation which however we could not include because of lack of space

Also the last chapter which deals with the descriptive set theory is meant to be just an introduction to the subject.

Several colleagues helped us with the preparation of the text. Dr M. Mączyński translated the main part of the book and Mr R. Kowalsky collaborated with him in this difficult task. Professor J. Łoś wrote a penetrating appraisal of the manuscript of the 1951 edition as well as of the present one. His remarks and criticism allowed us to eliminate many errors and inaccuracies. Mr W. Marek and Mr K. Wiśniewski read the manuscript and the galley proofs and helped us in improving our text. To all these persons we express our deep gratitude.

KAZIMIERZ KURATOWSKI
ANDRZEJ MOSTOWSKI

CONTENTS

CHAPTER I

ALGEBRA OF SETS

§ 1. Propositional calculus

Mathematical reasoning in set theory can be presented in a very clear form by making use of logical symbols and by basing argumentation on the laws of logic formulated in terms of such symbols. In this section we shall present some basic principles of logic in order to refer to them later in this chapter and in the remainder of the book.

We shall designate arbitrary sentences by the letters $p, q, r, \ldots$ We assume that all of the sentences to be considered are either true or false. Since we consider only sentences of mathematics, we shall be dealing with sentences for which the above assumption is applicable.

From two arbitrary sentences, p and q, we can form a new sentence by applying to p and to q any one of the connectives:

and, or, if ... then ..., if and only if.

The sentence p *and* q we write in symbols $p \wedge q$. The sentence $p \wedge q$ is called the *conjunction* or the logical *product* of the sentences p and q, which are the *components* of the conjunction. The conjunction $p \wedge q$ is true when both components are true. On the other hand, if any one of the components is false then the conjunction is false.

The sentence p *or* q, which we write symbolically $p \vee q$, is called the *disjunction* or the logical *sum* of the sentences p and q (the components of the disjunction). The disjunction is true if either of the components is true and is false only when both components are false.

The sentence *if* p *then* q is called the *implication* of q by p, where p is called the *antecedent* and q the *consequent* of the implication. Instead of writing *if p then q* we write $p \to q$. An implication is false if the consequent is false and the antecedent true. In all other cases the implication is true.

If the implication $p \to q$ is true we say that q *follows* from p; in case we know that the sentence p is true we may conclude that the sentence q is also true.

In ordinary language the sense of the expression "if ..., then ..." does not entirely coincide with the meaning given above. However, in mathematics the use of such a definition as we have given is useful.

The sentence *p if and only if q* is called the *equivalence* of the two component sentences p and q and is written $p \equiv q$. This sentence is true provided p and q have the same logical value; that is, either both are true or both are false. If p is true and q false, or if p is false and q true, then the equivalence $p \equiv q$ is false.

The equivalence $p \equiv q$ can also be defined by the conjunction

$$(p \to q) \wedge (q \to p).$$

The sentence *it is not true that p* we call the *negation* of p and we write $\neg p$. The negation $\neg p$ is true when p is false and false when p is true. Hence $\neg p$ has the logical value opposite to that of p.

We shall denote an arbitrary true sentence by V and an arbitrary false sentence by F; for instance, we may choose for V the sentence $2 \cdot 2 = 4$, and for F the sentence $2 \cdot 2 = 5$.

Using the symbols F and V, we can write the definitions of truth and falsity for conjunction, disjunction, implication, equivalence and negation in the form of the following true equivalences:

(1) $F \wedge F \equiv F, \quad F \wedge V \equiv F, \quad V \wedge F \equiv F, \quad V \wedge V \equiv V,$

(2) $F \vee F \equiv F, \quad F \vee V \equiv V, \quad V \vee F \equiv V, \quad V \vee V \equiv V,$

(3) $(F \to F) \equiv V, \quad (F \to V) \equiv V, \quad (V \to F) \equiv F, \quad (V \to V) \equiv V,$

(4) $(F \equiv F) \equiv V, \quad (F \equiv V) \equiv F, \quad (V \equiv F) \equiv F, \quad (V \equiv V) \equiv V,$

(5) $\neg F \equiv V, \quad \neg V \equiv F.$

Logical *laws* or *tautologies* are those expressions built up from the letters $p, q, r, \ldots$ and the connectives $\wedge, \vee, \to, \equiv, \neg$ which have the property that no matter how we replace the letters $p, q, r, \ldots$ by arbitrary sentences (true or false) the entire expression itself is always true.

The truth or falsity of a sentence built up by means of connectives from the sentences $p, q, r, \ldots$ does not depend upon the meaning of the sentences $p, q, r, \ldots$ but only upon their logical values. Thus we can test whether an expression is a logical law by applying the following method: in place of the letters $p, q, r, \ldots$ we substitute the values F and V in every possible manner. Then using equations (1)–(5) we calculate the logical value of the expression for each one of these substitutions. If this value is always true, then the expression is a tautology.

Example. The expression $(p \wedge q) \rightarrow (p \vee r)$ is a tautology. It contains three variables p, q and r. Thus we must make a total of eight substitutions, since for each variable we may substitute either F or V. If, for example, for each letter we substitute F, then we obtain $(F \wedge F) \rightarrow (F \vee F)$, and by (1) and (2) we obtain $F \rightarrow F$, namely V. Similarly, the value of the expression $(p \wedge q) \rightarrow (p \vee q)$ is true in each of the remaining seven cases.

Below we give several of the most important logical laws together with names for them. Checking that they are indeed logical laws is an exercise which may be left to the reader.

$(p \vee q) \equiv (q \vee p)$	*law of commutativity of disjunction,*
$[(p \vee q) \vee r] \equiv [p \vee (q \vee r)]$	*law of associativity of disjunction,*
$(p \wedge q) \equiv (q \wedge p)$	*law of commutativity of conjunction,*
$[p \wedge (q \wedge r)] \equiv [(p \wedge q) \wedge r]$	*law of associativity of conjunction,*
$[p \wedge (q \vee r)] \equiv [(p \wedge q) \vee (p \wedge r)]$	*first distributive law,*
$[p \vee (q \wedge r)] \equiv [(p \vee q) \wedge (p \vee r)]$	*second distributive law,*
$(p \vee p) \equiv p, \quad (p \wedge p) \equiv p$	*laws of tautology,*
$(p \wedge F) \equiv F, \quad (p \wedge V) \equiv p$ $(p \vee F) \equiv p, \quad (p \vee V) \equiv V$	*laws of absorption.*

In these laws the far reaching analogy between propositional calculus and ordinary arithmetic is made apparent. The major differences occur in the second distributive law and in the laws of tautology and absorption. In particular, the laws of tautology show that in the propositional calculus with logical addition and multiplication we need use neither coefficients nor exponents.

$[(p \to q) \wedge (q \to r)] \to (p \to r)$ *law of the hypothetical syllogism,*

$(p \vee \neg p) \equiv V$ *law of excluded middle,*

$(p \wedge \neg p) \equiv F$ *law of contradiction,*

$p \equiv \neg\neg p$ *law of double negation,*

$\neg(p \vee q) \equiv (\neg p \wedge \neg q)$

$\neg(p \wedge q) \equiv (\neg p \vee \neg q)$ *de Morgan's laws,*

$(p \to q) \equiv (\neg q \to \neg p)$ *law of contraposition,*

$(p \to q) \equiv (\neg p \vee q),$

$F \to p, \quad p \to p, \quad p \to V.$

Throughout this book whenever we shall write an expression using logical symbols, we shall tacitly state that the expression is true. Remarks either preceding or following such an expression will always refer to a proof of its validity.

§ 2. Sets and operations on sets

The basic notion of set theory is the concept of *set*. This basic concept is, in turn, a product of historical evolution. Originally the theory of sets made use of an intuitive concept of set, characteristic of the so-called "naive" set theory. At that time the word "set" had the same imprecisely defined meaning as in everyday language. Such, in particular, was the concept of set held by Cantor [1]), the creator of set theory.

Such a view was untenable, as in certain cases the intuitive concept proved to be unreliable. In Chapter II, §2 we shall deal with the antinomies of set theory, i.e. with the apparent contradictions which appeared at a certain stage in the development of the theory and

[1]) Georg Cantor (1845–1918) was a German mathematician, professor at the University of Halle. He published his studies in set theory in the journal Mathematische Annalen during the years 1879–1897.

were due to the vagueness of intuition associated with the concept of set in certain more complicated cases. In the course of the polemic which arose over the antinomies it became apparent that different mathematicians had different concept of sets. As a result it became impossible to base set theory on intuition.

In the present book we shall present set theory as an axiomatic system. In geometry we do not examine directly the meaning of the terms "point", "line", "plane" or other "primitive terms", but from a well-defined system of axioms we deduce all the theorems of geometry without resorting to the intuitive meaning of the primitive terms. Similarly, we shall base set theory on a system of axioms from which we shall obtain theorems by deduction. Although the axioms have their source in the intuitive concept of sets, the use of the axiomatic method ensures that the intuitive content of the word "set" plays no part in proofs of theorems or in definitions of set theoretical concepts.

Sometimes we shall illustrate set theory with examples furnished by other branches of mathematics. This illustrative material involving axioms not belonging to the axiom system of set theory will be distinguished by the sign # placed at the beginning and at the end of the text.

The primitive notions of set theory are "set" and the relation "to be an element of". Instead of *x is a set* we shall write $Z(x)$, and instead of *x is an element of y* we shall write $x \in y$[1]). The negation of the formula $x \in y$ will be written as x non $\in y$, or $x \notin y$ or $\neg(x \in y)$. To simplify the notation we shall use capital letters to denote sets; thus if a formula involves a capital letter, say A, then it is tacitly assumed that A is a set. Later on we shall introduce still one primitive notion: $x \,\mathrm{TR}\, y$ (*x is the relational type of y*). We shall discuss it in Chapter II.

For the present we assume four axioms:

1. AXIOM OF EXTENSIONALITY: *If the sets A and B have the same elements then they are identical.*

[1]) The sign $\in$, introduced by G. Peano, is an abbreviation of the Greek word ἐστὶ (to be).

A [1]). AXIOM OF UNION: *For any sets A and B there exists a set which contains all the elements of A and all the elements of B and which does not contain any other elements.*

B [1]). AXIOM OF DIFFERENCE: *For any sets A and B there exists a set which contains only those elements of A which are not elements of B.*

C [1]). AXIOM OF EXISTENCE: *There exists at least one set.*

The axiom of extensionality can be rewritten in the following form:

$$\textit{if, for every } x, \quad x \in A \equiv x \in B, \quad \textit{then } A = B,$$

where the equality sign between the two symbols indicates that they denote the same object.

It follows from axioms I and A that for any sets A and B there exists exactly one set satisfying the conditions of axiom A. In fact, if there were two such sets C_1 and C_2, then they would contain the same elements (namely those which belong either to A or to B) and, by axiom I, $C_1 = C_2$.

The unique set satisfying the conditions of axiom A is called the *sum* or the *union* of two sets A and B and is denoted by $A \cup B$. Thus for any x and for any sets A and B we have the equivalence

$$x \in A \cup B \equiv (x \in A) \vee (x \in B). \tag{1}$$

Similarly, from axioms I and B, it follows that for any sets A and B there exists exactly one set whose elements are all the objects belonging to A and not belonging to B. Such a set is called the *difference* of the sets A and B and denoted by $A - B$. For any x and for arbitrary sets A and B we have

$$x \in A - B \equiv (x \in A) \wedge (x \notin B). \tag{2}$$

By means of de Morgan's law and the law of double negation (§ 1, p. 4) it follows that

$$\neg(x \in A - B) \equiv \neg(x \in A) \vee (x \in B), \tag{3}$$

i.e. x is not an element of $A - B$ if x is not an element of A or x is an element of B.

[1]) In Chapter II these axioms will be replaced by more general ones.

Using the operations $\cup$ and $-$ we can define two other operations on sets.

The *intersection* $A \cap B$ of A and B we define by

$$A \cap B = A-(A-B).$$

From the definition of difference we have for any x

$$x \in A \cap B \equiv (x \in A) \wedge \neg(x \in A-B),$$

from which, by means of (3) and the first distributive law (see p. 3), it follows that

$$\begin{aligned} x \in A \cap B &\equiv (x \in A) \wedge [\neg(x \in A) \vee (x \in B)] \\ &\equiv [(x \in A) \wedge \neg(x \in A)] \vee [(x \in A) \wedge (x \in B)] \\ &\equiv F \vee [(x \in A) \wedge (x \in B)] \equiv [(x \in A) \wedge (x \in B)], \end{aligned}$$

and finally

(4) $$x \in A \cap B \equiv (x \in A) \wedge (x \in B).$$

Hence the intersection of two sets is the common part of the factors; the elements of the intersection are those objects which belong to both factors.

The *symmetric difference* of two sets A and B is defined as

(5) $$A \dot{-} B = (A-B) \cup (B-A).$$

The elements of the set $A \dot{-} B$ are those objects which belong to A and not to B together with those objects which belong to B and not to A.

Exercises

1. Define the operations $\cup, \cap, -$ by means of: (a) $\dot{-}, \cap$, (b) $\dot{-}, \cup$, (c) $-, \dot{-}$.

2. Show that it is not possible to define either the sum by means of the intersection and the difference, or the difference by means of the sum and the intersection.

§ 3. Inclusion. Empty set

A set A is said to be a *subset* of a set B provided every element of the set A is also an element of the set B. In this case we write $A \subset B$ or $B \supset A$ and we say that A is *included* in B. The relation $\subset$ is called the *inclusion relation.*

The following equivalence results from this definition

(1) $$\{\textit{for every } x \ (x \in A \rightarrow x \in B)\} \equiv A \subset B.$$

Clearly from $A = B$ it follows that $A \subset B$, but not conversely. If $A \subset B$ and $A \neq B$ we say that A is a *proper* subset of B. If A is a subset of B and B is a subset of A then $A = B$, i.e.

$$(A \subset B) \wedge (B \subset A) \rightarrow (A = B).$$

To prove this we notice that from the left-hand side of the implication we have for every x

$$x \in A \rightarrow x \in B \quad \text{and} \quad x \in B \rightarrow x \in A,$$

from which we obtain the equivalence $x \in A \equiv x \in B$, and thus $A = B$ by axiom I.

It is easy to show that, if A is a subset of B and B is a subset of C, then A is a subset of C:

(2) $$(A \subset B) \wedge (B \subset C) \rightarrow (A \subset C),$$

i.e. the inclusion relation is *transitive*.

The union of two sets contains both components; the intersection of two sets is contained in each component:

(3) $$A \subset A \cup B, \qquad B \subset A \cup B,$$

(4) $$A \cap B \subset A, \qquad A \cap B \subset B.$$

In fact, from $p \rightarrow (p \vee q)$ it follows that for every x

$$x \in A \rightarrow [(x \in A) \vee (x \in B)],$$

from which, by (1), § 2, p. 6,

$$x \in A \rightarrow x \in (A \cup B),$$

and by (1) we obtain $A \subset A \cup B$. The proof of the second formula of (3) is similar, the proof of (4) follows from the law $(p \wedge q) \rightarrow p$.

From (2), § 2 it follows that

$$A - B \subset A.$$

Thus the difference of two sets is contained in the minuend.

The inclusion relation can be defined by means of the identity relation and one of the operations $\cup$ or $\cap$. Namely, the following equivalences hold

(5) $$(A \subset B) \equiv (A \cup B = B) \equiv (A \cap B = A).$$

In fact, if $A \subset B$ then for every x, $x \in A \to x \in B$; thus by means of the law $(p \to q) \to [(p \vee q) \to q]$,

$$[(x \in A) \vee (x \in B)] \to (x \in B),$$

which proves that $A \cup B \subset B$. On the other hand, $B \subset A \cup B$ and hence $A \cup B = B$.

Conversely, if $A \cup B = B$, then by (3) $A \subset B$.

The second part of equivalence (5) can be proved in a similar manner.

It follows from axiom B that if there exists at least one set A then there also exists the set $A - A$, which contains no element. There exists only one such set. In fact, if there were two such set Z_1 and Z_2, then (for every x) we would have the equivalence

$$x \in Z_1 \equiv x \in Z_2.$$

This equivalence holds since both components are false. Thus, from axiom I, $Z_1 = Z_2$.

This unique set, which contains no element, is called the *empty set* and is denoted by 0. Thus for every x

$$x \notin 0,$$

i.e.

$$(x \in 0) \equiv F.$$

The implication $x \in 0 \to x \in A$ holds for every x since the antecedent of the implication is false. Thus

$$0 \subset A,$$

i.e. the empty set is a subset of every set.

Formula (1), § 2, p. 6 implies that

$$x \in (A \cup 0) \equiv (x \in A) \vee (x \in 0) \equiv (x \in A) \vee F \equiv x \in A,$$

because $p \vee F \equiv p$. From this we infer

$$A \cup 0 = A,$$

and from $\neg F \equiv V$

$$A - 0 = A.$$

The identity $A \cap B = 0$ indicates that the sets A and B have no common element, or—in other words—they are *disjoint*.

The equation $B - A = 0$ indicates that $B \subset A$.

The role played by the empty set in set theory is analogous to that played by the number zero in algebra. Without the set 0 the operations of intersection and subtraction would not always be performable and the calculus of sets would be considerably complicated.

§ 4. Laws of union, intersection, and subtraction

The operations of union, intersection, and subtraction on sets have many properties in common with operations on numbers: namely, union with addition, intersection with multiplication, and subtraction with subtraction. In this section we shall mention the most important of these properties. We shall also prove several theorems indicating the difference between the algebra of sets and arithmetic [1]).

The commutative laws:

(1) $$A \cup B = B \cup A, \qquad A \cap B = B \cap A.$$

These laws follow directly from the commutative laws for disjunction and conjunction.

The associative laws:

(2) $$A \cup (B \cup C) = (A \cup B) \cup C, \qquad A \cap (B \cap C) = (A \cap B) \cap C.$$

Again, these laws are direct consequences of the associative laws for disjunction and conjunction.

Formulas (1) allow us to permute the components of any union or intersection of a finite number of sets without changing the results. Similarly, formulas (2) allow us to group the components of such a finite union or intersection in an arbitrary manner. For example:

$$A \cup \{B \cup [C \cup (D \cup E)]\} = [A \cup (D \cup C)] \cup (B \cup E) = (E \cup C) \cup [B \cup (A \cup D)].$$

In other words, we may eliminate parentheses when performing the operation of union (or intersection) on a finite number of sets.

The distributive laws:

(3) $$\begin{aligned} A \cap (B \cup C) &= (A \cap B) \cup (A \cap C), \\ A \cup (B \cap C) &= (A \cup B) \cap (A \cup C). \end{aligned}$$

[1]) The theorems given in § 4 are due to the English mathematician G. Boole (1813–1864), whose works initiated investigations in mathematical logic.

The proofs follow from the distributive laws for conjunction over disjunction and disjunction over conjunction, given in § 1.

The first distributive law is completely analogous to the corresponding distributive law in arithmetic. Similarly, as in arithmetic, from this law it follows that in order to intersect two unions we may intersect each component of the first union with each component of the second union and take the union of those intersections:

$$(A \cup B \cup \ldots \cup H) \cap (X \cup Y \cup \ldots \cup T)$$
$$= (A \cap X) \cup (A \cap Y) \cup \ldots \cup (A \cap T) \cup (B \cap X) \cup (B \cap Y) \cup$$
$$\ldots \cup (B \cap T) \cup \ldots \cup (H \cap X) \cup (H \cap Y) \cup \ldots \cup (H \cap T).$$

The second distributive law has no counterpart in arithmetic.

The laws of tautology:

(4) $$A \cup A = A, \quad A \cap A = A.$$

The proof is immediate from the laws of tautology $(p \vee p) \equiv p$ and $(p \wedge p) \equiv p$.

We shall prove several laws of subtraction.

(5) $$A \cup (B - A) = A \cup B.$$

PROOF. By means of (1) and (2), § 2, p. 6 we have

$$x \in [A \cup (B - A)] \equiv (x \in A) \vee [(x \in B) \wedge \neg(x \in A)],$$

from which, by the distributive law for disjunction over conjunction

$$x \in [A \cup (B - A)] \equiv [(x \in A) \vee (x \in B)] \wedge [(x \in A) \vee \neg(x \in A)]$$
$$\equiv (x \in A) \vee (x \in B),$$

since $(x \in A) \vee \neg(x \in A) \equiv V$, and V may be omitted as a component of a conjunction. Thus

$$x \in [A \cup (B - A)] \equiv x \in (A \cup B),$$

which proves (5).

From (5) we conclude that the operation of forming difference of sets is not the inverse of the operation of forming their union. For example, if A is the set of even numbers and B the set of numbers divisible by 3 then the set $A \cup (B - A)$ is different from B, for it contains all even numbers.

On the other hand, in case $A \subset B$, we have by (5) and (5), § 3, p. 8,

$$A \cup (B-A) = B,$$

as in arithmetic.

(6) $$A-B = A-(A \cap B).$$

PROOF.

$$\begin{aligned} x \in A-(A \cap B) &\equiv (x \in A) \wedge \neg(x \in A \cap B) \equiv (x \in A) \wedge \neg[(x \in A) \wedge (x \in B)] \\ &\equiv (x \in A) \wedge [\neg(x \in A) \vee \neg(x \in B)] \\ &\equiv [(x \in A) \wedge \neg(x \in A)] \vee [(x \in A) \wedge \neg(x \in B)] \\ &\equiv F \vee [(x \in A) \wedge \neg(x \in B)] \equiv [(x \in A) \wedge \neg(x \in B)] \\ &\equiv x \in A-B. \end{aligned}$$

The distributive law for union over subtraction has in the algebra of sets the following form

(7) $$A \cap (B-C) = (A \cap B)-C.$$

This law follows from the equivalence

$$\begin{aligned} x \in A \cap (B-C) &\equiv [(x \in A) \wedge (x \in B) \wedge \neg(x \in C)] \\ &\equiv [(x \in A \cap B) \wedge \neg(x \in C)] \\ &\equiv x \in (A \cap B)-C. \end{aligned}$$

From (7) it follows that

$$A \cap (B-A) = (A \cap B)-A = (B \cap A)-A = B \cap (A-A) = B \cap 0 = 0.$$

Thus

$$A \cap (B-A) = 0.$$

De Morgan's laws for the calculus of sets take the following form

(8) $$\begin{aligned} A-(B \cap C) &= (A-B) \cup (A-C), \\ A-(B \cup C) &= (A-B) \cap (A-C). \end{aligned}$$

In the proofs we make use of de Morgan's laws for the propositional calculus.

The following identities are given without proof.

(9) $$(A \cup B)-C = (A-C) \cup (B-C),$$

(10) $$A-(B-C) = (A-B) \cup (A \cap C),$$

(11) $$A-(B \cup C) = (A-B)-C.$$

The following formulas illustrate the analogy between the inclusion relation and the "less than" relation in arithmetic:

(12) $$(A \subset B) \wedge (C \subset D) \rightarrow (A \cup C \subset B \cup D),$$

(13) $$(A \subset B) \wedge (C \subset D) \rightarrow (A \cap C \subset B \cap D),$$

(14) $$(A \subset B) \wedge (C \subset D) \rightarrow (A - D \subset B - C).$$

From (14) it follows as an easy consequence that

(15) $$(C \subset D) \rightarrow (A - D \subset A - C),$$

which is the counterpart of the arithmetic theorem:

$$x \leqslant y \rightarrow z - y \leqslant z - x.$$

Exercises

1. Prove the formula:

$$N(A \cup B) = N(A) + N(B) - N(A \cap B),$$

where $N(X)$ denotes the number of elements of the set X (under the assumption that X is finite).

Hint: Express $N(A-B)$ in terms of $N(A)$ and $N(A \cap B)$.

2. Generalize the result of Exercise 1 in the following way

$$N(A_1 \cup A_2 \cup \dots \cup A_n) = \sum_i N(A_i) - \sum_{i,j} N(A_i \cap A_j) + \sum_{i,j,k} N(A_i \cap A_j \cap A_k) - \dots,$$

where the indices of the summations take as values the numbers from 1 to n, and they are different from each other.

3. Applying the result of Exercise 2 show that the number of integers less than n and prime to n is given by the formula

$$n\left(1 - \frac{1}{p_1}\right)\left(1 - \frac{1}{p_2}\right) \dots \left(1 - \frac{1}{p_r}\right),$$

where $p_1, p_2, \dots, p_r$ denote all different prime factors of n.

§ 5. Properties of symmetric difference [1])

The symmetric difference $A \dot{-} B$ was defined in § 2, p. 7 by the formula:

(0) $$A \dot{-} B = (A - B) \cup (B - A).$$

[1]) The properties of symmetric difference were extensively investigated by M. H. Stone. See his *The theory of representations for Boolean Algebras*, Transactions of the American Mathematical Society **40** (1936) 37–111. See also F. Hausdorff, *Mengenlehre*, 3rd edition, Chapter X.

The operation $\dot{-}$ is commutative and associative:

(1) $$A \dot{-} B = B \dot{-} A,$$

(2) $$A \dot{-} (B \dot{-} C) = (A \dot{-} B) \dot{-} C.$$

Formula (1) follows directly from (0).

To prove (2) we transform the left-hand and right-hand sides of (2) by means of (0):

$$A \dot{-} (B \dot{-} C) = A \dot{-} [(B - C) \cup (C - B)]$$
$$= \{A - [(B - C) \cup (C - B)]\} \cup \{[(B - C) \cup (C - B)] - A\}.$$

Using (8), (9), (10), and (11), §4, p. 12, we obtain

$$\begin{aligned} A \dot{-} (B \dot{-} C) & \\ &= \{[A - (B - C)] \cap [A - (C - B)]\} \cup [(B - C) - A] \cup [(C - B) - A] \\ &= \{[(A - B) \cup (A \cap C)] \cap [(A - C) \cup (A \cap B)]\} \cup [B - (C \cup A)] \\ &\quad \cup [C - (B \cup A)] = [(A - B) \cap (A - C)] \cup [(A - B) \cap B] \\ &\quad \cup [(A - C) \cap C] \cup (A \cap B \cap C) \cup [(B - (C \cup A)] \cup [C - (B \cup A)] \\ &= [A - (B \cup C)] \cup [B - (C \cup A)] \cup [C - (A \cup B)] \cup (A \cap B \cap C). \end{aligned}$$

Thus the set $A \dot{-} (B \dot{-} C)$ contains the elements common to all the sets A, B, and C as well as the elements belonging to exactly one of them.

To transform the right-hand side of (2) it is not necessary to repeat the computation. It suffices to notice that by means of (1)

$$(A \dot{-} B) \dot{-} C = C \dot{-} (A \dot{-} B),$$

from which (substituting in the formula for $A \dot{-} (B \dot{-} C)$ the letters C, A, B for A, B, C respectively) we obtain

$$\begin{aligned} (A \dot{-} B) \dot{-} C & \\ &= [C - (A \cup B)] \cup [A - (B \cup C)] \cup [B - (C \cup A)] \cup (C \cap A \cap B) \\ &= [A - (B \cup C)] \cup [B - (C \cup A)] \cup [C - (A \cup B)] \cup (A \cap B \cap C). \end{aligned}$$

Thus the associativity of the operation has been proved. It follows from (1) and (2) that we may eliminate parentheses when performing the operation $\dot{-}$ on a finite number of sets.

The operation of intersection is distributive over $\dot{-}$, that is

$$A \cap (B \dot{-} C) = (A \cap B) \dot{-} (A \cap C). \tag{3}$$

In fact, it follows from (6) and (7), §4, p. 12 that

$$\begin{aligned} A \cap (B \dot{-} C) &= A \cap [(B-C) \cup (C-B)] \\ &= [(A \cap B)-C] \cup [(A \cap C)-B] = [B \cap (A-C)] \cup [C \cap (A-B)] \\ &= \{B \cap [A-(A \cap C)]\} \cup \{C \cap [A-(A \cap B)]\} \\ &= [(A \cap B)-(A \cap C)] \cup [(A \cap C)-(A \cap B)] \\ &= (A \cap B) \dot{-} (A \cap C). \end{aligned}$$

The empty set behaves as a zero element for the operation $\dot{-}$, that is

$$A \dot{-} 0 = A. \tag{4}$$

In fact, $(A-0) \cup (0-A) = A \cup 0 = A$.

The theorems which we have proved so far do not indicate any essential difference between the operations $\dot{-}$ and $\cup$. However, a difference can be seen in the following theorems.

$$A \dot{-} A = 0. \tag{5}$$

In fact, $A \dot{-} A = (A-A) \cup (A-A) = 0$.

The operation of union has no inverse operation. In particular, we have seen that the operation of subtraction is not an inverse of the union operation. However, there does exist operation inverse to the operation $\dot{-}$: for any sets A and C there exists exactly one set B such that $A \dot{-} B = C$, namely $B = A \dot{-} C$. In other words:

$$A \dot{-} (A \dot{-} C) = C, \tag{6}$$

$$A \dot{-} B = C \rightarrow B = A \dot{-} C. \tag{7}$$

In fact, (2), (4) and (5) imply

$$A \dot{-} (A \dot{-} C) = (A \dot{-} A) \dot{-} C = 0 \dot{-} C = C \dot{-} 0 = C,$$

which proves (6). If $A \dot{-} B = C$ then $A \dot{-} (A \dot{-} B) = A \dot{-} C$ and hence $B = A \dot{-} C$ by means of (6).

Thus (6) and (7) indicate that the operation $\dot{-}$ does have an inverse: the operation $\dot{-}$ itself.

In algebra and number theory we investigate systems of objects usually called *numbers* with two operations $+$ and $\cdot$ (called *addition* and *multiplication*). These operations are always performable on those objects and satisfy the following conditions:

(i) $$x+y = y+x,$$

(ii) $$x+(y+z) = (x+y)+z,$$

(iii) there exists a number 0 such that $x+0 = x$,

(iv) for arbitrary x and y there exists exactly one number $z = x-y$ (the *difference*) such that $y+z = x$,

(v) $$x\cdot y = y\cdot x,$$

(vi) $$x\cdot(y\cdot z) = (x\cdot y)\cdot z,$$

(vii) $$x\cdot(y+z) = (x\cdot y)+(x\cdot z).$$

Such systems are called *rings* (more exactly: *commutative rings*). If there exists a number 1 such that for every x

(viii) $$x\cdot 1 = x,$$

then we say that *the ring has a unit element*.

The algebraic computations in rings are performed exactly as in arithmetic. For, in proving arithmetic properties involving addition, subtraction and multiplication, we make use only of the fact that numbers form a commutative ring with unit.

Formulas (1)–(7) show that sets form a ring (without unit) if by "addition" we understand the operation $\dot{-}$ and by "multiplication" the operation $\cap$. A peculiarity of this ring is that the operation "subtraction" coincides with the operation "addition" and, moreover, "square" of every element is equal to that element.

Using $\dot{-}$ and $\cap$ as the basic operations, calculations in the algebra of sets are performed as in ordinary arithmetic. Moreover, we may omit all exponents and reduce all coefficients modulo 2 (i.e., $2kA = 0$ and $(2k+1)A = A$).

This result is significant because the operations $\cup$ and $-$ can be expressed in terms of $\dot{-}$ and $\cap$. Owing to this fact the entire algebra of sets treated above may be represented as the arithmetic of the ring of sets. In fact, it can easily be verified that:

(8) $$A \cup B = A \dot{-} B \dot{-} (A \cap B),$$

(9) $$A - B = A \dot{-} (A \cap B).$$

Formulas (8) and (4) imply the following theorem:

(10) *if A and B are disjoint, then* $A \cup B = A \dot{-} B$.

The role which symmetric difference plays in applications is illustrated by the following example.

Let X be a set and $\boldsymbol{I}$ a non-empty family of subsets of X; that is, $\boldsymbol{I}$ is a set whose elements are subsets of X. Suppose that

$$(11) \qquad \begin{gathered} (Y \subset Z) \wedge (Z \in \boldsymbol{I}) \rightarrow (Y \in \boldsymbol{I}), \\ (Y \in \boldsymbol{I}) \wedge (Z \in \boldsymbol{I}) \rightarrow (Y \cup Z \in \boldsymbol{I}). \end{gathered}$$

A family of sets satisfying these conditions is called an *ideal*. We say that two subsets A, B of X are *congruent modulo $\boldsymbol{I}$* if $A \dot{-} B \in \boldsymbol{I}$ and we denote this fact by $A \doteq B (\text{mod } \boldsymbol{I})$ or by $A \doteq B$ if the ideal $\boldsymbol{I}$ is fixed.

Since $0 \in \boldsymbol{I}$, it follows from (5) that $A \doteq A$, i.e. the relation $\doteq$ is reflexive. (1) implies that $(A \doteq B) \rightarrow (B \doteq A)$, i.e. the relation $\doteq$ is symmetric.

Finally, the identity $A \dot{-} B = (A \dot{-} C) \dot{-} (B \dot{-} C)$ implies that $A \dot{-} B \subset (A \dot{-} C) \cup (B \dot{-} C)$, because the symmetric difference of two sets is contained in their union. By means of (11) we infer that

$$(A \doteq B) \wedge (B \doteq C) \rightarrow (A \doteq C),$$

i.e. the relation $\doteq$ is transitive.

Replacing the sign $=$ by the sign $\doteq$ in the previous definitions we obtain new notions. For example, two sets A and B are said to be *disjoint modulo $\boldsymbol{I}$* provided $A \cap B \doteq 0$ (see p. 9); we say that *A is included in B modulo $\boldsymbol{I}$* if $A - B \doteq 0$, etc.

Exercises

1. Show that the set $A_1 \dot{-} A_2 \dot{-} \ldots \dot{-} A_n$ contains those and only those elements which belong to an odd number of sets A_i $(i = 1, 2, \ldots, n)$.

2. For A finite let $N(A)$ denote the number of elements of A. Prove that if the sets $A_1, A_2, \ldots, A_n$ are finite then

$$\begin{aligned} N(A_1 \dot{-} A_2 \dot{-} \ldots \dot{-} A_n) &= \sum_i N(A_i) - 2 \sum_{i,j} N(A_i \cap A_j) + 4 \sum_{i,j,k} N(A_i \cap A_j \cap A_k) \\ &\quad - 8 \sum_{i,j,k,l} N(A_i \cap A_j \cap A_k \cap A_l) + \cdots \end{aligned}$$

3. Show that

$$(A_1 \cup A_2 \cup \dots \cup A_n) \dot{-} (B_1 \cup B_2 \cup \dots \cup B_n) \subset (A_1 \dot{-} B_1) \cup \dots \cup (A_n \dot{-} B_n),$$

$$(A_1 \cap A_2 \cap \dots \cap A_n) \dot{-} (B_1 \cap B_2 \cap \dots \cap B_n) \subset (A_1 \dot{-} B_1) \cup \dots \cup (A_n \dot{-} B_n)$$

(Hausdorff).

4. Show that for any ideal I the condition $A \doteq B$ implies

$$A \cup C \doteq B \cup C, \quad A \cap C \doteq B \cap C, \quad A - C \doteq B - C, \quad C - A \doteq C - B.$$

5. For any real number t denote by $[t]$ the largest integer $\leqslant t$. Let A_t be the set of rational numbers of the form $[nt]/n$, $n = 1, 2, \dots$. Prove that if I is the ideal composed of all finite subsets of the set of rational numbers, then $\neg(A_x \doteq A_y \pmod{I})$ and A_x is disjoint (modulo I) from A_y for all irrational numbers $x, y > 0$, $x \neq y$.

§ 6. The set 1, complement

In many applications of set theory we consider only sets contained in a given fixed set. For instance, in geometry we deal with sets of points in a given space, and in arithmetic with sets of numbers.

In this section $A, B, \dots$ will denote sets contained in a certain fixed set which will be referred to either as the space or the *universe* and will be denoted by 1. Thus for every A

$$A \subset 1,$$

from which it follows that

(1) $$A \cap 1 = A, \quad A \cup 1 = A.$$

The set $1 - A$ is called the *complement* of A and is denoted by A^c or $-A$:

$$-A = A^c = 1 - A.$$

Clearly,

(2) $$A \cap -A = 0, \quad A \cup -A = 1.$$

Since $--A = 1-(1-A)$, we obtain by (10), § 4, p. 12 the following *law of double complementation*

(3) $$--A = A.$$

Setting $A = 1$ in de Morgan's laws ((8), § 4, p. 12) and substituting A and B for B and C, we obtain

(4) $$-(A \cap B) = -A \cup -B, \quad -(A \cup B) = -A \cap -B.$$

Thus *the complement of the intersection of two sets is equal to the union of their complements and the complement of the union of two sets is equal to the intersection of their complements.*

It is worth noting that the formulas which we obtained by introducing the notion of complementation are analogous to those of propositional calculus discussed in § 1. To obtain the laws of propositional calculus (see p. 2–4) it suffices to substitute in (1)–(4) the equivalence sign for the sign of identity and to interpret the letters A, B, ... as propositional variables and the symbols $\cup$, $\cap$, $-$, 0, 1 as disjunction, conjunction, negation, the false sentence and the true sentence, respectively. Conversely, theorems of the algebra of sets can be obtained from the corresponding laws of the propositional calculus simply by changing the meaning of symbols. From this point of view calculations on sets contained in a fixed set 1 can be simplified by using the operations $\cup$, $\cap$, $-$.

Subtraction can be defined by means of the operation $-$ and one of the operations $\cup$ or $\cap$. In fact, we have

$$A-B = A \cap (1-B) = A \cap -B$$

and

$$A-B = A \cap -B = -(-A \cup B).$$

The inclusion relation between two sets can be expressed by the identity

$$(A \subset B) \equiv (A \cap -B = 0). \tag{5}$$

For assuming $A \subset B$ and multiplying both sides of the inclusion by $-B$ we obtain $A \cap -B \subset B \cap -B$ and since $B \cap -B = 0$, we have $A \cap -B = 0$. Conversely, if $A \cap -B = 0$, then

$$\begin{aligned} A &= A \cap 1 = A \cap (B \cup -B) \\ &= (A \cap B) \cup (A \cap -B) = (A \cap B) \cup 0 = A \cap B \subset B. \end{aligned}$$

Since $(A = B) \equiv (A \subset B) \wedge (B \subset A)$, it follows from (5) that

$$(A = B) \equiv (A \cap -B = 0) \wedge (B \cap -A = 0),$$

and, since the condition $(X = 0) \wedge (Y = 0)$ is equivalent to $X \cup Y = 0$,

$$(A = B) \equiv [(A \cap -B) \cup (B \cap -A) = 0] \equiv (A \dot{-} B = 0). \tag{6}$$

It follows directly from (5) that

$$(A \subset B) \equiv (-B \subset -A). \tag{7}$$

(compare with the law of contraposition p. 4).

The system of all sets contained in 1 forms a ring where the operation $\dot{-}$ is understood as addition and $\cap$ as multiplication. This ring differs from the ring of sets considered in § 5 in that it has a unit element. The unit is namely the set 1. In fact, formula (1) states that the set 1 satisfies condition (viii), § 5, p. 16 characterizing the unit element of a ring.

Hence calculations in the algebra of sets are formally like those in the algebra of numbers.

Exercise

The quotient of two sets is defined as follows $A:B = A \cup -B$. Find formulas for $A:(B \cup C)$ and for $A:(B \cap C)$ (counterpart of de Morgan's laws). Compute $A \cap (B:C)$.

§ 7. Constituents

In this section we shall consider sets which can be obtained from arbitrary n sets by applying the operations of union, intersection, and difference. We shall show that the total number of such sets is finite and that they can be represented in a certain definite form (*normal form*).

Let $A_1, A_2, \ldots, A_n$ be arbitrary subsets of the space 1. Throughout this section these subsets will remain fixed.

Let

$$A_i^1 = 1 - A_i, \quad A_i^0 = A_i \quad \text{for } i = 1, 2, \ldots, n.$$

Each set of the form

$$A_1^{i_1} \cap A_2^{i_2} \cap \ldots \cap A_n^{i_n} \quad (i_k = 0 \text{ or } i_k = 1 \text{ for } k = 1, 2, \ldots, n)$$

will be called a *constituent*.

The total number of distinct constituents is at most 2^n, because each of the superscripts i_k may have either one of the values 0 and 1. The number of constituents may be less than 2^n; for instance, if $n = 2$ and $A_1 = 1 - A_2$, then there are only three constituents:

$$0 = A_1^0 \cap A_2^0 = A_1^1 \cap A_2^1, \quad A_1 = A_1^0 \cap A_2^1, \quad A_2 = A_1^1 \cap A_2^0.$$

Distinct constituents are always disjoint.

In fact, if

$$S_1 = A_1^{i_1} \cap A_2^{i_2} \cap \ldots \cap A_n^{i_n} \quad \text{and} \quad S_2 = A_1^{j_1} \cap A_2^{j_2} \cap \ldots \cap A_n^{j_n}$$

and if for at least one $k \leqslant n$, $i_k \neq j_k$, for instance $i_k = 0$ and $j_k = 1$, then $A_k^{i_k} \cap A_k^{j_k} = 0$. Hence $S_1 \cap S_2 = 0$.

The union of all constituents is the space 1.

It suffices to notice that

$$1 = (A_1^0 \cup A_1^1) \cap (A_2^0 \cup A_2^1) \cap \ldots \cap (A_n^0 \cup A_n^1).$$

By applying the distributive law of intersection with respect to union on the right-hand side of the equation we obtain the union of all the constituents.

The set A_i is a union of all constituents which contain the component A_i^0.

If $S_1, S_2, \ldots S_h$ are all constituents, then

$$1 = S_1 \cup S_2 \cup \ldots S_h.$$

Therefore

$$A_i = (A_i \cap S_1) \cup (A_i \cap S_2) \cup \ldots \cup (A_i \cap S_h).$$

If S_p contains the component A_i^1, then $A_i \cap S_p = 0$ because $A_i \cap A_i^1 = A_i \cap (1 - A_i) = 0$. On the other hand, if S_p contains the component A_i^0, then $A_i \cap S_p = S_p$. Thus A_i is the union of those constituents which contain the component A_i^0. Q.E.D.

We shall now prove the following

THEOREM 1: *Each non-empty set obtained from the sets $A_1, A_2, \ldots, A_n$ by applying the operations of union, intersection and subtraction is the union of a certain number of constituents.*

PROOF. The theorem is true for the sets $A_1, A_2, \ldots, A_n$. It suffices to show that if X and Y are unions of a certain number of constituents then the sets $X \cup Y$, $X \cap Y$, $X - Y$ can also be represented as the union of constituents (provided $X \cup Y$, $X \cap Y$, $X - Y$ are non-empty).

Assume that X and Y can be represented as unions of constituents:

$$X = S_1 \cup S_2 \cup \ldots \cup S_k, \qquad Y = \overline{S}_1 \cup \overline{S}_2 \cup \ldots \cup \overline{S}_l.$$

It follows that

$$X \cup Y = (S_1 \cup \ldots \cup S_k) \cup (\overline{S}_1 \cup \ldots \cup \overline{S}_l).$$

Thus $X \cup Y$ is a union of constituents.

From the distributive law for intersection with respect to union, it follows that

$$X \cap Y = (S_1 \cap \overline{S}_1) \cup (S_1 \cap \overline{S}_2) \cup \ldots \cup (S_1 \cap \overline{S}_l) \cup \ldots \\ \cup (S_i \cap \overline{S}_j) \cup \ldots \cup (S_k \cap \overline{S}_l).$$

$S_i \cap \overline{S}_j = 0$ if $S_i \neq \overline{S}_j$; otherwise $S_i \cap \overline{S}_j = S_i$. Thus $X \cap Y$ is a union of constituents

$$X \cap Y = S_{i_1} \cup S_{i_2} \cup \ldots \cup S_{i_p},$$

or else is empty.

If among the constituents $S_{i_1}, S_{i_2}, \ldots, S_{i_p}$ occur all of the constituents $S_1, S_2, \ldots, S_k$, then

$$X - Y = X - (X \cap Y) \subset (S_1 \cup \ldots \cup S_k) - (S_1 \cup \ldots \cup S_k) = 0.$$

Otherwise, let $S_{j_1}, S_{j_2}, \ldots, S_{j_q}$ be those constituents among $S_1, S_2, \ldots, S_k$ which do not occur among the constituents $S_{i_1}, S_{i_2}, \ldots, S_{i_p}$.

We have

$$\begin{aligned} X - Y &= X - (X \cap Y) \\ &= [(S_{i_1} \cup \ldots \cup S_{i_p}) \cup (S_{j_1} \cup \ldots \cup S_{j_q})] - (S_{i_1} \cup \ldots \cup S_{i_p}) \\ &= (S_{j_1} \cup \ldots \cup S_{j_q}) - (S_{i_1} \cup \ldots \cup S_{i_p}) \\ &= (S_{j_1} \cup \ldots \cup S_{j_q}) - [(S_{j_1} \cup \ldots \cup S_{j_q}) \cap (S_{i_1} \cup \ldots \cup S_{i_p})] \\ &= S_{j_1} \cup \ldots \cup S_{j_q}, \end{aligned}$$

because

$$(S_{j_1} \cup \ldots \cup S_{j_q}) \cap (S_{i_1} \cup \ldots \cup S_{i_p}) = 0.$$

Thus $X \cup Y$, $X \cap Y$ and $X - Y$ are representable as unions of constituents. Q. E. D.

THEOREM 2: *From n sets by applying the operations of union, intersection, and subtraction at most* 2^{2^n} *sets can be constructed.*

In fact, each such set, with the exception of the empty set, is a union of constituents. Because the number of constituents cannot be greater than 2^n, the number of distinct unions constructed from some (non-zero) number of constituents cannot be greater than $2^{2^n} - 1$.

Of particular importance is the case where all of the constituents are different from 0. In this case, we say that the sets $A_1, \ldots, A_n$ are *independent* [1]).

[1]) The notion of independent sets plays an important role in problems connected with the foundations of probability theory. See E. Marczewski, *Indépendence d'ensembles et prolongement de mesures,* Colloquium Mathematicum **1** (1948) 122–132.

THEOREM 3: *If the sets $A_1, \ldots, A_n$ are independent, then the number of distinct constituents equals 2^n.*

PROOF. If

$$S = A_1^{i_1} \cap \ldots \cap A_n^{i_n} = A_1^{j_1} \cap \ldots \cap A_n^{j_n} \tag{0}$$

and not all of the equations $i_1 = j_1, \ldots, i_n = j_n$ hold, then $S = 0$. In fact, if for example, $i_p = 1$ and $j_p = 0$, then intersecting both sides of the last equation in (0) with A_p^1 we obtain $S = 0$. Thus if the sets $A_1, \ldots, A_n$ are independent then equation (0) holds if and only if $i_1 = j_1, \ldots, i_n = j_n$. Q. E. D.

Example. Let the set D_m consist of sequences $(z_1, \ldots, z_n)$ such that each z_i equals either 0 or 1 but $z_m = 0$. The sets $D_1, \ldots, D_n$ are independent. In fact, $D_m^{i_m}$ consists of those sequences $(z_1, \ldots, z_n)$ for which $z_m = i_m$. Thus $(i_1, \ldots, i_n) \in D_1^{i_1} \cap \ldots \cap D_n^{i_n}$.

We shall apply the concept of constituents to a discussion of the following *problem of elimination*. We introduce the abbreviations

$$\Gamma_n^0(A) \equiv \{A \text{ contains at least } n \text{ elements}\},$$
$$\Gamma_n^1(A) \equiv \{A \text{ contains exactly } n \text{ elements}\}.$$

Let $i_1, \ldots, i_n$, $j_1, \ldots, j_n$ be sequences of the numbers 0 and 1. Let $p_1, \ldots, p_n$, $q_1, \ldots, q_n$ be sequences of non-negative integers. We are interested in finding necessary and sufficient conditions for the existence of a set X satisfying the conjunction of the following conditions:

$$\text{(i)} \quad \begin{array}{l} \Gamma_{p_1}^{i_1}(X \cap A_1),\ \Gamma_{p_2}^{i_2}(X \cap A_2),\ \ldots,\ \Gamma_{p_n}^{i_n}(X \cap A_n), \\ \Gamma_{q_1}^{j_1}(-X \cap A_1),\ \Gamma_{q_2}^{j_2}(-X \cap A_2),\ \ldots,\ \Gamma_{q_n}^{j_n}(-X \cap A_n). \end{array}$$

We assume at first that $n = 1$. Writing i, j, p, q, A instead of i_1, j_1, p_1, q_1, A_1, we obtain the solution:

$$[(i = j = 1) \wedge \Gamma_{p+q}^1(A)] \vee \Gamma_{p+q}^0(A). \tag{ii}$$

In fact, if there exists a set X satisfying (i) and $i = j = 1$, then A is the union of two sets containing respectively p and q elements, and in this case A contains exactly $p+q$ elements. If $i = 0 \vee j = 0$ then A is the union of two sets, one of which contains at least p elements and the other at least q elements. Therefore A contains at least $p+q$ elements. Conversely, if condition (ii) is satisfied, then it suffices to choose as X any subset of A containing p elements.

Assume that $n > 1$ and $A_1, \ldots, A_n$ are pairwise disjoint. If there exists a set X satisfying (i), then writing $X_s = X$, $s = 1, 2, \ldots, n$, we conclude that

(iii) $\quad \Gamma_{p_s}^{i_s}(X_s \cap A_s) \wedge \Gamma_{q_s}^{j_s}(-X_s \cap A_s) \quad$ for $\quad s = 1, 2, \ldots, n,$

and by virtue of (ii)

(iv) $\quad [(i_s = j_s = 1) \wedge \Gamma_{p_s+q_s}^{1}(A_s)] \vee \Gamma_{p_s+q_s}^{0}(A_s), \qquad s = 1, 2, \ldots, n.$

Conversely, if (iv) holds then for every s $(1 \leqslant s \leqslant n)$ there exists a set X_s satisfying (iii). Let

$$X = [(X_1 \cap A_1) \cup (X_2 \cap A_2) \cup \ldots \cup (X_n \cap A_n)] \cup (-A_1 \cap -A_2 \cap \ldots \cap -A_n).$$

Therefore

$$-X = [(-X_1 \cup -A_1) \cap (-X_2 \cup -A_2) \cap \ldots \cap (-X_n \cup -A_n)] \cap (A_1 \cup \ldots \cup A_n).$$

Since the sets A_i are disjoint, we have $X \cap A_s = X_s \cap A_s$ and $-X \cap A_s = -X_s \cap A_s$. By applying (iii) we obtain (i).

Next we assume that for all r, s $(1 \leqslant r, s \leqslant n)$ either $A_r = A_s$ or $A_r \cap A_s = 0$. We shall designate conditions (i) by $W_1, W_2, \ldots, W_n, V_1, V_2, \ldots, V_n$. We shall show that if $A_r = A_s$ then $W_r \to W_s$, or $W_s \to W_r$, or else $W_r \wedge W_s \equiv F$. Indeed, if $i_r = i_s = 0$, then $W_s \to W_r$ if $p_r \leqslant p_s$, and $W_r \to W_s$ if $p_s < p_r$. If $i_r = 1$ and $i_s = 0$, then $W_r \to W_s$ in case $p_r \geqslant p_s$, and in case $p_r < p_s$, $W_r \wedge W_s \equiv F$. Finally if $i_r = i_s = 1$ then $W_r \to W_s$ for $p_r = p_s$ and otherwise $W_r \wedge W_s = F$. Similarly it can be shown that either $V_r \to V_s$, or $V_s \to V_r$, or $V_r \wedge V_s \equiv F$. We conclude that either the conjunction of (i) is false or else we may omit from (i) certain components and obtain an equivalent conjunction in which none of the sets A_s occurs more than once. Thus this case is reduced to the preceding case.

Now we shall reduce the general case to the case in which the sets A_s are either identical or disjoint. For this purpose we note that if $M \cap N = 0$, then

$$\Gamma_p^0(M \vee N) \equiv \Gamma_p^0(M) \vee [\Gamma_{p-1}^1(M) \wedge \Gamma_1^0(N)] \vee [\Gamma_{p-2}^1(M) \wedge \Gamma_2^0(N)] \vee \ldots \vee [\Gamma_0^1(M) \wedge \Gamma_p^0(N)],$$

$$\Gamma_p^1(M \cup N) \equiv [\Gamma_p^1(M) \wedge \Gamma_0^1(N)] \vee [\Gamma_{p-1}^1(M) \wedge \Gamma_1^1(N)] \vee \\ \ldots \vee [\Gamma_0^1(M) \wedge \Gamma_p^1(N)].$$

By induction, if the sets $S_1, \ldots, S_h$ are pairwise disjoint, then the condition of the form $\Gamma_p^i(S_1 \cup \ldots \cup S_h)$ can be expressed equivalently as a disjunction of conjunctions, where each conjunction has the form

$$\Gamma_{p_1}^{j_1}(S_1) \wedge \ldots \wedge \Gamma_{p_h}^{j_h}(S_h).$$

Represent the sets A_s as unions of constituents; then according to the above remark, each of the conditions (i) can be expressed as a disjunction of conjunctions each of which has the form

$$\Gamma_{v_1}^{u_1}(X \cap S_1) \wedge \ldots \wedge \Gamma_{v_h}^{u_h}(X \cap S_h),$$

or respectively,

$$\Gamma_{z_1}^{w_1}(-X \cap S_1) \wedge \ldots \wedge \Gamma_{z_h}^{w_h}(-X \cap S_h).$$

Applying the distributive law for conjunction over disjunction, we express the conjunction of conditions (i) as a disjunction, each of which is a conjunction whose components have either the form $\Gamma_f^e(X \cap S_g)$ or the form $\Gamma_f^e(-X \cap S_g)$. Sets occurring in each such conjunction are either identical or disjoint. Thus the general case is reduced to the preceding one.

Example. We shall find necessary and sufficient conditions for the existence of a set X satisfying the conditions

$$X \cap A \cap B \neq 0, \qquad -X \cap A \cap B \neq 0,$$

$$X \cap A \not\subset B, \qquad X \cap B \not\subset A.$$

These conditions can be expressed equivalently as the conjunction of the following six conditions:

$$\Gamma_1^0(X \cap A \cap B), \qquad \Gamma_1^0(X \cap A \cap -B), \qquad \Gamma_1^0(X \cap -A \cap B),$$

$$\Gamma_1^0(-X \cap A \cap B), \qquad \Gamma_0^0(-X \cap A \cap -B), \qquad \Gamma_0^0(-X \cap -A \cap B).$$

Hence we obtain the desired condition

$$\Gamma_2^0(A \cap B) \wedge \Gamma_1^0(A \cap -B) \wedge \Gamma_1^0(-A \cap B).$$

In other terms, $A \cap -B$ and $B \cap -A$ have to be non-empty and $A \cap B$ has to contain at least two elements [1]).

Exercises

1. Assuming that the set 1 is infinite and that $A_1, \dots, A_n$ are finite, describe a method of obtaining necessary and sufficient conditions for the existence of a finite set X satisfying the conjunction of conditions (i).

2. Let I be the unit n-dimensional cube, that is, the set of sequences $(x_1, \dots, x_n)$ such that $0 \leqslant x_i \leqslant 1$ $(i = 1, 2, \dots, n)$. Let I_m consist of those sequences $(x_1, \dots, x_n) \in I$ where $1/2 \leqslant x_m \leqslant 1$. Show that the sets $I_1, \dots, I_n$ are independent. Give a geometrical interpretation for $n = 2$ and $n = 3$.

§ 8. Applications of the algebra of sets to topology [2])

In order to illustrate applications which the calculus developed in the preceding sections has outside of the general theory of sets, we shall examine the axioms of general topology and apply the algebra of sets to establish several results.

In general topology we study a set 1, called the *space*, whose elements are called *points*. We assume, moreover, that to every set A contained in 1 there corresponds a set $\overline{A}$ also contained in 1 and called the *closure* of A. The space 1 is called *topological* if it satisfies the following axioms (see also p. 119)

$$\overline{A \cup B} = \overline{A} \cup \overline{B}, \tag{1}$$

$$\overline{\overline{A}} = \overline{A}, \tag{2}$$

$$A \subset \overline{A}, \tag{3}$$

$$\overline{0} = 0. \tag{4}$$

[1]) The elimination method given above is due to Skolem, *Untersuchungen über die Axiome des Klassenkalkuls ...*, Skrifter utgit av Videnskapsselskapet i Kristiania, I Klasse, No 3 (Oslo 1919).

[2]) For more details on topological calculus developed in this section see K. Kuratowski, *Topology I*, Academic Press 1966, Chapt. I. For further investigations on this calculus from an algebraical point of view see the paper of J.C.C. Mc Kinsey and A. Tarski, *The algebra of topology*, Annals of Mathematics **45** (1944) 141–191.

In §8 we apply not only axioms I, A, B, C but also axioms (1)–(4). However, we can deduce all theorems given in this section from the full axiom system of set theory given in Chapter II, treating axioms (1)–(4) as assumptions about the operation of closure.

In axioms (1)–(3) the letters A and B denote arbitrary subsets of the space 1.

Axioms (1)–(4) are satisfied if, for example, 1 is the set of points of the plane and if the closure operation $\overline{A}$ consists of adding to the set A all points p such that every circle around p contains elements of A. This interpretation will be referred to as the *natural interpretation* of the axioms (1)–(4).

We shall show how, using only laws of the calculus of sets, it is possible to deduce a variety of properties of the closure operation.

$$(5) \qquad \overline{1} = 1.$$

PROOF. For every A we have $\overline{A} \subset 1$, and by axiom (3), $1 \subset \overline{1}$.

$$(6) \qquad \overline{A} - \overline{B} \subset \overline{A - B}.$$

PROOF. From $B \cup (A - B) = A \cup B$ applying axiom (1) we obtain $\overline{B} \cup \overline{A - B} = \overline{A} \cup \overline{B}$. This implies that $\overline{A} \subset \overline{B} \cup \overline{A - B}$ and thus

$$\overline{A} - \overline{B} \subset (\overline{B} \cup \overline{A - B}) - \overline{B} = \overline{A - B} - \overline{B} \subset \overline{A - B},$$

which proves (6).

$$(7) \qquad A \subset B \to \overline{A} \subset \overline{B}.$$

PROOF. $A \subset B$ is equivalent to the equation $A \cup B = B$. By axiom (1), $\overline{A} \cup \overline{B} = \overline{B}$, thus $\overline{A} \subset \overline{B}$ (cf. § 3, (5), p. 8).

$$(8) \qquad \overline{A \cap B} \subset \overline{A} \cap \overline{B}.$$

PROOF. Since $A \cap B \subset A$ and $A \cap B \subset B$, theorem (7) implies $\overline{A \cap B} \subset \overline{A}$ and $\overline{A \cap B} \subset \overline{B}$, from which it follows that $\overline{A \cap B} \subset \overline{A} \cap \overline{B}$.

(9) *If* $A = \overline{A}$ *and* $B = \overline{B}$, *then* $\overline{A \cap B} = A \cap B$.

PROOF. In fact, $A \cap B \subset \overline{A \cap B}$ by axiom (3). But by (8) and by the hypothesis of (9), $\overline{A \cap B} \subset \overline{A} \cap \overline{B} = A \cap B$. Therefore $A \cap B = \overline{A \cap B}$.

We call a set *closed* if it is equal to its closure. Theorem (9) states that the intersection of two closed sets is closed, and axiom (3) that the union of two closed sets is closed.

We call a set *open* if it is the complement of a closed set. By de Morgan's laws it follows that the union and intersection of two open sets is open.

In the natural interpretation of axioms (1)–(4) *closed sets are those sets which contain all their accumulation points* (cf. p. 32). Open sets have the property: for every point p contained in the open set A there exists a circle with center p entirely contained in A.

The set[1])

$$\mathrm{Int}(A) = 1-\overline{1-A} = A^{c-c}$$

is called the *interior* of the set A. The interior of any set is clearly an open set. # In the natural interpretation of axioms (1)–(4), the set $\mathrm{Int}(A)$ consists exactly of those points p for which there exists a circle with center p entirely contained in A. #

(10) $$\mathrm{Int}(A) \subset A.$$

PROOF. By axiom (3), $A^c \subset A^{c-}$, from which, by applying equation (7), § 6, p. 19, we obtain

$$1-A^{c-} \subset 1-A^c,$$

hence

$$A^{c-c} \subset A^{cc} = A.$$

In particular, the relation $\mathrm{Int}(\mathrm{Int}(A)) \subset \mathrm{Int}(A)$ is a special case of (10). This relation may be strengthened as follows:

(11) $$\mathrm{Int}(\mathrm{Int}(A)) = \mathrm{Int}(A).$$

PROOF. It follows from the definition of $\mathrm{Int}(A)$ that

$$\mathrm{Int}(A) = A^{c-c}, \qquad \mathrm{Int}(\mathrm{Int}(A)) = [\mathrm{Int}(A)]^{c-c} = [A^{c-c}]^{c-c}.$$

By the law of double complementation we may eliminate two consecutive occurrences of the operation A^c; we thus obtain

$$\mathrm{Int}(\mathrm{Int}(A)) = A^{c--c},$$

and because $A^{c--} = A^{c-}$ by axiom (2), we obtain

$$\mathrm{Int}(\mathrm{Int}(A)) = A^{c-c} = \mathrm{Int}(A).$$

(12) $$\mathrm{Int}(A \cap B) = \mathrm{Int}(A) \cap \mathrm{Int}(B).$$

PROOF. By de Morgan's laws

$$(A \cap B)^{c-c} = (A^c \cup B^c)^{-c},$$

[1]) Instead of $\overline{A}$ we sometimes write A^-.

whence by axiom (1)

$$\mathrm{Int}(A \cap B) = (A \cap B)^{c-c} = (A^{c-} \cup B^{c-})^{c},$$

and a final application of de Morgan's laws gives

$$\mathrm{Int}(A \cap B) = A^{c-c} \cap B^{c-c} = \mathrm{Int}(A) \cap \mathrm{Int}(B).$$

As a simple consequence of (12) we have:

$$(13) \qquad A \subset B \rightarrow \mathrm{Int}(A) \subset \mathrm{Int}(B).$$

In fact, the assumption $A \subset B$ gives us $A \cap B = A$, from which it follows that

$$\mathrm{Int}(A) = \mathrm{Int}(A \cap B) = \mathrm{Int}(A) \cap \mathrm{Int}(B) \subset \mathrm{Int}(B).$$

$$(14) \qquad \overline{\mathrm{Int}(\overline{\mathrm{Int}(A)})} = \overline{\mathrm{Int}(A)}.$$

PROOF. By (10)

$$\mathrm{Int}(\overline{\mathrm{Int}(A)}) \subset \overline{\mathrm{Int}(A)},$$

whence by (7) and (2)

$$(14_1) \qquad \overline{\mathrm{Int}(\overline{\mathrm{Int}(A)})} \subset \overline{\mathrm{Int}(A)}.$$

On the other hand, by (11), (3), and (13)

$$\mathrm{Int}(A) = \mathrm{Int}(\mathrm{Int}(A)) \subset \mathrm{Int}(\overline{\mathrm{Int}(A)}),$$

and by (7) it follows that

$$(14_2) \qquad \overline{\mathrm{Int}(A)} \subset \overline{\mathrm{Int}(\overline{\mathrm{Int}(A)})}.$$

Inclusions (14_1) and (14_2) imply (14).

Replacing $\mathrm{Int}(X)$ by X^{c-c} in (14), we obtain

$$(15) \qquad A^{c-c-c-c-} = A^{c-c-}.$$

Moreover, substituting A^c for A and applying the law of double complementation we obtain

$$(16) \qquad A^{-c-c-c-} = A^{-c-}.\,[1]$$

Equations (15) and (16) show that if we apply in succession the operations of complementation and closure to the set A, then we obtain

[1] Formula (16) was given by K. Kuratowski in the paper: *Sur l'opération $\bar{A}$ d'Analysis Situs*, Fundamenta Mathematicae **3** (1922) 182–199.

only a finite number of sets. Namely, if we start with the operation of complementation, then we obtain the sets

$$A,\ A^{c},\ A^{c-},\ A^{c-c},\ A^{c-c-},\ A^{c-c-c},\ A^{c-c-c-},\ A^{c-c-c-c}.$$

The next set in this sequence would be $A^{c-c-c-c-}$, but by (15) this set equals A^{c-c-}.

If, on the other hand, we start by applying the operation $^-$, then we obtain the sets

$$A^{-},\ A^{-c},\ A^{-c-},\ A^{-c-c},\ A^{-c-c-},\ A^{-c-c-c}.$$

The next set would be $A^{-c-c-c-}$ but by (16) it is equal to the set A^{-c-}.

Hence by applying the operations of complementation and closure to an arbitrary set A we obtain at most 14 distinct sets.

Formulas (17) and (18) will be used in § 9.

(17) *If* $B = X^{-c-}$, *then* $\operatorname{Int}[\overline{\operatorname{Int}(A-B)} \cap B] = 0$.

PROOF. Clearly $A - B \subset B^c$, whence by (13) and (7)

$$\operatorname{Int}[\overline{\operatorname{Int}(A-B)} \cap B] \subset \operatorname{Int}[\overline{\operatorname{Int}(B^c)} \cap B].$$

Thus it suffices to show that

$$\operatorname{Int}[\overline{\operatorname{Int}(B^c)} \cap B] = 0.$$

Since $\overline{\operatorname{Int}(B^c)} = B^{cc-c-} = B^{-c-} = X^{-c---c-} = X^{-c-c-}$, it follows by formulas (12), (16), and (10) that

$$\begin{aligned}\operatorname{Int}[\overline{\operatorname{Int}(B^c)} \cap B] &= \operatorname{Int}[\overline{\operatorname{Int}(B^c)}] \cap \operatorname{Int}(B) = X^{-c-c-c-c} \cap B^{c-c}\\ &= X^{-c-c} \cap B^{c-c} = B^c \cap B^{c-c} = 0.\end{aligned}$$

(18) *If* $A = \overline{A}$ *or* $B = \overline{B}$ *then* $\overline{\operatorname{Int}(A)} \cup \overline{\operatorname{Int}(B)} = \overline{\operatorname{Int}(A \cup B)}$.

PROOF. From theorem (13) we conclude that $\operatorname{Int}(A) \subset \operatorname{Int}(A \cup B)$ and $\operatorname{Int}(B) \subset \operatorname{Int}(A \cup B)$, which implies that $\operatorname{Int}(A) \cup \operatorname{Int}(B) \subset \operatorname{Int}(A \cup B)$. Applying the closure to both sides of the inclusion we obtain by (1) and (7)

(18_1) $$\overline{\operatorname{Int}(A)} \cup \overline{\operatorname{Int}(B)} \subset \overline{\operatorname{Int}(A \cup B)}.$$

For the proof of the opposite inclusion we suppose that, for instance, $\overline{B} = B$. We apply the identity

$$A \cup B \cup [1-(A \cup B)] = 1,$$

from which by axiom (3) it follows that

$$A \cup B \cup \overline{1-(A \cup B)} = 1,$$

whence

$$B \cup \overline{1-(A \cup B)} \supset 1-A.$$

Applying closure to both sides we obtain (since $\overline{B} = B$):

$$B \cup \overline{1-(A \cup B)} \supset \overline{1-A},$$

from which it follows that

$$[1-\overline{1-A}] \cup B \cup \overline{1-(A \cup B)} = 1,$$

whence

$$\mathrm{Int}(A) \cup B \cup \overline{1-(A \cup B)} = 1.$$

It follows from this equation that

$$\mathrm{Int}(A) \cup \overline{1-(A \cup B)} \supset 1-B,$$

and thus

$$\overline{\mathrm{Int}(A)} \cup \overline{1-(A \cup B)} \supset \overline{1-B}.$$

Adding to both sides of this equation the set $1-\overline{1-B} = \mathrm{Int}(B)$ we obtain

$$\overline{\mathrm{Int}(A)} \cup \mathrm{Int}(B) \cup \overline{1-(A \cup B)} = 1,$$

thus

$$\overline{\mathrm{Int}(A)} \cup \mathrm{Int}(B) \supset 1-\overline{1-(A \cup B)} = \mathrm{Int}(A \cup B).$$

Applying closure to both sides of the inclusion we obtain by (1) and (3)

$$(18_2) \qquad \overline{\mathrm{Int}(A)} \cup \overline{\mathrm{Int}(B)} \supset \overline{\mathrm{Int}(A \cup B)}.$$

Inclusions (18_1) and (18_2) prove theorem (18).

Exercises

1. Prove that if the set A is open, then

$$\overline{A \cap \overline{X}} = \overline{A \cap X}$$

for every set X.

2. Let $\mathrm{Fr}(A) = \overline{A} \cap \overline{1-A}$ (the *boundary* of A).
Prove that:

(a) $\mathrm{Fr}(A \cup B) \cup \mathrm{Fr}(A \cap B) \cup [\mathrm{Fr}(A) \cap \mathrm{Fr}(B)] = \mathrm{Fr}(A) \cup \mathrm{Fr}(B)$, [A.H. Stone]

(b) $\mathrm{Fr}(A) = (A \cap \overline{1-A}) \cup (\overline{A}-A)$,

(c) $A \cup \text{Fr}(A) = \overline{A}$,

(d) $\text{Fr}[\text{Int}(A)] \subset \text{Fr}(A)$,

(e) $\overline{\text{Int}[\text{Fr}(A)]} = \overline{A \cap \text{Int}[\text{Fr}(A)]} = \overline{\text{Int}[\text{Fr}(A)] - A}$.

3. We call the set A *boundary* if $\overline{1-A} = 1$. The set A is called *nowhere dense* if $\overline{A}$ is boundary.

Prove that

(a) the union of a boundary set and a nowhere dense set is boundary;

(b) the union of two nowhere dense sets is nowhere dense;

(c) in order that the set $\text{Fr}(A)$ be nowhere dense it is necessary and sufficient that A be the union of an open set and a nowhere dense set.

4. Let 1 be a space satisfying besides axioms (1)–(4) the following axiom (where $\{p\}$ denotes the set consisting of the single element p):

$$\overline{\{p\}} = \{p\}.$$

We say that the point p is an *accumulation point* of the set A if $p \in \overline{A-\{p\}}$ (for the plane this condition is equivalent to the condition that $p = \lim\limits_{n=\infty} p_n$, where $p_n \in A-\{p\}$). By A^c we denote the set of all accumulation points of the set A, called the *derivative* of the set A. Prove the formulas:

$$(A \cup B)^c = A^c \cup B^c, \qquad A^c - B^c \subset (A-B)^c, \qquad A^{cc} \subset A^c, \qquad \overline{A} = A \cup A^c, \qquad \overline{A^c} = A^c.$$

5. Let 1 denote the space considered in exercise 4. We call the set A *dense in itself* if $A \subset A^c$.

Prove that

(a) if the space 1 is dense in itself, then every open set is also dense in itself;

(b) if sets A and $1-A$ are boundary, then 1 is dense in itself;

(c) the sets $\text{Int}[\text{Fr}(A)]$ and $A \cap \text{Int}[\text{Fr}(A)]$ are dense in themselves.

6. Conditions (1)–(3) are equivalent to the condition

$$A \cup \overline{A} \cup \overline{\overline{B}} = \overline{A \cup B} \qquad \text{[Iseki].}$$

§ 9. Boolean algebras

We shall conclude this chapter with certain considerations of axiomatic character. If we examine the theorems of §§ 2–8, we notice that the symbol $\in$ does not occur in the majority of them, though of course it does appear in the definitions and proofs. This suggests developing a separate theory to cover that part of the calculus of sets which does not make reference to the $\in$ relation. In this theory we shall speak only of the equality or inequality between objects and terms resulting from these objects by performing certain operations on them. We shall base this theory on a system of axioms, from which we shall be able to prove all theorems of the preceding sections in which the $\in$ symbol does not occur. This theory, which is called *Boolean algebra*, has applications in many areas of mathematics[1]).

Let K be an arbitrary set of elements, $\triangle$ and $\wedge$ operations of two arguments always performable on elements of K and having values in K. Finally, let o denote a particular element of K. We say that K is a *Boolean ring* or *Boolean algebra* with respect to these operations and to the element o if for arbitrary $a, b, c \in K$ the following equations hold (axioms of Boolean algebra):

(1) $$a \triangle b = b \triangle a,$$

(2) $$a \triangle (b \triangle c) = (a \triangle b) \triangle c,$$

(3) $$a \triangle o = a,$$

(4) $$a \triangle a = o,$$

(5) $$a \wedge b = b \wedge a,$$

(6) $$a \wedge (b \wedge c) = (a \wedge b) \wedge c,$$

(7) $$a \wedge o = o,$$

(8) $$a \wedge a = a,$$

(9) $$a \wedge (b \triangle c) = (a \wedge b) \triangle (a \wedge c).$$

We define the sum and the difference of elements of K by the equations

$$a \vee b = a \triangle [b \triangle (a \wedge b)],$$

$$a - b = a \triangle (a \wedge b).$$

We call $a \triangle b$ the *symmetric difference* of a and b, $a \wedge b$ the *product* of a and b, and o the zero element[2]).

[1]) There is a number of books with exposition of Boolean algebras. Among them let us mention R. Halmos, *Lectures on Boolean Algebras* (Princeton 1963) and the monograph of R. Sikorski, *Boolean Algebras*, 2nd edition (Berlin 1964).

[2]) The fact that we are using the same symbols for operations in Boolean algebras and for logical operations should not lead to misunderstanding.

An example of a Boolean algebra is the family of all subsets of a given fixed set 1 where the operations $\triangle$ and $\wedge$ are the set-theoretical operations of symmetric difference and intersection and where o denotes the empty set. We dealt with this interpretation of axioms (1)–(9) in §6[1]).

More generally, instead of considering all the subsets of the space 1, we may limit ourselves to the consideration of any family of subsets K of 1 where the symmetric difference and intersection of two sets belonging to K also belong to K. Such a family is a Boolean algebra with respect to the same operations as in the preceding example. Each Boolean algebra of the type just described is called a *field of sets.*

We introduce *Boolean polynomials.* Let $x_1, x_2, \ldots$ be arbitrary letters. The symbols

(i) o,

(ii) $x_1, x_2, \ldots$

are polynomials; if f and g are polynomials then the expressions

(iii) $(f) \triangle (g)$,

(iv) $(f) \wedge (g)$

are polynomials. A polynomial is to be understood as a sequence of symbols.

Let us suppose that K is a Boolean algebra and that to every letter x_j there corresponds a certain element $a_j \in K$. We define inductively the value of a polynomial with respect to this correlation. The *value of polynomial* (i) is the zero element of the algebra K, the values of polynomials (ii) are the corresponding elements in K; if the values of f and g are the elements a and b, then the value of polynomial (iii) is $a \triangle b$ and the value of (iv) is $a \wedge b$.

The value of the polynomial f is denoted by $f_K(a_1, a_2, \ldots)$; clearly $f_K(a_1, a_2, \ldots) \in K$.

Let the polynomial f have the form $\ldots (h') \triangle (h'') \ldots$, and the poly-

[1]) Similarly as in §8, our exposition is based not only on the axioms of set theory but also on the axioms of Boolean algebra and, in part, also on topological axioms. As a matter of fact, we can deduce all theorems from the axioms of set theory given in Chapter II, treating the axioms of Boolean algebra as assumptions about the operations $\triangle$, $\wedge$ and the element o and the axioms of topology — as assumptions about the closure operation. Similar remarks apply to §10.

nomial g the form ... $(h'') \triangle (h')$ ... where the periods denote sequences of symbols which occur both in f and in g, and where h' and h'' are polynomials. In this case we say that the polynomial g is *immediately transformable into* the polynomial f by means of axiom (1). Similarly we define immediate transformability by means of the remaining axioms (2)–(9). We say that the polynomial g is *transformable into* f if there exists a finite sequence of polynomials $f = f_1, f_2, \ldots, f_k = g$ such that for each i $(1 \leqslant i < k)$ the polynomial f_{i+1} is immediately transformable into the polynomial f_i by means of one of the axioms. In this case we write $f \sim g$.

Clearly, $f \sim f$, $f \sim g \to g \sim f$ and $f \sim g \sim h \to f \sim h$. If $f \sim g$ then $f_K(a_1, a_2, \ldots) = g_K(a_1, a_2, \ldots)$ for every Boolean algebra K and arbitrary elements $a_j \in K$.

Polynomials resulting from the expression $f_1 \triangle f_2 \triangle \ldots \triangle f_k$ (or from the expression $f_1 \wedge f_2 \wedge \ldots \wedge f_k$) by an arbitrary placement of parentheses are mutually transformable into each other by means of axiom (2) (or axiom (6)). For this reason we shall always omit parantheses when writing such polynomials. Moreover, we shall not take notice of the difference in the order of polynomials to which we apply successively either one of the symbols $\triangle$ or $\wedge$.

THEOREM 1: *Every polynomial is either transformable into o or into some polynomial of the form $s_1 \triangle s_2 \triangle \ldots \triangle s_h$, where each of the polynomials s_j has the form $x_{i_1} \wedge x_{i_2} \wedge \ldots \wedge x_{i_t}$ $(i_1 < i_2 < \ldots < i_t, t \geqslant 1)$, and no two components s_j, s_k $(1 \leqslant j < k \leqslant h)$ are identical.*[1]

PROOF. The theorem is clear for polynomials (i) and (ii). Assume that it holds for polynomials f and g. If $f \sim o$ (or $g \sim o$), then $(f) \triangle (g) \sim g$ and $(f) \wedge (g) \sim o$ (or $(f) \triangle (g) \sim f$ and $(f) \wedge (g) \sim o$). At this point we may assume that $f \sim s_1 \triangle s_2 \triangle \ldots \triangle s_h$ and $g \sim t_1 \triangle t_2 \triangle \ldots \triangle t_k$. Thus $(f) \triangle (g) \sim s_1 \triangle s_2 \triangle \ldots \triangle s_h \triangle t_1 \triangle t_2 \triangle \ldots \triangle t_k$. By applying (3) and (4) we eliminate all redundant occurrences of components and thus obtain $(f) \triangle (g)$ in the desired form. The theorem, therefore, holds for formula (iii).

In the case of polynomial (iv) we apply axioms (9) and (5) and

[1]) Theorem 1, as well as Theorem 2, is a scheme: for each polynomial f we obtain a separate theorem.

obtain

$$(f) \wedge (g) \sim [(s_1 \triangle \ldots \triangle s_h) \wedge t_1] \triangle \ldots \triangle [(s_1 \triangle \ldots \triangle s_h) \wedge t_k]$$
$$\sim (s_1 \wedge t_1) \triangle \ldots \triangle (s_p \wedge t_q) \triangle \ldots \triangle (s_h \wedge t_k).$$

By means of (5) and (8) each of the polynomials $s_p \wedge t_q$ is transformable into the product of individual variables. Omitting as in the previous case redundancies we obtain the desired form. The theorem, therefore, holds for formula (iv). Q.E.D.

THEOREM 2: *Let K be the field of all subsets of the non-empty set* 1. *If f is a polynomial such that* $\neg(f \sim o)$, *then there exist sets* $A_1, A_2, \ldots$ *belonging to K such that* $f_K(A_1, A_2, \ldots) \neq 0$.

PROOF. By Theorem 1 we may limit ourselves to consideration of the case where f has the form $s_1 \triangle s_2 \triangle \ldots \triangle s_h$ and where each of the polynomials s_j is a product of letters x_i. Let n be the number of distinct letters x_i occurring in f. We shall prove the theorem by induction on n.

For $n = 1$, $f \sim x_i$, thus we may choose any non-empty set for the set A_i. Assume that the theorem holds for all numbers less than n and that the polynomial f contains exactly n distinct variables. If one of the variables x_p occurs in each of the expressions s_j, then $f \sim x_p \wedge g$ where g contains less than n variables. By the induction hypothesis there exist sets $A_1, A_2, \ldots$ such that $g_K(A_1, A_2, \ldots) \neq 0$. Replacing A_p by 1 we leave the value of g unchanged (because g does not contain x_p) and we obtain the set $1 \cap g_K(A_1, A_2, \ldots) \neq 0$ as the value of f.

If none of the letters x_p occurs in each of the s_j, then we substitute in f the symbol o everywhere for some arbitrary x_p. Thus we obtain the polynomial g of fewer variables than f and $\neg(g \sim o)$. Hence in this case the theorem follows from the induction hypothesis.

THEOREM 3: *Every equation* $f = g$ *which is true for arbitrary sets (and even for arbitrary subsets of a given non-empty set) is derivable from axioms* (1)–(9).

PROOF. If the polynomial $f \triangle g$ has the value o for all $A_1, A_2, \ldots$ contained in a non-empty set 1, then $f \triangle g \sim o$ and thus $f \sim g$. Therefore polynomial g arises from f by transformation by means of axioms (1)–(9) and by the general rule of logic which states that equal elements may be substituted for each other.

Theorem 3 shows that the equations derivable from axioms (1)–(9) are identical with the equations true for arbitrary sets. Moreover, this theorem provides a mechanical procedure for deciding when an equation of the form $f = g$ is derivable from axioms (1)–(9). Namely, it suffices to reduce the polynomial $f \triangle g$ by the method given in the proof of Theorem 1 and to determine whether or not it is transformed into o.

We introduce an *order relation* in Boolean algebra by the definition:

$$a \leqslant b \equiv a \wedge b = a.$$

THEOREM 4: $a \leqslant b \equiv a \vee b = b$.

PROOF. If $a \wedge b = a$, then $a \vee b = a \triangle b \triangle (a \wedge b) = a \triangle b \triangle a = b$. Conversely, if $a \vee b = b$, then $a \triangle b \triangle (a \wedge b) = b$. Thus $a \triangle b \triangle b \triangle (a \wedge b) = b \triangle b = o$ and $a \triangle o \triangle (a \wedge b) = o$, whence $a \triangle a \triangle (a \wedge b) = a \triangle o = a$ and $o \triangle (a \wedge b) = a$; that is, $a \wedge b = a$.

We call an element i of the Boolean algebra K a *unit* of K if

$$a \wedge i = a \tag{10}$$

for all elements $a \in K$.

It is easy to prove that *a unit, if it exists, is unique.*

In an algebra with unit we define the *complement* of the element a by the equation:

$$-a = i \triangle a.$$

Axioms (1)–(9) are very convenient in most calculations but are seldom used to describe Boolean algebra. In the next theorem we shall present a different system of axioms, which is usually taken as the basis of Boolean algebra. We shall limit ourself to the consideration of Boolean algebras with unit.

THEOREM 5: *If K is a Boolean algebra with unit, then the following equations hold for all $a, b, c \in K$:*

(i) $a \vee b = b \vee a$, (i′) $a \wedge b = b \wedge a$,

(ii) $a \vee (b \vee c) = (a \vee b) \vee c$, (ii′) $a \wedge (b \wedge c) = (a \wedge b) \wedge c$,

(iii) $a \vee o = a$, (iii′) $a \wedge i = a$,

(iv) $a \vee -a = i$, (iv′) $a \wedge -a = o$,

(v) $a \wedge (b \vee c) = (a \wedge b) \vee (a \wedge c)$, (v′) $a \vee (b \wedge c) = (a \vee b) \wedge (a \vee c)$.

PROOF. Equations (i), (i′) (ii), (ii′), (iii), (v), (v′) are true for arbitrary sets and thus are consequences of axioms (1)–(9). Equation (iii′) is identical with (10). We establish (iv) and (iv′) as follows:

$$\begin{aligned} a \wedge -a &= a \wedge (i \triangle a) && \text{by the definition of } -a, \\ &= a \triangle (a \wedge a) && \text{from (9) and (10)} \\ &= a \triangle a && \text{from (8)} \\ &= o && \text{from (4).} \end{aligned}$$

$$\begin{aligned} a \vee -a &= a \triangle (i \triangle a) \triangle [a \wedge (i \triangle a)] && \text{by the definition of sum,} \\ &= a \triangle (i \triangle a) \triangle o && \text{from (iv)} \\ &= (a \triangle a) \triangle i && \text{from (1), (2), (3)} \\ &= o \triangle i && \text{from (4)} \\ &= i && \text{from (3).} \end{aligned}$$

A partial converse to Theorem 5 holds:

THEOREM 6: *If* K *is a set,* o, $i \in K$, *and if* $\vee$, $\wedge$, $-$ *are operations defined on elements of* K *satisfying equations* (i)–(v′), *then* K *is a Boolean algebra with respect to the operations* $a \triangle b = (a \wedge -b) \vee (b \wedge -a)$, $a \wedge b$ *and the element* o.

The proof of the theorem is not difficult and is left to the reader.

Equations (i)–(v′) are most often used as axioms for Boolean algebra. In particular, it is worth noting the symmetry of these equations with respect to the operations $\vee$ and $\wedge$.

We shall conclude this section by giving an interesting example of a Boolean algebra.

Let 1 be an arbitrary topological space with a closure operator (see § 8, p. 26). We call $A \subset 1$ a *regular closed set* if

$$A = \overline{\mathrm{Int}(A)}.$$

By $\boldsymbol{K}$ we denote the family of all regular closed sets contained in 1. Clearly 0 and 1 belong to $\boldsymbol{K}$ since

$$\overline{\mathrm{Int}(0)} = \overline{0} = 0 \quad \text{and} \quad \overline{\mathrm{Int}(1)} = \overline{1} = 1.$$

If $A \in \boldsymbol{K}$ then $\overline{A} = A$, because

$$\overline{A} = \overline{\overline{\mathrm{Int}(A)}} = \overline{\mathrm{Int}(A)} = A.$$

Thus every set belonging to $\boldsymbol{K}$ is closed (see § 8, p. 27). By theorem (18), § 8, p. 30, it follows that if A, $B \in \boldsymbol{K}$ then

$$A \cup B = \overline{\mathrm{Int}(A)} \cup \overline{\mathrm{Int}(B)} = \overline{\mathrm{Int}(A \cup B)},$$

which proves that $A \cup B \in \boldsymbol{K}$.

For $A \in \boldsymbol{K}$ and $B \in \boldsymbol{K}$ let

$$A \odot B = \overline{\mathrm{Int}(A \cap B)}, \qquad A' = \overline{\mathrm{Int}(-A)}, \qquad A \circ B = (A \odot B') \cup (B \odot A').$$

It follows from this definition and from formula (14), § 8, p. 29 that if $A \in \boldsymbol{K}$ and $B \in \boldsymbol{K}$, then $A \odot B \in \boldsymbol{K}$, $A' \in \boldsymbol{K}$ and $A \circ B \in \boldsymbol{K}$.

THEOREM 7: *$\boldsymbol{K}$ is a Boolean algebra with unit with respect to the operations $\circ$ and $\odot$.*

PROOF. It suffices to show that the operations $\cup$, $\odot$ and $'$ satisfy axioms (i)–(v′) of Theorem 5.

Axioms (i)–(iii) are clearly satisfied. Axiom (i′) follows from the equation

$$A \odot B = \overline{\mathrm{Int}(A \cap B)} = \overline{\mathrm{Int}(B \cap A)} = B \odot A.$$

It is equally easy to show that axiom (iii′) holds:

$$A \odot 1 = \overline{\mathrm{Int}(A \cap 1)} = \overline{\mathrm{Int}(A)} = A.$$

To show that axiom (ii′) holds we apply (12) and (8) from § 8 and obtain

$$\mathrm{Int}[(A \odot B) \cap C] = \mathrm{Int}(A \odot B) \cap \mathrm{Int}(C),$$

$$A \odot B = \overline{\mathrm{Int}(A \cap B)} = \overline{\mathrm{Int}(A) \cap \mathrm{Int}(B)} \subset \overline{\mathrm{Int}(A)} \cap \overline{\mathrm{Int}(B)} = A \cap B;$$

it follows by (10), § 8 that

$$(*) \qquad \mathrm{Int}[(A \odot B) \cap C] \subset (A \odot B) \cap C \subset A \cap B \cap C \subset B \cap C.$$

Thus

$$\mathrm{Int}\{\mathrm{Int}[(A \odot B) \cap C]\} \subset \mathrm{Int}(B \cap C);$$

that is (see (11), § 8),

$$\mathrm{Int}[(A \odot B) \cap C] \subset \mathrm{Int}(B \cap C) \subset \overline{\mathrm{Int}(B \cap C)} = B \odot C.$$

Since (by $(*)$) $\mathrm{Int}[(A \odot B) \cap C] \subset A$, we have

$$\mathrm{Int}[(A \odot B) \cap C] \subset A \cap (B \odot C),$$

whence we obtain

$$\mathrm{Int}\{\mathrm{Int}[(A \odot B) \cap C]\} \subset \mathrm{Int}[A \cap (B \odot C)],$$

and hence

$$\operatorname{Int}[(A \odot B) \cap C] \subset \operatorname{Int}[A \cap (B \odot C)].$$

Taking closure on both sides of the inclusion we obtain

$$\overline{\operatorname{Int}[(A \odot B) \cap C]} \subset \overline{\operatorname{Int}[A \cap (B \odot C)]},$$

that is, $(A \odot B) \odot C \subset A \odot (B \odot C)$. The opposite inclusion is obtained in an entirely similar manner. Thus we may consider the equation $(A \odot B) \odot C = A \odot (B \odot C)$ as proved.

We examine axiom (v). We have

$$A \odot (B \cup C) = \overline{\operatorname{Int}[A \cap (B \cup C)]} = \overline{\operatorname{Int}[(A \cap B) \cup (A \cap C)]}.$$

The sets A, B and C are closed, thus (see (9) §8, p. 27) $\overline{A \cap B} = A \cap B$ and $\overline{A \cap C} = A \cap C$. By (18) §8, p. 30 we conclude that

$$\begin{aligned}\overline{\operatorname{Int}[(A \cap B) \cup (A \cap C)]} &= \overline{\operatorname{Int}(A \cap B)} \cup \overline{\operatorname{Int}(A \cap C)} \\ &= (A \odot B) \cup (A \odot C).\end{aligned}$$

Thus

$$A \odot (B \cup C) = (A \odot B) \cup (A \odot C).$$

We check axiom (v′) as follows. From the definitions,

$$A \cup (B \odot C) = \overline{\operatorname{Int}(A)} \cup \overline{\operatorname{Int}(B \cap C)}.$$

By (18) §8, p. 30, the right-hand side of the equation equals $\overline{\operatorname{Int}[A \cup (B \cap C)]}$, which equals $\overline{\operatorname{Int}[(A \cup B) \cap (A \cup C)]}$, that is, $(A \cup B) \odot (A \cup C)$.

Axiom (iv′) is an easy consequence of theorem (17) §8, p. 30 and of the fact that every regular closed set has the form X^{-c-}.

Finally we prove that axiom (iv) holds. By (18) §8, p. 30 we have

$$A \cup A' = \overline{\operatorname{Int}(A)} \cup \overline{\operatorname{Int}(-A)} = \overline{\operatorname{Int}(A \cup -A)},$$

since $\bar{A} = A$. Thus we conclude immediately that $A \cup A' = \overline{\operatorname{Int}(1)} = 1$.

Theorem 7 is thus proved.

Let us take the plane as the space 1. Every circle together with its boundary is clearly a regular closed set. Since every non-empty set of the form $\operatorname{Int}(A)$ contains some circle, we conclude that the Boolean algebra of regular closed sets in the plane has the following property:

If $A \in \boldsymbol{K}$ and $A \neq 0$, then there exists B such that $B \in \boldsymbol{K}$, $0 \neq B \subset A$ and $B \neq A$. #

Exercises

1. From every equation written in terms of variables, the symbols o and i and the operations $\vee$, $\wedge$ and $-$ we obtain a new equation by interchanging the symbols o and i and the operations $\vee$ and $\wedge$. If the original equation is true in Boolean algebra, then so is the equation obtained from it in this way (*Principle of Duality*).

2. Show that axioms (ii) and (ii′) are derivable from axioms (i), (i′), (iii)–(v), (iii′)–(v′). (Huntington)

§ 10. Lattices [1])

The concept of lattice is more general than that of Boolean algebra. Let L be an arbitrary set of elements, upon which are defined the operations $\vee$ and $\wedge$. We say that L is a *lattice* with respect to the operations $\vee$ and $\wedge$ if the following equations hold (axioms of lattice theory)

(1) $$a \vee a = a, \qquad a \wedge a = a,$$

(2) $$a \vee b = b \vee a, \qquad a \wedge b = b \wedge a,$$

(3) $$a \vee (b \vee c) = (a \vee b) \vee c, \qquad a \wedge (b \wedge c) = (a \wedge b) \wedge c,$$

(4) $$a \wedge (a \vee b) = a, \qquad a \vee (a \wedge b) = a.$$

We call a lattice *distributive* if

(5) $$a \wedge (b \vee c) = (a \wedge b) \vee (a \wedge c), \qquad a \vee (b \wedge c) = (a \vee b) \wedge (a \vee c).$$

We introduce an *order relation* between elements of a lattice just as we did for Boolean algebras:

(6) $$a \leqslant b \equiv a \vee b = b$$

or, equivalently,

(7) $$a \leqslant b \equiv a \wedge b = a.$$

Similarly we define the elements o and i (if they exist in the given lattice) as the elements satisfying conditions

(8) $$a \vee o = a, \qquad a \wedge i = a$$

for all $a \in L$.

[1]) A detailed exposition of lattice theory is given in the book: G. Birkhoff, *Lattice theory*, 2nd edition (New York 1948).

See footnote [1]) on p. 34.

It is easy to show that *o is the smallest element in the lattice and that i is the largest*, namely,

$$o \leqslant a \leqslant i \tag{9}$$

for every $a \in L$.

Referring to Theorem 5, p. 37 we observe that *every Boolean algebra with unit is a distributive lattice with zero and unit.* The converse does not hold, as is shown by the following counter-example which of itself is important for numerous applications in topology. The family of all closed subsets of an arbitrary topological space is a lattice (with the natural interpretation of the operations: $a \vee b = a \cup b$, $a \wedge b = a \cap b$). However, this family is not in general a Boolean algebra, since the difference of two closed sets need not be closed (for example, when the space is the space of real numbers).

On the other hand, the following theorem holds.

THEOREM: *If A is a distributive lattice with o and i and if for every $a \in A$ there exists an element $-a \in A$ satisfying the equations*

$$a \vee (-a) = i, \qquad a \wedge (-a) = o, \tag{10}$$

then (i) *the element $-a$ is unique, and* (ii) *A is a Boolean algebra with zero and unit with respect to the operations $\vee$, $\wedge$, and $-$.*

PROOF. Suppose that the element a' also satisfies conditions (10). Then $a' = a' \wedge i = a' \wedge (a \vee -a) = (a' \wedge a) \vee (a' \wedge -a) = o \vee (a' \wedge -a) = a' \wedge -a$. Similarly, $-a = -a \wedge a'$, therefore $a' = -a$.

For the proof of the second part of the theorem it suffices to show that axioms (i)–(v′) from p. 37 are satisfied. Axioms (i), (i′), (ii) and (ii′) hold in every lattice, (iii) and (iii′) follow from the assumption that o and i are zero and unit in A, (iv) and (iv′) follow from the assumption that condition (10) holds, and finally (v) and (v′) from the assumption that the lattice is distributive.

The concept of *Brouwerian lattice* [1]) is intermediate between that of lattice and Boolean algebra. We call a lattice with unit *Brouwerian* if

[1]) Brouwerian lattices were investigated in detail in the paper: J. C. C. Mc Kinsey and A. Tarski, *On closed elements in closure algebras,* Annals of Mathematics **47** (1946) 122–162. The term "Brouwerian algebra" was introduced in this paper because of a close connection between these algebras and logic of Brouwer.

for arbitrary elements $a, b \in L$ there exists an element of L called the *pseudo-difference* of a and b and denoted by the symbol $a \overset{*}{-} b$ such that

$$(a \overset{*}{-} b \leqslant c) \equiv (a \leqslant b \vee c).$$

The family of closed subsets of a given space considered above is a Brouwerian lattice, where the pseudo-difference of two closed sets A and B is the closed set $\overline{A-B}$.

We denote by $\overset{*}{-} a$ the *pseudo-complement* of a, namely $\overset{*}{-} a = i \overset{*}{-} a$. Notice that, in contrast to the operation of ordinary complementation, the equation $(\overset{*}{-} a) \wedge a = 0$ does not hold. This corresponds to the fact that the law of the excluded middle does not hold in intuitionistic logic. In the topological interpretation this means that the nowhere dense set $\overline{X-A} \cap A$, namely the frontier of A, is not necessarily empty. On the other hand, the validity of the equation $(\overset{*}{-} a) \vee a = i$ corresponds to the law of contradiction in Brouwerian logic.

Examples and exercises

1. The set of natural numbers is a lattice with respect to the operation of taking the greatest common divisor as the operation $\vee$ and the least common multiple for the operation $\wedge$. The formula $a \leqslant b$ means that b is a divisor of a. The number 1 is the unit of the lattice, and there is no zero element.

2. We consider euclidean n-space $\mathcal{E}^n$ and the family L_n of its linear subsets (points, lines, planes and in general, k-dimensional subspaces where $k \leqslant n$) passing through the origin. The family L_n is a lattice with respect to the operations $\vee$ and $\wedge$ defined by: $A \wedge B$ is the intersection of A and B; $A \vee B$ is the least linear subspace of $\mathcal{E}^n$ containing A and B. For example, if A and B are two planes, then $A \cup B$ is a 3-dimensional space if $A \cap B$ is a straight line, and is a 4-dimensional space if $A \cap B$ is a point. The relation $\leqslant$ is the ordinary inclusion relation. The zero element of the lattice L_n is the one-point set consisting of the origin and the unit is the entire space L_n.

The lattice L_n is not distributive but is modular. Namely, we call a lattice *modular* if

$$(a \leqslant c) \rightarrow [a \vee (b \wedge c) = (a \vee b) \wedge c].$$

It is worth noticing that in the lattice L_n every increasing sequence $a_1 < a_2 < \dots$ contains at most $n+1$ elements.

3. The set of sentences of an arbitrary mathematical theory is a lattice with respect to the operations of conjunction and disjunction when we identify sentences which are equivalent in terms of the propositional calculus. The zero element of the lattice is the false sentence and the unit element is the true sentence. The formula $a \leqslant b$ means that a implies b. #

4. Prove that the formula

$$(a \leqslant c) \rightarrow [a \vee (b \wedge c) \leqslant (a \vee b) \wedge c]$$

holds in every lattice.

5. Prove that the equations given in (5) are equivalent.

6. Prove that the following formulas hold in every Brouwerian lattice (see Mc Kinsey-A. Tarski, *op. cit.*, p. 124):

$$(x \leqslant y) \rightarrow (x \overset{*}{-} z \leqslant y \overset{*}{-} z) \wedge (z \overset{*}{-} y \leqslant z \overset{*}{-} x),$$

$$(x \leqslant y) \equiv (x \overset{*}{-} y = o),$$

$$z \overset{*}{-} (x \wedge y) = (z \overset{*}{-} x) \vee (z \overset{*}{-} y),$$

$$(x \vee y) \overset{*}{-} z = (x \overset{*}{-} z) \vee (y \overset{*}{-} z),$$

$$\overset{*}{-}(\overset{*}{-} x) \leqslant x,$$

$$\overset{*}{-}\overset{*}{-}\overset{*}{-} x = \overset{*}{-} x.$$

7. The family of compact subsets of a topological space is a lattice with respect to the ordinary set theoretical operations $\cup$ and $\cap$. If the space itself is not compact, then the lattice does not have a unit; on the other hand, the lattice always has a zero (see p. 139 for the definition of compact space).

CHAPTER II

AXIOMS OF SET THEORY. RELATIONS. FUNCTIONS

§ 1. Propositional functions. Quantifiers

We shall begin this chapter, like the previous one, by reviewing certain logical notions.

In the propositional calculus, as outlined in § 1, Chapter I, we dealt with sentences which have constant logical values. Now we shall consider *propositional functions*. They are expressions which contain variables. If each variable is replaced by the name of an arbitrary element, then the propositional function becomes a sentence. For instance,

$$x > 0, \qquad x^2 < 5, \qquad X \text{ is a non-empty set}$$

are examples of propositional functions. By substitution we obtain, e.g., the following sentences:

$1 > 0, \quad 25 < 5,$ the set of prime numbers is a non-empty set.

We say that the object *a satisfies the propositional function* $\Phi(x)$ if the sentence $\Phi(a)$ arising from $\Phi(x)$ by substituting the name of the object a for the argument x is true.

When dealing with propositional functions we shall often assume that the variable x may be replaced only by names of elements belonging to a certain fixed set A. In this case we say that *the domain of the propositional function is limited to the set* A. For example, the domain of the propositional function $x > 0$ is limited to the set of numbers (real, natural or rational, etc.). On the other hand, the propositional function $x = x$ has unlimited domain.

If every element of the set A satisfies $\Phi(x)$, then we write

$$\bigwedge_{x \in A} \Phi(x),$$

which is read: *for every x belonging to A,* $\Phi(x)$.

For propositional functions with domain limited to the set A we write

$$\bigwedge_{x} \Phi(x) \quad \text{instead of} \quad \bigwedge_{x \in A} \Phi(x).$$

Similarly, if $\Phi(x)$ is a propositional function with unlimited domain, then $\bigwedge_{x} \Phi(x)$ means that for all x, $\Phi(x)$. For example, the sentence $\bigwedge_{x} (x = x)$ is true.

The formulas

$$\bigvee_{x \in A} \Phi(x), \qquad \bigvee_{x} \Phi(x)$$

are read respectively: *for some x belonging to A, $\Phi(x)$*; and: *for some x, $\Phi(x)$*.

The symbols $\bigwedge$ and $\bigvee$ are called *quantifiers*, $\bigwedge$ is the *universal quantifier*, $\bigvee$ the *existential quantifier* [1]). Thus quantifiers are logical operators which allow us to form sentences from propositional functions of one variable and, more generally, propositional functions of $n-1$ variables from propositional functions of n variables.

In the sequel we assume that $A \neq 0$. If A contains a finite number of elements, $a_1, a_2, \ldots, a_n$, then the statement that every element of the set A satisfies the condition $\Phi(x)$ is clearly equivalent to the conjunction of the n sentences $\Phi(a_1), \Phi(a_2), \ldots, \Phi(a_n)$; and the statement that some element of the set A satisfies the condition $\Phi(x)$ is equivalent to the disjunction of these sentences:

$$\bigwedge_{x \in A} \Phi(x) \equiv [\Phi(a_1) \wedge \Phi(a_2) \wedge \ldots \wedge \Phi(a_n)],$$

$$\bigvee_{x \in A} \Phi(x) \equiv [\Phi(a_1) \vee \Phi(a_2) \vee \ldots \vee \Phi(a_n)].$$

Hence the universal quantifier is a generalized logical conjunction and the existential quantifier a generalized logical disjunction.

In the case where A is the empty set we let

$$\bigwedge_{x \in 0} \Phi(x) \equiv V \quad \text{and} \quad \bigvee_{x \in 0} \Phi(x) \equiv F.$$

[1]) Several authors use other symbols for quantifiers: for example, $(\forall x)$ or (x) for the universal quantifier and $(\exists x)$ or (Ex) for the existential one.

The following theorems (laws of logic) hold:

(1) *If* $a \in A$ *then* $\bigwedge\limits_{x \in A} \Phi(x) \rightarrow \Phi(a)$ *and* $\Phi(a) \rightarrow \bigvee\limits_{x \in A} \Phi(x)$.

The second formula states that to prove an existential sentence of the form $\bigvee\limits_{x \in A} \Phi(x)$ it suffices to find an object a belonging to the set A and satisfying the condition $\Phi(x)$. Such a proof of an existential sentence is called *effective.*

(2) $$\bigwedge_x [\Phi(x) \wedge \Psi(x)] \equiv [\bigwedge_x \Phi(x) \wedge \bigwedge_x \Psi(x)],$$

(3) $$\bigvee_x [\Phi(x) \vee \Psi(x)] \equiv [\bigvee_x \Phi(x) \vee \bigvee_x \Psi(x)].$$

Thus the universal quantifier is distributive over conjunction and the existential quantifier is distributive over disjunction.

(4) $$[\bigwedge_x \Phi(x) \vee \bigwedge_x \Psi(x)a] \rightarrow [\bigwedge_x [\Phi(x) \vee \Psi(x)],$$

(5) $$\bigvee_x [\Phi(x) \wedge \Psi(x)] \rightarrow [\bigvee_x \Phi(x) \wedge \bigvee_x \Psi(x)].$$

By means of simple counter-examples we conclude that the converse implications are not, in general, true. The universal quantifier is not distributive over disjunction and the existential quantifier is not distributive over conjunction.

(6) $$\neg[\bigwedge_x \Phi(x)] \equiv \bigvee_x [\neg \Phi(x)],$$

(7) $$\neg[\bigvee_x \Phi(x)] \equiv \bigwedge_x [\neg \Phi(x)].$$

Laws (6) and (7) are called *de Morgan's laws.* It follows from them that:

(6′) $$\neg \bigwedge_x [\neg \Phi(x)] \equiv \bigvee_x \Phi(x),$$

(7′) $$\neg \bigvee_x [\neg \Phi(x)] \equiv \bigwedge_x \Phi(x).$$

Hence the existential quantifier can be defined in terms of the universal quantifier (and conversely, the universal quantifier in terms of the existential).

The first equivalence above shows that the existential sentence $\bigvee_x \Phi(x)$ can be proved by deriving a contradiction from the assumption $\bigwedge_x \neg\Phi(x)$. Such proofs of existential sentences are often used but, in general, are not effective, i.e. they do not give any method of constructing the object satisfying the propositional function $\Phi(x)$.

Sentences can be considered as propositional functions without arguments. Clearly, we have

(8) $$\bigwedge_x p \equiv p,$$

(9) $$\bigvee_x p \equiv p.$$

Moreover, it is easy to check that

(10) $$\bigwedge_x [p \vee \Phi(x)] \equiv [p \vee \bigwedge_x \Phi(x)],$$

(11) $$\bigvee_x [p \wedge \Phi(x)] \equiv [p \wedge \bigvee_x \Phi(x)].$$

By means of the law of the propositional calculus $[p \to \Phi(x)] \equiv [\neg p \vee \Phi(x)]$ it follows easily from (10) that

(12) $$[p \to \bigwedge_x \Phi(x)] \equiv \bigwedge_x [p \to \Phi(x)].$$

Observe that

(13) $$[(\bigwedge_x \Phi(x)) \to p] \equiv \bigvee_x [\Phi(x) \to p].$$

In fact, it follows from (6) that the left-hand side of (13) is equivalent to the disjunction $\bigvee_x \neg\Phi(x) \vee p$, and then by (9), to the disjunction $\bigvee_x \neg\Phi(x) \vee \bigvee_x p$. By (3) we obtain $\bigvee_x [\neg\Phi(x) \vee p]$ or $\bigvee_x [\Phi(x) \to p]$.

Propositional functions may involve several variables. For instance:

$$x > y, \qquad x \in X, \qquad x^2+y^2+z^2 \neq 0.$$

Propositional functions containing two variables are denoted by $\Phi(x, y)$, $\Psi(x, y)$, ...

Laws (1)–(13) are also valid for propositional functions of several variables. Instead of p in (7)–(13) we can have any function which does not contain the variable x.

Note the following laws concerning propositional functions of two variables:

(14) $$\bigwedge_x \bigwedge_y \Phi(x,y) \equiv \bigwedge_y \bigwedge_x \Phi(x,y),$$

(15) $$\bigvee_x \bigvee_y \Phi(x,y) \equiv \bigvee_y \bigvee_x \Phi(x,y).$$

Thus it makes no difference in which order we write universal or existential quantifiers when they occur together. We usually write $\bigwedge_{xy}$ instead of $\bigwedge_x \bigwedge_y$ and $\bigvee_{xy}$ instead of $\bigvee_x \bigvee_y$.

(16) $$[\bigwedge_x \Phi(x) \vee \bigwedge_x \Psi(x)] \equiv \bigwedge_x \bigwedge_y [\Phi(x) \vee \Psi(y)]$$
$$\equiv \bigwedge_{xy} [\Phi(x) \vee \Psi(y)].$$

(17) $$[\bigvee_x \Phi(x) \wedge \bigvee_x \Psi(x)] \equiv \bigvee_x \bigvee_y [\Phi(x) \wedge \Psi(y)]$$
$$\equiv \bigvee_{xy} [\Phi(x) \wedge \Psi(y)].$$

To prove (16) we substitute in (10) $\bigwedge_y \Psi(y)$ for p and observe that $\bigwedge_y \Psi(y) \vee \Phi(x) \equiv \bigwedge_y [\Psi(y) \vee \Phi(x)]$ by means of the same law (10). The proof of (17) is similar.

(18) $$\bigvee_x \bigwedge_y \Phi(x,y) \rightarrow \bigwedge_y \bigvee_x \Phi(x,y).$$

PROOF. Using (1) twice we obtain $\bigwedge_y \Phi(x,y) \rightarrow \Phi(x,y)$ and $\Phi(x,y) \rightarrow \bigvee_x \Phi(x,y)$. These implications hold for any x, y, hence

$$\bigwedge_x \bigwedge_y [\bigwedge_y \Phi(x,y) \rightarrow \bigvee_x \Phi(x,y)].$$

By means of (12) and (13) we obtain (18).

As an application of (18) we shall discuss the difference between uniform and ordinary convergence of a sequence of functions. By the definition of limit, the sentence $\bigwedge_x [\lim_{n=\infty} f_n(x) = f(x)]$ is equivalent to the following

$$\bigwedge_{\varepsilon>0} \bigwedge_x \bigvee_k \bigwedge_n |f_{n+k}(x) - f(x)| < \varepsilon.$$

Interchanging the quantifiers $\bigwedge_x$ and $\bigvee_k$ we obtain the definition of uniform convergence making k independent of x. The fact that k is independent of x and depends only on ε is apparent in the above formula with the interchanged quantifiers. #

The following diagram gives several other theorems concerning interchanging of quantifiers:

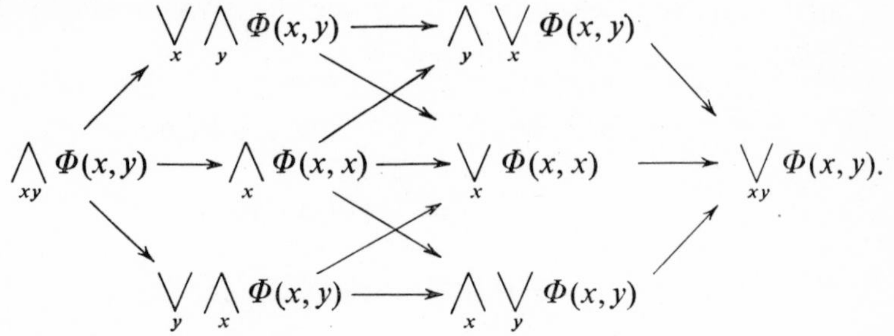

By means of simple counter-examples it is easy to check that none of the above implications can be inverted.

In set theory with primitive terms "set" and "membership" (cf. p. 5) a special role is played by a class $\mathfrak{K}$ of propositional functions obtained by applying the operations of propositional calculus and quantifiers to propositional functions of the form

(i) $Z(x)$ (i.e., x is a set), $x \in y$ and $x = y$.

The following clauses constitute an inductive definition of $\mathfrak{K}$:

(A) Propositional functions (i) (and all the propositional functions analogous to (i), differing from (i) only by the choice of symbols x, y which can be replaced arbitrarily by any other symbols).

(B) If Φ and Ψ are propositional functions belonging to $\mathfrak{K}$, then $\Phi \vee \Psi$, $\Phi \wedge \Psi$, $\Phi \rightarrow \Psi$, $\Phi \equiv \Psi$, $\neg \Phi$ belong to $\mathfrak{K}$ as well.

(C) If Φ belongs to the class $\mathfrak{K}$, then the propositional functions $\bigvee_x \Phi$ and $\bigwedge_x \Phi$ (where x may be replaced by any other letter) belong to the class $\mathfrak{K}$ as well.

(D) Every propositional function of the class $\mathfrak{K}$ arises by a finite number of applications of rules (A)–(C).

The propositional functions mentioned in (A) are called the *atomic formulas* of the class $\mathfrak{K}$.

Extending the list of atomic formulas but preserving (B), (C) and (D) we obtain classes larger than $\mathfrak{K}$. For instance, if we add new atomic formulas

$$xPy, \quad xQy, \ldots$$

(where again, the letters $x, y, \ldots$ could by replaced by any others), then we obtain the class of *propositional functions of general set theory extended by the primitive terms $P, Q, \ldots$*. This class will be denoted by $\mathfrak{K}[P, Q, \ldots]$. The propositional functions of this class will play a role when we admit primitive notions other than Z and $\in$.

§ 2. Axioms of set theory

We shall introduce axioms upon which we shall base the rest of our exposition of set theory. The new axioms will allow us to form new sets from given sets, and in this sense they do not differ from the axioms in Chapter I. On the other hand, the essential difference between the new axioms and the old ones is that we shall now deal with sets whose elements are also sets. [1])

First of all we retain the axiom of extensionality:

I. (Axiom of extensionality.) *If the sets A and B have the same elements, they are identical. In symbols*

$$\bigwedge_x [x \in A \equiv x \in B] \rightarrow (A = B).$$

II. (Axiom of the empty set.) *There exists a set* 0 *such that no x is an element of* 0; *symbolically*:

$$\bigvee_P \bigwedge_x (x \notin P).$$

Obviously, there is only one empty set (see p. 9).

[1]) To make the terminology clearer we shall use the term a *family of sets* instead of a *set of sets*. Families of sets will be denoted by capital letters printed in bold-faced italics $\boldsymbol{A}, \boldsymbol{B}, \boldsymbol{X}, \boldsymbol{Y}$, etc.

II'. (AXIOM OF PAIRS.)[1]) *For arbitrary a, b, there exists a set which contains only a and b.* In symbols:

$$\bigvee_P \bigwedge_x \{(x \in P) \equiv [(x = a) \vee (x = b)]\}.$$

III. (AXIOM OF UNIONS.) *Let* $\boldsymbol{A}$ *be a family of sets. There exists a set S such that x is an element of S if and only if x is an element of some set X belonging to* $\boldsymbol{A}$.

Symbolically:

$$x \in S \equiv \bigvee_X [(x \in X) \wedge (X \in \boldsymbol{A})]. \tag{1}$$

By axiom I there exists at most one set S satisfying axiom III for a given family of sets $\boldsymbol{A}$. In fact, if

$$x \in S_1 \equiv \bigvee_X [(x \in X) \wedge (X \in \boldsymbol{A})]$$

and

$$x \in S_2 \equiv \bigvee_X [(x \in X) \wedge (X \in \boldsymbol{A})],$$

then for any x

$$x \in S_1 \equiv x \in S_2,$$

and, by axiom I, $S_1 = S_2$.

Axiom III states that there exists at least one set S satisfying formula (1). We infer that for any $\boldsymbol{A}$ this set is unique. This set is called the *union* of the sets belonging to $\boldsymbol{A}$ and is denoted by $S(\boldsymbol{A})$ or $\bigcup_{X \in \boldsymbol{A}} X$.

IV. (AXIOM OF POWER SETS.) *For every set A there exists a family of sets* $\boldsymbol{P}$ *which consists exactly of all the subsets of the set A*:

$$(X \in \boldsymbol{P}) \equiv (X \subset A).$$

It is easy to prove that the set $\boldsymbol{P}$ is uniquely determined by A. This set $\boldsymbol{P}$ is called the *power set* of A and is denoted by 2^A.

V. (AXIOM OF INFINITY.) *There exists a family of sets* $\boldsymbol{A}$ *satisfying the conditions:* $0 \in \boldsymbol{A}$; *if* $X \in \boldsymbol{A}$, *then there exists an element* $Y \in \boldsymbol{A}$ *such that Y consists exactly of all the elements of X and the set X itself.*

[1]) This axiom can be derived from the remaining ones; therefore we do not give it a separate number.

Symbolically,

$$\bigvee_{A} \Big((0 \in A) \wedge \bigwedge_{X \in A} \bigvee_{Y \in A} \bigwedge_{x} \{ (x \in Y) \equiv [(x \in X) \vee (x = X)] \} \Big).$$

Thus the set 0 belongs to A, moreover, the set N_1 whose unique element is 0 also belongs to A. Similarly the set N_2 whose elements are 0 and N_1 belongs to A, etc.

VI. (Axiom of choice.) *For every family A of disjoint non-empty sets there exists a set B which has exactly one element in common with each set A:*

$$\bigwedge_{X, Y \in A} \{ [X \neq 0] \wedge [(X \neq Y) \rightarrow (X \cap Y = 0)] \} \rightarrow \bigvee_{B} \bigwedge_{X \in A} \bigvee_{x} \bigwedge_{y} [(y \in B \cap X) \equiv (y = x)].$$

For easier reading of the formula, observe that the propositional function $\bigvee_{x} \bigwedge_{y} [(y \in B \cap X) \equiv (y = x)]$ states that there exists an element x such that the conditions $y \in B \cap X$ and $y = x$ are equivalent. Thus the element x is the unique element of the intersection $B \cap X$ and the propositional function above asserts that this intersection contains exactly one element.

Not all mathematicians accept the axiom of choice without reserve, some of them view this axiom with a certain measure of distrust. They claim that proofs involving the axiom of choice are of a different nature than proofs not involving it, because it predicates the existence of a set B without giving a method of constructing it (i.e., it is not effective).[1]) Moreover, among the consequences of the axiom of choice there are many very peculiar ones. On the other

[1]) This is the position of, for example, Borel and Lebesgue (see E. Borel, *Eléments de la théorie des ensembles* (Paris 1949, p. 200), contrary to the position of, for example, Hausdorff and Fraenkel, who accept the axiom of choice without reserve attributing to it the same degree of "evidence" as to axioms I – V.

A detailed analysis of numerous proofs involving the axiom of choice was made by W. Sierpiński in his paper *L'axiome de M. Zermelo et son rôle dans la théorie des ensembles et l'analyse,* Bulletin de l'Académie de Sciences de Cracovie (1918) 97–152.

hand, it is unquestionable that many important discoveries in mathematics would never be made without appealing to this axiom.

In the sequel we shall mark theorems which are proved using the axiom of choice with the superscript °. As a rule the axiom of choice will be used only in proofs of theorems which have not yet been proved without the use of this axiom.

For each propositional function $\Phi(x)$ of the class $\mathfrak{K}$ we assume the following axiom[1]):

VI'_{Φ}. (AXIOM OF SUBSETS FOR THE PROPOSITIONAL FUNCTION Φ.) *For any set A there exists a set which contains the elements of A satisfying the propositional function Φ and which contains no other elements.*

Symbolically this axiom can be written in the following form:

$$\textit{There exists a set } B \textit{ such that } \bigwedge_x \{(x \in B) \equiv [(x \in A) \wedge \Phi(x)]\}$$

(we suppose that the variable B does not occur in Φ).

If $\Phi(x)$ contains free variables different from x, then they act as parameters upon which B depends.

Clearly, the set B is uniquely determined by the propositional function Φ. It is denoted by $\{x \in A\colon \Phi(x)\}$, which is read "the set of x which belong to A and for which $\Phi(x)$".

Finally, for every propositional function of the class $\mathfrak{K}$ in which variables z and B do not occur we have the following axiom:

VII_{Φ}. (AXIOM OF REPLACEMENT FOR THE PROPOSITIONAL FUNCTION Φ.) *If for every x there exists exactly one y such that $\Phi(x, y)$, then for every set A there exists a set B which contains those and only those elements y for which the condition $\Phi(x, y)$ holds for some $x \in A$.*

Symbolically,

$$\{\bigwedge_x \bigvee_z \bigwedge_y [\Phi(x, y) \equiv (y = z)]\} \to \bigwedge_A \bigvee_B \bigwedge_y [(y \in B) \equiv \bigvee_{x \in A} \Phi(x, y)].$$

The intuitive content of this axiom is as follows. Suppose that the antecedent of the implication holds, namely, for every x there exists exactly one element y satisfying $\Phi(x, y)$. In this case we say that y corresponds to x. The axiom states that for every set A there exists a

[1]) This axiom is dependent on the remaining ones, therefore we do not give it a separate number.

set B which contains all the elements y corresponding to elements of A and which contains no other elements.

For instance, if $\Phi(x, y)$ is the propositional function $Z(x) \wedge (y = 2^x)$, then the element corresponding to the set X is the power set 2^X. By the axiom of replacement, for every family of sets $\boldsymbol{A}$ there exists a family of sets $\boldsymbol{B}$ which consists of all the power sets 2^X where $X \in \boldsymbol{A}$.

Observe that we have defined not just one axiom of replacement but actually an infinite number of them. In fact, for every propositional function belonging to the class $\mathfrak{K}$ and not involving the variables B and z we have a separate axiom. Similarly, axioms VI'_Φ form an infinite collection of axioms.

If the uniqueness condition occurring in the antecedent of axiom VII_Φ is satisfied, then the set B whose existence is asserted in the conclusion of the axiom is unique. The proof follows immediately from axiom I. We call the set B the *image* of A obtained by the transformation Φ and we denote it by $\{\Phi\}$ “A.

Axioms I–VI and all of the axioms VII_Φ where Φ is an arbitrary propositional function of the class $\mathfrak{K}$ constitute an infinite system of axioms, which will be denoted by Σ°. Eliminating the axiom of choice from the system Σ° we obtain the axiom system denoted by Σ.

As already mentioned on p. 51 we shall introduce later new primitive notions $P, Q, \ldots$ into set theory. Then we shall use axioms I–VI and all axioms of the form VII_Φ, where Φ is an arbitrary propositional function of the class $\mathfrak{K}[P, Q, \ldots]$. This system, which includes the system Σ°, will be denoted by $\Sigma^\circ[P, Q, \ldots]$. If we omit the axiom of choice then we shall be dealing with the system which we denote by $\Sigma[P, Q, \ldots]$.

We can fully appraise the meaning which individual axioms have for set theory only after acquainting ourselves with conclusions which follow from them. At this time we shall be content to make a few remarks of a general character.

Axioms III, IV, VI, and VII are axioms of conditional existence, that is, they allow us to conclude the existence of certain sets assuming the existence of others.

Constructions of sets based on axioms III, IV and VII are unique. On the other hand, axiom VI does not assert the existence of a unique set: for a given family A of non-empty disjoint sets there exist, in general, many sets B satisfying the axiom of choice.

Axioms II and V are existential axioms: they postulate the existence of certain sets independently of any assumptions concerning the existence of other sets.

We make a few more remarks of a more general nature. Axioms in mathematical theories can play one of two roles. There are cases where the axioms completely characterize the theory, i.e., they constitute in some sense a definition of the primitive notions of the theory. Such is the case, for instance, in group theory: we define a group as a set and operations satisfying the axioms of group theory. In other cases the axioms formalize only certain chosen properties of the primitive notions of the theory. In this case the purpose of the axioms is not to give a complete description of the primitive notions but rather to give a systematization of the intuitive concept. This second point of view is that taken in this book. There arise, of course, problems of a philosophical nature related to establishing the intuitive truth of the axioms. However we shall not treat these problems here.

Since the intuitive content of the notion of set is not completely characterized by axioms I–VII, it is not surprising that the axioms do not suffice for establishing certain results from intuitive set theory. As an example of an intuitively obvious property of sets which cannot be derived from the axioms I–VII we give the following:

If A is a non-empty family of sets, then there exists a set X such that

$$X \in A \quad \textit{and} \quad X \cap A = 0.$$

Some authors accept the so-called *axiom of regularity*, which states that every family of sets has the property described above.

From the axiom of regularity it follows in particular that $X \in X$ for no X and, more generally, $X_1 \in X_2 \in \ldots \in X_n \in X_1$ for no $X_1, X_2, \ldots, X_n$.

In this book we will not use the axiom of regularity.

In Chapter X we shall treat certain other axioms independent of the axioms I–VII.

Some historical and bibliographical remarks on the axiomatization of set theory are in order. The first axiomatization of set theory is due to E. Zermelo (*Untersuchungen über die Grundlagen der Mengen-*

lehre I, Mathematische Annalen **65** (1908) 261–281). The primitive notions of his axiom system were "set" and $\in$, as in the system Σ°. Axioms I, IV, V and VI occur in Zermelo's set theory in the same form as in Σ°. Instead of the infinite collection of axioms VII (of replacement) Zermelo used the axiom of subsets VI′. The ambiguous formulation of this axiom was a source of much discussion. The definite form of the axiom was proposed by Th. Skolem (see the paper of 1922 cited below).

Axiom VII was formulated at about the same time by three authors: by D. Mirimanov in *Les antinomies de Russell et de Burali-Forti et le problème fondamental de la théorie des ensembles*, Enseignement Mathématique **19** (1917) 37–52, A. Fraenkel in *Zu den Grundlagen der Cantor-Zermeloschen Mengenlehre*, Mathematische Annalen (1922) 230–237, and by Th. Skolem in *Einige Bemerkungen zur axiomatischen Begründung der Mengenlehre*, Wissenschaftliche Vorträge gehalten auf dem fünften Kongress der Skandinavischen Mathematiker in Helsingfors (Helsingfors 1922) 217–232.

The most influential of these papers was that of Fraenkel, and for this reason axiom VII is often credited to Fraenkel.

The axiom of regularity is basically due to Mirimanov (see his paper cited above).

Axiom systems of set theory in which the axiom of replacement is written as a scheme of axioms dependent upon an arbitrary propositional function Φ (as it is in Σ°) are called *Zermelo–Fraenkel set theories*. If instead of the axiom of replacement only the axiom of subsets is assumed, then the system is said to be a *Zermelo set theory.*

A different axiomatization of set theory was proposed by v. Neumann (*Die Axiomatisierung der Mengenlehre*, Mathematische Zeitschrift **27** (1928), 669–752). Von Neumann introduced into set theory a new primitive notion which entered into his formulations of the axiom of replacement and the axiom of subsets and which allowed him to dispense with referring to the propositional function Φ. As first suggested by Bernays (*A system of axiomatic set theory I*, Journal of Symbolic Logic **2** (1937) 65–77), we can take the notion of a class as this primitive notion. Intuitively, X is a class if it is the collection of all objects satisfying some propositional function. Such a collection is not in general a set (see p. 61).

In this intuitive explanation of the notion of class we use such unclear notions as "collection" and "satisfying". In the formulations of the axiomatic system such notions do not occur. All axioms are stated in terms of the primitive notions "set", "class", "membership of an element in a class", and "membership of an element in a set".

In the literature, systems involving these primitive notions are said to be *Gödel–Bernays systems.* An advantage of these systems over systems of the Zermelo-Fraenkel type is finite axiomatizability; a disadvantage is a less natural choice of primitive notions[1]).

The most famous work based upon a Gödel–Bernays type formulation of set theory was done by K. Gödel (*The consistency of the axiom of choice and of the generalized continuum hypothesis with the axioms of set theory*, Annals of Mathematics Studies, 2nd edition (Princeton 1951)). See also A. A. Fraenkel and P. Bernays, *Axiomatic set theory* (Amsterdam 1958).

In general it seems that the axiomatization of set theory has not yet reached its most perfect form.

A critical exposition of different systems proposed as a basis for set theory is given in the book *Foundations of Set Theory* (Amsterdam 1958) by A. A. Fraenkel and Y. Bar-Hillel. This book contains a complete bibliography concerning the philosophical and mathematical foundations of set theory. The book by Hao Wang and R. Mc Naughton *Les systèmes axiomatiques de la théorie des ensembles* (Paris–Louvain 1953) contains a brief but useful description of the work done in the field.

Exercise

Show that axioms III, IV and VII can be replaced by a single axiom stating the existence of the set $S(\{\Phi\}\text{``}\, 2^A)$ for every set A and for every propositional function Φ belonging to $\mathfrak{K}$. [Hao Wang]

§ 3. Some simple consequences of the axioms

Starting with this paragraph, our exposition of set theory will be based upon the axioms of the system Σ°. Theorems dependent upon the axiom of choice will be marked by °.

[1]) Of course whether a notion is natural or not is not its objective property, but depends on psychological and historical motives.

THEOREM 1: (THE EXISTENCE OF PAIR.) *For arbitrary a, b there exists a unique set whose only elements are a and b.*

PROOF. Uniqueness follows from axiom I and existence from axiom II'.

The set, whose uniqueness and existence are stated in Theorem 1, is called the *unordered pair* of elements a, b and is denoted by $\{a, b\}$. If $a = b$ then we simply write $\{a\}$.

THEOREM 2: (THE EXISTENCE OF UNION.) *For arbitrary sets A and B there exists a set C such that*

$$(x \in C) \equiv [(x \in A) \vee (x \in B)].$$

In fact, $C = \bigcup_{X \in \{A,B\}} X$.

Theorem 2 asserts that axiom A (p. 6) is a consequence of the axioms Σ.

THEOREM 3: (THE EXISTENCE OF UNORDERED TRIPLES, QUADRUPLES, ETC.) *For arbitrary, a, b, c, ..., m there exist sets: $\{a, b, c\}$ whose only elements are a, b and c; $\{a, b, c, d\}$ whose only elements are a, b, c and d, ...; $\{a, b, ..., m\}$ whose only elements are a, b, ..., m.*

In fact, $\{a, b, c\} = \{a, b\} \cup \{c\}$, $\{a, b, c, d\} = \{a, b, c\} \cup \{d\}$, etc.

The set

$$\langle a, b \rangle = \{\{a\}, \{a, b\}\} \tag{1}$$

is called an *ordered pair*. We call a the *first term* of $\langle a, b \rangle$ and b the *second term* of $\langle a, b \rangle$ [1]).

THEOREM 4: *In order that $\langle a, b \rangle = \langle c, d \rangle$ it is necessary and sufficient that $a = c$ and $b = d$.*

PROOF. The sufficiency of the condition is obvious. To prove its necessity, suppose that $\langle a, b \rangle = \langle c, d \rangle$. By means of (1), it follows that

$$\{c\} \in \langle a, b \rangle \quad \text{and} \quad \{c, d\} \in \langle a, b \rangle,$$

[1]) This definition of an ordered pair was given by K. Kuratowski in the paper *Sur la notion de l'ordre dans la théorie des ensembles*, Fundamenta Mathematicae **2** (1921) 161–171. See also: N. Wiener, *A simplification of the logic of relations*, Proceedings of the Cambridge Philosophical Society **17** (1912–1914) 387–390.

that is

(i) $\{c\} = \{a\}$ or (ii) $\{c\} = \{a, b\}$,

and

(iii) $\{c, d\} = \{a\}$ or (iv) $\{c, d\} = \{a, b\}$.

Formula (ii) holds if $a = c = b$. Formulas (iii) and (iv) are then equivalent and it follows that $c = d = a$. Hence we obtain $a = c = b = d$ in which case the theorem holds. Similarly, one can check that the theorem holds for case (iii). It remains to be shown that the theorem holds for cases (i) and (iv). We have then $c = a$ and either $c = b$ or $d = b$. If $c = b$ then (ii) holds and this case has already been considered. If $d = b$ then $a = c$ and $b = d$, which proves the theorem.

COROLLARY: *If* $\langle a, b\rangle = \langle b, a\rangle$ *then* $a = b$.

By the definition of the set $\{x \in A\colon \Phi(x)\}$ axiom VI'_{Φ} implies the following theorem:

THEOREM 5:

$$t \in \{x \in A\colon \Phi(x)\} \equiv [\Phi(t) \wedge (t \in A)]. \tag{2}$$

In particular, if $\Phi(x) \to (x \in A)$ (i.e. if the domain of the propositional function Φ is limited to A), then

$$t \in \{x\colon \Phi(x)\} \equiv \Phi(t). \tag{3}$$

Equivalence (3) leads easily to the following theorems (with the assumption that the domains of Φ and Ψ are limited to A):

$$\{x\colon \Phi(x) \vee \Psi(x)\} = \{x\colon \Phi(x)\} \cup \{x\colon \Psi(x)\}, \tag{4}$$

$$\{x\colon \Phi(x) \wedge \Psi(x)\} = \{x\colon \Phi(x)\} \cap \{x\colon \Psi(x)\}, \tag{5}$$

$$\{x\colon \neg\Phi(x)\} = A - \{x\colon \Phi(x)\}. \tag{6}$$

As an example we shall prove (4). For this purpose we apply equivalence (3) to the propositional function $\Phi(x) \vee \Psi(x)$ and we obtain

$$t \in \{x\colon \Phi(x) \vee \Psi(x)\} \equiv [\Phi(t) \vee \Psi(t)]. \tag{i}$$

According to (3) we have

$$\Phi(t) \equiv t \in \{x\colon \Phi(x)\} \quad \text{and} \quad \Psi(t) \equiv t \in \{x\colon \Psi(x)\},$$

thus it follows from (i) that

$$\begin{aligned} t \in \{x: \Phi(x) \vee \Psi(x)\} &\equiv t \in \{x: \Phi(x)\} \vee t \in \{x: \Psi(x)\} \\ &\equiv t \in \{x: \Phi(x)\} \cup \{x: \Psi(x)\}, \end{aligned}$$

which proves (4).

THEOREM 6: *For every non-empty family of sets A there exists a unique set containing just those elements which are common to all the sets of the family A.*

This set is called the *intersection* of the sets belonging to the family A and is denoted by $P(A)$ or $\bigcap_{X \in A} X$.

For we have:

$$P(A) = \{x \in S(A): \bigwedge_X [(X \in A) \to (x \in X)]\}.$$

If the family A is composed of sets $X_1, X_2, \ldots, X_n$ (n finite), then $P(A) = X_1 \cap X_2 \cap \ldots \cap X_n$. In case $A = 0$, the operation $P(A)$ is not performable.

We conclude this section with a remark on so-called *antinomies of set theory*. A naïve intuition of set would incline us to accept an axiom (stronger than axiom VI'_{Φ}) stating that for any propositional function there exists a set B containing those and only those elements which satisfy this function.

The creator of set theory, Cantor, believed (at least at the beginning of his work) that such an axiom was true[1]).

However, it became very early apparent that the axiom formulated in this way leads to a contradiction (to an *antinomy*).

Let us take as an example the propositional function

$$\Phi(x) \equiv (x \text{ is a set}) \wedge (x \notin x),$$

which leads to *Russell's antinomy*[2]).

We shall prove

THEOREM 7: *There exists no set Z such that*

$$\bigwedge_x [(x \in Z) \equiv \Phi(x)].$$

[1]) See G. Cantor, *Über unendliche, lineare Punktmannigfaltigkeiten*, Mathematische Annalen **20** (1882) 113–121.

[2]) This antinomy was first published in the appendix to the book of G. Frege, *Grundgesetze der Arithmetik*, vol. 2 (Jena 1903).

PROOF. If such a set existed, then the equivalence

$$(x \in Z) \equiv (x \text{ is a set}) \wedge (x \notin x)$$

would hold. From the assumption that Z is a set we obtain the contradiction $Z \in Z \equiv \neg(Z \in Z)$.

Interdependence of the axioms.

We have shown that axiom A (p. 6) follows from Σ. Axiom B (p. 6) follows from Σ as well, because $A - B = \{x \in A: \neg(x \in B)\}$. Axiom C (p. 6) follows directly from axiom II (the axiom of empty set) or from axiom V (the axiom of infinity).

Axiom II′ follows from the other axioms of the system Σ. In fact, let A be a family of sets such that $0 \in A$ and such that there exists at least one non-empty set belonging to A. This family exists by the axiom of infinity. The set $\{a, b\}$ is the set $\{\Phi\}$"A where Φ is the propositional function

$$[(x = 0) \wedge (y = a)] \vee [(x \neq 0) \wedge (y = b)].$$

Axiom VI'_Φ (of subsets) is also a consequence of the other axioms of the system Σ. In fact, let A be a set and $\Phi(x)$ a propositional function. If $\bigwedge_x [(x \in A) \to \neg\Phi(x)]$, then the empty set satisfies the axiom of subsets. Otherwise, let a be an arbitrary element of A such that $\Phi(a)$. Denote by $\Psi(x, y)$ the propositional function $[\Phi(x) \wedge (y = x)] \vee [\neg\Phi(x) \wedge (x = a)]$. For every x there exists exactly one y such that $\Psi(x, y)$; namely this element y is x or a, depending on whether $\Phi(x)$ or $\neg\Phi(x)$. The set $\{\Psi\}$"A clearly satisfies the thesis of axiom VI'_Φ.

Exercises

Show that

1. If $X \in A$, then $P(A) \subset X \subset S(A)$.
2. $S(A_1 \cup A_2) = S(A_1) \cup S(A_2)$.
3. If $A_1 \cap A_2 \neq 0$, then $P(A_1 \cap A_2) \supset P(A_1) \cap P(A_2)$.

§ 4. Cartesian products. Relations

The *cartesian product* of two sets X and Y is defined to be the set of all ordered pairs $\langle x, y \rangle$ such that $x \in X$ and $y \in Y$.

The existence of this set can be proved as follows. If $x \in X$ and $y \in Y$, then $\{x, y\} \subset X \cup Y$ and $\{x\} \subset X \cup Y$, whence

$$\langle x, y\rangle = \{\{x\}, \{x, y\}\} \in 2^{2^{X \cup Y}}.$$

The set

$$\{t \in T: \bigvee_{x \in X} \bigvee_{y \in Y} (t = \langle x, y\rangle)\}, \quad \text{where} \quad T = 2^{2^{X \cup Y}},$$

exists by means of axioms IV, VI′ and Theorem 2, p. 59. This set contains every ordered pair $\langle x, y\rangle$, where $x \in X$, $y \in Y$, and contains no other elements. Hence this set is the cartesian product of X and Y.

Since there exists at most one set containing exactly the pairs $\langle x, y\rangle$, $x \in X$, $y \in Y$, the cartesian product is uniquely determined by X and Y. This product is denoted by $X \times Y$.

If $X = 0$ or $Y = 0$ then obviously $X \times Y = 0$.

In spite of the arbitrary nature of X and Y, their cartesian product can be treated in geometrical terms: the elements of the set $X \times Y$ are called *points*, the sets X and Y the *coordinate axes*. If $z = \langle x, y\rangle$ then x is called the *abscissa* and y the *ordinate* of z. The fact that the set of points in a plane can be treated as the cartesian product $\mathcal{E} \times \mathcal{E}$ where $\mathcal{E}$ is the set of real numbers justifies the use of this terminology.

Certain properties of cartesian products are similar to the properties of multiplication of numbers. For instance, the distributive laws hold:

$$(X_1 \cup X_2) \times Y = X_1 \times Y \cup X_2 \times Y,$$
$$Y \times (X_1 \cup X_2) = Y \times X_1 \cup Y \times X_2,$$
$$(X_1 - X_2) \times Y = X_1 \times Y - X_2 \times Y,$$
$$Y \times (X_1 - X_2) = Y \times X_1 - Y \times X_2.$$

As an example we shall prove the first of these equations:

$$\begin{aligned}\langle x, y\rangle \in (X_1 \cup X_2) \times Y &\equiv (x \in X_1 \cup X_2) \wedge (y \in Y)\\ &\equiv (x \in X_1 \vee x \in X_2) \wedge (y \in Y)\\ &\equiv (x \in X_1 \wedge y \in Y) \vee (x \in X_2 \wedge y \in Y)\\ &\equiv (\langle x, y\rangle \in X_1 \times Y) \vee (\langle x, y\rangle \in X_2 \times Y)\\ &\equiv \langle x, y\rangle \in (X_1 \times Y \cup X_2 \times Y).\end{aligned}$$

The cartesian product is distributive over intersection:

$$(X_1 \cap X_2) \times Y = (X_1 \times Y) \cap (X_2 \times Y),$$
$$Y \times (X_1 \cap X_2) = (Y \times X_1) \cap (Y \times X_2).$$

The proof is similar to the previous one.

The cartesian product is monotone with respect to the inclusion relation, that is,

(*) *If* $Y \neq 0$, *then* $(X_1 \subset X_2) \equiv (X_1 \times Y \subset X_2 \times Y) = (Y \times X_1 \subset Y \times X_2)$.

In fact, let $y \in Y$. Suppose that $X_1 \subset X_2$. Since (for $i = 1, 2$)

$$(\langle x, y\rangle \in X_i \times Y) \equiv (x \in X_i) \wedge (y \in Y),$$

we have the following implication

$$(\langle x, y\rangle \in X_1 \times Y) \rightarrow (\langle x, y\rangle \in X_2 \times Y);$$

hence $X_1 \times Y \subset X_2 \times Y$.

Conversely, if $X_1 \times Y \subset X_2 \times Y$ and $y \in Y$, then

$$\begin{aligned}(x \in X_1) \rightarrow (x \in X_1) \wedge (y \in Y) \equiv (\langle x, y\rangle \in X_1 \times Y) \rightarrow (\langle x, y\rangle \in X_2 \times Y)\\ \equiv (x \in X_2) \wedge (y \in Y) \rightarrow (x \in X_2),\end{aligned}$$

thus $X_1 \subset X_2$.

The proof of the second part of (*) is similar.

Using cartesian products we can perform certain logical transformations. For instance, the formulas (p. 49)

$$\bigwedge_x \bigwedge_y \Phi(x, y) \equiv \bigwedge_{xy} \Phi(x, y) \equiv \bigwedge_z \Phi(z),$$

$$\bigvee_x \bigvee_y \Phi(x, y) \equiv \bigvee_{xy} \Phi(x, y) \equiv \bigvee_z \Phi(z)$$

allow us to replace two consecutive universal or existential quantifiers by one quantifier binding the variable $z = \langle x, y\rangle$ which runs over the cartesian product $X \times Y$.

A subset R of a cartesian product $X \times Y$ is called a *(binary) relation.*

Instead of writing $\langle a, b\rangle \in R$, where R denotes a relation, we sometimes write aRb and read: *a is in the relation R to b*, or *the relation R holds between a and b*.

The *left domain* (D_l) (or simply the *domain*) of a relation R is defined to be the set of all x such that $\langle x, y\rangle \in R$ for some y; the *right domain* (D_r)—the set of all y such that $\langle x, y\rangle \in R$ for some x. The right domain of a relation is sometimes called the *range*, or the *counter-domain*, or the *converse domain*. The union $F(R)$ of the left and right domains of R is called the *field* of R.

In geometrical terminology we say that D_l is the *projection* of R on the X axis and D_r is the projection of R on the Y axis.

Thus we have

(1) $D_1 = \{x \in X: \bigvee_y \langle x, y\rangle \in R\}, \quad D_r = \{y \in Y: \bigvee_x \langle x, y\rangle \in R\}.$

These formulas prove the existence of the sets D_1 and D_r.

If the arguments of the propositional function $\Phi(x, y)$ are limited to the sets X and Y respectively, then the set $R = \{\langle x, y\rangle: \Phi(x, y)\}$ is a relation. Clearly, $\Phi(x, y) \equiv xRy \equiv \langle x, y\rangle \in R$. Hence it follows from formula (1) that:

THEOREM: *The projection of the set* $\{\langle x, y\rangle: \Phi(x, y)\}$ *on the X-axis is the set* $\{x: \bigvee_y \Phi(x, y)\}$.

The relation $\{\langle x, y\rangle: yRx\}$ is called the *inverse* of R and is denoted by R^c. Obviously $D_1(R^c) = D_r(R)$ and $D_r(R^c) = D_1(R)$.

The relation $\{\langle x, y\rangle: \bigvee_z (xSz \wedge zRy)\}$ is called the *composition* of R and S and is denoted by $R \circ S$[1]. Obviously, $D_1(R \circ S) \subset D_1(S)$ and $D_r(R \circ S) \subset D_r(R)$.

The operation $\circ$ is associative. In fact,

$$\begin{aligned} x(R \circ S) \circ Ty &\equiv \bigvee_z (xTz \wedge zR \circ Sy) \\ &\equiv \bigvee_z \bigvee_t (xTz \wedge zSt \wedge tRy) \\ &\equiv \bigvee_t \bigvee_z (xTz \wedge zSt \wedge tRy) \\ &\equiv \bigvee_t [\bigvee_z (xTz \wedge zSt) \wedge tRy] \\ &\equiv \bigvee_t (xS \circ Tt \wedge tRy) \\ &\equiv xR \circ (S \circ T)y. \end{aligned}$$

Because of the associativity of $\circ$ we may omit parantheses in expressions of the form $R \circ S \circ \ldots \circ U$.

We shall prove the formula

$$(R \circ S)^c = S^c \circ R^c.$$

[1]) We use this notation instead of the more natural $S \circ R$, because composing transformations we normally write on the second place the symbol of the operation which is carried out first (for example, $\sin(\log x)$).

In fact,

$$\begin{aligned} x(R \circ S)^c y &\equiv yR \circ Sx \\ &\equiv \bigvee_z (ySz \wedge zRx) \\ &\equiv \bigvee_z (xR^c z \circ zS^c y) \\ &\equiv xS^c \circ R^c y. \end{aligned}$$

Other properties of the operations ^{c} and $\circ$ are given in the exercises.

Examples and exercises

1. Let $X = Y = \mathcal{E}$ (the set of real numbers). The set $\{\langle x, y\rangle : x < y\}$ is that part of the plane which lies above the straight line $x = y$. The set $\{\langle x, y\rangle : y = x^2\}$ is a parabola, its projection on the Y axis is the set $\{y: \bigvee_x (y = x^2)\}$.

2. Let A be a family of subsets of $X \times Y$. Let $F(Z)$ denote the projection of the set Z (where $Z \subset X \times Y$) on the X axis and $F(A)$ the family of all projections $F(Z)$, $Z \in A$. Prove that

$$F[S(A)] = S[F(A)],$$

i.e. the projection of a union is equal to the union of the projections.

3. Give an example showing that the projection of an intersection may be different from the intersection of the projections.

4. Prove the formulas $(R \cup S)^c = R^c \cup S^c$, $(R \cap S)^c = R^c \cap S^c$ and $(R^c)^c = R$.

5. Prove the formulas

$$(R \cup S) \circ T = (R \circ T) \cup (S \circ T), \quad T \circ (R \cup S) = (T \circ R) \cup (T \circ S),$$
$$(R \cap S) \circ T \subset (R \circ T) \cap (S \circ T), \quad T \circ (R \cap S) \subset (T \circ R) \cap (T \circ S).$$

6. Prove that $(X \times Y)^c = Y \times X$. Compute $(X \times Y) \circ (Z \times T)$.

§ 5. Equivalence relations

Equivalence relations form an important and frequently encountered class of relations. A relation R is called an *equivalence relation* if for all $x, y, z \in F(R)$, the following conditions are satisfied:

$$xRx \qquad (\textit{reflexivity}),$$
$$xRy \to yRx \qquad (\textit{symmetry}),$$
$$xRy \wedge yRz \to xRz \qquad (\textit{transitivity}).$$

Examples

1. Let x, y be straight lines lying in a plane. Let xRy if and only if x is parallel to y. Then R is an equivalence relation.

2. Let C be a set of Cauchy sequences $\langle a_1, a_2, \ldots, a_n, \ldots \rangle$ of rational numbers. The relation R which holds between two sequences if and only if $\lim (a_n - b_n) = 0$ is an equivalence relation.

3. Let X be the set of real numbers x such that $0 \leqslant x < 1$. The relation R which holds between two numbers $a, b \in X$ if and only if the difference $a-b$ is a rational number is an equivalence relation. #

4. Let X be any set, $\boldsymbol{K} = 2^X$ and let $\boldsymbol{I}$ be an ideal (see p. 17). The relation $\doteq$ which holds between two sets $X, Y \in \boldsymbol{K}$ if and only if $X \dot{-} Y \in \boldsymbol{I}$ is an equivalence relation.

5. Example 4 can be generalized in the following way. Let $\boldsymbol{K}$ be an arbitrary Boolean algebra and $\boldsymbol{I}$ any subset of $\boldsymbol{K}$ satisfying the conditions:

$$a \leqslant b \in \boldsymbol{I} \rightarrow a \in \boldsymbol{I}, \qquad (a \in \boldsymbol{I}) \wedge (b \in \boldsymbol{I}) \rightarrow (a \vee b \in \boldsymbol{I}).$$

Then $\boldsymbol{I}$ is an ideal of $\boldsymbol{K}$ and the relation $\doteq$ (Example 4) is an equivalence relation.

We shall now give several theorems which describe the structure of an arbitrary equivalence relation.

Let C be any set. A family $\boldsymbol{A}$ of subsets of C $(\boldsymbol{A} \subset 2^C)$ is called a *partition* of C if $0 \notin \boldsymbol{A}$, $S(\boldsymbol{A}) = C$ and the sets belonging to $\boldsymbol{A}$ are pairwise disjoint (i.e. for any $X, Y \in \boldsymbol{A}$ either $X = Y$ or $X \cap Y = 0$).

THEOREM 1: *If $\boldsymbol{A}$ is a partition of C, then the relation $R_{\boldsymbol{A}}$ defined by the formula*

$$x R_{\boldsymbol{A}} y \equiv \bigvee_{Y \in \boldsymbol{A}} [(x \in Y) \wedge (y \in Y)]$$

is an equivalence relation whose field is C.

The proof of this theorem is left to the reader.

THEOREM 2: *If $\boldsymbol{A}$ and $\boldsymbol{B}$ are two different partitions of C, then $R_{\boldsymbol{A}} \neq R_{\boldsymbol{B}}$.*

PROOF. Suppose that $R_{\boldsymbol{A}} = R_{\boldsymbol{B}}$; we shall show that $\boldsymbol{A} = \boldsymbol{B}$. Because of the symmetry of the assumptions it suffices to prove that $\boldsymbol{A} \subset \boldsymbol{B}$. So let $Y \in \boldsymbol{A}$ and let $y \in Y$. Since $S(\boldsymbol{B}) = C$, there exists $Z \in \boldsymbol{B}$ such that $y \in Z$. If $x \in Y$ then $x R_{\boldsymbol{A}} y$ and hence $x R_{\boldsymbol{B}} y$. Because Z is the unique element of $\boldsymbol{B}$ containing y, we have $x \in Z$. Similarly we can show that $x \in Z \rightarrow x \in Y$, which proves that $Y = Z$ and hence $Y \in \boldsymbol{B}$.

THEOREM 3: *For any equivalence relation R with field $C \neq 0$ there exists a partition A of the set C such that $R = R_A$.*

PROOF. Let

$$A = \{Y \subset C: \bigvee_{y \in C} \bigwedge_{u \in C} (uRy \equiv u \in Y)\}.$$

Because of the reflexivity of R the elements of the family A are non-empty and $S(A) = C$. If $Y \in A$ and $Z \in A$, then for some $y, z \in C$ the following formulas hold:

$$\bigvee_u (u \in Y \equiv uRy), \quad \bigwedge_u (u \in Z = uRz).$$

From the symmetry and transitivity of R we infer that if sets Y and Z have a common element, then they are identical. This proves that the family A is a partition of C.

We show now that $R = R_A$.

Suppose that uRv. Denoting the set $\{z \in C: zRu\}$ by Y_u we obtain $Y_u \in A$ and $v \in Y_u$; hence uR_Av and $R \subset R_A$.

Now suppose that uR_Av; then there exist Y in A and an element y such that $\bigwedge_z (zRy \equiv z \in Y)$ and $u \in Y$ and $v \in Y$. Therefore uRy and vRy; by the symmetry and transitivity of R, it follows that uRv. This proves that $R_A \subset R$. Hence $R = R_A$, Q.E.D.

It follows from Theorems 1–3 that every equivalence relation with field $C \neq 0$ defines exactly one partition A of the set C and vice versa.

If $R = R_A$ then sets of the family A are called *equivalence classes* of R. The equivalence class containing an element x is denoted by x/R, the family A itself is denoted by C/R. This family is called the *quotient class of C with respect to R.*

Examples

For the relation R of Example 1 each equivalence class consists of all straight lines lying in the same direction (i.e. mutually parallel). For the relation R of Example 2 each equivalence class consists of all sequences of rational numbers convergent to the same real number. Cantor defined real numbers as the equivalence classes with respect to this relation. #

A *set of representatives* of an equivalence relation with field C is a subset of C which has exactly one element in common with each equivalence class.

The existence of a set of representatives for any equivalence relation follows from the axiom of choice. Without the axiom of choice we cannot prove the existence of a set of representatives even for very simple relations. Such is the case for the relation of Example 3[1]).

Exercises

1. Let $I = \{x\colon 0 \leqslant x < 1\}$; for $X \subset I$ let $X(r)$ denote the set of numbers belonging to I and having the form $x+r+n$ where $x \in X$ and n is an integer. Show that if Z is a set of representatives for the relation R of Example 3, then

a) $Z(r) \cap Z(s) = 0$ for all rational numbers r, s $(r \neq s)$;

b) $I = \bigcup_r Z(r)$, where the union is over all rational numbers.

2. Show that the condition $R_A \subset R_B$ is equivalent to the following: every set $Y \in A$ is the union of some family $A' \subset B$.

3. Show that if M is a non-empty family of equivalence relations with common field C, then $P(M)$ is also an equivalence relation with field C.

4. Preserving the notation of Exercise 3 prove that there exists an equivalence relation U with field C such that

a) $R \in M \to R \subset U$;

b) if V is an equivalence relation with field C and $\bigwedge_R [R \in M \to R \subset V]$, then $U \subset V$.

5. Assuming in Exercises 3 and 4 that $M = \{R_A, R_B\}$, describe $P(M)$ and U.

§ 6. Functions

A relation $R \subset X \times Y$ is called a *function*[2]) if

$$(1) \qquad \bigwedge_{x, y_1, y_2} [xRy_1 \wedge xRy_2 \to (y_1 = y_2)].$$

Functions are denoted by letters $f, g, h, \ldots$. The sets $D_l(f)$ and $D_r(f)$ are called respectively the *domain* and the *range* of the func-

[1]) As was shown by G. Vitali, *Sul problema della misura dei gruppi di punti di una retta* (Bologna 1905), every set of representatives for the relation in Example 3 is non-measurable in the sense of Lebesgue.

[2]) This definition of a function is due to G. Peano, *Sulla definizione di funzione*, Atti della Reale Accademia dei Lincei, Classe di scienze fisiche, matematiche e naturali **20** (1911) 3–5.

tion f. The following terminology will be used: if $D_l(f) = X$ and $D_r(f) \subset Y$ then f is called a *mapping* (or a *transformation*) *of* X *into* Y; if, moreover, $D_r(f) = Y$ then f is called a *mapping of* X *onto* Y. When $D_l(f) = X$, we say that the function f is defined on X.

The set of all mappings of X into Y is denoted by Y^X. Instead of the formula $f \in Y^X$ we often use the more suggestive formulas $f: X \rightarrow Y$ or $X \xrightarrow{f} Y$.

If $f \in Y^X$ and $x \in X$, then by the definition of domain there exists at least one element $y \in Y$ such that xfy. On the other hand, it follows from the definition of function that there exists at most one such element. Hence the element y is uniquely determined. It is called the *value* of f at x and is denoted by $f(x)$. Therefore, the formula $y = f(x)$ has the same meaning as xfy.

For f, g belonging to Y^X the following obvious equivalence holds:

$$(f = g) \equiv \bigwedge_{x,y \in X} [f(x) = g(x)].$$

If ordered pairs are identified with points of a plane, the first term with the abscissa and the second term with the ordinate, then it turns out that a function is identical with its graph.

DEFINITION: A function f is said to be a *one-to-one function* if different elements of the domain have different values under the function f:

$$[f(x_1) = f(x_2)] \rightarrow [x_1 = x_2],$$

where x_1 and x_2 are arbitrary elements of the domain.

THEOREM 1: *If* $f \in Y^X$ *then* f^c *is a function if and only if* f *is one-to-one. Moreover,* $f^c \in X^{Y_1}$ *where* Y_1 *is the range of* f *and* f^c *is also a one-to-one function.*

PROOF. The relation f^c is a function if and only if

$$\bigwedge_{x_1, x_2, y} [yf^c x_1 \wedge yf^c x_2 \rightarrow x_1 = x_2].$$

that is if

$$\bigwedge_{x_1, x_2, y} [y = f(x_1) \wedge y = f(x_2) \rightarrow x_1 = x_2].$$

Clearly, this formula is equivalent to (1). The second part of the theorem follows from the formulas for the domain and range of an inverse relation (p. 65).

THEOREM 2: *If* $f \in Y^X$ *and* $g \in Z^Y$ *then the relation* $g \circ f$ *is a function and* $g \circ f \in Z^X$ *(in other words: if* $X \xrightarrow[f]{} Y \xrightarrow[g]{} Z$ *then* $X \xrightarrow[g \circ f]{} Z$*).*

PROOF. The definition of the composition of two relations implies the equivalences:

$$\begin{aligned} x g \circ f z &\equiv \bigvee_y [(xfy) \wedge (ygz)] \\ &\equiv \bigvee_y [(f(x) = y) \wedge (g(y) = z)] \\ &\equiv g(f(x)) = z; \end{aligned}$$

it follows that

$$\bigwedge_{x, z_1, z_2} [(x g \circ f z_1) \wedge (x g \circ f z_2) \to z_1 = z_2]$$

and that every element of X belongs to the domain of $g \circ f$.

Since the domain of this relation is included in the range of g, $g \circ f \in Z^X$.

Theorem 2 implies the following formula

$$g \circ f(x) = g(f(x)) \quad \text{for} \quad x \in X.$$

THEOREM 3: *If* $f \in Y^X$, $g \in Z^Y$ *and the functions* f *and* g *are one-to-one, then their composition is also one-to-one.*

In fact,

$$g(f(x)) = g(f(x')) \to f(x) = f(x') \to x = x'.$$

DEFINITION: A one-to-one function whose domain and range are the same set X is called a *permutation* of the set X.

The simplest permutation of X is the identity permutation I_X, that is, the function defined by the formula $I_X(x) = x$ for all $x \in X$.

THEOREM 4: *If* $f \in Y^X$ *and* f *is a one-to-one function, then* $f^c \circ f = I_X$ *and* $f \circ f^c = I_{Y_1}$ *where* Y_1 *is the range of* f.

In fact, the equivalence $f^c(y) = x \equiv f(x) = y$ implies $f^c(f(x)) = x$, thus $f^c \circ f = I_X$. The proof of the second formula is similar.

Let $f \in Y^X$, $g \in Z^X$, $\varphi \in T^Y$ and $\psi \in T^Z$. Hence the range of the function $\varphi \circ f$ is contained in T and the same holds for the function $\psi \circ g$. If $\varphi \circ f = \psi \circ g$ then we say that the following diagram

$$\begin{array}{ccc} X & \xrightarrow{f} & Y \\ {\scriptstyle g}\downarrow & & \downarrow{\scriptstyle \varphi} \\ Z & \xrightarrow{\psi} & T \end{array}$$

is *commutative*. This diagram shows that starting with an element $x \in X$ we can obtain the element $\varphi \circ f(x) = \psi \circ g(x)$ in two ways: through an element of the set Y or through an element of the set Z.

An example of a commutative diagram will be given on page 79.

DEFINITION: A function g is said to be an *extension* of a function f if $f \subset g$. We also say that f is a *restriction* of g.

THEOREM 5: *In order that $f \subset g$ it is necessary and sufficient that $D_1(f) \subset D_1(g)$ and $f(x) = g(x)$ for all $x \in D_1(f)$.*

PROOF. *Necessity*: Suppose that $f \subset g$. Then $D_1(f) \subset D_1(g)$, for the projection of a subset is a subset of the projection (see p. 66). If $x \in D_1(f)$ and $y = f(x)$ then $\langle x, y\rangle \in f$, hence $\langle x, y\rangle \in g$ and $y = g(x)$.

Sufficiency: Suppose that $D_1(f) \subset D_1(g)$ and $f(x) = g(x)$ for all $x \in D_1(f)$. If $\langle x, y\rangle \in f$ then $y = f(x) = g(x)$, therefore $\langle x, y\rangle \in g$, which shows that $f \subset g$.

The restriction f of g for which $D_1(f) = A$ will be denoted by $g|A$.

The notion of function should be distinguished from the notion of operation. By an operation we mean a propositional function $\Phi(x, y)$ of two variables satisfying the following conditions:

$$\text{(W)} \qquad \bigwedge_x \bigvee_y \Phi(x, y), \qquad \bigwedge_{x, y_1, y_2} [\Phi(x, y_1) \wedge \Phi(x, y_2) \rightarrow (y_1 = y_2)].$$

These conditions state that for every x there exists exactly one object y such that $\Phi(x, y)$. This object might be denoted by $F(x)$. If, however, the domain of the propositional function $\Phi(x, y)$ is unlimited, then there may exist no set of all the pairs $\langle x, y\rangle$ such that $\Phi(x, y)$, i.e. there may exist no function f such that $\Phi(x, y) \equiv [y = f(x)]$. For instance, such a function does not exist if $\Phi(x, y)$ is the propositional function $x = y$ (see p. 61). On the other hand, the following theorem holds:

THEOREM 6: *If a propositional function $\Phi(x, y)$ satisfies conditions* (W) *and A is an arbitrary set, then there exists a function f_A with domain A*

and such that for arbitrary $x \in A$ *and arbitrary* y

$$[y = f_A(x)] \equiv \Phi(x, y).$$

Namely, the required function f_A is the set

$$\{t \in A \times B\colon \bigvee_{xy} [(t = \langle x, y\rangle) \wedge \Phi(x, y)]\}$$

where B denotes the image of A under the propositional function Φ (see p. 55).

In particular, if a propositional function Φ is of the form $\ldots x \ldots = y$ (where on the left-hand side of the equation we have an expression written in terms of the letter x, constants, and operation symbols), then the function f_A will be denoted by $\underset{x \in A}{F}[\ldots x \ldots]$. For example, using this notation,

$$I_X = \underset{x \in X}{F}[x], \qquad f = \underset{x \in D_1(f)}{F}[f(x)].$$

Functions of more than one variable

Let $X \times Y \times Z = X \times (Y \times Z)$, $X \times Y \times Z \times T = X \times (Y \times Z \times T)$ and similarly for any number of sets. If $X = Y = Z$ then instead of $X \times X \times X$ we write X^3 and similarly for $X \times X \times X \times X$. Subsets of the cartesian product of n sets are called *n-ary relations*.

If the domain of a function f is the cartesian product $X \times Y$, then f is said to be a *function of two variables*. Similarly, if the domain of f is the cartesian product $X \times Y \times Z$, then we say that f is a function of three variables. Instead of $f(\langle x, y\rangle)$ we write $f(x, y)$.

°THEOREM 7: *If a function f is a one-to-one mapping of the set* $X \times Y$ *onto the set* Z, *then there exist functions* α *and* β, *mapping the set* Z *onto* X *and* Y *respectively, such that* $f(\alpha(z), \beta(z)) = z$ *for every* $z \in Z$.

PROOF. It suffices to take for α the set of pairs $\langle z, x\rangle$ satisfying the condition $\bigvee_{y} [f(x, y) = z]$ and for β the set of pairs $\langle z, y\rangle$ satisfying the condition $\bigvee_{x} [f(x, y) = z]$.

To conclude this section we give a formulation of the axiom of choice using the notation of function.

°THEOREM 8: *If* A *is a non-empty family of sets and* $0 \notin A$, *then there exists a function* $f \in (S(A))^A$ *such that* $f(X) \in X$ *for every* $X \in A$.

PROOF. Let $h = \underset{X\in A}{F}\,[\{X\}\times X]$. For $X\in A$ we have thus $h(X)\neq 0$ and, moreover, $h(X)\cap h(Y) = 0$ for $X\neq Y$. Applying the axiom of choice to the family $D_r(h)$ we obtain a set which has exactly one element in common with each set $h(X)$, $X\in A$. As it is easy to show, this set is the required function f.

A function with the properties mentioned in Theorem 8 is called a *choice function* for the family A.

Theorem 8 shows that from the axioms Σ° it is possible to derive the existence of a choice function for an arbitrary non-empty family of sets not containing the empty set. Conversely, it can be shown that the axiom of choice follows from Theorem 8 and the axioms Σ.

Exercise

1. Let $n\geqslant 3$ and let

$$X = A_0\cup\ldots\cup A_{n-1},$$

$$B_k = A_{k+1}\cup\ldots\cup A_{k+n-1},\qquad C_k = A_{k+1}\cup\ldots\cup A_{k+n-2},$$

where the indices are reduced modulo n. Let $f_k\in Y^{B_k}$, $k = 0,\ldots,n-1$, be a system of functions satisfying the condition

$$f_k(x) = f_{k+1}(x)\quad\text{for}\quad x\in C_{k+1}.$$

There exists a function $f\in Y^X$ satisfying the equation $f_k = f|B_k$ for every $k = 0,\ldots,n-1$.

§ 7. Images and inverse images

Let A and B be arbitrary sets and R a relation such that $R\subset A\times B$. For $X\subset A$ let

$$R^1(X) = \{y\colon \bigvee_{x\in X}(xRy)\}.$$

This set is called the *image* of X under the relation R. Clearly,

$$R^1\colon 2^A\to 2^B.$$

In particular, if f is a function then $f^1(X)$ consists of values of the function f on the set X. We shall write $f^1(X) = \{f(x)\colon x\in X\}$.

The same symbol will be used for operations, e.g. $\{\langle x,y\rangle\colon x\in X\}$, $\{S(X)\colon X\in A\}$, etc. As we know, there exists neither a function whose value for any x is the pair $\langle x,y\rangle$ nor a function whose value for any family X is the set $S(X)$. However, every such operation determines a function if we limit its domain to an arbitrary given set (see Theorem 6, p. 72). Thus strictly speaking it would be necessary to replace the symbols $\langle x, y\rangle$, $S(X)$, etc., in the formulas $\{\langle x, y\rangle : x \in X\}$, $\{S(X): X \in A\}$ by symbols for values of functions with domains X and A, respectively.

It follows from the definition of inverse relation (p. 65) that if $Y \subset B$ then the image of Y under the relation R^c is

$$R^{-1}(Y) = \{x: \bigvee_{y \in Y} (y R^c x)\} = \{x: \bigvee_{y \in Y} (x R y)\}.$$

This set is called the *inverse image* of Y under R. If $R = f$ is a function, then

$$f^{-1}(Y) = \{x: \bigvee_{y \in Y} (f(x) = y)\} = \{x: f(x) \in Y\},$$

i.e. the following equivalence holds:

$$x \in f^{-1}(Y) \equiv f(x) \in Y.$$

If Y reduces to the one-element set $\{y\}$, then the set $f^{-1}(Y)$ is called a *coset* of f determined by y. Distinct cosets are always disjoint, the union of all cosets is the domain of f.

We shall now establish several simple properties of images and inverse images.

THEOREM 1: *If* $R \subset A \times B$ *and* X_1, X_2 *are subsets of* A, *then*

(1) $$R^1(X_1) \cup R^1(X_2) = R^1(X_1 \cup X_2),$$

(2) $$X_1 \subset X_2 \to R^1(X_1) \subset R^1(X_2),$$

(3) $$R^1(X_1 \cap X_2) \subset R^1(X_1) \cap R^1(X_2).$$

PROOF. Formula (1) follows from the equivalence

$$\begin{aligned} y \in R^1(X_1 \cup X_2) &\equiv \bigvee_x \{[(x \in X_1) \vee (x \in X_2)] \wedge (x R y)\} \\ &\equiv \bigvee_x [(x \in X_1) \wedge (x R y)] \vee \bigvee_x [(x \in X_2) \wedge (x R y)] \\ &\equiv y \in R^1(X_1) \vee y \in R^1(X_2) \\ &\equiv y \in R^1(X_1) \cup R^1(X_2). \end{aligned}$$

To prove (2) it suffices to notice that if $X_1 \subset X_2$ then $X_2 = X_1 \cup X_2$. Thus by means of (1) it follows that

$$R^1(X_2) = R^1(X_1) \cup R^1(X_2) \supset R^1(X_1).$$

Finally, formula (3) follows from the remark that $X_1 \cap X_2 \subset X_i$ for $i = 1, 2$, whence, by (2), $R^1(X_1 \cap X_2) \subset R^1(X_1)$ and $R^1(X_1 \cap X_2) \subset R^1(X_2)$; and, in turn, we obtain $R^1(X_1 \cap X_2) \subset R^1(X_1) \cap R^1(X_2)$.

THEOREM 2: *If $f \in B^A$ and $Y_1 \subset B$, $Y_2 \subset B$, then*

$$f^{-1}(Y_1 \cup Y_2) = f^{-1}(Y_1) \cup f^{-1}(Y_2), \tag{4}$$

$$f^{-1}(Y_1 \cap Y_2) = f^{-1}(Y_1) \cap f^{-1}(Y_2), \tag{5}$$

$$f^{-1}(Y_1 - Y_2) = f^{-1}(Y_1) - f^{-1}(Y_2). \tag{6}$$

PROOF. (4) is a special case of (1). Formula (5) follows from the equivalence

$$\begin{aligned} x \in f^{-1}(Y_1 \cap Y_2) &\equiv f(x) \in Y_1 \cap Y_2 \\ &\equiv (f(x) \in Y_1) \wedge (f(x) \in Y_2) \\ &\equiv (x \in f^{-1}(Y_1)) \wedge (x \in f^{-1}(Y_2)) \\ &\equiv (x \in f^{-1}(Y_1) \cap f^{-1}(Y_2)). \end{aligned}$$

The proof of (6) is similar.

Theorems 1 and 2 show that the operation of forming the image under an arbitrary relation is additive, but it is not multiplicative. On the other hand, the operation of obtaining the inverse image is both additive and multiplicative.

THEOREM 3: *If $f\colon A \to B$ and if f is a one-to-one function, then for any $X_1, X_2 \subset A$ the following formulas hold:*

$$f^1(X_1 \cap X_2) = f^1(X_1) \cap f^1(X_2), \qquad f^1(X_1 - X_2) = f^1(X_1) - f^1(X_2).$$

For the proof, substitute f^c for f in Theorem 2.

THEOREM 4: *If $f\colon A \to B$, $Y \subset f^1(A)$ and $X \subset A$, then*

$$f^1(f^{-1}(Y)) = Y, \qquad f^{-1}(f^1(X)) \supset X.$$

The proof of the first formula can be obtained from the equivalence

$$\begin{aligned} y \in f^1(f^{-1}(Y)) &\equiv \bigvee_x [(x \in f^{-1}(Y)) \wedge (y = f(x))] \\ &\equiv \bigvee_x [(f(x) \in Y) \wedge (y = f(x))] \equiv (y \in Y). \end{aligned}$$

The proof of the second formula follows from the implication

$$(x \in X) \to (f(x) \in f^1(X)) \equiv x \in f^{-1}(f_1(X)).$$

In the formula just proved the inclusion sign cannot in general be replaced by the equality sign. For instance, if f is a function of the real variable x and $f(x) = x^2$, then for $X = \{x: x \geqslant 0\}$ we have $f^{-1}(f^1(X)) \neq X$. But for one-to-one functions we ooviously have $f^{-1}(f^1(X)) = X$.

Finally, let us note the following important

THEOREM 5: *If* $S \subset A \times B$ *and* $R \subset B \times C$, *then* $(R \circ S)^1(X) = R^1(S^1(X))$ *for every set* $X \subset A$.

PROOF.

$$\begin{aligned} y \in (R \circ S)^1(X) &\equiv \bigvee_{x \in X} (xR \circ Sy) \\ &\equiv \bigvee_{x \in X} \bigvee_{z} [(xSz) \wedge (zRy)] \\ &\equiv \bigvee_{z} \bigvee_{x \in X} [(xSz) \wedge (zRy)] \\ &\equiv \bigvee_{z} [(z \in S^1(X)) \wedge (zRy)] \\ &\equiv y \in R^1(S^1(X)). \end{aligned}$$

In particular, it follows from Theorem 5 that if $f: A \to B$ and $g: B \to C$, then $(g \circ f)^1(X) = g^1(f^1(X))$ for every set $X \subset A$.

Exercises

1. Prove that $f^1(X_1) - f^1(X_2) \subset f^1(X_1 - X_2)$ and $f^1(X \cap f^{-1}(Y)) = f^1(X) \cap Y$.

2. If $g = f|A$, then $g^{-1}(Y) = A \cap f^{-1}(Y)$.

3. A value y of a function f is said to be of *order* n if the set $f^{-1}(\{y\})$ consists of n elements. We say that a *function* f *is of order* $\leqslant n$ if all of its values are of order $\leqslant n$.

Prove that if a function f defined on a set X is of order $\leqslant n$ and $A \subset X$, then the restriction $f|\big(f^{-1}(f^1(A)) - A\big)$ is of order $\leqslant n-1$.

4. We are given a system of $r+1$ disjoint sets $A_0, A_1, \ldots, A_r$ included in X and a function of order $\leqslant n$ defined on X $(n \geqslant r)$. Let $B = f^1(A_0) \cap \ldots \cap f^1(A_r)$. Prove that the restriction $f|(A_i \cap f^{-1}(B))$ is of order $\leqslant n-r$.

5. Images and inverse images are used in topology, in particular to define the notion of a continuous function.

Let X and Y be two topological spaces and let $f: X \to Y$. We say that f is *continuous* if the inverse image of any open set in Y is an open set in X.

Prove that the following conditions are necessary and sufficient for a function f to be continuous:

(a) inverse images of closed sets are closed,

(b) $f^1(\overline{A}) \subset \overline{f^1(A)}$,

(c) $\overline{A} \subset f^{-1}\overline{[f^1(A)]}$,

(d) $\overline{f^{-1}(B)} \subset f^{-1}(\bar{B})$,

(e) $f^1\,\overline{[f^{-1}(B)]} \subset \bar{B}$,

where $A \subset X$ and $B \subset Y$.

6. Let f be a one-to-one mapping of X onto Y (hence $f^c: Y \to X$). We say that f is a *homeomorphism* if f and f^c are continuous.

Show that each of the conditions arising from (b)–(e) by substituting the equality sign for the inclusion sign is a necessary and sufficient condition for a function f to be a homeomorphism.

7. Show by means of an example that the image of an open set need not be open even though the function is continuous.

The same for closed sets.

8. Prove that the composition of two continuous functions is continuous.

§ 8. Functions consistent with a given equivalence relation. Factor Boolean algebras

The construction to be given in this section is one of basic importance in abstract algebra.

Let R be an equivalence relation whose field is X, f a function of two variables belonging to $X^{X \times X}$.

DEFINITON: The function f is *consistent with* R if

$$\bigwedge_{x, x_1, y, y_1} [(xRx_1) \wedge (yRy_1) \to (f(x,y) R f(x_1, y_1))].$$

A similar definition can be adopted for a function of arbitrarily many arguments.

It results from the equivalence $xRy \equiv (x \in y/R) \equiv (x/R = y/R)$ that the definition of consistency can be expressed as follows: if $x \in x_1/R$ and $y \in y_1/R$, then $f(x,y)/R = f(x_1, y_1)/R$. In other words, the equivalence class $f(x,y)/R$ depends on the classes x/R and y/R but not on the elements x, y themselves. This implies that there exists a function φ with domain $(X/R) \times (X/R)$ satisfying for any $x, y \in X$ the formula:

$$\varphi(x/R, y/R) = f(x,y)/R.$$

Namely, φ is the set of all pairs of the form $\langle\langle k', k''\rangle, k\rangle$, where $k, k', k'' \in X/R$ and

$$\bigvee_{x, y} [(x \in k') \wedge (y \in k'') \wedge (f(x,y) \in k)].$$

We say that the function φ is *induced from* f *by* R.

The function $k \in (X/R)^X$ defined by the formula $k(x) = x/R$ is called the *canonical mapping* of X onto X/R. The function of two variables k^2 defined by the formula

$$k^2(x, y) = \langle x/R, y/R \rangle$$

is also called the *canonical mapping* of X^2 onto $(X/R)^2$. A similar definition can be given for functions of three and more variables.

THEOREM 1: *If a function $f \in X^{X \times X}$ is consistent with an equivalence relation R and φ is the function induced from f by R, then the diagram*

$$\begin{array}{ccc} X^2 & \xrightarrow{f} & X \\ {\scriptstyle k^2}\downarrow & & \downarrow{\scriptstyle k} \\ (X/R)^2 & \xrightarrow[\varphi]{} & X/R \end{array}$$

is commutative.

PROOF. For any pair $\langle x, y \rangle \in X^2$ the following formulas hold:

$$k \circ f(x, y) = k\big(f(x, y)\big) = f(x, y)/R,$$

$$\varphi \circ k^2(x, y) = \varphi\big(k^2(x, y)\big) = \varphi(x/R, y/R) = f(x, y)/R.$$

Hence $k \circ f = \varphi \circ k^2$.

Example. Let $X = \boldsymbol{K}$ be a field of sets with unit U, $\boldsymbol{I}$ any ideal in $\boldsymbol{K}$, R the relation $\doteq$ mod $\boldsymbol{I}$ (see p. 17). The set $\boldsymbol{K}/R$ is denoted by $\boldsymbol{K}/\boldsymbol{I}$ and is called a *factor Boolean algebra.*

The functions $f(X, Y) = X \cup Y$, $g(X, Y) = X \cap Y$, and $h(X) = U - X$ are consistent with the relation $\doteq$ (see Exercise 4, p. 18). The functions induced from f, g, h by the relation $\doteq$ will be denoted by $\vee$, $\wedge$, and $-$, respectively. Hence

$$(X/R) \vee (Y/R) = (X \cup Y)/R, \qquad (X/R) \wedge (Y/R) = (X \cap Y)/R,$$

$$-(X/R) = (U - X)/R.$$

THEOREM 2: *The set $\boldsymbol{K}/\boldsymbol{I}$ is a Boolean algebra with respect to the operations $\vee$, $\wedge$, $-$, with $0/R$ and U/R as the zero and the unit element, respectively.*

PROOF. It is sufficient to show that the operations $\vee$, $\wedge$, $-$ and the elements $0/R$ and U/R satisfy axioms (i)–(v′), p. 37. For instance, we check axiom (i). Let $a = X/R$ and $b = Y/R$; then $a \vee b = (X \cup Y)/R$

and $b \vee a = (Y \cup X)/R$ and hence $a \vee b = b \vee a$. The remaining axioms can be checked similarly.

REMARK. The conditions $X \dot{=} 0$ (mod $\boldsymbol{I}$) and $X \in \boldsymbol{I}$ are equivalent. This proves that $0/R = \boldsymbol{I}$.

The factor algebras $\boldsymbol{K}/\boldsymbol{I}$ may have properties quite different from those of $\boldsymbol{K}$. Thus the construction leading from $\boldsymbol{K}$ to $\boldsymbol{K}/\boldsymbol{I}$ allows us to build new and interesting examples of rings.

Exercises

1. Generalize the example given above by taking any Boolean algebra as $\boldsymbol{K}$ and any subset of $\boldsymbol{K}$ satisfying the conditions of Example 5, p. 67, as $\boldsymbol{I}$.

2. Let $\boldsymbol{K}$ be the field of all subsets of an infinite set U, and let $\boldsymbol{I}$ be the ideal of all finite subsets of U. Show that every non-zero element of the factor ring $\boldsymbol{K}/\boldsymbol{I}$ can be represented as $x \vee y$ where $x \neq \boldsymbol{I}$ and $y \neq \boldsymbol{I}$.

§ 9. Order relations

DEFINITION 1: A relation R is said to be an *order relation* if it is reflexive, transitive, and antisymmetric. The last condition means that

$$(xRy) \wedge (yRx) \rightarrow (x = y).$$

A relation which is only reflexive and transitive is said to be a *quasi-order relation*[1]).

Instead of xRy we usually write $x \leqslant_R y$ or $x \leqslant y$. We also say that the field of R is ordered (or quasi-ordered) without explicitly mentioning R. It is necessary to remember, however, that an ordering is by no means an intrinsic property of the set. The same set may be ordered by different relations.

REMARKS. In former terminology an order relation was understood to be a relation which has the property of connectedness, i.e. $(x \neq y) \rightarrow [xRy \vee yRx]$, in addition to the properties given in Definition 1. The order relations (in our sense) were called *partial order*

[1]) According to Bourbaki, a *proto-order relation (préordre)* is a transitive relation satisfying the condition:

$$(xRy) \rightarrow (xRx) \wedge (yRy).$$

See: *Théorie des ensembles*, Chap. 3, § 1, No. 2 (1963).

relations. Order relations which are also connected are called *linear order relations* and will be considered in detail in Chapter VI.

Examples

1. Every family of sets is ordered by the inclusion relation. If it is linearly ordered by this relation, then it is called a *monotone family*.

2. Every lattice (in particular, every Boolean algebra) is ordered by the relation $a \leqslant b$.

3. The set of natural numbers is ordered by the relation of divisibility.

4. A family $\boldsymbol{P}$ is said to be a *cover* of a set A if $A = S(\boldsymbol{P})$. A cover $\boldsymbol{P}_1$ is said to be a *refinement* of a cover $\boldsymbol{P}_2$ if for every $X \in \boldsymbol{P}_1$ there exists $Y \in \boldsymbol{P}_2$ such that $X \supset Y$. The relation R, defined by

$$\boldsymbol{P}_2 R \boldsymbol{P}_1 \equiv (\boldsymbol{P}_1 \text{ is a refinement of } \boldsymbol{P}_2),$$

is a quasi-order relation in the set of all covers of A. It is not, however, an order relation, that is, there may exist two distinct $\boldsymbol{P}_1$ and $\boldsymbol{P}_2$ such that $\boldsymbol{P}_1 R \boldsymbol{P}_2$ and $\boldsymbol{P}_2 R \boldsymbol{P}_1$.

On the other hand, if we limit the field of R to covers which consist of non-empty disjoint sets (such covers are called *partitions*; cf. p. 67), then R is an order relation.

DEFINITION 2: A set A ordered (or quasi-ordered) by the relation $\leqslant$ is said to be *directed* if for every pair $x \in A$ and $y \in A$ there exists $z \in A$ such that $x \leqslant z$ and $y \leqslant z$.

5. Every lattice is a directed set since $x \leqslant x \vee y$ and $y \leqslant x \vee y$. In particular, the family of all subsets of a given set X, as well as the family of all closed subsets of a given topological space, is directed with respect to the inclusion relation (either $\subset$ or $\supset$).

6. The set of all covers of a given set A is directed with respect to the relation R considered in Example 4. For, given two covers $\boldsymbol{P}_1$ and $\boldsymbol{P}_2$, denote by $\boldsymbol{P}_3$ the family of all intersections of the form $X \cap Y$ where $X \in \boldsymbol{P}_1$, $Y \in \boldsymbol{P}_2$. It is easy to check that $\boldsymbol{P}_3$ is a cover and $\boldsymbol{P}_1 R \boldsymbol{P}_3$ as well as $\boldsymbol{P}_2 R \boldsymbol{P}_3$.

DEFINITION 3: An ordered set A is said to be *cofinal* with its subset B if for every $x \in A$ there exists $y \in B$ such that $x \leqslant y$. Analogously we can define *coinitial* sets.

Example. The set of real numbers is cofinal and coinitial with the set of integers.

If an ordered set A contains a greatest element, then A is cofinal with the set composed of this element.

The greatest (least) element should be distinguished from the maximal (minimal) element. Namely, an element x of an ordered set A is said to be *maximal* (*minimal*) if there is no element y in A such that $x < y$ ($y < x$). In linearly ordered sets the notions of greatest (least) element and of maximal (minimal) element coincide. This is not always the case for arbitrary ordered sets.

DEFINITION 4: Let A be an ordered set, T any set and let $f \in A^T$. An element $u \in A$ is said to be the *least upper bound of* $\{f_t\}$ if $f_t \leqslant u$ and u is the least element having this property:

(i) $\bigwedge_{t \in T} (f_t \leqslant u)$,

(ii) $\bigwedge_{t \in T} (f_t \leqslant v) \rightarrow (u \leqslant v)$.

Replacing $\leqslant$ by $\geqslant$ we obtain the definition of the *greatest lower bound.*

The least upper bound, if it exists, is uniquely determined. For suppose that besides (i) and (ii) we have

(i') $\bigwedge_{t \in T} (f_t \leqslant u')$,

(ii') $\bigwedge_{t \in T} (f_t \leqslant v) \rightarrow (u' \leqslant v)$.

Setting $v = u$ in (ii') and applying (i), we obtain $u' \leqslant u$. Likewise, it follows from (ii) and (i') that $u \leqslant u'$. Hence $u = u'$, since the relation $\leqslant$ is antisymmetric.

The proof of the uniqueness of the greatest lower bound is similar.

The least upper bound, if it exists, is denoted in the theory of ordered sets by $\bigvee_{t \in T} f_t$, the greatest lower bound by $\bigwedge_{t \in T} f_t$. If T is a finite set $T = \{1, 2, \ldots, n\}$ and $f_1 = a$, $f_2 = b$, $\ldots$, $f_n = h$, then the least upper bound of these elements is also denoted by $a \vee b \vee \ldots \vee h$, and the greatest lower bound by $a \wedge b \wedge \ldots \wedge h$.

The greatest lower bound of all elements of A, if it exists, is called the *zero element* and is denoted by 0_A or simply 0. Analogously, the least upper bound of all the elements of A, if it exists, is called the *unit element* and is denoted by 1_A or 1.

Obviously, $a \wedge b \leqslant a$ and $a \wedge b \leqslant b$ if $a \wedge b$ exists; similarly $a \leqslant a \vee b$ and $b \leqslant a \vee b$ provided $a \vee b$ exists (in this case A is a directed set).

If $a \leqslant b$, then $a \vee b$ and $a \wedge b$ exist and they equal b and a, respectively. This implies that if $a \wedge b$ and $a \vee b$ exist for all $a, b \in A$, A is a lattice.

DEFINITION 5: An ordering of a set A is said to be *complete* if for every T and for every $f \in A^T$ there exist $\bigwedge_{t \in T} f_t$ and $\bigvee_{t \in T} f_t$.

Since every lattice is a set ordered by the relation $a \leqslant b$, this definition also explains the meaning of the term "complete lattice".

Examples and exercises

7. 2^X *is a complete lattice* (for an arbitrary set X) *with respect to the operations* $\cap$, $\cup$. The existence of the least upper bound is a consequence of Axiom III, § 2, the existence of the greatest lower bound follows from Theorem 6, § 3.

This example will be used in Chapter IV, § 1.

8. *The family of all closed subsets of an arbitrary topological space is a complete lattice under the operations* $\cap$, $\cup$. In this case $\bigvee_t X_t$ is the closure of the union of the sets X_t, $\bigwedge_t X_t$ is the intersection of X_t.

9. Let A be any set. *The family* 2^{A^2} (i.e. the family of relations with fields included in A) *is ordered by the inclusion relation.* Prove that the family of all transitive relations is a lattice and describe the meaning of the operations $\wedge$ and $\vee$.

10. The same problem as in 9 for the family of all equivalence relations.

DEFINITION 6: Two sets A and B ordered by the relations R and S respectively are said to be *similar* if there exists a one-to-one function f mapping the set A onto B and satisfying for arbitrary $x, y \in A$ the equivalence

$$x R y \equiv f(x) S f(y).$$

In this case we say that the function establishes the similarity of the sets A and B (under the relations R and S).

For example, defining $f(x) = -x$ for $x \in \mathcal{E}$ we obtain similarity between the set $\mathcal{E}$ ordered by $\leqslant$ and the same set $\mathcal{E}$ ordered by $\geqslant$.

The notion of similarity is a special case of the more general notion of isomorphism which will be treated in the next section.

§ 10. Relational systems, their isomorphisms and types

Let A be a set, $R_0, R_1, \ldots$ relations respectively of $p_0, p_1, \ldots, p_{k-1}$ arguments in A; in other words, $R_j \subset A^{p_j}$ for $j < k$. The sequence

$$\langle A, R_0, R_1, \ldots, R_{k-1} \rangle$$

is called a *relational system of characteristic* $(p_0, p_1, \ldots, p_{k-1})$ and the set A is called the *field of the system.*

Relational systems are investigated in many branches of mathematics, especially in algebra. We may, for instance, consider a group, as a relational system of characteristic (3) and a ring as a relational system of characteristic (3,3). Boolean algebras (see p. 32) may also be treated as relational systems.

In order to simplify our treatment we shall investigate systems of characteristic (2), that is, systems of the form $\langle A, R \rangle$, where $R \subset A \times A$. However, all proofs can easily be generalized to arbitrary systems.

Definition: Two relational systems $\langle A, R \rangle$ and $\langle B, S \rangle$ are said to be *isomorphic* if there exists a one-to-one function f mapping A onto B such that for all $x, y \in A$

$$xRy \equiv f(x)Sf(y).$$

Then we write $\langle A, R \rangle \approx \langle B, S \rangle$ or briefly $R \approx S$ if no confusion can arise about the sets A and B.

The proof of the following theorem is immediate.

Theorem 1: *The relation $\approx$ is reflexive, symmetric, and transitive.*

We shall show that every property of the system $\langle A, R \rangle$ which can be expressed by means of the propositional calculus and quantifiers limited to the field of the relational system, is also a property of every system isomorphic to $\langle A, R \rangle$. We say that the property in question is *invariant under isomorphism.*

Let Φ be a propositional function involving free variables x, y. Besides x, y, Φ may involve an arbitrary number of other variables $u_0, u_1, \ldots, u_{k-1}$. Suppose that Φ arises from propositional functions of the form

$$u_i = u_j, \tag{1}$$

$$\langle u_i, u_j \rangle \in y \tag{2}$$

by means of operations of the propositional calculus and by means of the quantifiers $\bigvee_{u \in x}$ and $\bigwedge_{u \in x}$. Thus the variables x and y are not bounded by quantifiers. For such propositional functions we have

THEOREM 2[1]: *If a function f is an isomorphism of the relational systems $\langle A, R \rangle$ and $\langle B, S \rangle$ and if $a_0, a_1, \ldots, a_{k-1} \in A$, then*

$$\Phi(A, R, a_0, \ldots, a_{k-1}) \equiv \Phi(B, S, f(a_0), \ldots, f(a_{k-1})). \tag{3}$$

PROOF. If Φ is the propositional function (1), then the equivalence (3) follows from the assumption that f is one-to-one. If Φ is the propositional function (2), then (3) follows from the assumption that f is an isomorphism.

Suppose now that (3) holds for propositional functions Φ and Φ'. By the laws of the propositional calculus it follows that (3) also holds for the functions $\neg\Phi$ and $\Phi \vee \Phi'$. This implies that (3) holds for all the propositional functions which can be obtained from Φ and Φ' by applying operations of the propositional calculus. Hence, to prove the theorem for all propositional functions it suffices to show that (3) holds for propositional functions arising from Φ by applying a quantifier (existential or universal) to Φ. It suffices to consider only one of these quantifiers, for instance, the existential quantifier.

Let Ψ be the propositional function $\bigvee_{u_0 \in x} \Phi$ and suppose that $a_1, \ldots, a_{k-1} \in A$. If $\Psi(A, R, a_1, \ldots, a_{k-1})$ then for some a_0 belonging to A we have $\Phi(A, R, a_0, a_1, \ldots, a_{k-1})$. By the induction hypothesis we thus obtain $\Phi(B, S, f(a_0), f(a_1), \ldots, f(a_{k-1}))$, and it follows that $\Psi(B, S, f(a_1), \ldots, f(a_{k-1}))$. Hence we have proved the implication

$$\Psi(A, R, a_1, \ldots, a_{k-1}) \rightarrow \Psi(B, S, f(a_1), \ldots, f(a_{k-1})).$$

[1]) Theorem 2 is a scheme: for each propositional function we obtain a separate theorem.

The proof of the converse implication is similar.

Example. The following properties of the system $\langle A, R\rangle$ are by Theorem 2 invariant under isomorphism:

1. *Reflexivity:* $\bigwedge_{x\in A} xRx.$
2. *Irreflexivity:* $\bigwedge_{x\in A} \neg(xRx).$
3. *Symmetry:* $\bigwedge_{x,y\in A} [xRy \to yRx].$
4. *Asymmetry:* $\bigwedge_{x,y\in A} [xRy \to \neg(yRx)].$
5. *Antisymmetry:* $\bigwedge_{x,y\in A} [(xRy)\wedge(yRx) \to (x=y)].$
6. *Transitivity:* $\bigwedge_{x,y,z\in A} [(xRy)\wedge(yRz) \to (xRz)].$
7. *Connectedness:* $\bigwedge_{x,y\in A} [(xRy)\vee(x=y)\vee(yRx)].$

Two isomorphic systems are said to be of the same *type*. The mere use of the word "type" in this expression does not presuppose that there are objects which we call "types". All the theorems of set theory could indeed be expressed without using this notion. However, the introduction of the notion of type simplifies the axiomatic treatment of the theory. Moreover, the use of this notion is justified by the fact that Cantor himself developed set theory using this concept.

We introduce a new primitive notion TR. The formula $\alpha\,\mathrm{TR}\langle A, R\rangle$ is read: α *is the type of the relational system* $\langle A, R\rangle$. We also introduce a new axiom.

AXIOM VIII (OF RELATIONAL SYSTEMS): *For every system* $\langle A, R\rangle$ *where* $R\subset A^2$ *there exists exactly one object* α *such that* $\alpha\,\mathrm{TR}\langle A, R\rangle$. *Moreover, for any systems* $\langle A, R\rangle$ *and* $\langle B, S\rangle$ *the following formula holds*

$$(\alpha\,\mathrm{TR}\langle A,R\rangle)\wedge(\beta\,\mathrm{TR}\langle B,S\rangle)\to[(\alpha=\beta)\equiv\langle A,R\rangle\approx\langle B,S\rangle].$$

The unique object α such that $\alpha\,\mathrm{TR}\langle A, R\rangle$ is denoted by $\overline{\langle A, R\rangle}$ or, if there is no confusion, by $\overline{R}$[1]).

[1]) Cantor dealt not with relational types of general systems but with types of linearly ordered sets (cf. § 9). His use of the notion of type was imprecise. He defined the type of a linearly ordered set as that property which remains if we

The object α is called a *relational type* if and only if there exists some system $\langle A, R\rangle$ such that $\alpha \,\mathrm{TR}\, \langle A, R\rangle$.

Exercises

1. Let A have n elements and let r_n be the number of relational types of systems with field A.

Show that the number r_n satisfies the inequality

$$2^{n^2}/n! < r_n < 2^{n^2}.$$

2. Prove that $r_2 = 10$ and $r_3 = 104$ [1]).

disregard the nature of its elements but not their order. The single dash over the symbol of set was meant to indicate this single process of abstraction.

[1]) R.L. Davis (Proc. Amer. Math. Soc. **4** (1953) 494) states that $r_4 = 3044$ and $r_5 = 291968$.

CHAPTER III

NATURAL NUMBERS. FINITE AND INFINITE SETS

In this chapter all theorems will be derived from axioms of Σ° (cf. p. 55). As usual, theorems not marked by ° do not involve the axiom of choice in their proofs.

§ 1. Natural numbers

Let for any set X,

$$X' = X \cup \{X\}.$$

The set X' will be called the *successor* of X.

THEOREM 1: *There exists exactly one family of sets N such that*

(i) $0 \in N$;

(ii) $X \in N \rightarrow X' \in N$;

(iii) *if $\boldsymbol{K}$ satisfies* (i) *and* (ii), *then* $N \subset \boldsymbol{K}$.

PROOF. It follows from the axiom of infinity that there exists at least one family $\boldsymbol{R}$ satisfying conditions (i) and (ii). Let $\boldsymbol{\Phi}$ be the family of all those subsets of $\boldsymbol{R}$ which satisfy (i) and (ii):

$$\boldsymbol{\Phi} = \{\boldsymbol{S} \subset \boldsymbol{R}\colon\ 0 \in \boldsymbol{S} \wedge \bigwedge_X (X \in \boldsymbol{S} \rightarrow X' \in \boldsymbol{S})\}.$$

It is easy to show that $P(\boldsymbol{\Phi})$ is the required family.

The elements of N are $0, \{0\}, \{0, \{0\}\}$, etc. These sets can be considered as the counterparts of natural numbers $0, 1, 2, \ldots$, the operation $'$ as the counterpart of $+1$. We shall prove several theorems of arithmetic which hold for the elements of N[1]).

[1]) The reader, who feels it unnatural that in our exposition the role of natural numbers is played by sets, can take a natural numbers some objects which are in one-to-one correspondence with the sets belonging to N. Such objects may be, for instance, the types of relational systems $S(n) = \langle n, n \times n\rangle$, where $n \in N$. This method

In order to simplify the notation, the elements of N will be denoted by the letters $m, n, p, \ldots$. A set K is said to be *inductive* if it satisfies conditions (i) and (ii).

(1) $$m \in n \to m' \subset n.$$

PROOF. Let $K = \{n: \bigwedge_m (m \in n \to m' \subset n)\}$. To prove (1) it suffices to show that $N \subset K$ or, in other words, to show that the set K is inductive. Condition (i) clearly holds. To prove (ii), let $n \in K$ and $m \in n'$. Hence $m \in n$ or $m = n$. In the first case, $m \subset n$ by the definition of K, in the second case, $m \subset n$ because the sets are equal. Thus $m \subset n'$, and consequently $n' \in K$, which proves the theorem. The proof of (1) is an example of a proof by induction.

(2) $$n \notin n.$$

The proof by induction consists in showing that the set $\{n: n \notin n\}$ is inductive.

(3) $$m' = n' \to m = n.$$

PROOF. It follows from $m' = n'$ that $m \in n'$, thus $m \in n$ or $m = n$ and by (1) $m \subset n$. Similarly we prove that $n \subset m$.

Peano showed that the arithmetic of natural numbers can be based upon the following axioms:

(a) *zero is a natural number;*

(b) *every natural number has a successor;*

(c) *zero is not a successor of any natural number;*

(d) *natural numbers having the same successor are equal;*

will be used in Chapter V, where we introduce cardinal numbers. Identifying natural numbers with the elements of the family N, we can base our treatment of arithmetic on the axioms $\Sigma°$ only (mostly even on the axioms Σ without the axiom of replacement); whereas in order to identify them with the types of the systems $S(n)$ we would have to appeal to the axioms $\Sigma°$ [TR] and VIII.

A detailed analysis of the problem of what axioms of set theory are necessary to justify the laws of arithmetic and analysis was made by P. Bernays in his series of papers under the common title: *A system of axiomatic set theory,* published in Journal of Symbolic Logic **2** ((1937) 65–77; **6** (1941) 1–17 and 133–145; **8** (1943) 89–106; **13** (1948) 65–79; and **19** (1954) 81–96). See also P. Bernays and A. A. Fraenkel, *Axiomatic set theory* (Amsterdam 1958).

(e) *a set which contains zero and which contains the successor of every number belonging to this set contains all natural numbers.*

It follows from (i), (ii), (3), (iii) and $n' \neq 0$ that the elements of the set N satisfy Peano's axioms.

(4) *For arbitrary m, n exactly one of the following formulas holds:*

$$m \in n, \qquad m = n, \qquad n \in m.$$

PROOF. (1) and (2) imply that every two of the above conditions are mutually contradictory. To prove that for every pair m, n one of these formulas holds, we use induction. Let

$$K(n) = \{m\colon\ m \in n \vee m = n \vee n \in m\}.$$

Theorem (4) is equivalent to $\bigwedge\limits_{n} (N \subset K(n))$, thus it suffices to prove that every set $K(n)$ is inductive.

The set $K(0)$ is inductive, for $K(0)$ consists of the set 0 and of those m for which $0 \in m$ and it is obvious that $0 \in m \rightarrow 0 \in m'$. Suppose that the set $K(n)$ is inductive, i.e. that $N \subset K(n)$. We shall prove that $K(n')$ is also inductive.

Condition (i): $n' \in N \subset K(0)$ implies that $n' \in 0 \vee n' = 0 \vee 0 \in n'$. Since the first two components of this disjunction are false, $0 \in n'$ and $0 \in K(n')$.

Condition (ii): Suppose that $m \in K(n')$, that is, either $m \in n', m = n'$ or $n' \in m$. In the second and the third case we obviously have $n' \in m'$ and hence $m' \in K(n')$. In the first case either $m = n$ or $m \in n$ holds. If $m = n$ then $m' = n'$ and hence $m' \in K(n')$. If $m \in n$ then $m \in K(n)$ and hence $m' \in K(n)$, for $K(n)$ is inductive by assumption. We thus obtain $m' \in n \vee m' = n \vee n' \in m$. The third component of this disjunction is false, for it implies $n \in n$, which contradicts (2). Hence we have only the two possibilites, $m' \in n$ and $m' = n$, which since $n \subset n'$, prove that $m' \in K(n')$. This completes the proof of Theorem (4).

(5) *The set $Z = \{m\colon\ n \in m\}$ is identical with the intersection P of all families $K \subset N$ such that $n' \in K$ and K satisfies* (ii).

PROOF. Since $m \subset m'$, the set Z satisfies (ii). This proves that $P \subset Z$, for obviously $n' \in Z$. It remains to be shown that if K satisfies (ii) and $n' \in K$, then $Z \subset K$. For this purpose, let $L = \{n\colon\ n \in Z \rightarrow n \in K\}$. It suffices to show that $N \subset L$ or, in other words, that L is an inductive family.

Condition (i) obviously holds, for $0 \notin Z$.

To prove that L satisfies (ii), suppose that $m \in L$. This means that either $m \in K$ or $m \notin Z$. In the first case $m' \in K$, for K satisfies (ii), and we obtain $m' \in L$. The second case splits into three subcases depending upon whether $n \in m$, $n = m$ or $m \in n$. The first subcase contradicts the assumption $m \notin Z$. The second subcase implies $m' = n'$ and hence $m' \in K$ and finally $m' \in L$, for $K \subset L$. In the last subcase we have by (4) either $m' \in n$ or $m' = n$ or $n \in m'$. If either $m' \in n$ or $m' = n$, then by (4) $n \notin m'$; hence $m' \notin Z$ and finally $m' \in L$. The condition $n \in m'$ leads to a contradiction, for it implies that $n \in m \vee n = m$ whereas by assumption we have $m \in n$.

In ordinary arithmetic the set of all numbers greater than n is defined to be the common part of all sets which contain the successor of n and which contain the successor of every number b which they contain. Theorem (5) shows that the membership relation $\in$ in N is the counterpart of the relation "less than" between numbers. We shall often write $m < n$ or $m \leqslant n$ instead of $m \in n$ or $m \in n'$, respectively.

The existence of the set N allows us to define in set theory notions analogous to those found in arithmetic and analysis. For example, a function f whose domain is the set N is called an *infinite sequence* and is sometimes denoted by $(f_0, f_1, \ldots, f_n, \ldots)$. If $n \in N$ then a function with domain n is said to be a *finite sequence of n terms.*

The set of all infinite sequences whose terms belong to A is clearly A^N, the set of all finite sequences of n terms in A is A^n. The set of all finite sequences with terms in A can be defined as

$$\{R \subset N \times A\colon (R \text{ is a function}) \wedge \bigvee_{n \in N} (D_1(R) = n)\}.$$

This definition implies the existence of the set of all finite sequences with terms in A.

Exercises

1. Show that if $m, n \in N$, then $m \in n \equiv (m \subset n) \wedge (m \neq n)$.

2. Show that if $0 \neq K \subset N$, then $P(K) \in N \cap K$.

3. Prove that every non-empty family $K \subset N$ contains an element k such that $k \cap K = 0$ (cf. the axiom of regularity, p. 56).

§ 2. Definitions by induction

Inductive definitions are the most characteristic feature of the arithmetic of natural numbers. The simplest case is the definition of a sequence φ (with terms belonging to a certain set Z) satisfying the following conditions:

(a) $$\varphi(0) = z, \quad \varphi(n') = e(\varphi(n), n)$$

where $z \in Z$ and e is a function mapping $Z \times N$ into Z.

More generally, we consider a mapping f of the cartesian product $Z \times N \times A$ into Z and seek a function $\varphi \in Z^{N \times A}$ satisfying the conditions:

(b) $$\varphi(0,a) = g(a), \quad \varphi(n', a) = f(\varphi(n, a), n, a),$$

where $g \in Z^A$. This is a definition by induction with parameter a ranging over the set A.

Schemes (a) and (b) correspond to induction "from n to $n+1$", i.e. $\varphi(n')$ or $\varphi(n', a)$ depends upon $\varphi(n)$ or $\varphi(n, a)$, respectively. More generally, $\varphi(n')$ may depend upon all values $\varphi(m)$ where $m \leqslant n$ (i.e. $m \in n'$). In the case of induction with parameter $\varphi(n')$ may depend upon all values $\varphi(m, a)$, where $m \leqslant n'$; or even upon all values $\varphi(m, b)$, where $m \leqslant n'$ and $b \in A$. In this way we obtain the following schemes of definitions by induction:

(c) $$\varphi(0) = z, \quad \varphi(n') = h(\varphi | n', n),$$

(d) $$\varphi(0, a) = g(a), \quad \varphi(n', a) = H(\varphi | (n' \times A), n, a).$$

In the scheme (c), $z \in Z$ and $h \in Z^{C \times N}$, where C is the set of finite sequences whose terms belong to Z; in the scheme (d) $g \in Z^A$ and $H \in Z^{T \times N \times A}$, where T is the set of functions whose domain is included in $N \times A$ and whose values belong to Z [1]).

Examples of definition by induction

1. The function $m+n$:

$$m+0 = m, \quad m+n' = (m+n)'.$$

[1]) Scheme (c) could be generalized by assuming that the domain of the function h is not the whole set $C \times N$, but only the set of pairs of the form (c, n) where $c \in Z^n$. However, this generalization is not of greater importance.

This definition is obtained from (b) if we set $Z = A = N$, $g(a) = a$, $f(p, n, a) = p'$.

2. The function $\binom{n}{2}$:

$$\binom{0}{2} = 0, \quad \binom{n'}{2} = \binom{n}{2} + n.$$

This follows from (a) if we set $Z = N$, $z = 0$, $e(p, n) = p + n$.

3. Let $Z = A = X^X$, $g(a) = I_X$ and $f(u, n, a) = u \circ a$ in (b). Then (b) takes on the form

$$\varphi(0, a) = I_X, \quad \varphi(n', a) = \varphi(n, a) \circ a.$$

The function $\varphi(n, a)$ is denoted by a^n and is called nth iteration of the function a. We thus have:

$$a^0(x) = x, \quad a^{n'}(x) = a^n(a(x)) \quad \text{for } x \in X,\ a \in X^X \text{ and } n \in N.$$

4. Let $A = N^N$. Let $g(a) = a_0$ and $f(u, n, a) = u + a_{n'}$ in (b). Then (b) takes on the form

$$\varphi(0, a) = a_0, \quad \varphi(n', a) = \varphi(n, a) + a_{n'}.$$

The function defined in this way is denoted by $\sum_{i=0}^{n} a_i$. Similarly we define $\prod_{i=0}^{n} a_i$, $\max_{i \leqslant n} a_i$.

It is clear that the scheme (d) is the most general of all the schemes discussed above. By appropriate choice of functions we can obtain from (d) any of the schemes (a)–(d). For example, taking the function defined by

$$H(c, n, a) = f(c(n, a), n, a) \quad \text{for} \quad a \in A,\ n \in N,\ c \in Z^{N \times A}$$

as H in (d), we obtain (b).

We shall now show that, conversely, the scheme (d) can be obtained from (a). Let g and H be functions belonging to Z^A and $Z^{T \times N \times A}$ respectively, and let φ be a function satisfying (d). We shall show that the sequence $\Psi: \Psi_n = \varphi|(n' \times A)$ can be defined by (a).

Obviously $\Psi_n \in T$ for every n. The first term of the sequence Ψ is equal to $\varphi|(0' \times A)$, i.e. to the set

$$z^* = \{\langle\langle 0, a\rangle, g(a)\rangle : a \in A\}.$$

The relation between $\Psi_{n'}$ and Ψ_n is given by the formula

$$\Psi_{n'} = \Psi_n \cup \varphi|(\{n'\} \times A),$$

where the second component is

$$\{\langle\langle n', a\rangle, \varphi(n', a)\rangle : a \in A\} = \{\langle\langle n', a\rangle, H(\Psi_n, n, a)\rangle : a \in A\}.$$

Thus we see that the sequence Ψ can be defined by (a) if we substitute T for Z, z^* for z and let

$$e(c, n) = c \cup \{\langle\langle n', a\rangle, H(c, n, a)\rangle : a \in A\} \quad \text{for} \quad c \in T.$$

Now we shall prove the existence and uniqueness of the function satisfying (a). This theorem shows that we are entitled to use definitions by induction of the type (a). According to the remark made above, this will imply the existence of functions satisfying the formulas (b), (c), and (d). Since the uniqueness of such functions can be proved in the same manner as for (a), we shall use in the sequel definitions by induction of any of the types (a) – (d).

THEOREM 1: *If Z is any set, $z \in Z$ and $e \in Z^{Z \times N}$, then there exists exactly one sequence φ satisfying formulas* (a).

PROOF. *Uniqueness:* Suppose that φ_1 and φ_2 satisfy (a) and let $K = \{n: \varphi_1(n) = \varphi_2(n)\}$. Then (a) implies that K is inductive. Hence $N \subset K$ and $\varphi_1 = \varphi_2$.

Existence: Let $\Phi(z, n, t)$ be the propositional function $e(z, n) = t$ and let $\Psi(n, z, F)$ be the following propositional function

$$(F \text{ is a function}) \wedge (D_1(F) = n') \wedge (F(0) = z) \wedge \bigwedge_{m \in n} \Phi(F(m), m, F(m')).$$

In other words, F is a function defined on the set of numbers $\leqslant n$ such that $F(0) = z$ and $F(m') = e(F(m), m)$ for all $m < n$.

We prove by induction that there exists exactly one function F_n such that $\Psi(n, z, F_n)$. The proof of the uniqueness of this function is similar to that given in the first part of Theorem 1. The existence of F_n can be proved as follows: for $n = 0$ it suffices to take $\{\langle 0, z\rangle\}$ as F_n; if $n \in N$ and F_n satisfies $\Psi(n, z, F_n)$, then $F_{n'} = F_n \cup \{\langle n', e(F_n(n), n)\rangle\}$ satisfies the condition $\Psi(n', z, F_{n'})$.

Now, we take as φ the set of pairs $\langle n, s\rangle$ such that $n \in N$, $s \in Z$ and $\bigvee_F [\Psi(n, z, F) \wedge (s = F(n))]$.

Since F is the unique function satisfying $\Psi(n, z, F)$, it follows that φ is a function. For $n = 0$ we have $\varphi(0) = F_0(0) = z$; if $n \in N$, then $\varphi(n') = F_{n'}(n') = e(F_n(n), n)$ by the definition of F_n; hence we obtain $\varphi(n') = e(\varphi(n), n)$. Theorem 1 is thus proved.

We frequently define not one but several functions (with the same range Z) by a simultaneous induction:

$$\varphi(0) = z, \qquad \psi(0) = t,$$
$$\varphi(n') = f(\varphi(n), \psi(n), n) \qquad \psi(n') = g(\varphi(n), \psi(n), n),$$

where z, $t \in Z$ and f, $g \in Z^{Z \times Z \times N}$.

This kind of definitions can be reduced to the previous one. It suffices to notice that the sequence $\vartheta_n = \langle \varphi_n, \psi_n \rangle$ satisfies the formulas:

$$\vartheta_0 = \langle z, t\rangle, \qquad \vartheta_{n'} = e(\vartheta_n, n),$$

where we set $e(u, n) = \langle f(K(u), L(u), n), g(K(u), L(u), n)\rangle$, and K, L denote functions such that $K(\langle x, y\rangle) = x$ and $L(\langle x, y\rangle) = y$, respectively. Thus the function ϑ is defined by induction by means of (a). We now define φ and ψ by

$$\varphi(n) = K(\vartheta_n) \quad \text{and} \quad \psi(n) = L(\vartheta_n).$$

The theorem on inductive definitions can be generalized to the case of operations. We shall discuss only one special case. Let Φ be a propositional function such that

$$\bigwedge_z \bigwedge_{n \in N} \bigvee_t \Phi(z, n, t),$$

$$\bigwedge_z \bigwedge_{n \in N} \bigwedge_{t_1, t_2} [\Phi(z, n, t_1) \wedge \Phi(z, n, t_2) \rightarrow t_1 = t_2].$$

THEOREM 2 [1]): *For any set S there exists exactly one sequence φ such that*

$$\varphi_0 = S \quad \textit{and} \quad \bigwedge_{n \in N} \Phi(\varphi_n, n, \varphi_{n'}).$$

Uniqueness can be proved as in Theorem 1.

[1]) Theorem 2 is a scheme: for each propositional function we have a separate theorem.

To prove the existence of φ, let us consider the following propositional function $\Psi^*(n, S, F)$.

$$(F \text{ is a function}) \wedge \big(D_1(F) = n'\big) \wedge \big(F(0) = S\big) \wedge \bigwedge_{m \in n} \Phi\big(F(m), m, F(m')\big).$$

As in the proof of Theorem 1, it can be shown that there exists exactly one function F_n such that $\Psi^*(n, S, F_n)$. To proceed further we must make certain that there exists a set containing all the elements of the form $F_n(n)$ where $n \in N$. (In the case considered in Theorem 1 this set is Z, for the domain of the last variable of the propositional function Φ which we used in the proof of Theorem 1 was limited to the set Z.) In the case under consideration, the existence of the required set Z follows from the axiom of replacement.

In fact, the uniqueness of F_n implies that the propositional function

$$\bigvee_F [\Psi^*(n, S, F) \wedge (y = F(n))]$$

satisfies the assumption of axiom VII. Hence by means of axiom VII the image of N obtained by this propositional function exists. This image is the required set Z containing all the elements $F_n(n)$.

The remainder of the proof is analogous to that of Theorem 1.

Example. Let $\Phi(S, t)$ be the propositional function $t = 2^S$. Thus for any set S there exists a sequence φ such that $\varphi_0 = S$ and $\varphi_{n'} = 2^{\varphi_n}$ for every natural number n.

§ 3. The mapping J of the set $N \times N$ onto N and related mappings

Using definitions by induction we shall now define several mappings important in the sequel.

1. *The mapping J of the set $N \times N$ onto N.* Let for $x, y \in N$

$$J(x, y) = \binom{x+y+1}{2} + x.$$

THEOREM 1: *J is a one-to-one mapping of $N \times N$ onto N.*

PROOF. Suppose that $J(x, y) = J(a, b)$. We shall first prove that $x = a$. In fact, if we suppose $x > a$, then $x = a+r$, $r > 0$. Thus we would obtain

$$(1) \qquad \binom{a+r+y+1}{2} + r = \binom{a+b+1}{2}.$$

This implies $b > r+y$, for $\binom{x}{2}$ is an increasing function. Hence $b = r+y+s$ where $s > 0$. Substituting this value for b in (1) and letting $c = a+r+y+1$, we obtain $\binom{c}{2}+r = \binom{c+s}{2}$. But this is not true, for $r < c$, since $\binom{c}{2}+r < \binom{c}{2}+c = \binom{c+1}{2} \leqslant \binom{c+s}{2}$. In the same way it can be shown that $x < a$ does not hold. Hence $x = a$ and we obtain $\binom{a+y+1}{2} = \binom{a+b+1}{2}$. If $y < b$ then we would have $b = y+t$, $t > 0$; and we would obtain $\binom{a+b+1}{2} \geqslant \binom{a+y+2}{2} > \binom{a+y+1}{2}$. Likewise we can derive a contradiction from the assumption that $y > b$. Therefore the function J is one-to-one.

Now we shall prove that the range Z of J is identical with N. It follows from $J(0,0) = 0$ and $J(0,1) = 1$ that $0, 1 \in Z$. Suppose that $n \in Z$, i.e. that $n = J(x,y)$ for some x and y. If $y > 0$ then

$$n+1 = J(x,y)+1 = \binom{x+y+1}{2}+x+1 = J(x+1,\, y-1) \in Z.$$

If $y = 0$ then

$$n = \binom{x}{2}+x = \binom{x+1}{2}, \qquad \text{thus} \qquad n+1 = \binom{x+1}{2}+1.$$

Assuming that $x > 0$ we can write $\binom{x+1}{2}+1$ in the form $\binom{1+(x-1)+1}{2}+1 = J(1, x-1)$; hence $n+1 \in Z$. Finally, if $x = y = 0$ then $n = 0$ and $n+1 = 1$. Hence $n+1 \in Z$. Theorem 1 is thus proved.

THEOREM 2: *There exist functions K, L mapping N onto N such that $J(K(x), L(x)) = x$. Moreover, these functions satisfy the inequalities*

(2) $$K(x) \leqslant x, \qquad L(x) \leqslant x.$$

The existence of the functions K and L follows from Theorem 7, p. 73, the inequalities follow from $x \leqslant J(x,y)$ and $y \leqslant J(x,y)$.

REMARK: The intuitive meaning of the functions J, K, L can be illustrated by arranging the pairs $\langle x,y\rangle$ of natural numbers into the following infinite array:

(3) $$\begin{array}{cccc} \langle 0,0\rangle & \langle 0,1\rangle & \langle 0,2\rangle & \ldots \\ \langle 1,0\rangle & \langle 1,1\rangle & \langle 1,2\rangle & \ldots \\ \langle 2,0\rangle & \langle 2,1\rangle & \langle 2,2\rangle & \ldots \\ \ldots & \ldots & \ldots & \ldots \end{array}$$

and then ordering them in the sequence

(4) $\langle 0,0\rangle,\ \langle 0,1\rangle,\ \langle 1,0\rangle,\ \langle 0,2\rangle,\ \langle 1,1\rangle\ \langle 2,0\rangle,\ \ldots$

The pair $\langle x,y\rangle$ occurs in the $J(x,y)$th position in this sequence. The nth term of this sequence occurs in the $(K(n)+1)$st row and the $(L(n)+1)$st column of (3).

2. *The mapping of the set N^{n+1} onto N.* We shall define by induction a sequence of one-to-one functions such that the kth term of this sequence (denoted by τ_k) is a one-to-one mapping of the set N^{k+1} onto N. Identifying every one-term sequence with its only term, we let

$$\tau_0(x) = x \quad \text{for} \quad x\in N,$$
$$\tau_{k+1}(e) = J\big(\tau_k(e|k'), e_{k+1}\big) \quad \text{for} \quad e\in N^{k+2}.$$

THEOREM 3: *The function τ_k maps N^{k+1} onto N and is one-to-one.*

PROOF. For $k=0$ the theorem is obvious. Suppose now that it holds for the number k. If $e\in N^{k+2}$ then $e|k'\in N^{k+1}$, whence $\tau_k(e|k')\in N$ and, by definition, $\tau_{k+1}(e)\in N$. The function τ_{k+1} thus maps N^{k+1} into N. The fact that τ_{k+1} is one-to-one follows from the implications:

$$\tau_{k+1}(e) = \tau_{k+1}(e^*) \to \big(\tau_k(e|k') = \tau_k(e^*|k')\big)\wedge(e_{k+1} = e^*_{k+1})$$
$$\to (e|k' = e^*|k')\wedge(e_{k+1} = e^*_{k+1}) \to (e = e^*).$$

It remains to be shown that for every number n there exists a sequence $e\in N^{k+2}$ such that $\tau_k(e) = n$. By the inductive assumption there exists a sequence $f\in N^{k+1}$ such that $\tau_k(f) = K(n)$. We let e to be the sequence whose $k+1$ initial terms coincide with those of f and whose last term is $L(n)$. For this sequence e the following formula holds by definition:

$$\tau_{k+1}(e) = J\big(\tau_k(f), L(n)\big) = J\big(K(n), L(n)\big) = n.$$

3. *The mapping of the set of all finite sequences of natural numbers onto the set N.* Let for $e\in N^{k+1}$

$$\sigma_0(e) = J\big(k, \tau_k(e)\big).$$

This function is a one-to-one mapping of the set of all non-empty finite sequences of natural numbers onto N. We have the following:

THEOREM 4: *There exists a one-to-one mapping σ of the set S of all finite sequences of natural numbers onto N which satisfies the condition* $\sigma(0) = 0$.

To prove this it suffices to let $\sigma(e) = 1 + \sigma_0(e)$ for non-empty sequences e and $\sigma(0) = 0$.

4. *The mapping J' of the set $N^{n+1} \times N^{n+1}$ onto the set N^{n+1} and of the set $N^N \times N^N$ onto the set N^N.* Let n be a natural number. For e, $f \in N^{n+1}$, let

$$J'(e,f) = \underset{k \leqslant n}{F} [J(e_k, f_k)],$$

$$K'(e) = \underset{k \leqslant n}{F} [K(e_k)], \quad L'(e) = \underset{k \leqslant n}{F} [L(e_k)].$$

Hence if e and f are sequences with $n+1$ terms e_k and f_k $(k \leqslant n)$ respectively, then $J'(e,f)$ is the sequence of $n+1$ terms $J(e_k, f_k)$ $(k \leqslant n)$; and $K'(e)$ and $L'(e)$ are sequences with the terms $K(e_k)$ and $L(e_k)$ $(k \leqslant n)$ respectively.

Similar definitions will be applied to infinite sequences of natural numbers. Let φ, $\psi \in N^N$ and let

$$J^*(\varphi, \psi) = \underset{k \in N}{F} [J(\varphi_k, \psi_k)],$$

$$K^*(\varphi) = \underset{k \in N}{F} [K(\varphi_k)], \quad L^*(\varphi) = \underset{k \in N}{F} [L(\varphi_k)].$$

$J^*(\varphi, \psi)$ is thus an infinite sequence whose kth term is $J(\varphi_k, \psi_k)$, $K^*(\varphi)$ and $L^*(\varphi)$ are infinite sequences whose kth terms are $K(\varphi_k)$ and $L(\varphi_k)$, respectively.

THEOREM 5: *The function J' restricted to the set $N^{n+1} \times N^{n+1}$ is a one-to-one mapping of this set onto N^{n+1}; the function J^* is a one-to-one mapping of $N^N \times N^N$ onto N^N.*

THEOREM 6: *For any $e \in N^{n+1}$ and for any $\varphi \in N^N$ the following formulas hold*:

$$J'(K'(e), L'(e)) = e, \quad J^*(K^*(\varphi), L^*(\varphi)) = \varphi.$$

The proof of these theorems is left to the reader.

5. *The mapping of the set N^N onto the set $(N^N)^N$.* For $k \in N$ and for $\varphi \in N^N$ let

$$\varphi^{(k)} = \underset{n \in N}{F} [\varphi_{J(k,n)}];$$

thus the sequence $\varphi^{(k)}$ has as terms $\varphi_{J(k,0)}, \varphi_{J(k,1)}, \varphi_{J(k,2)}, \ldots$.

THEOREM 7: *The function M: $\varphi \to \underset{k \in N}{F} [\varphi^{(k)}]$ (which associates with every sequence φ the sequence $\varphi^{(0)}, \varphi^{(1)}, \varphi^{(2)}, \ldots$) is a one-to-one mapping of the set N^N onto the set $(N^N)^N$.*

PROOF. For every $\varphi \in N^N$ we clearly have $M(\varphi) \in (N^N)^N$. The function M is one-to-one. In fact, it follows from $M(\varphi) = M(\psi)$ that $\varphi^{(k)} = \psi^{(k)}$ for every natural number k. Thus $\varphi_{J(k,m)} = \psi_{J(k,m)}$ for any k, m, and by letting $k = K(n)$ and $m = L(n)$ we obtain $\varphi_n = \psi_n$ for all n. Finally, every element of the set $(N^N)^N$, that is, every infinite sequence t whose terms t_k are elements of N^N for all natural k, can be represented as $M(\varphi)$ for some φ. In fact, if φ is the sequence $\varphi_n = t_{K(n)}\big(L(n)\big)$, then $\varphi^{(k)}$ is the sequence whose nth term is $t_{K(J(k,n))}\big(L(J(k,n))\big) = t_k(n)$, i.e. $\varphi^{(k)} = t_k$ for arbitrary k. Hence $M(\varphi) = t$. Q.E.D.

§ 4. Finite and infinite sets

The notions introduced in § 1 and § 2 of this chapter allow us to derive basic properties of finite and infinite sets from the axioms of set theory.

DEFINITION: We say that *a set X has n elements* and we write $|X| = n$ (where $n \in N$) if there exists a one-to-one sequence with domain n and range X. Such a sequence is called a *one-to-one sequence with n terms*.

A set X is *finite* if $|X| = n$ for some $n \in N$, otherwise we say that the set X is *infinite*.

A set X has 0 elements if and only if $X = 0$, for the only one-to-one sequence with 0 terms is the empty sequence.

For every $p \in N$ the set p has p elements; in fact, the function I_p defined by $I_p(x) = x$ for every $x \in p$ is a one-to-one sequence of p terms whose range is p.

THEOREM 1: *If f is a one-to-one mapping of the set X onto the set Y, then $|X| = n$ if and only if $|Y| = n$.*

PROOF. If e is a one-to-one sequence of n terms with range X, then $f \circ e$ is also a one-to-one sequence (see p. 71) of n terms whose range is Y.

LEMMA: *If f is a one-to-one function, $D_l(f) = X \cup \{a\}$, $D_r(f) = Y \cup \{b\}$ and $a \notin X$, $b \notin Y$, then there exists a one-to-one function g such that $X \underset{g}{\to} Y$ and such that Y is the range of g.*

PROOF. Let $f(a) = a_1$, $f^c(b) = b_1$. If $a_1 = b$ then $b_1 = a$ and the function f maps X onto Y; thus it suffices to take $g = f|X$.

If $a_1 \neq b$ then $a_1 \in Y$ and similarly $b_1 \in X$. In this case, g is defined as follows:

$$g(x) = f(x) \quad \text{if} \quad x \neq b_1, \qquad g(b_1) = a_1.$$

Checking that this function satisfies the lemma is left to the reader.

THEOREM 2: *Let* $n \in N$. *The following conditions are equivalent*:

(i) $|X| = n'$.

(ii) *There exists a set* $X_1 \subset X$ *and an element* $a_1 \notin X_1$ *such that* $|X_1| = n$ *and* $X = X_1 \cup \{a_1\}$.

(iii) $X \neq 0$ *and for every* X_2 *and* a_2, *if* $a_2 \notin X_2$ *and* $X = X_2 \cup \{a_2\}$ *then* $|X_2| = n$.

PROOF. (i) → (ii). Let e be a one-to-one sequence of n' terms with range X. Condition (ii) is satisfied when $a = e_n$, $X_1 = X - \{a\}$.

(ii) → (iii). The condition $X \neq 0$ is an immediate consequence of (ii). Letting X_1 and a_1 denote respectively the set and element satysfying (ii) we infer that $X_2 \cup \{a_2\} = X_1 \cup \{a_1\}$; and thus there exists a one-to-one function mapping $X_1 \cup \{a_1\}$ onto $X_2 \cup \{a_2\}$. By means of the lemma there exists a one-to-one function g mapping X_1 onto X_2 and hence, by Theorem 1, $|X_2| = n$.

(iii) → (i). Let a be any element of X and let $X_1 = X - \{a\}$. By (iii) we have $|X_1| = n$ and thus X_1 is the range of a one-to-one sequence e of n terms. The sequence e' of n' terms defined by $e'_p = e_p$ for $p \in n$, $e'_n = a$, is one-to-one and its range is X. Hence $|X| = n'$.

THEOREM 3: *If* $|X| = m$ *and* $|Y| = n$, *then* $m \leqslant n$ *if and only if there exists a set* $Y_1 \subset Y$ *such that the set* X *is a one-to-one image of* Y_1.

PROOF. If $m \leqslant n$ then $m \subset n$ (see p. 89 and 91). Suppose that Y is the range of a one-to-one sequence e of n terms and X is the range of a one-to-one sequence f of m terms. The function $e \circ f^c$ is thus one-to-one and maps X onto a subset of Y (for $f^{c1}(X) = m \subset n$).

Suppose now that there exist a set $Y_1 \subset Y$ and a one-to-one function f mapping Y_1 onto X. To prove that $m \leqslant n$ we shall use induction on n.

If $n = 0$ then $Y = 0$; hence $Y_1 = X = 0$ and, moreover, $m = 0$ and $m \leqslant n$. Suppose that the theorem holds for some $n \in N$ and let $|Y| = n'$. Hence $Y = Y_2 \cup \{a\}$, where $|Y_2| = n$ and $a \notin Y_2$. Since $X = f^1(Y_1)$, we have $f^1(X) = f^1(Y_2 \cap Y_1) \cup f^1(\{a\} \cap Y_1)$. The set $\{a\} \cap Y_1$ is either empty or equal to $\{a\}$. In the first case we have $|Y_2 \cap Y| = m$. The formulas $Y_2 \cap Y_1 \subset Y_1$ and $|Y_1| = m$ show that the inductive hypothesis holds; hence $m \leqslant n$ and thus $m < n'$. In the second case Theorem 2 implies $m = p'$ where p is a number such that $|Y_2 \cap Y_1| = p$. By the inductive hypothesis, $p \leqslant n$, hence $m = p' \leqslant n'$. Thus the theorem is proved.

THEOREM 4: *If* $|X| = m$, $|Y| = n$ *and* $X \cap Y = 0$, *then* $|X \cup Y| = m+n$.

PROOF. The proof is by induction on n. For $n = 0$ we have $Y = 0$, and the theorem holds. Suppose that the theorem holds for the number n and let $|Y| = n'$. Thus $Y = Y_1 \cup \{a\}$ where $a \notin Y_1$ and hence $X \cup Y = (X \cup Y_1) \cup \{a\}$, where $a \notin Y$. It follows from the inductive hypothesis that $|X \cup Y_1| = m+n$ and, by Theorem 2, $|X \cup Y_1 \cup \{a\}| = (m+n)'$. This proves the theorem because $(m+n)' = m+n'$ by the definition of addition (see p. 92).

COROLLARY 5: *For an arbitrary U the finite sets contained in U form an ideal.*

In fact, a subset of a finite set is finite by Theorem 3, and the union of finite sets is finite by Theorems 3 and 4.

THEOREM 6: *If* $|X| = m$ *and* $|Y| = n$, *then the set X is a one-to-one image of Y if and only if* $m = n$.

PROOF. If $m = n$, then X is obviously a one-to-one image of Y, because there exist one-to-one sequences mapping the set n onto X and Y. Now suppose that X is a one-to-one image of Y. Then m is a one-to-one image of n. We shall prove by induction that $m = n$.

For $n = 0$ the theorem is obvious. Suppose that it is true for some n and let m be a one-to-one image of n'. Hence $m \neq 0$ and we may assume $m = p'$. Because $p' = p \cup \{p\}$ and $n' = n \cup \{n\}$, p is, according to the lemma, a one-to-one image of n. Hence by the inductive hypothesis $p = n$ and finally $m = p' = n'$, which proves the theorem.

COROLLARY 7: (The so-called *drawer principle of Dirichlet.*) *If* $|X| = m$, $|Y| = n$, $m > n$ *and f is a function such that* $f^1(X) = Y$, *then the function f is not one-to-one.*

Dirichlet formulated this theorem as follows:

If m objects are put into n drawers and $m > n$, *then at least one of the drawers contains at least two objects.*

Obviously, our function f is the function assigning to each object the drawer in which it is contained.

We shall now apply the theorems just proved to draw certain conclusions about infinite sets.

THEOREM 8: *If a set X is infinite and $X \subset Y$, then the set Y is infinite.*

This is an immediate consequence of Theorem 3.

THEOREM 9: *If X is infinite and Y finite, then the difference $X-Y$ is infinite.*

This follows from Theorem 4.

THEOREM 10: *The set N is infinite.*

PROOF. By way of a contradiction suppose that $|N| = n$ where $n \in N$. Since $n' \subset N$, we infer from Theorem 3 that the set n' has m elements, where m is a certain element of N such that $m \leqslant n$. Because $|p| = p$ for every $p \in N$, we obtain $n' \leqslant n$, which contradicts formula (4) (p. 90).

COROLLARY 11: *The range of a one-to-one infinite sequence is infinite.*

In fact, such a set is a one-to-one image of N. If it were finite then, by Theorem 1, N would also be finite.

From this theorem and from Theorem 8 we obtain

THEOREM 12: *If a set X contains a subset which is the set of terms of an infinite one-to-one sequence, then X is infinite.*

A set satisfying the hypothesis of Theorem 12 is called a *Dedekind infinite set*[1]). Theorem 12 can thus be expressed as follows:

If a set is Dedekind infinite, then it is infinite.

The converse theorem is also true, but its proof requires the axiom of choice.

° THEOREM 13: *If a set X is infinite, then it is Dedekind infinite.*

PROOF. Let f be a choice function for the family $2^X - \{0\}$. We extend f by letting $f(0) = x$, where x is an arbitrary fixed element of X. Thus f assigns an element of X to every subset of X and in particular $f(Y) \in Y$ if $Y \neq 0$.

[1]) It was R. Dedekind in his book *Was sind und was sollen die Zahlen*, Braunschweig 1881, who first called attention to the necessity of defining the notions of finite and infinite sets. The definition proposed there is equivalent to the one above.

Now let us define by induction two sequences $A \in (2^X)^N$ and $a \in X^N$:

$$a_0 = x, \qquad A_0 = \{x\},$$

$$a_{n'} = f(X - A_n), \qquad A_{n'} = A_n \cup \{a_{n'}\}.$$

We can prove by induction that the set A_n is finite and $A_m \subset A_n$ for $m \leqslant n$. Hence $X - A_n \neq 0$ and thus $a_{n'} \in X - A_n$ and $a_n \in A_n$ for every $n \in N$. The sequence a is one-to-one. In fact, if $k < j$ then $a_k \in A_k$, but $a_j \notin A_k$, for, letting $j = n'$, we have $A_k \subset A_n$ and $a_j = a_{n'} \in X - A_n \subset X - A_k$. Hence $a_j \neq a_k$. The set X is therefore Dedekind infinite, because it contains the subset $\{a_n : n \in N\}$, which is the set of terms of an infinite one-to-one sequence.

Exercises

1. If $f \in X^Y$, Y is an infinite set and X is finite, then at least one of the cosets of f is infinite (*Dirichlet's principle for infinite sets*).

2. If $|X| = m$ and $|Y| = n$, then $|X \times Y| = m \cdot n$ and $|X^Y| = m^n$.

3. If $|X_i| = m$ for $i = 1, 2, 3$, $|X_j \cap X_k| = n_{jk}$ for $j, k = 1, 2, 3$, $|X_1 \cap X_2 \cap X_3| = n_{123}$, then

$$|X_1 \cup X_2 \cup X_3| = n_1 + n_2 + n_3 - n_{12} - n_{23} - n_{31} + n_{123}.$$

Generalize this formula for the case of an arbitrary (finite) number of sets.

4. Prove that a set $X \subset N$ is infinite if and only if $\bigwedge_m \bigvee_{x \in X} (m < x)$.

§ 5. König's infinity lemma

Let A and B be sets, $B \subset A$, and let $f \in A^B$. A finite sequence $c \in A^n$ (resp. an infinite sequence $c \in A^N$) is called a *branch of length n* (resp. an *infinite branch*) if $c_m = f(c_{m'})$ and $c_{m'} \in B$ for every m such that $m' \in n$ (resp. for every $m' \in N$). The element c_0 (which need not belong to B) is called the *initial vertex* of the branch.

If c is a branch of length n (or an infinite branch) and $m \in n$ (or $m \in N$), then $c|m$ is a branch of length m.

°KÖNIG'S INFINITY LEMMA [1]): *Suppose that all the cosets of f are finite. If $x \in A$ and for every $n \in N$ there exists a branch of length n with initial vertex x, then there also exists at least one infinite branch with initial vertex x.*

[1]) Denes König, *Über eine Schlussweise aus dem Endlichen ins Unendliche*, Acta Litt. ac. sci. Hung. Fran. Josephinae, Sectio sci. math. **3** (1927) 121–130.

PROOF. Denote by K the set of elements $u \in A$ such that for every $n \in N$ there exists a branch of length n with initial vertex x. By assumption $x \in K$.

LEMMA: *If* $u \in K$ *then* $f^{-1}(\{u\}) \cap K \neq 0$.

In fact, suppose that $f^{-1}(\{u\}) \subset A - K$. Let e be a sequence of length m whose range is $W = f^{-1}(\{u\})$. Thus for every $j \in m$ there exists a number $n \in N$ such that there is no branch of length n with the initial vertex e_j. Let n_j denote the least number with this property and let $p = (\max_{j \in m} n_j)'$. Hence $n_j \in p$ for all $j \in m$ and thus for every element v of the coset $f^{-1}(\{u\})$ there exists no branch of length p with initial vertex v. On the other hand, it follows from the assumption $u \in K$ that there does exist a branch g of length p' and with the initial vertex u. Letting $c_j = g_{j'}$ for $j \in p'$, we obtain a branch of length p with initial vertex g_1. But this leads to a contradiction, for $g_1 \in f^{-1}(\{u\})$.

Now, let φ be a choice function for the family of non-empty sets of the form $K \cap f^{-1}(\{u\})$ where $u \in A$. Let us extend the function φ by defining $\varphi(0) = x$. Thus φ assigns an element of A to each set of the form $f^{-1}(\{u\}) \cap K$. Define a sequence c by induction letting

$$c_0 = x, \qquad c_{n'} = \varphi(f^{-1}(\{c_n\}) \cap K).$$

We shall show that for every $n \in N$ the following formula holds:

$$c_{n'} \in f^{-1}(\{c_n\}) \cap K. \tag{1}$$

In fact, for $n = 0$ we have $c_0 = x$, thus $c_0 \in K$ and, by the lemma, $f^{-1}(\{c_0\}) \cap K \neq 0$. Hence by means of the definition of choice function $c_{0'} \in f^{-1}(\{c_0\}) \cap K$. If (1) holds for some $n \in N$, then by the lemma we obtain $f^{-1}(\{c_{n'}\}) \cap K \neq 0$. Hence

$$c_{n''} = \varphi(f^{-1}(\{c_{n'}\}) \cap K) \in f^{-1}(\{c_{n'}\}) \cap K.$$

Formula (1) is thus proved by induction. It follows from (1) that $f(c_{n'}) = c_n$. Therefore c is an infinite branch with initial vertex x. Q.E.D.

The proof above uses the theorem asserting the existence of a choice function (see p. 73). Thus we have used the axiom of choice. It is worth noticing, on the other hand, that we have not applied the full axiom of choice but rather a special case guaranteeing the existence of a choice function for an arbitrary family of finite sets. One can even show that it is sufficient to assume the existence of a choice function for a countable family of finite sets.

It can be shown that it is impossible to eliminate the axiom of choice entirely from the proof of König's Lemma. In other words, this theorem is not a consequence of the axioms Σ.

Example. Let I be the closed interval $[0, 1] = \{x: 0 \leqslant x \leqslant 1\}$ and suppose that $I_{j,n} = \{x: j/2^n \leqslant x \leqslant (j+1)/2^n\}$ for $j < 2^n, n \in N$. Let G be a family of open intervals such that $S(G) = I$. We say that G *covers* $I_{j,n}$ if there exists an interval $D \in G$ such that $I_{j,n} \subset D$.

THEOREM: *Let G and $I_{j,n}$ be as defined above. Then there exists a number n such that G covers all the intervals $I_{j,n}$ for $j = 1, \ldots, 2^n - 1$.*

PROOF. Let A be the family of all the intervals $I_{j,n}$ and let B be the family of all the intervals $I_{j,n+1}$, $n \in N$ which are not covered by G. Let $f(I_{j,n+1})$ be that interval $I_{k,n}$ which contains $I_{j,n+1}$. Thus we have defined a function, belonging to A^B, whose cosets are finite. To prove the theorem it suffices to show that there exists a number n such that there is no branch with initial vertex I and length n.

Suppose the contrary. By means of König's lemma there exists an infinite branch, that is, a sequence of intervals $I_{j_n,n}$ such that each interval is contained in the previous one and none is covered by G. Let x be a point common to all the intervals of this sequence. Since $I = S(G)$, there exists an interval D in G such that $x \in D$. Hence for some n we have $I_{j_n,n} \subset D$. Thus G covers $I_{j_n,n}$, which contradicts the assumption that $I_{j_n,n} \in B$. #

Exercises

1. Give an example of a function $f \in N^N$ such that for every n there exists a branch of length n with initial vertex 0 and such that there exists no infinite branch with initial vertex 0 (the cosets of f cannot be all finite).

2. Prove that if A is a set of finite sequences of the terms 0 or 1 such that $\bigwedge_n [c \in A \to c|n \in A]$ and such that for every n there exists a sequence of at least n terms in A, then there exists an infinite sequence φ such that for every n the restriction $\varphi|n$ belongs to A. Does this theorem hold for an arbitrary set A of sequences of natural terms?

3. Let A be a set of binary relations between natural numbers, $A \subset 2^{N \times N}$, satisfying the following condition:

1. For every $n \in N$ there exists a relation in A whose field contains n.
2. If $R \in A$ and $n \in N$, then $R \cap (n \times n) \in A$.

Prove that there exists a relation R_0 with field N such that $R_0 \cap (n \times n) \in A$ for every $n \in N$.

4. If mankind is to last forever, then at least one man living now will have a male descendant in every generation. [König]

§ 6. Graphs. Ramsey's theorem

Every set G whose elements are unordered pairs of distinct elements is called a *graph*. The set $S(G)$ is called the *field of the graph*, its elements are called *vertices*. If $\{a, b\} \in G$ then the pair $\{a, b\}$ is called an edge of the graph. In this case we also say that the vertices a and b are joined to each other. This terminology is motivated by the geometrical interpretation of a graph in case the field consists of a finite number of linearly independent points in $\mathcal{E}^2$. This geometrical interpretation is given by a figure consisting of polygonal lines (edges) having no points in common except their vertices. An example of a graph is the set consisting of all the pairs $\{x, y\}$ where $x, y \in X$ and $x \neq y$. This graph is denoted by $[X]_2$ and is called the *complete graph with field X*. If G is a graph with field X, then the difference $G' = [X]_2 - G$ is also a graph and is called the *complement* of G.

A graph H is said to be a *subgraph* of G if $H \subset G$.

The study of graphs is equivalent to the investigation of symmetric and irreflexive relations, that is, relations satisfying the conditions:

$$xRy \to yRx, \qquad x \text{ non-}R\, x.$$

In fact, every graph G can be associated with such a relation by letting $R_G = \{\langle x, y\rangle : \{x, y\} \in G\}$. Conversely, every symmetric and irreflexive relation R determines a graph $G = \{\{x, y\} : [xRy]\}$ where $R = R_G$.

RAMSEY'S THEOREM: *If G is a graph with infinite field, then either G or G' contains a complete subgraph with infinite field.*

PROOF. Let f be a choice function for the family $2^{S(G)} - \{0\}$ and let $K(x) = \{y : \{x, y\}\} \in G$, $L(x) = \{y : \{x, y\}\} \in G'$. Thus the set $K(x)$ consists of the vertices joined to x in the graph G and $L(x)$ consists of the vertices joined to x in G'.

Now we define by induction four sequences $T \in (2^{S(G)})^N$, $A \in (2^{S(G)})^N$, $a \in (S(G))^N$ and $\varphi \in N^N$. Namely, let

$$T_0 = A_0 = S(G), \quad a_0 = f(S(G)), \quad \varphi_0 = 0,$$

$$T_{n'} = \{x\colon (x \in A_n) \wedge (\text{the set } K(x) \cap A_n \text{ is infinite})\},$$

$$a_{n'} = \begin{cases} f(T_{n'}), \\ a_0, \end{cases} \quad A_{n'} = \begin{cases} K(a_{n'}) \cap A_n, \\ 0, \end{cases} \quad \varphi_{n'} = \begin{cases} 0 & \text{if } T_{n'} \neq 0, \\ 1 & \text{if } T_{n'} = 0. \end{cases}$$

We consider two cases.

Case 1. $\varphi_{n'} = 0$ *for all* $n \in N$. In this case we prove by induction that for all n the following formulas hold:

(1) $$a_{n'} \in T_{n'},$$

(2) $$\text{The set } K(a_{n'}) \cap A_n \text{ is infinite},$$

(3) $$A_{n'} \subset K(a_{n'}) \cap A_n,$$

(4) $$T_{n'} \subset A_n.$$

If $k > j > 0$ then it follows from (3) that $A_k \subset A_{k-1} \subset A_j$. Since $a_k \in A_{k-1} - A_k$ (by (1) and (4)), $a_k \in A_j - A_k$. Hence the set of all terms of the sequence a is infinite and the complete graph whose field is this set is contained in G. Thus the theorem is proved for this case.

Case 2. *There exists* j *such that* $\varphi_{j'} = 1$. Let j_0 denote the least among such numbers. Thus $T_j \neq 0$ for $j \leqslant j_0$, which implies $a_{j_0} \in T_{j_0}$. The set A_{j_0} is infinite, for it equals either $S(G)$ (if $j_0 = 0$) or $K(a_{j_0}) \cap A_{j_0-1}$. Both sets are infinite, the former by assumption and the latter because $a_{j_0} \in T_{j_0}$.

We define by induction a sequence B of subsets of A_{j_0} and a sequence b of elements of A_{j_0}.

$$B_0 = A_{j_0}, \qquad b_0 = f(B_0),$$

$$B_{j+1} = \begin{cases} L(b_j) \cap B_j, \\ 0, \end{cases} \qquad b_{j+1} = \begin{cases} f(B_j) & \text{if } B_j \neq 0, \\ a_0 & \text{if } B_j = 0. \end{cases}$$

The sets B_j form a descending sequence: $B_{j'} \subset B_j$ for $j \in N$; the set B_0 is infinite. We shall prove by induction that each set B_j is infinite. In fact, suppose that this is the case for some $j \in N$. If the set B_{j+1} were finite, then for every $x \in [B_j - L(b_j)] - \{b_j\}$ we would have $\{b_j, x\}$

$\in G$, whence the sets $K(b_j) \cap B_j$ and $K(b_j) \cap A_{j_0}$ would be infinite. This implies $b_j \in T_{j'_0}$, which contradicts the fact that $T_{j'_0}$ is empty.

It follows from the above that for all j we have $b_j \in B_j$. If $k > j$ then $b_k \in B_k \subset B_j \subset L(b_j)$, hence $\{b_k, b_j\} \in G'$. Letting Y be the set of all the terms of b we obtain $[Y]_2 \subset G'$. The theorem is thus proved, because the set Y is infinite.

Example. Let $X \subset N$ and let G be the set all unordered pairs $\{x, y\}$, where $x, y \in X$ and x and y are relatively prime. Applying Ramsey's theorem we conclude that if X is infinite, then either X contains an infinite subset Y where every two numbers belonging to Y are relatively prime, or else X contains an infinite subset Y where no two numbers belonging to Y are relatively prime.

REMARKS 1. Ramsey's theorem may be illustrated as follows. Let every edge of the complete graph $[X]_2$ where X is an infinite set be coloured either white or black. Then X necessarily contains an infinite subset Y such that all the edges of the graph $[Y]_2$ are of the same colour.

2. Ramsey's theorem has a counterpart, also due to Ramsey, in the finite case:

For any natural number n there exists a natural number q such that, if the set X contains at least q elements, then for every graph $G \subset [X]_2$ there exists a subset $Y \subset X$ of n elements such that either $[Y]_2 \subset G$ or $[Y]_2 \subset G'$.

In other words, *if G is a graph whose field consists of q elements, then either G or G' contains a complete subgraph with field consisting of n elements.*

The theorems given in Exercises 1 and 2 below may also be stated to hold for finite sets.

Exercises

1. If G is a graph with infinite field and $G = G_1 \cup G_2 \cup \dots \cup G_k$, where $G_i \cap G_j = 0$ for $i \neq j$, then at least one G_i contains a complete subgraph with infinite field. [Ramsey]

2. Generalize Ramsey's theorem in the following way. Suppose that X is an infinite set. Let $[X]_n$ be the family of all subsets of X consisting of n elements and let $[X]_n = M_1 \cup M_2 \cup \dots \cup M_k$ where $M_i \cap M_j = 0$ for $i \neq j$. Then there exists an infinite subset $Z \subset X$ such that $[Z]_n \subset M_j$ for some j.

3. A graph G is said to contain a triangle provided there exist three distinct elements a, b, c such that $\{a, b\}$, $\{b, c\}$, $\{a, c\} \in G$. Show that if X has at least 6 elements and $G \subset [X]_2$, then either G or G' contains a triangle.

4. Let $N = \bigcup_{k<p} A_k$ where the sets A_k are pairwise disjoint. Show that for any natural number q there exist an increasing infinite sequence φ of natural numbers and a number $j_0 < p$ such that $\sum_{i=n}^{n+q} \varphi_i \in A_{j_0}$ for every n[1]).

[1]) From the great number of publications devoted to Ramsey's theorem, let us mention only: F. P. Ramsey, *On a problem of formal logic*, Proc. London Math. Soc. **30** (1929), 2nd series, pp. 264–286; Th. Skolem, *Ein kombinatorischer Satz mit Anwendung auf ein logisches Entscheidungsproblem*, Fund. Math. **20** (1933) 254–261; R. Rado, *Direct composition of partitions*, Journal of the London Math. Soc. **29** (1954) 71–83; P. Erdös and R. Rado, *A partition calculus in set theory*, Bull. Amer. Math. Soc. **62** (1965) 427–489. The last paper contains a detailed bibliography of the subject.

CHAPTER IV

GENERALIZED UNION, INTERSECTION AND CARTESIAN PRODUCT

In the present chapter our treatment will be based upon the axioms Σ° as in the preceding chapters. Theorems which are not marked by the symbol $^\circ$ are theorems of the system Σ.

The purpose of this chapter is to generalize the operations of union, intersection and cartesian product for an arbitrary number of sets.

§ 1. Generalized union and intersection

Let F be a function from a non-empty set T into the family of all subsets of a given fixed set $\mathcal{X}$. Thus $F \in (2^{\mathcal{X}})^T$. Instead of $F(t)$ we shall write F_t.

Let W be the range of F, that is, the family of sets F_t where $t \in T$. The union of the sets belonging to the family W is denoted by $S(W)$ or $\bigcup (W)$ (see p. 52), the intersection is denoted by $P(W)$ or $\bigcap (W)$ (see p. 61).

The following notation will be used.

$$S(W) = \bigcup_t F_t, \quad P(W) = \bigcap_t F_t.$$

It is easy to show that

(1) $$x \in \bigcup_t F_t \equiv \bigvee_t (x \in F_t), \qquad x \in \bigcap_t F_t \equiv \bigwedge_t (x \in F_t).$$

If the set T consists of the single element a, then

$$\bigcup_{t \in T} F_t = F_a = \bigcap_{t \in T} F_t;$$

on the other hand, if T consists of two elements a and b, then

$$\bigcup_{t \in T} F_t = F_a \cup F_b \quad \text{and} \quad \bigcap_{t \in T} F_t = F_a \cap F_b.$$

Thus these notions are indeed generalizations of the notions of union and intersection of sets to the case of an arbitrary family of sets.

It follows from (1) that the following equations hold for arbitrary propositional function $\Phi(x, y)$ of two variables with a limited domain:

$$\bigcup_y \{x\colon \Phi(x,y)\} = \{x\colon \bigvee_y \Phi(x,y)\},$$
(2)
$$\bigcap_y \{x\colon \Phi(x,y)\} = \{x\colon \bigwedge_y \Phi(x,y)\}.$$

In fact, let $F_y = \{x\colon \Phi(x,y)\}$; we obtain

$$\Phi(z,y) \equiv z \in \{x\colon \Phi(x,y)\} \equiv z \in F_y,$$

and thus

$$z \in \{x\colon \bigvee_y \Phi(x,y)\} \equiv \bigvee_y \Phi(z,y)$$
$$\equiv \bigvee_y (z \in F_y) \equiv z \in \bigcup_y F_y \equiv z \in \bigcup_y \{x\colon \Phi(x,y)\}.$$

The proof of the second equation in (2) is similar.

By (1), the formulas concerning quantifiers given in § 1, Chapter II, lead to the following formulas for the generalized operations:

(3) $$\bigcap_t F_t \subset F_t \subset \bigcup_t F_t,$$

(4) $$\bigcap_t (F_t \cap G_t) = \bigcap_t F_t \cap \bigcap_t G_t,$$

(5) $$\bigcup_t (F_t \cup G_t) = \bigcup_t F_t \cup \bigcup_t G_t,$$

(6) $$\bigcap_t F_t \cup \bigcap_t G_t = \bigcap_{ts} (F_t \cup G_s) \subset \bigcap_t (F_t \cup G_t),$$

(7) $$\bigcup_t (F_t \cap G_t) \subset \bigcup_{ts} (F_t \cap G_s) = \bigcup_t F_t \cap \bigcup_t G_t,$$

(8) $$-(\bigcap_t F_t) = \bigcup_t (-F_t),$$

(9) $$-(\bigcup_t F_t) = \bigcap_t (-F_t),$$

(10) $$\bigcap_t (A \cup F_t) = A \cup \bigcap_t F_t,$$

(11) $$\bigcup_t (A \cap F_t) = A \cap \bigcup_t F_t,$$

(12) $$[\bigwedge_t (A \subset F_t)] \to [A \subset (\bigcap_t F_t)],$$

(13) $$[\bigwedge_t (F_t \subset A)] \to [(\bigcup_t F_t) \subset A].$$

In formulas (8) and (9) the symbol $-$ denotes complementation with respect to the set $\mathcal{X}$.

The proofs of the formulas above follow directly from the respective formulas in §1, Chapter II. As an example we prove de Morgan's law (8):

$$\begin{aligned} x \in -(\bigcap_t F_t) &\equiv \neg (x \in \bigcap_t F_t) \\ &\equiv \neg [\bigwedge_t (x \in F_t)] \\ &\equiv \bigvee_t (x \in -F_t) \\ &\equiv x \in \bigcup_t (-F_t); \end{aligned}$$

where we apply successively formulas (2), p. 6, (6), p. 47, and (1) above.

The diagram on page 50 also leads to formulas for the generalized operations. It suffices to replace the implication sign $\to$ by the inclusion sign $\subset$, and Φ by a function F of two arguments having sets as values. In particular, the following important formula holds:

(14) $$\bigcup_t \bigcap_s F_{ts} \subset \bigcap_s \bigcup_t F_{ts}.$$

This inclusion cannot in general be reversed (see p. 50).

THEOREM 1: *The union* $\bigcup_t F_t$ *is the unique set* S *satisfying the conditions*:

(15) $$\bigwedge_t (F_t \subset S),$$

(16) $$\bigwedge_X \{[\bigwedge_t (F_t \subset X)] \to (S \subset X)\}.$$

The intersection $\bigcap_t F_t$ *is the unique set* P *satisfying the conditions:*

(15′) $$\bigwedge_t (P \subset F_t),$$

(16′) $$\bigwedge_X \{[\bigwedge_t (X \subset F_t)] \to (X \subset P)\}.$$

In other words, the union $\bigcup_t F_t$ is the *smallest* set containing all the sets F_t and the intersection $\bigcap_t F_t$ is the *largest* set included in each of the sets F_t.

PROOF. It follows from (3) and (13) that the union $\bigcup_t F_t$ satisfies conditions (15) and (16). Conversely, assuming that the set S satisfies these conditions we infer from (15) and (13) that $\bigcup_t F_t \subset S$. Setting $X = \bigcup_t F_t$ in (16) and applying (3), we obtain $S \subset \bigcup_t F_t$. Hence $S = \bigcup_t F_t$.

The proof for intersection is similar.

THEOREM 2: (GENERALIZED ASSOCIATIVE LAWS.) *If* $T = \bigcup_{u \in U} H_u$ *where* H *is a set-valued function with domain* U (i.e. $H \in (2^T)^U$), *then*

$$\bigcup_{t \in T} F_t = \bigcup_{u \in U} \bigcup_{t \in H_u} F_t, \tag{17}$$

$$\bigcap_{t \in T} F_t = \bigcap_{u \in U} \bigcap_{t \in H_u} F_t. \tag{18}$$

PROOF. Letting

$$S = \bigcup_{t \in T} F_t \quad \text{and} \quad S_u = \bigcup_{t \in H_u} F_t,$$

we reduce equation (17) to the form

$$S = \bigcup_{u \in U} S_u. \tag{19}$$

By assumption we have $S \supset F_t$ for every $t \in T$, in particular, for every $t \in H_u$. Thus $S \supset S_u$ by Theorem 1. On the other hand, suppose that $X \supset S_u$ for arbitrary $u \in U$. If $t \in T$, then there exists $u \in U$ such that $t \in H_u$, whence it follows that $S_u \supset F_t$, and thus $X \supset F_t$. Since t is arbitrary, we conclude that $X \supset S$. Applying Theorem 1 we obtain (19).

The proof of (18) is similar.

THEOREM 3: (GENERALIZED COMMUTATIVE LAWS.) *If φ is a permutation of the elements of a set T, then*

$$\bigcup_{t\in T} F_t = \bigcup_{t\in T} F_{\varphi(t)}, \qquad \bigcap_{t\in T} F_t = \bigcap_{t\in T} F_{\varphi(t)}.$$

PROOF. Let $S = \bigcup_t F_{\varphi(t)}$. If $t \in T$, then $t = \varphi(\varphi^c(t))$, and because $S \supset F_{\varphi(u)}$ for arbitrary $u \in T$, in particular for $u = \varphi^c(t)$, we have $S \supset F_t$. Conversely, if X is a set such that $X \supset F_t$ for $t \in T$, then $X \supset F_{\varphi(t)}$, because $\varphi(t) \in T$. Thus $X \supset S$, which shows that S is the smallest set containing all the sets F_t (i.e. $S = \bigcup_t F_t$).

The proof of the second formula is similar.

THEOREM 4: (GENERALIZED DISTRIBUTIVE LAWS.)[1]) *If*

$$M = \bigcup_{u\in U} T_u \quad \textit{and} \quad \boldsymbol{K} = \{Y \in 2^M\colon \bigwedge_{u\in U} (Y \cap T_u \neq 0)\},$$

then

(20) $$\bigcap_{u\in U} \bigcup_{t\in T_u} F_t = \bigcup_{Y\in K} \bigcap_{t\in Y} F_t,$$

(21) $$\bigcup_{u\in U} \bigcap_{t\in T_u} F_t = \bigcap_{Y\in K} \bigcup_{t\in Y} F_t.$$

PROOF. Suppose that $Y \in \boldsymbol{K}$ and $u \in U$. By the definition of the family $\boldsymbol{K}$ we have $Y \cap T_u \neq 0$, thus there exists $t_0 \in Y \cap T_u$. This implies by (3) that

$$\bigcap_{t\in Y} F_t \subset F_{t_0} \subset \bigcup_{t\in T_u} F_t.$$

Since this inclusion holds for any $u \in U$ (where Y is constant), we infer from Theorem 1 that

$$\bigcap_{t\in Y} F_t \subset \bigcap_{u\in U} \bigcup_{t\in T_u} F_t.$$

Since Y is arbitrary, we obtain by (3) the following inclusion:

(22) $$\bigcup_{Y\in K} \bigcap_{t\in Y} F_t \subset \bigcap_{u\in U} \bigcup_{t\in T_u} F_t.$$

To prove the opposite inclusion, suppose that

(23) $$a \in \bigcap_{u\in U} \bigcup_{t\in T_u} F_t.$$

Let

(24) $$Y = \{t \in M\colon a \in F_t\}.$$

If $u \in U$ then by (23) $a \in \bigcup_{t\in T_u} F_t$. Thus there exists $t \in T_u$ such that

[1]) See: A. Tarski, *Zur Grundlegung der Boole'schen Algebra I*, Fundamenta Mathematicae **24** (1935) 195.

$a \in F_t$; hence $t \in Y$, which proves that $Y \cap T_u \neq 0$. By the definition of K we have $Y \in K$. It now follows from (24) that $\bigwedge_{t \in Y} (a \in F_t)$; that is, $a \in \bigcap_{t \in Y} F_t$. This shows that

$$a \in \bigcup_{Y \in K} \bigcap_{t \in Y} F_t. \tag{25}$$

This together with (22) gives (20). To prove (21), replace F_t in (20) by $S - F_t$, where $S = \bigcup_{t \in M} F_t$. Then we obtain:

$$\bigcap_{u \in U} \bigcup_{t \in T_u} (S - F_t) = \bigcup_{Y \in K} \bigcap_{t \in Y} (S - F_t),$$

whence, by de Morgan's laws (8) and (9) and by $-(-F_t) = F_t$, we obtain (21).

We shall now generalize formulas (1)–(4), § 8, Chapter II, concerning images and inverse images of finite unions and intersections, to the case of arbitrary unions and intersections.

THEOREM 5: *Let* $F \in (2^{\mathcal{X}})^T$ *and let* $f \in Y^{\mathcal{X}}$. *Then*

$$f^1(\bigcup_t F_t) = \bigcup_t f^1(F_t), \tag{26}$$

$$f^1(\bigcap_t F_t) \subset \bigcap_t f^1(F_t). \tag{27}$$

If the function f is one-to-one, then the inclusion sign in (27) *can be replaced by the identity sign.*

PROOF. It follows from the definition of image that

$$\begin{aligned} y \in f^1(\bigcup_t F_t) &\equiv \bigvee_x [(x \in \bigcup_t F_t) \wedge (y = f(x))] \\ &\equiv \bigvee_x [\bigvee_t ((x \in F_t) \wedge (y = f(x)))] \\ &\equiv \bigvee_t [\bigvee_x ((x \in F_t) \wedge (y = f(x)))] \\ &\equiv \bigvee_t (y \in f^1(F_t)) \equiv y \in \bigcup_t f^1(F_t), \end{aligned}$$

which proves (26). Similarly, by means of (18) on p. 49, we obtain the following equivalences:

$$\begin{aligned} y \in f^1(\bigcap_t F_t) &\equiv \bigvee_x [(x \in \bigcap_t F_t) \wedge (y = f(x))] \\ &\equiv \bigvee_x \bigwedge_t [(x \in F_t) \wedge (y = f(x))] \end{aligned}$$

$$\rightarrow \bigwedge_t \bigvee_x [(x \in F_t) \wedge (y = f(x))]$$

$$\equiv \bigwedge_t (y \in f^1(F_t)) \equiv y \in \bigcap_t f^1(F_t),$$

whence it follows that (27) holds.

If the function f is one-to-one, then using (27) for the inverse function f^c and for the sets $f^1(F_t)$ we obtain

$$f^{-1}(\bigcap_t f^1(F_t)) \subset \bigcap_t f^{-1}(f^1(F_t)) = \bigcap_t F_t,$$

and by (2), p. 75, it follows

$$\bigcap_t f^1(F_t) \subset f^1(\bigcap_t (F_t)).$$

Since (27) also holds, Theorem 5 is proved.

THEOREM 6: *If* $G \in (2^Y)^T$ *and* $f \in Y^{\mathfrak{X}}$ *then*

$$f^{-1}(\bigcup_t G_t) = \bigcup_t f^{-1}(G_t), \tag{28}$$

$$f^{-1}(\bigcap_t G_t) = \bigcap_t f^{-1}(G_t). \tag{29}$$

The proof can be obtained from the following equivalences, which are consequences of the definition of the inverse image (see p. 75).

$$y \in f^{-1}(\bigcup_t G_t) \equiv f(y) \in \bigcup_t G_t \equiv \bigvee_t [f(y) \in G_t]$$

$$\equiv \bigvee_t [y \in f^{-1}(G_t)] \equiv y \in \bigcup_t f^{-1}(G_t);$$

$$y \in f^{-1}(\bigcap_t G_t) \equiv f(y) \in \bigcap_t G_t \equiv \bigwedge_t [f(y) \in G_t]$$

$$\equiv \bigwedge_t [y \in f^{-1}(G_t)] \equiv y \in \bigcap_t f^{-1}(G_t).$$

Formulas (26) and (28) assert the additivity of the operation of forming images and inverse images. Formula (29) asserts that the operation of forming inverse images is multiplicative. The operation of forming images is multiplicative, however, only for one-to-one functions.

Examples

Let the set 1 be a topological space (see Chapter I, § 8).

1. *If F is a function whose values are closed sets* (see p. 27), *then the intersection $P = \bigcap_t F_t$ is also a closed set.*

PROOF. Since $P \subset F_t$, we have $\overline{P} \subset \overline{F_t}$ for every t; thus $\overline{P} \subset F_t$, because $\overline{F_t} = F_t$. This implies that $\overline{P} \subset \bigcap_t F_t = P$, hence $\overline{P} = P$, for $P \subset \overline{P}$ by Axiom (3), § 8, Chapter I, p. 26.

2. *If G is a function whose values are open sets, then the union $S = \bigcup_t G_t$ is an open set.*

PROOF. The sets $1-G_t$ are closed, thus the intersection $\bigcap_t (1-G_t)$ is also closed. By de Morgan's law (9) the set $1-S$ is closed; hence the set S is open.

3. *If D is a function whose values are regular closed sets* (cf. p. 38), *then the set $S_0 = \overline{\bigcup_t D_t}$ is a regular closed set containing all the sets D_t. Moreover, every regular closed set containing all the sets D_t also contains the set S_0.*

PROOF. Clearly $S_0 \supset D_t$, so that $\mathrm{Int}(S_0) \supset \mathrm{Int}(D_t)$, thus

$$\text{(i)} \qquad \overline{\mathrm{Int}(S_0)} \supset \overline{\mathrm{Int}(D_t)} = D_t.$$

Since t is arbitrary, we infer by Theorem 1 that

$$\overline{\mathrm{Int}(S_0)} \supset \bigcup_t D_t \quad \text{and} \quad \overline{\mathrm{Int}(S_0)} \supset \overline{\bigcup_t D_t} = S_0.$$

On the other hand, $\mathrm{Int}(S_0) \subset S_0$. Thus

$$\overline{\mathrm{Int}(S_0)} \subset \overline{S_0} = S_0,$$

which proves that $S_0 = \overline{\mathrm{Int}(S_0)}$. Hence the set S_0 is regular closed. It follows from (i) that S_0 contains each set D_t.

If Z is a regular closed set and $Z \supset D_t$ for every t, then

$$Z \supset \bigcup_t D_t, \quad \text{thus} \quad Z = \overline{Z} \supset \overline{\bigcup_t D_t} = S_0.$$

4. *If D is a function whose values are regular closed sets, then the set $P_0 = \overline{\mathrm{Int}(\bigcap_t D_t)}$ is a regular closed set included in each set D_t. Moreover, every regular closed set included in each set D_t is also included in P_0.*

PROOF. Let $X = \bigcap_t D_t$. We thus have

$$P_0 = \overline{\mathrm{Int}(X)} = X^{c-c-} \quad \text{hence} \quad \overline{\mathrm{Int}(P_0)} = X^{c-c-c-c-}.$$

Applying formula (15), § 8, Chapter I, p. 29 we have

$$\overline{\mathrm{Int}(P_0)} = X = P_0.$$

Hence the set P_0 is regular closed.

Since $X \subset D_t$, we have $\mathrm{Int}(X) \subset \mathrm{Int}(D_t)$ and $\overline{\mathrm{Int}(X)} \subset \overline{\mathrm{Int}(D_t)}$, that is, $P_0 \subset \overline{\mathrm{Int}(D_t)} = D_t$ for every t.

Finally, if Z is a regular closed set and $Z \subset D_t$ for every t, then $Z \subset \bigcap_t D_t$. Hence $\mathrm{Int}(Z) \subset \mathrm{Int}(X)$ and $Z = \overline{\mathrm{Int}(Z)} \subset \overline{\mathrm{Int}(X)} = P_0$.

5. As a result of the theorems proved in Examples 1 and 2, it is possible to define a topological space by taking as primitive notion either that of open set or that of closed set instead of closure.

Namely, we may conceive of a *topological space* as a set with a distinguished family of subsets $\boldsymbol{F}$. Subsets belonging to the family $\boldsymbol{F}$ are called *closed sets*. We suppose that $\boldsymbol{F}$ satisfies two conditions:

(i) *If* $\boldsymbol{W} \subset \boldsymbol{F}$, *then* $P(\boldsymbol{W}) \in \boldsymbol{F}$ (*that is, the interesection of an arbitrary family of closed sets is closed*).

(ii) *If a family* $\boldsymbol{W}$ *is finite and* $\boldsymbol{W} \subset \boldsymbol{F}$, *then* $S(\boldsymbol{W}) \in \boldsymbol{F}$ (*that is, the union of a finite number of closed set is closed*).

We obviously assume that $P(0)$ is the whole space.

If we take the notion of open set as primitive, then denoting the family of open sets by $\boldsymbol{G}$ we assume axioms dual to (i) and (ii):

(i′) *If* $\boldsymbol{W} \subset \boldsymbol{G}$ *then* $S(\boldsymbol{W}) \in \boldsymbol{G}$.

(ii′) *If a family* $\boldsymbol{W}$ *is finite and* $\boldsymbol{W} \subset \boldsymbol{G}$, *then* $P(\boldsymbol{W}) \in \boldsymbol{G}$.

The system of axioms (i)–(ii) is equivalent to the system (1)–(4) given in Chapter I, p. 26. The axioms (1)–(4) are satisfied if we define $\overline{A}$ by the formula $\overline{A} = P(\boldsymbol{W}_A)$, where $\boldsymbol{W}_A$ is the family of all closed sets containing the set A. Then we have $(A = \overline{A}) \equiv (A \in \boldsymbol{F})$.

A similar remark can be made for the system (i′)–(ii′).

6. A family $\boldsymbol{R} \subset \boldsymbol{F}$ is said to be a *closed base* for the topological space if for every $A \in \boldsymbol{F}$ there exists $\boldsymbol{W} \subset \boldsymbol{R}$ such that $A = P(\boldsymbol{W})$. A family

$\boldsymbol{R} \subset \boldsymbol{F}$ is a *closed subbase* if the family of all finite unions of the sets belonging to $\boldsymbol{R}$ is a closed base.

7. The notion of *open base* and *subbase* can be defined dually replacing $\boldsymbol{F}$ by $\boldsymbol{G}$ (= the family of open sets), intersection by union and union by intersection.

Exercises

1. Let $F \in (2^{\mathcal{X}})^T$, $f \in \mathcal{Y}^{\mathcal{X}}$ and $\mathcal{X} = \bigcup_t F_t$. Let $f_t = f|F_t$. Prove that

$$f^{-1}(Y) = \bigcup_t f_t^{-1}(Y) \quad \text{for every } Y \subset \mathcal{Y}.$$

2. Prove that

$$\Big(\bigcup_t F_t\Big) \times \Big(\bigcup_u G_u\Big) = \bigcup_{t,u} (F_t \times G_u),$$
$$\Big(\bigcap_t F_t\Big) \times \Big(\bigcap_u G_u\Big) = \bigcap_{t,u} (F_t \times G_u).$$

3. Let T be any set and let $\boldsymbol{K} \subset 2^T$. Let the operation $D_{\boldsymbol{K}}$ on $F \in (2^X)^T$ be defined by the formula

$$x \in D_{\boldsymbol{K}}(F) \equiv \{t: x \in F_t\} \in \boldsymbol{K}.$$

Find $\boldsymbol{K}$ for which the operation $D_{\boldsymbol{K}}$ coincides with the operations of union and intersection discussed above.

4. Show that if $\boldsymbol{I}$ is an ideal in 2^T and $\boldsymbol{K} = 2^T - \boldsymbol{I}$, then the operation $D_{\boldsymbol{K}}$ is distributive over finite union; that is,

$$\bigwedge_t (F_t = G_t \cup H_t) \to \big(D_{\boldsymbol{K}}(F) = D_{\boldsymbol{K}}(G) \cup D_{\boldsymbol{K}}(H)\big).$$

5. Prove that the family of all intervals $r < x < s$, where r and s are rational numbers, is a base for the space $\mathcal{E}$ of real numbers.

Prove that the sets $\{x: r < x\}$ and $\{x: x < r\}$, where r is rational, form an open subbase for this space.

6. Let X be any set and $\boldsymbol{R}$ be any family of its subsets. Prove that the set X can be considered as a topological space with the family $\boldsymbol{R}$ as an open subbase (resp. closed subbase).

7. If X is a topological space and R is an equivalence relation with field X, then X/R becomes a topological space when we assume that a set $U \subset X/R$ is open if and only if the union $S(U) = \bigcup_{Z \in U} Z$ is an open set in X.

8. Prove that the canonical mapping $X \to X/R$ is continuous if X/R has the quotient topology defined in Exercise 7.

§ 2. Operations on infinite sequences of sets

We shall now consider a special case of the previous operations; namely, where the domain T of the function F coincides with N, that is, where F is an infinite sequence of sets. In analogy with infinite series and products of real numbers, we write

$$\bigcup_n F_n \text{ or } \bigcup_{n=0}^{\infty} F_n \text{ or } F_0 \cup F_1 \cup \ldots \quad \text{instead of} \quad \bigcup_{n\in N} F_n;$$

$$\bigcap_n F_n \text{ or } \bigcap_{n=0}^{\infty} F_n \text{ or } F_0 \cap F_1 \cap \ldots \quad \text{instead of} \quad \bigcap_{n\in N} F_n.$$

The following formulas follow immediately from formulas (2), § 1

(1)
$$\bigcup_{n=0}^{\infty} \{x\colon \Phi(n,x)\} = \{x\colon \bigvee_{n=0}^{\infty} \Phi(n,x)\},$$
$$\bigcap_{n=0}^{\infty} \{x\colon \Phi(n,x)\} = \{x\colon \bigwedge_{n=0}^{\infty} \Phi(n,x)\},$$

where $\Phi(n,x)$ denotes a propositional function of two variables, n is limited to N and x to a given set X.

Besides infinite union and intersection we consider the operations

$\operatorname{Lim\,sup}_{n=\infty} F_n$ (*limit superior* of the sequence $F_0, F_1, \ldots$),

$\operatorname{Lim\,inf}_{n=\infty} F_n$ (*limit inferior* of the sequence $F_0, F_1, \ldots$),

defined as follows

$$\operatorname{Lim\,sup}_{n=\infty} F_n = \bigcap_{n=0}^{\infty}\bigcup_{k=0}^{\infty} F_{n+k}, \qquad \operatorname{Lim\,inf}_{n=\infty} F_n = \bigcup_{n=0}^{\infty}\bigcap_{k=0}^{\infty} F_{n+k}.$$

It is easy to check that $\operatorname{Lim\,sup} F_n$ is the set of those elements x which belong to F_n for infinitely many n. Analogously, x belongs to $\operatorname{Lim\,inf} F_n$ if and only if it belongs to F_n for almost all n; that is, if it belongs to all but a finite number of the F_n.

It is easily seen that

(2)
$$\operatorname{Lim\,inf}_{n=\infty} F_n \subset \operatorname{Lim\,sup}_{n=\infty} F_n.$$

(see formula (18), p. 49).

If the inclusion sign in (2) can be replaced by the equality sign, that is, if the superior and inferior limits are equal, then their common value is denoted by

$$\operatorname{Lim}_{n=\infty} F_n,$$

and is called the *limit* of the sequence $F_0, F_1, \ldots$. In this case we also say that the sequence is *convergent*.

This terminology is similar to that used in the theory of real numbers. In order to emphasize this analogy, let us consider the notion of the characteristic function of a given set.

Let the set 1 be given and $X \subset 1$. The function with domain 1

$$f_X(x) = \begin{cases} 1 & \text{if} \quad x \in X, \\ 0 & \text{if} \quad x \in 1 - X \end{cases} \tag{3}$$

is said to be the *characteristic function* of the set X[1]).

It is easy to show that the sequence $F_0, F_1, \ldots$ of subsets of 1 is convergent if and only if the sequence of the characteristic functions of these sets is convergent to the characteristic function of $\operatorname*{Lim}_{n=\infty} F_n$.

It is also easy to show that the following conditions are equivalent[2]):

$$\operatorname*{Lim}_{n=\infty} (F_n \dot{-} A) = 0, \tag{4}$$

$$\operatorname*{Lim}_{n=\infty} F_n = A, \tag{4'}$$

where the sign $\dot{-}$ denotes the symmetric difference of two sets. The same equivalence holds for real numbers if we replace $F_n \dot{-} A$ by $|F_n - A|$.

Proof. Condition (4) is equivalent to the following: every element x belongs to $F_n \dot{-} A$ for at most finitely many n. In other words, for every x there exists n_0 such that $n > n_0$ implies

$$x \in F_n \equiv x \in A. \tag{5}$$

Suppose that $x \in \operatorname{Lim\,sup} F_n$, i.e. that x belongs to F_n for infinitely many n. It follows from (5) that $x \in A$ and that $x \in F_n$ for all $n > n_0$; that is, $x \in \operatorname{Lim\,inf} F_n$. Thus we have proved that (4) implies

$$\operatorname*{Lim\,sup}_{n=\infty} F_n \subset A \subset \operatorname*{Lim\,inf}_{n=\infty} F_n, \tag{6}$$

from which (4') follows by (2).

[1]) See: Ch. de la Vallée Poussin, *Intégrales de Lebesgue, fonctions d'ensemble, classes de Baire*, 2nd ed. (Paris 1936).

[2]) See: E. Marczewski, *Concerning the symmetric difference in the theory of sets and in Boolean Algebras*, Colloq. Math. **1** (1948) 200–202.

Conversely, suppose that (6) holds and $x \in A$. Thus $x \in \operatorname{Lim\,inf} F_n$ and $x \in F_n$ for all n greater than some n_0. If, on the other hand, $x \notin A$, then $x \notin \operatorname{Lim\,sup} F_n$ and hence $x \notin F_n$ from an n_0 on. Hence condition (6) implies that (5) holds for every x if $n > n_0$.

We shall still prove several more special laws concerning interchanging the symbols $\cap$ and $\cup$ and replacing two operations of the same kind by one such operation.

Let F be a function defined on the set $N \times N$, F' a function defined on the set $N^N \times N^N$ and F'' a function defined on the set $N \times N^N$, where the values of these functions are sets. We use the notation introduced on p. 96–100.

(7) $$\bigcup_m \bigcup_n F_{m,n} = \bigcup_p F_{K(p),L(p)}, \qquad \bigcap_m \bigcap_n F_{m,n} = \bigcap_p F_{K(p),L(p)}.$$

We shall prove only the first of these formulas. Clearly, $F_{K(p),L(p)} \subset \bigcup_m \bigcup_n F_{m,n}$, and thus $\bigcup_p F_{K(p),L(p)} \subset \bigcup_m \bigcup_n F_{m,n}$. On the other hand, if $x \in \bigcup_m \bigcup_n F_{m,n}$, then for some m, n we have $x \in F_{m,n}$; hence $x \in F_{K(p),L(p)}$ where $p = J(m, n)$.

(8) $$\bigcap_m \bigcup_n F_{m,n} = \bigcup_{\varphi \in N^N} \bigcap_m F_{m,\varphi(m)}.$$

In fact, it is clear that $F_{m,\varphi(m)} \subset \bigcup_n F_{m,n}$, thus $\bigcap_m F_{m,\varphi(m)} \subset \bigcap_m \bigcup_n F_{m,n}$. Since φ is arbitrary, we have

$$\bigcup_{\varphi \in N^N} \bigcap_m F_{m,\varphi(m)} \subset \bigcap_m \bigcup_n F_{m,n}.$$

If $x \in \bigcap_m \bigcup_n F_{m,n}$, then for every $m \in N$ there exists n such that $x \in F_{m,n}$. Letting $\varphi(m) = \min_n (x \in F_{m,n})$ we infer that $x \in \bigcap_m F_{m,\varphi(m)}$; hence $x \in \bigcup_\varphi \bigcap_m F_{m,\varphi(m)}$.

(9) $$\bigcup_\varphi \bigcup_\psi F'_{\varphi,\psi} = \bigcup_\vartheta F'_{K^*(\vartheta),L^*(\vartheta)}, \qquad \bigcap_\varphi \bigcap_\psi F'_{\varphi,\psi} = \bigcap_\vartheta F'_{K^*(\vartheta),L^*(\vartheta)}.$$

The proof is similar to that of (7).

°(10) $$\bigcap_m \bigcup_\varphi F''_{m,\varphi} = \bigcup_\varphi \bigcap_m F''_{m,\varphi(m)}.$$

In fact, $\varphi^{(m)} \in N^N$, thus $F''_{m,\varphi^{(m)}} \subset \bigcup_{\varphi} F''_{m,\varphi}$, whence it follows that $\bigcap_{m} F''_{m,\varphi^{(m)}} \subset \bigcap_{m} \bigcup_{\varphi} F''_{m,\varphi}$. To prove the opposite inclusion, suppose that $x \in \bigcap_{m} \bigcup_{\varphi} F''_{m,\varphi}$ and let $Z_m = \{\varphi \colon x \in F''_{m,\varphi}\}$. Hence $Z \neq 0$ for every $m \in N$, and so there exists a choice function h for the family consisting of all the sets Z_m. Letting $h(Z_m) = f(m)$, we infer that $f(m) \in N^N$ and $x \in F''_{m,f(m)}$ for every $m \in N$.

It follows from Theorem 7, p. 99 that there exists a sequence $\varphi \in N^N$ such that $\varphi^{(m)} = f(m)$ for every $m \in N$. Thus $x \in F''_{m,\varphi^{(m)}}$ for every $m \in N$, that is,

$$x \in \bigcap_{m} F''_{m,\varphi^{(m)}} \subset \bigcup_{\varphi} \bigcap_{m} F''_{m,\varphi^{(m)}}.$$

Using formulas (7)–(10) we shall obtain a formula to be used in Chapter X. In this formula G is a function of four variables, with domain $N^N \times N^N \times N \times N$, whose values are sets.

$$°(11) \quad \bigcup_{\psi} \bigcap_{m} \bigcup_{\varphi} \bigcap_{n} G_{\psi,\varphi,m,n} = \bigcup_{\vartheta} \bigcap_{p} G_{K^*(\vartheta),L^*(\vartheta)^{(K(p))},K(p),L(p)}.$$

In fact, replacing $F''_{m,\varphi}$ in (10) by $\bigcap_{n} G_{\psi,\varphi,m,n}$ (where ψ is an arbitrary but fixed function), we obtain

$$\bigcap_{m} \bigcup_{\varphi} \bigcap_{n} G_{\psi,\varphi,m,n} = \bigcup_{\varphi} \bigcap_{m} \bigcap_{n} G_{\psi,\varphi^{(m)},m,n},$$

thus the left-hand side of (11) equals $\bigcup_{\psi} \bigcup_{\varphi} \bigcap_{m} \bigcap_{n} G_{\psi,\varphi^{(m)},m,n}$. Applying (7) and (9) we obtain (11).

Exercises

1. Prove that the characteristic function defined by (3) satisfies the following conditions:

(a) $f_0(x) = 0$,
(b) $f_1(x) = 1$,
(c) $f_{-X}(x) = 1 - f_X(x)$,
(d) $f_{A \cap B}(x) = f_A(x) \cdot f_B(x)$,
(e) $f_{A-B}(x) = f_A(x) - f_{A \cap B}(x)$.

2. Prove that if $F_0 \subset F_1 \subset F_2 \subset \ldots$, then $\bigcup_{n=0}^{\infty} F_n = \operatorname{Lim}_{n=\infty} F_n$.

3. Prove that if $F_0 \supset F_1 \supset \dots$, then $\bigcap_{n=0}^{\infty} F_n = \operatorname{Lim}_{n=\infty} F_n$.

4. Prove that if $F_0 = 1$, then

$$1 = (F_0 - F_1) \cup (F_1 - F_2) \cup (F_2 - F_3) \cup \dots \cup \bigcap_{n=0}^{\infty} F_n.$$

If, moreover, $F_0 \supset F_1 \supset F_2 \supset \dots$, then

$$(F_1 - F_2) \cup (F_3 - F_4) \cup \dots \cup \bigcap_{n=0}^{\infty} F_n = 1 - [(F_0 - F_1) \cup (F_2 - F_3) \cup \dots].$$

5. Prove that if $k_1 < k_2 < \dots$, then

$$\operatorname{Lim\,inf}_{n=\infty} F_n \subset \operatorname{Lim\,inf}_{n=\infty} F_{k_n}, \qquad \operatorname{Lim\,sup}_{n=\infty} F_{k_n} \subset \operatorname{Lim\,sup}_{n=\infty} F_n.$$

6. Prove that if $\bigcap_{n=1}^{\infty} A_n \cap \bigcap_{n=1}^{\infty} B_n = 0$, then

$$\bigcap_{n=1}^{\infty} A_n \subset \bigcup_{n=1}^{\infty} [A_n \cap (B_{n-1} - B_n)]$$

where $B_0 = 1$.

7. $\bigcup_{n=1}^{\infty} A_n = \bigcup_{n=1}^{\infty} B_n$, where $B_1 = A_1$ and $B_n = A_n - (A_1 \cup \dots \cup A_{n-1})$ for $n > 1$.

8. Let $\bigcup_n \bigcap_m B_{n,m} = A = \bigcap_m \bigcup_n C_{n,m}$ and let $\bigcup_{n,m} C_{n,m+1} \subset \bigcup_{n,m} C_{n,m}$. Prove that

$$A = \operatorname{Lim}_{n=\infty} A_n, \quad \text{where} \quad A_n = \bigcup_{k=1}^{\infty} (B_{k,1} \cap \dots \cap B_{k,n}) \cap (C_{1,k} \cup \dots \cup C_{n,k}).$$

9. Prove that
(a) $\operatorname{Lim\,inf}(-A_n) = -\operatorname{Lim\,sup} A_n$,
(b) $\operatorname{Lim}(-A_n) = -(\operatorname{Lim} A_n)$,
(c) $\operatorname{Lim\,inf}(A_n \cap B_n) = \operatorname{Lim\,inf} A_n \cap \operatorname{Lim\,inf} B_n$,
(d) $\operatorname{Lim\,sup}(A_n \cup B_n) = \operatorname{Lim\,sup} A_n \cup \operatorname{Lim\,sup} B_n$,
(e) $\bigcap_{n=1}^{\infty} A_n \subset \operatorname{Lim\,inf} A_n \subset \operatorname{Lim\,sup} A_n \subset \bigcup_{n=1}^{\infty} A_n$,
(f) $\operatorname{Lim\,inf} A_n \cup \operatorname{Lim\,inf} B_n \subset \operatorname{Lim\,inf}(A_n \cup B_n)$,
(g) $\operatorname{Lim\,sup}(A_n \cap B_n) \subset \operatorname{Lim\,sup} A_n \cap \operatorname{Lim\,sup} B_n$,
(h) $A \dot{-} \operatorname{Lim\,inf} A_n \subset \operatorname{Lim\,sup}(A \dot{-} A_n)$,
$A \dot{-} \operatorname{Lim\,sup} A_n \subset \operatorname{Lim\,sup}(A \dot{-} A_n)$;
show that the opposite inclusions do not hold in general.

10. A function f from sets into sets is said to be *continuous* if for every convergent sequence $F_1, F_2, \dots$ the following identity holds:

$$f(\operatorname{Lim}_{n=\infty} F_n) = \operatorname{Lim}_{n=\infty} f(F_n).$$

Show that the functions $X \cup Y$, $X \cap Y$, $-X$ and generally $\bigcup_n F_n$ and $\bigcap_n F_n$ are continuous with respect to each component.

11. Prove the following condition for a sequence F_n to be convergent: for every sequence of pairs $\langle m_i, n_i \rangle$ such that $\lim_{i=\infty} m_i = \lim_{i=\infty} n_i = \infty$, we have

$$\bigcap_i (F_{m_i} \dot{-} F_{n_i}) = 0. \qquad \text{[Marczewski]}$$

12. If K is a family of subsets of N such that the complement of every set in K is finite, $D_K(F) = \operatorname{Lim\,inf} F_n$; if K is a family of infinite subsets of N then $D_K(F) = \operatorname{Lim\,sup} F_n$ (see § 1, Exercise 3). Using this result, generalize the operations Limsup, Liminf for the case where the argument is a function defined on an arbitrary set T (not necessarily on the set N).

§ 3. Families of sets closed under given operations

Let X be a fixed set and f a function of an arbitrary number of variables, where each variable ranges over the subsets of X. For simplicity let us suppose that f is a function of two variables; that is, the domain of f is the cartesian product $2^X \times 2^X$.

A family $R \subset 2^X$ is said to be *closed under a given function* f if

$$\bigwedge_{Y_1, Y_2} \big[(Y_1 \in R) \wedge (Y_2 \in R) \rightarrow \big(f(Y_1, Y_2) \in R\big)\big].$$

THEOREM 1: *For each family $R \subset 2^X$ there exists a family R_1 such that*: 1. $R \subset R_1 \subset 2^X$; 2. *the family R_1 is closed under the operation f*; 3. *the family R_1 is the least family satisfying conditions* 1 *and* 2, *that is, if R' satisfies the following two conditions*

$$(1) \quad R \subset R' \subset 2^X \quad \textit{and} \quad \bigwedge_{Y_1, Y_2} [(Y_1 \in R') \wedge (Y_2 \in R') \rightarrow (f(Y_1, Y_2) \in R')],$$

then $R_1 \subset R'$.

PROOF. Let K be the set of all families R' satisfying (1). K is a non-empty set, for $2^X \in K$. The required family is the intersection $\bigcap_{R' \in K} R'$.

The family R_1 satisfying conditions 1–3 is uniquely determined. In fact, if R_2 also satisfies the same conditions, then $R_1 \subset R_2$, since R_1 is the least such family. Similarly we obtain $R_2 \subset R_1$. Hence $R_1 = R_2$. We denote this family by R^*.

THEOREM 2: *For arbitrary families* $\boldsymbol{R}, \boldsymbol{R}_1$ *and* $\boldsymbol{R}_2$ *the following conditions hold*

(i) $\boldsymbol{R} \subset \boldsymbol{R}^*$,

(ii) $\boldsymbol{R}_1 \subset \boldsymbol{R}_2 \rightarrow \boldsymbol{R}_1^* \subset \boldsymbol{R}_2^*$,

(iii) $\boldsymbol{R}^{**} = \boldsymbol{R}^*$.

PROOF. Formula (i) follows from Theorem 1 (condition 1). Formula (ii) follows from the fact that $\boldsymbol{R}_2^*$ is a family closed under f and containing $\boldsymbol{R}_1$, thus by minimality, $\boldsymbol{R}_2^* \supset \boldsymbol{R}_1^*$. Finally, condition (iii) can be proved as follows: (i) implies $\boldsymbol{R}^* \subset \boldsymbol{R}^{**}$; since $\boldsymbol{R}^* \supset \boldsymbol{R}^*$ and $\boldsymbol{R}^*$ is closed under f, we obtain $\boldsymbol{R}^{**} \subset \boldsymbol{R}^*$ by minimality.

Theorems similar to 1 and 2 also hold for the case where there is given not one function f but an arbitrary family of such functions and $\boldsymbol{R}^*$ denotes the least family containing $\boldsymbol{R}$ and closed under all these functions. Moreover, the domains of these functions may be sequences of subsets of X. We shall not, however, formulate all of these generalizations.

Example 1. Let f denote the union of sets, i.e. $f(Y_1, Y_2) = Y_1 \cup Y_2$. The least family of sets containing $\boldsymbol{R}$ and closed under f is denoted by $\boldsymbol{R}_s$. This family consists of finite unions of the form $\bigcup_{i<n} Y_i$ where $n \in N$, $n \neq 0$ and $Y = (Y_0, Y_1, \ldots, Y_{n-1})$ is a sequence of sets belonging to $\boldsymbol{R}$; in other words, $Y \in \boldsymbol{R}^n$.

Similarly, if g is the function defined by $g(Y_1, Y_2) = Y_1 \cap Y_2$, then the least family containing $\boldsymbol{R}$ and closed under g is denoted by $\boldsymbol{R}_d$. This family consists of all intersections of the form $\bigcap_{i<n} Y_i$ where $n \in N$, $n \neq 0$, $Y \in \boldsymbol{R}^n$.

Example 2. The least family containing $\boldsymbol{R}$ and closed under the operations f and g defined in Example 1 is called the *lattice of sets generated* by $\boldsymbol{R}$.

THEOREM 3: *The lattice of sets generated by* $\boldsymbol{R}$ *is identical with the family* $\boldsymbol{R}_{sd}$. *Moreover,* $\boldsymbol{R}_{sd} = \boldsymbol{R}_{ds}$.

PROOF. First we prove the second part of the theorem. Let $Z \in \boldsymbol{R}_{sd}$, that is, $Z = \bigcap_{i<n} Y_i$, where $n \in N$, $n \neq 0$ and $Y_i \in \boldsymbol{R}_s$ for $i < n$. We show by induction that $Z \in \boldsymbol{R}_{ds}$. For $n = 1$ we have $Z = Y_0 \in \boldsymbol{R}_s$ and $\boldsymbol{R}_s \subset \boldsymbol{R}_{ds}$ because $\boldsymbol{R} \subset \boldsymbol{R}_d$. Suppose that the theorem holds for $n = k$ and let Z be the intersection of $k+1$ components Y_i belonging to $\boldsymbol{R}_s$. In particular, let $Y_k = \bigcup_{j<m} T_j$ where $m \in N$, $m \neq 0$ and $T_j \in \boldsymbol{R}$ for $j < m$. Let $Z' = \bigcap_{i<k} Y_i$. By the induction hypothesis, $Z' \in \boldsymbol{R}_{ds}$, thus $Z' = \bigcup_{h<p} V_h$ where $p \in N$, $p \neq 0$ and $V_h \in \boldsymbol{R}_d$ for $h < p$. Since $Z = Z' \cap Y_k$, we have

$$Z = Z' \cap \bigcup_{j<m} T_j = \bigcup_{j<m} (Z' \cap T_j) = \bigcup_{j<m} \bigcup_{h<p} (V_h \cap T_j).$$

It follows now from $V_h \cap T_j \in \boldsymbol{R}_d$ that $Z \in \boldsymbol{R}_{ds}$. We have thus proved that $\boldsymbol{R}_{sd} \subset \boldsymbol{R}_{ds}$. In a similar way we prove the opposite inclusion.

Now let us show that $\boldsymbol{R}_{sd}$ is the lattice of sets generated by $\boldsymbol{R}$. It is clear that the family $\boldsymbol{R}_{sd}$ is included in this lattice, for the operations of union and intersection do not lead out of the lattice. On the other hand, $\boldsymbol{R}_{sd} = (\boldsymbol{R}_{sd})_d = \boldsymbol{R}_{ds} = (\boldsymbol{R}_{ds})_s$; thus the family $\boldsymbol{R}_{sd}$ is closed under both union and intersection. Hence it contains the lattice generated by $\boldsymbol{R}$.

Exercises

1. Let $\boldsymbol{R}_r$ be the least family of subsets of X closed under the operation $Y_1 - Y_2$. Prove that

(a) $\boldsymbol{R}_d \subset \boldsymbol{R}_r$;

(b) if $X \in \boldsymbol{R}$ then $\boldsymbol{R}_s \subset \boldsymbol{R}_r$.

Show that the assumption $X \in \boldsymbol{R}$ in theorem (b) is essential.

2. Prove that the least field of sets containing $\boldsymbol{R}$ is $(\boldsymbol{R} \cup c\boldsymbol{R})_{sd}$ where $c\boldsymbol{R} = \{X - Y\colon Y \in \boldsymbol{R}\}$.

3. Let $\boldsymbol{R}_\Sigma$, resp. $\boldsymbol{R}_\Delta$, denote the least family containing $\boldsymbol{R}$ and such that for every non-empty family $\boldsymbol{S} \subset \boldsymbol{R}$ we have $\bigcup_{Y \in \boldsymbol{S}} Y \in \boldsymbol{R}_\Sigma$, resp. $\bigcap_{Y \in \boldsymbol{S}} Y \in \boldsymbol{R}_\Delta$. Prove that $\boldsymbol{R}_{\Sigma\Delta} = \boldsymbol{R}_{\Delta\Sigma}$.

Hint. Use Theorem 4, p. 115.

§ 4. σ-additive and σ-multiplicative families of sets

A family $\boldsymbol{R}$ of sets is said to be *σ-additive* (resp. *σ-multiplicative*) if for every sequence $H \in \boldsymbol{R}^N$ the formula $\bigcup_n H_n \in \boldsymbol{R}$ (resp. $\bigcap_n H_n \in \boldsymbol{R}$) holds.

The next theorems follow from Theorems 1 and 2, § 3, p. 126 and 127 generalized for the case of functions whose domains are sequences of sets.

THEOREM 1: *For every family* $\boldsymbol{R}$ *there exists a unique family* $\boldsymbol{B}(\boldsymbol{R})$ *which is σ-additive, σ-multiplicative, contains* $\boldsymbol{R}$ *and is the least family with these properties.*

THEOREM 2: *For every family* $\boldsymbol{R}$ *the following formulas hold:*

(1) $$\boldsymbol{R} \subset \boldsymbol{B}(\boldsymbol{R});$$

(2) $$\boldsymbol{R}_1 \subset \boldsymbol{R}_2 \to \boldsymbol{B}(\boldsymbol{R}_1) \subset \boldsymbol{B}(\boldsymbol{R}_2),$$

(3) $$\boldsymbol{B}(\boldsymbol{B}(\boldsymbol{R})) = \boldsymbol{B}(\boldsymbol{R}).$$

Performing the operation $\bigcup_n$ resp. $\bigcap_n$ on sequences whose terms belong to $\boldsymbol{B}(\boldsymbol{R})$, we obtain sets belonging to $\boldsymbol{B}(\boldsymbol{R})$. This remark allows us to obtain a classification of sets belonging to $\boldsymbol{B}(\boldsymbol{R})$. Namely, for any family $\boldsymbol{R}$ let $\boldsymbol{R}_\sigma$ denote the family of sets of the form $\bigcup_n H_n$ where $H \in \boldsymbol{R}^N$ and $\boldsymbol{R}_\delta$ the family of sets of the form $\bigcap_n H_n$, where $H \in \boldsymbol{R}^N$. It is clear that $\boldsymbol{R} \subset \boldsymbol{R}' \to (\boldsymbol{R}_\sigma \subset \boldsymbol{R}'_\sigma) \wedge (\boldsymbol{R}_\delta \subset \boldsymbol{R}'_\delta)$.

We define a σ-additive family as a family $\boldsymbol{R}$ such that $\boldsymbol{R} = \boldsymbol{R}_\sigma$ and a σ-multiplicative family as a family $\boldsymbol{R}$ such that $\boldsymbol{R} = \boldsymbol{R}_\delta$. Since $\boldsymbol{B}(\boldsymbol{R})$ is both σ-additive and σ-multiplicative, we obtain $(\boldsymbol{B}(\boldsymbol{R}))_\sigma = \boldsymbol{B}(\boldsymbol{R}) = (\boldsymbol{B}(\boldsymbol{R}))_\delta$. From $\boldsymbol{R} \subset \boldsymbol{B}(\boldsymbol{R})$ we have:

THEOREM 3: *The family* $\boldsymbol{B}(\boldsymbol{R})$ *contains each of the following families*

$$\boldsymbol{R}_\sigma, \boldsymbol{R}_{\sigma\delta}, \boldsymbol{R}_{\sigma\delta\sigma}, \ldots,$$

$$\boldsymbol{R}_\delta, \boldsymbol{R}_{\delta\sigma}, \boldsymbol{R}_{\delta\sigma\delta}, \ldots$$

In general, no two of these families are equal; moreover, they do not exhaust the whole family $\boldsymbol{B}(\boldsymbol{R})$.

We shall describe a method which often allows us to decide whether or not an individual set defined by a propositional function belongs to $\boldsymbol{B}(\boldsymbol{R})$ [1]).

[1]) See K. Kuratowski and A. Tarski, *Les opérations logiques et les ensembles projectifs*, Fundamenta Mathematicae **17** (1931) 240-248; K. Kuratowski, *Évaluation de la classe borelienne ou projective d'un ensemble de points à l'aide des symboles logiques*, ibid., 249–272.

Let $\Phi(i,j,\ldots,k,x)$ be a propositional function where the range of $i,j,\ldots,k$ is limited to N. Let

$$Z_{i,j,\ldots,k} = \{x\colon \Phi(i,j,\ldots,k,x)\},$$
$$W = \{x\colon \Omega'_i \Omega''_j \ldots \Omega^{(h)}_k \Phi(i,j,\ldots,k,x)\},$$

where each of the symbols $\Omega', \Omega'', \ldots, \Omega^{(h)}$ is either the universal or the existential quantifier. We have

THEOREM 4: *If for any $i,j,\ldots,k \in N$ the set $Z_{i,j,\ldots,k}$ belongs to $\boldsymbol{B}(\boldsymbol{R})$, then $W \in \boldsymbol{B}(\boldsymbol{R})$.*

PROOF. The proof is by induction on the number of quantifiers. If $h = 0$, then $W = Z_{i,j,\ldots,k}$; thus $W \in \boldsymbol{B}(\boldsymbol{R})$ by assumption. If the theorem holds for $h-1$ quantifiers, then each of the sets

$$W_i = \{x\colon \Omega''_j \ldots \Omega^{(h)}_k \Phi(i,j,\ldots,k,x)\}$$

belongs to $\boldsymbol{B}(\boldsymbol{R})$. Since $W = \bigcup_{i\in N} W_i$ when Ω' is the existential quantifier, and $W = \bigcap_{i\in N} W_i$ when Ω' is the universal quantifier, we have in both cases $W \in \boldsymbol{B}(\boldsymbol{R})$. Q.E.D.

We obtain most important examples by taking as $\boldsymbol{R}$ the family $\boldsymbol{F}$ of closed sets in an arbitrary topological space X. In this case, $\boldsymbol{B}(\boldsymbol{R})$ is called the *family of Borel sets* of the space X[1]).

As an example we consider a sequence f_n of continuous functions and show that points x for which the sequence $f_n(x)$ converges is an $\boldsymbol{F}_{\sigma\delta}$ set.

The Cauchy condition for the convergence of a sequence of real numbers $a_1, a_2, \ldots, a_n, \ldots$ can be written in the following form

$$\bigwedge_k \bigvee_m \bigwedge_i [|a_{m+i} - a_m| \leqslant 1/k].$$

This implies that the set Z of points at which the values of the sequence of continuous functions $f_1, f_2, \ldots, f_n, \ldots$ converge is

(i) $$Z = \Big\{x\colon \bigwedge_k \bigvee_m \bigwedge_i [|f_{m+i}(x) - f_m(x)| \leqslant 1/k]\Big\}.$$

[1]) After the name of the French mathematician E. Borel who first investigated them.

Letting
$$Z_{k,m,i} = \{x: |f_{m+i}(x) - f_m(x)| \leqslant 1/k\},$$
we infer from (i) that
$$Z = \bigcap_{k=1}^{\infty} \bigcup_{m=1}^{\infty} \bigcap_{i=1}^{\infty} Z_{k,m,i}.$$

Since the set $Z_{k,m,i}$ (for fixed indices) is closed (because the functions considered are continuous), the set Z is $\boldsymbol{F}_{\sigma\delta}$. #

Exercises

1. Prove that

(a) the intersection of two $\boldsymbol{F}_\sigma$-sets is an $\boldsymbol{F}_\sigma$-set,

(b) the union of an infinite sequence of $\boldsymbol{F}_\sigma$-sets is an $\boldsymbol{F}_\sigma$-set.

Prove the analogous properties for $\boldsymbol{F}_{\sigma\delta}$-sets and for Borel sets.

2. Prove that every set open in $\mathcal{E}^n$ is an $\boldsymbol{F}_\sigma$-set.

3. Prove that the Borel sets in $\mathcal{E}^n$ constitute the least σ-additive and σ-multiplicative family containing the family $\boldsymbol{G}$ of all open sets.

4. Prove the formulas which are obtained from (1)-(3) replacing $\boldsymbol{B}(\boldsymbol{R})$ by $\boldsymbol{R}_\sigma$ or by $\boldsymbol{R}_\delta$.

5. Give examples of (finite) families $\boldsymbol{R}$ such that $\boldsymbol{R} = \boldsymbol{R}_\sigma = \boldsymbol{R}_{\sigma\delta}$ and examples of families $\boldsymbol{R}$ such that $\boldsymbol{R} \neq \boldsymbol{R}_\sigma \neq \boldsymbol{R}_{\sigma\delta} = \boldsymbol{R}_{\sigma\delta\sigma}$ [1]).

§ 5. Generalized cartesian products

As in § 1, let F be a function whose values are subsets of the set X and whose domain is a set $T \neq 0$.

DEFINITION: The *cartesian product* $\prod_{t \in T} F_t$ is the set of all functions f whose domain is T and which satisfy the condition $f(t) \in F_t$ for every $t \in T$. That is,
$$\prod_{t \in T} F_t = \{f \in \Phi: \bigwedge_{t \in T} [f(t) \in F_t]\}, \quad \text{where} \quad \Phi = X^T.$$

If $T = N$ we write $\prod_{n=0}^{\infty} F_n$ instead of $\prod_{n \in N} F_n$. The elements of this cartesian product are sequences φ such that $\varphi_n \in F_n$ for $n \in N$.

[1]) Exercise 5 is connected with the problem posed by Kolmogorov, see Fundamenta Mathematicae **25** (1935) 578. The following special case of this problem is still open: *does there exist a family* $\boldsymbol{R}$ *such that* $\boldsymbol{R}_{\sigma\delta\sigma} \neq \boldsymbol{R}_{\sigma\delta\sigma\delta} = \boldsymbol{R}_{\sigma\delta\sigma\delta\sigma}$? See also W. Sierpiński, *Algèbre de Ensembles*, Monografie Matematyczne (Warszawa 1951), p. 171.

If all the sets F_t are identical, $F_t = Y$, then we have $\prod_{t \in T} F_t = Y^T$. In this case the symbol $\prod_{t \in T} F_t$ denotes the set of functions with domain T and range Y.

The set Y^T is called a *cartesian power* of the set Y.

For $Y \subset \prod_{t \in T} F_t$ let Y^t denote the projection of Y on F_t. Thus Y^t is the set $\{f(t) : f \in Y\}$. Clearly, $Y_1 \subset Y_2 \to Y_1^t \subset Y_2^t$ for every $t \in T$.

REMARK: Let $T = \{1, 2\}$. The cartesian product $\prod_{t \in T} F_t$ and the product $F_1 \times F_2$ are not identical. In fact, the first product has as elements two-term sequences, the second product, ordered pairs. These two notions are distinct. In practice, however, the distinction between these two kinds of products is inessential, for we can always associate with every pair $\langle x, y \rangle$ of $F_1 \times F_2$ the sequence $\{\langle 1, x \rangle, \langle 2, y \rangle\}$ belonging to $\prod_{t \in T} F_t$ in a one-to-one manner.

If $F_{t_0} = 0$ *for some* t_0, *then* $\prod_{t \in T} F_t = 0$.

In fact, if $f \in \prod_{t \in T} F_t$, then $f(t_0) \in F_{t_0}$; thus $F_{t_0} \neq 0$.

THEOREM 1. *If a set* T *has a finite number of elements and* $F_t \neq 0$ *for every* $t \in T$, *then* $\prod_{t \in T} F_t \neq 0$.

The proof is by induction on the number of elements of T. If T is composed of one element, then the theorem clearly holds. Suppose that it holds for the case where T is composed of n elements. Let $T_1 = T \cup \{a\}$ where $a \notin T$. Suppose further that $F_t \neq 0$ for $t \in T_1$. We shall show that $\prod_{t \in T_1} F_t \neq 0$. In fact, the induction hypothesis gives $\prod_{t \in T} F_t \neq 0$; thus let $f \in \prod_{t \in T} F_t$. Let $t_0 \in F_a$. The set $f_1 = f \cup \{\langle a, t_0 \rangle\}$ is a function belonging to $\prod_{t \in T_1} F_t$. Consequently, the set $\prod_{t \in T_1} F_t$ is non-empty.

Theorem 1 also holds for arbitrary T if all factors F_t are equal.

THEOREM 2: *If* $Y \neq 0$, *then* $Y^T \neq 0$.

In the general case the proof that the cartesian product is non-empty requires the axiom of choice.

°THEOREM 3: *If* $F_t \neq 0$ *for* $t \in T$, *then* $\prod_{t \in T} F_t \neq 0$ [1].

PROOF. A choice function for the family $\{F_t\colon t \in T\}$ is an element of $\prod_{t \in T} F_t$.

In applications of cartesian products (e.g. in algebra, in topology) we deal mostly with cases where certain operations are defined on the sets F_t or where the sets F_t are topological spaces. We discuss first the case where only one operation is defined on each set F_t. For convenience, we assume that this operation is binary. In other words, we suppose that besides the function $F \in (2^X)^T$ we are given a function G such that $G_t \in (F_t)^{F_t \times F_t}$ for every $t \in T$.

The function G induces a binary operation φ on the elements of the cartesian product $\prod_{t \in T} F_t$. Namely, we let for $f, g \in \prod_{t \in T} F_t$

$$\varphi(f, g) = \underset{t \in T}{F}\left[G_t\big(f(t), g(t)\big)\right].$$

Thus $\varphi(f, g)$ is that element h of the cartesian product for which $h(t) = G_t\big(f(t), g(t)\big)$ for every t. The operation φ is called the *cartesian product of the operations* G_t.

In a similar way we define the cartesian product of *relations*. Let R be a function such that (for every $t \in T$) R_t is a relation with field included in F_t. The *cartesian product of these relations* is the relation ϱ, whose field is included in $\prod_{t \in T} F_t$, such that

$$\langle f, g \rangle \in \varrho \equiv \bigwedge_t [\langle f(t), g(t) \rangle \in R_t].$$

It should be pointed out that ϱ is not the cartesian product $\prod_{t \in T} R_t$, because ϱ is a binary relation; that is, ϱ is a set of ordered pairs, whereas $\prod_{t \in T} R_t$ is a set of functions. However, we can associate in a natural way the

[1]) B. Russell took Theorem 3 as an axiom instead of the axiom of choice. He called this axiom the *multiplicative axiom*. See A. N. Whitehead and B. Russell, *Principia Mathematica*, vol. I, 2nd ed. (Cambridge 1925), p. 536.

cartesian product $\prod_{t\in T} R_t$ with the relation which holds between functions f and g if and only if the function h defined by $h(t) = \langle f(t), g(t)\rangle$ (that is, the function $\underset{t\in T}{F}[\langle f(t), g(t)\rangle]$) belongs to $\prod_{t\in T} R_t$. This relation coincides with the relation ϱ defined above.

Clearly, the definitions can be applied without modifications to the case where not just one but several operations (or relations) are defined on each F_t.

Example. Suppose that F_t is a Boolean algebra with respect to the operations $\vee_t$, $\wedge_t$, $-_t$ and the elements 0_t, 1_t. Let $\vee$, $\wedge$, $-$ denote the cartesian products of the operations $\vee_t$ $\wedge_t$, $-_t$, respectively, and let ξ, ι denote the functions such that $\xi(t) = 0_t$ and $\iota(t) = 1_t$ for all $t \in T$.

THEOREM 4: *The cartesian product $\prod_{t\in T} F_t$ is a Boolean algebra under the operations* $\vee$, $\wedge$, $-$, ξ, ι.

PROOF. To prove the theorem it suffices to check that axioms given on p. 37 hold. For instance, we check axiom (iv). Let $f \in \prod_{t\in T} F_t$; it follows from the definition that $f \vee -f$ is the function g such that $g(t) = f(t) \vee -_t f(t)$ for every t. Since axiom (iv) holds in F_t, we have $g(t) = 1_t$, thus $g = \iota$.

The Boolean algebra $\prod_{t\in T} F_t$ is called the *direct product* of the Boolean algebras F_t.

In a similar way we can define the direct product of groups, rings, and other algebraic systems.

Exercises

1. Prove that a Boolean algebra of 2^n elements is the direct product of n Boolean algebras of two elements.

Hint: Use induction on n.

2. Prove that if the relations R_t are (a) reflexive, (b) symmetric, (c) transitive, then their cartesian product has the same properties. Give an example of a property which does not hold for cartesian products although it holds for the individual factors. In other words, find a function R and a property which holds for all relations R_t but does not hold for their cartesian product.

In the following two exercises we assume that H is a function such that

$H_t \in F_t^{F_t \times F_t}$, R_t is an equivalence relation in F_t, φ is the cartesian product of the operations H_t and ϱ is the cartesian product of the relations R_t.

3. Show that if each function H_t is consistent with R_t, then φ is consistent with ϱ.

4. Let X be the function such that, for every t, X_t is the quotient function induced from H_t by means of R_t and let χ be the quotient function induced from φ by ϱ. Show that the following diagram is commutative:

$$\begin{array}{ccc} H & \longrightarrow & \varphi \\ \downarrow & & \downarrow \\ X & \longrightarrow & \chi \end{array}$$

§ 6. Cartesian products of topological spaces

For every $t \in T$, let F_t be a topological space and let $C_t X$ denote the closure of the set $X \subset F_t$ in the space F_t. Hence C is a function such that

$$C_t \in (2^{F_t})^{2^{F_t}} \qquad \text{for every } t.$$

Clearly, there are many different ways to define the closure operation on the space $\prod_{t \in T} F_t$. In fact, an arbitrary set can be made into a topological space in many different ways. Here we shall discuss one of the special topologies on the space $\prod_{t \in T} F_t$, introduced by Tychonoff [1]).

Let S be a finite subset of T and let G_s be an open set in the space F_s for every $s \in S$. We define the neighborhood determined by S and by the sets G_s to be the following subset of the cartesian product $\Pi = \prod_{t \in T} F_t$:

$$\Gamma = \{f \in \Pi : \bigwedge_{s \in S} f(s) \in G_s\}.$$

We shall prove that the intersection of two neighborhoods is a neighborhood. In fact, if Γ is the neighborhood determined by a finite set S and by open sets G_s ($s \in S$) and Γ' is the neighborhood determined by a finite set S' and by open sets G'_s ($s \in S'$), then

[1]) A. Tychonoff, *Über topologische Erweiterung von Räumen*, Mathematische Annalen **102** (1930) 544–561.

$$\Gamma \cap \Gamma' = \{f \in \Pi: \bigwedge_{s \in S} \bigwedge_{s' \in S'} (f(s) \in G_s) \wedge (f(s') \in G'_{s'})\}$$
$$= \{f \in \Pi: \bigwedge_{s \in S - S'} (f(s) \in G_s) \wedge \bigwedge_{s' \in S' - S} (f(s') \in G'_{s'})$$
$$\wedge \bigwedge_{s \in S \cap S'} (f(s) \in G_s \cap G'_s)\}.$$

Thus $\Gamma \cap \Gamma'$ is the neighborhood determined by the finite set $S \cup S'$ and by the open sets G''_t, where the sets G''_t are defined as follows: $G''_t = G_t$ for $t \in S - S'$, $G''_t = G'_t$ for $t \in S' - S$, and $G''_t = G_t \cap G'_t$ for $t \in S \cap S'$.

We define the closure of a set $X \subset \Pi$ to be the set CX of all $f \in \Pi$ such that each neighborhood Γ containing f also contains at least one element of X:

$$(*) \qquad \bigwedge_{\Gamma} [(\Gamma \text{ is a neighborhood}) \wedge (f \in \Gamma) \rightarrow (\Gamma \cap X \neq 0)].$$

THEOREM 1: *The cartesian product* $\prod_{t \in T} F_t$ *is a topological space with respect to the closure defined by* $\overline{X} = CX$ *for* $X \subset \prod_{t \in T} F_t$.

PROOF. It is necessary to check that axioms (1)–(4), p. 26 hold. Axioms (3) and (4) clearly hold.

Axiom (1). Let $f \in \overline{A}$; thus every neighborhood Γ containing f also contains at least one element of A. Hence $\Gamma \cap (A \cup B) \neq 0$, which implies $f \in \overline{A \cup B}$, and thus $\overline{A} \subset \overline{A \cup B}$. Similarly, $\overline{B} \subset \overline{A \cup B}$. Hence $\overline{A} \cup \overline{B} \subset \overline{A \cup B}$.

Now suppose that $f \in \overline{A \cup B}$ and $f \notin \overline{A}$. Thus for every neighborhood Γ containing f we have $\Gamma \cap (A \cup B) \neq 0$ and for some Γ_0 containing f we have $\Gamma_0 \cap A = 0$. If Γ is an arbitrary neighborhood containing f, then $\Gamma \cap \Gamma_0$ is also a neighborhood containing f. Therefore $\Gamma \cap \Gamma_0 \cap (A \cup B) \neq 0$, whence $\Gamma \cap \Gamma_0 \cap B \neq 0$ and hence $\Gamma \cap B \neq 0$. This shows that $f \in \overline{B}$.

Axiom (2). It suffices to show that $\overline{\overline{X}} \subset \overline{X}$. Let $f \in \overline{\overline{X}}$ and let Γ be any neighborhood containing f. Thus $\Gamma \cap \overline{X} \neq 0$; let $g \in \Gamma \cap \overline{X}$. Hence Γ is a neighborhood containing g. Since $g \in \overline{X}$, we have $\Gamma \cap X \neq 0$. This shows that the condition $(*)$ holds; hence $f \in \overline{X}$. ·

Examples of cartesian products of topological spaces

1. *The Cantor set.* This is the set $C = \{0, 1\}^N$ or, in other words, the cartesian power of a two-element set. If we define a topology on the set $\{0, 1\}$ by letting $\overline{X} = X$ (the discrete topology), then C becomes a topological space with the Tychonoff topology.

By assigning the real number $\sum_{n=0}^{\infty} 2f(n)/3^{n+1}$ to the element $f \in C$ we obtain a one-to-one mapping φ of the set C onto the set of those real numbers of the closed interval [0, 1] whose triadic expansion contains only the digits 0 and 2.

2. The *generalized Cantor set* C_T is the cartesian power $\{0, 1\}^T$. The Tychonoff topology may be defined on this set similarly as on the set C.

The generalized Cantor set may also be defined as the set of all characteristic functions of subsets of T. In practice, we may identify the set C_T with 2^T. Therefore at times we shall treat the family 2^T as a topological space. Similarly, the elements of the set $C_{T\times T} = \{0, 1\}^{T\times T}$ can be identified with the set of all relations on T. In fact, each element of the set $C_{T\times T}$ is a characteristic function of a set of ordered pairs of elements of T.

THEOREM 2: *The family $K_t = \{X \subset T: t \in X\}$ is both open and closed in C_T; the family $\{R \subset T\times T: tRs\}$ is both closed and open in $C_{T\times T}$.*

PROOF. Let Γ denote the neighborhood in C_T, determined by the set $S = \{t\}$ and by the open set $G_t = \{1\}$. Then $f \in \Gamma \equiv f(t) = 1$; thus Γ consists of the characteristic functions of the sets belonging to the family K_t. Hence this family is an open set. Likewise, the neighborhood determined by the set S and the open set $G_t' = \{0\}$ consists of the characteristic functions of the sets belonging to the family $2^T - K_t$. This shows that the family K_t is closed in C_T.

The second part of the theorem follows from the first.

3. *The Baire space.* This is the cartesian power N^N or, in other words, the set of infinite sequences of natural numbers. The topology in N^N is defined as the Tychonoff topology, where we define the closure operation in N to be $\overline{X} = X$.

If $a = (a_0, a_1, \ldots, a_{n-1})$ is a sequence of n terms ($a \in N^n$), then the set $N_a = N_{a_0, \ldots, a_{n-1}} = \{e\colon e|n = a\}$ is both open and closed in N^N. To see this, we notice that N_a is the set of sequences satisfying the conditions $\varphi_j = a_j$ where $j < n$; it thus coincides with the neighborhood Γ in N determined by the set $S = \{0, 1, \ldots, n-1\}$ and the open sets $G'_j = \{a_j\}$ for $j < n$. The complement of Γ is open in N^N, because it coincides with the union of neighborhoods determined by the sets $\{j\}$ and by the open sets $G'_j = N - \{a_j\}$, $j < n$.

Assigning the number

$$x = \frac{1\ |}{|\ \varphi_0+1} + \frac{1\ |}{|\ \varphi_1+1} + \frac{1\ |}{|\ \varphi_2+1} + \ldots$$

to the element $\varphi \in N^N$, we obtain a one-to-one mapping of the space N^N onto the set of irrational numbers in the open interval (0, 1). In practice, we may identify the Baire space with the set of irrational numbers in the open interval (0, 1). #

4. The *cartesian product of a finite number of spaces.* The construction described in this section is used both in case where the set T in the formula $X = \prod_{t \in T} F_t$ is finite and also in the case where T is infinite.

If T is a finite set, for instance $T = \{0, 1, \ldots, n-1\}$, then the cartesian products $\prod_{t<n} V_t$, where for every t the set V_t is open in F_t, form an open base of $\prod_{t<n} F_t$.

In particular, we may take $F_t = \mathcal{E}$ where $\mathcal{E}$ is the set of real numbers. In this case the space X is the *n-dimensional Euclidean space.* In the future, we shall make little use of this space because it has not been defined exclusively by means of set theoretical notions (in contrast to the other spaces discussed above).

In later chapters we shall make use of the following theorem.

THEOREM 3: *If $X = \prod_{t \in T} F_t$ is a cartesian product of topological spaces (with Tychonoff topology), $Z_t \subset F_t$ and Z_t is a closed set in F_t for every $t \in T$, then the set $\prod_{t \in T} Z_t$ is also closed.*

PROOF. Let $P = \prod_{t \in T} Z_t$ and let $f \notin P$. For some $s \in T$ we thus have $f(s) \notin Z_s$. The element of the subbase of X determined by the one-element set $\{s\}$ and by the open set $F_s - Z_s$ contains f and is disjoint from P.

Exercises

1. The set of reflexive relations whose fields are included in T is closed in $C_{T\times T}$. Prove that the same holds for the sets of symmetric relations, the set of transitive relations and the set of equivalence relations.

2. Prove that each neighborhood in the Baire space contains some neighborhood of the form $N_{\boldsymbol{a}}$, where $\boldsymbol{a}$ is a finite sequence.

3. Show that every set which is both open and closed in the Baire space is the union of a finite number of sets $N_{\boldsymbol{a}}$.

4. Show that the set $\{X \subset N: X \text{ is a finite set}\}$ is a Borel set in the space C_N.

5. Let I be any ideal in 2^T. Show that taking as neighborhoods the sets of the form $\{g: \bigwedge_{s\in S} (g(s) \in G_s)\}$, where $S \in I$ and G_s are open sets in F_s for $s \in S$ and defining the closure operation by (*), we obtain the function satisfying the axioms of topology (1)-(4) given on p. 26.

§ 7. The Tychonoff theorem

A family $\boldsymbol{R}$ of subsets of the set X is said *to have the finite intersection property* if every finite subfamily of $\boldsymbol{R}$ has a non-empty intersection.

A topological space X (that is, a set with an operation defined on subsets of X and satisfying axioms (1)-(4), p. 26) is said to be *compact* if every family of closed subsets of X which has the finite intersection property has a non-empty intersection. This definition implies that a topological space is compact if and only if every family of open sets, whose union is X, contains a finite subfamily whose union is also X.

Although the following theorem belongs to topology rather than to general set theory, we give it here because it has numerous applications in mathematical theories in general and in set theory in particular. Moreover, the means used in proving this theorem involve little more than set-theoretical techniques.

°THEOREM 1: (Tychonoff.) *If for every $t \in T$ the space F_t is compact, then the space $P = \prod_{t\in T} F_t$ is also compact (relative to the Tychonoff topology).*

In the proof of this theorem we make use of a lemma to be proved in Chapter VII, p. 267.

°LEMMA: *If $\boldsymbol{R}_0$ is a family of subsets of X with the finite intersection property, then there exists the maximal family $\boldsymbol{R} \subset 2^X$ containing $\boldsymbol{R}_0$*

which also has the finite intersection property. That is to say, every family of subsets of X containing $\boldsymbol{R}$ and different from $\boldsymbol{R}$ contains a finite subfamily with empty intersection.

We shall make use of the following two properties of maximal families $\boldsymbol{R}$ with the finite intersection property.

(i) *If $A \in \boldsymbol{R}$ and $B \in \boldsymbol{R}$, then $A \cap B \in \boldsymbol{R}$.*

Suppose the contrary. Then the family arising from $\boldsymbol{R}$ by adding to it $A \cap B$ does not have the finite intersection property. Thus it contains a finite subfamily with empty intersection. Clearly the set $A \cap B$ belongs to this subfamily. Hence we conclude that there exists a finite subfamily $\boldsymbol{R}' \subset \boldsymbol{R}$ such that $A \cap B \cap \bigcap_{Y \in \boldsymbol{R}'} Y = 0$, which contradicts the assumption that the family $\boldsymbol{R}$ has the finite intersection property.

(ii) *If $A \subset X$ and $A \cap Y \neq 0$ for every $Y \in \boldsymbol{R}$, then $A \in \boldsymbol{R}$.*

In fact, if $A \notin \boldsymbol{R}$, then the family $\boldsymbol{R} \cup \{A\}$ does not have the finite intersection property. Thus there exists a finite subfamily $\boldsymbol{R}' \subset \boldsymbol{R}$ such that $A \cap \bigcap_{Y \in \boldsymbol{R}'} Y = 0$. The intersection $\bigcap_{Y \in \boldsymbol{R}'} Y$ belongs to $\boldsymbol{R}$ by (i). This contradicts the assumption that $A \cap Y \neq 0$ for every $Y \in \boldsymbol{R}$.

Now to prove the Tychonoff theorem, let $\boldsymbol{R}_0$ be a family of closed subsets of P with the finite intersection property. Let $\boldsymbol{R}$ denote any maximal family of subsets of P with the finite intersection property, containing $\boldsymbol{R}_0$. For the proof of the theorem it now suffices to show that $\bigcap_{Y \in \boldsymbol{R}} \overline{Y} \neq 0$.

For arbitrary $Z \subset P$ let Z^t denote the projection of Z into F_t and let $\boldsymbol{R}^t = \{\overline{Y^t}: Y \in \boldsymbol{R}\}$. The family $\boldsymbol{R}^t$ consists of closed subsets of F_t. If the sets $\overline{Y_j^t}$, $j < n$, belong to $\boldsymbol{R}^t$ and $Y_j \in \boldsymbol{R}$, then $\bigcap_{j<n} Y_j \neq 0$ because the family $\boldsymbol{R}$ has the finite intersection property. This implies that $\bigcap_{j<n} Y_j^t \neq 0$ (see p. 132), whence $\bigcap_{j<n} \overline{Y_j^t} \neq 0$. Thus the family $\boldsymbol{R}^t$ has the finite intersection property. From the assumption that every F_t is compact we infer that $\bigcap_{Y \in \boldsymbol{R}} \overline{Y^t} \neq 0$. It now follows that there is an $f \in P$ such that for every $t \in T$, $f(t) \in \bigcap_{Y \in \boldsymbol{R}} \overline{Y^t}$. We shall prove that $f \in \bigcap_{Y \in \boldsymbol{R}} \overline{Y}$.

For this purpose suppose that $Y \in \boldsymbol{R}$ and that Γ is a neighborhood containing f. We have to show that $\Gamma \cap Y \neq 0$.

Let Γ be the neighborhood determined by a finite set $S \subset T$ and open sets $G_s \subset F_s$ $(s \in S)$, where clearly $f(s) \in G_s$ for $s \in S$. Letting $\Gamma_s = \{g: g(s) \in G_s\}$ we have $\Gamma = \bigcap_{s \in S} \Gamma_s$.

If Z is an arbitrary set belonging to $\boldsymbol{R}$, then $f(s) \in \overline{Z^s}$; thus $G_s \cap Z^s \neq 0$. This means that there exists $z_s \in G_s$ such that for some function $g \in Z$ we have $g(s) = z_s$; hence $g \in \Gamma_s$. Thus for any $Z \in \boldsymbol{R}$ we have $\Gamma_s \cap Z \neq 0$.

By (ii) it follows that $\Gamma_s \in \boldsymbol{R}$ and by (i) $\bigcap_{s \in S} \Gamma_s \in \boldsymbol{R}$; that is, $\Gamma \in \boldsymbol{R}$, which implies $\Gamma \cap Y \neq 0$. Thus every neighborhood containing f has elements in common with Y, consequently $f \in \overline{Y}$.

Examples

1. The sets $C, C_T, C_{T \times T}$ are compact.

2. Let $\Phi(R, x_1, \ldots, x_n)$ be a propositional function constructed from the propositional functions

$$(*) \qquad x_i = x_j, \qquad \langle x_i, x_j \rangle \in R$$

by applying only the operations of the propositional calculus. Such propositional functions are called *open*. For $a_1, \ldots, a_n \in T$ and for an arbitrary open propositional function Φ let

$$Z_\Phi = Z_\Phi(a_1, \ldots, a_n) = \{R \in T \times T: \ \Phi(R, a_1, \ldots, a_n)\}.$$

The set Z_Φ is both open and closed in $C_{T \times T}$. This fact follows from Theorem 2, § 6, when Φ is one of the propositional functions (*). For other open propositional functions, this property follows from the relationships between logical and set-theoretical operations as well as from the remark that the finite union, intersection, and complement of sets which are both open and closed are again both open and closed.

Now, let Φ_j be an open propositional function of the variables $x_{j1}, x_{j2}, \ldots, x_{jn_j}$ and let $a_{j1}, a_{j2}, \ldots, a_{jn_j}$ be elements of T $(j \in N)$. Since the set $C_{T \times T}$ is compact, we have

THEOREM 2. *If for every $k \in N$ the intersection* $\bigcap_{j<k} Z_{\Phi_j}(a_{j1}, \ldots, a_{jn_j})$

is non-empty, then the intersection $\bigcap_{j\in N} Z_{\Phi_j}(a_{j1}, \ldots, a_{jn_j})$ *is also non-empty.*

This theorem asserts that if there exist relations R_k which satisfy the conditions Φ_j for $j < k$ $(k = 1, 2, \ldots)$, then there also exists a "universal" relation R which satisfies all of these conditions.

Exercises

1. Derive König's lemma (p. 104) from the Tychonoff theorem.

2. Show that the Baire space is not compact.

§ 8. Reduced direct products

By combining the operation of cartesian product with forming of equivalence classes we obtain new operations which have found interesting applications in mathematical logic [1]).

Let T be any set and F a function defined on T whose values are non-empty sets. Let f_t be a function whose domain is $F_t \times F_t$ and whose range is included in F_t. Finally, let R_t be a binary relation with field included in F_t. All arguments below can be generalized for the case where the number of functions or relations is greater than 1.

Let $\boldsymbol{I}$ be an ideal in 2^T. Define the relation $\sim_I$ in $P = \prod_{t\in T} F_t$ by the formula

$$f \sim_I g \equiv \{t\colon f(t) \neq g(t)\} \in \boldsymbol{I}.$$

THEOREM 1: *The relation* $\sim_I$ *is an equivalence relation in* P.

The reflexivity of $\sim_I$ follows from $0 \in \boldsymbol{I}$, symmetry is obvious, and transitivity follows from the remark that for any $f, g, h \in P$,

$$\{t\colon f(t) \neq g(t)\} \subset \{t\colon f(t) \neq h(t)\} \cup \{t\colon h(t) \neq g(t)\}.$$

THEOREM 2: *The cartesian product* φ *of the functions* f_t *is consistent with* $\sim_I$.

[1]) These operations were first defined by J. Łoś in his paper *Quelques remarques, théorèmes et problèmes sur les classes définissables d'algèbres,* published in the book *Mathematical interpretations of formal systems* (Amsterdam 1955). See also T. Frayne, A. C. Morel and D. Scott, *Reduced direct products,* Fundamenta Mathematicae **51** (1962) 195–228.

PROOF. It is necessary to show that if e', e'', d', $d'' \in P$, then

$$(e' \sim_I e'') \wedge (d' \sim_I d'') \to [\varphi(e', d') \sim_I \varphi(e'', d'')].$$

Let $h' = \varphi(e', d')$, $h'' = \varphi(e'', d'')$ and $A = \{t: h'(t) \neq h''(t)\}$. It follows from the definition of φ that $h'(t) = f_t(e'(t), d'(t))$ and similarly $h''(t) = f_t(e''(t), d''(t))$. Hence $t \in A \to [e'(t) \neq e''(t)] \vee [d'(t) \neq d''(t)]$, whence it follows that

$$A \subset \{t: e'(t) \neq e''(t)\} \cup \{t: d'(t) \neq d''(t)\} \in \boldsymbol{I}.$$

From Theorems 1, 2 and from § 5, Chapter II, it follows that the quotient class $P/\boldsymbol{I}$ of P with respect to the relation $\sim_I$ and the operation $\varphi/\boldsymbol{I}$, induced from φ by $\sim_I$ exist.

We still define in $P/\boldsymbol{I}$ a relation $\varrho/\boldsymbol{I}$. It holds between the equivalence classes of two functions $e, d \in P$ if and only if $\{t: \langle e(t), d(t)\rangle \notin R_t\} \in \boldsymbol{I}$.

The set $P/\boldsymbol{I}$ is called the *direct product of the sets* F_t *reduced with respect to* $\boldsymbol{I}$ (shortly: *reduced* mod $\boldsymbol{I}$). Similarly, the function $\varphi/\boldsymbol{I}$ (resp. the relation $\varrho/\boldsymbol{I}$) is called the *direct product of the functions* f_t (resp. *of the relations* R_t) *reduced* mod $\boldsymbol{I}$.

Let $\Phi(x, y, z)$ be an arbitrary propositional function. The main problem of the theory of reduced products can be formulated as follows: When the sets $\{t: \Phi(F_t, f_t, R_t)\}$ are known, under what conditions do the set $P/\boldsymbol{I}$, the function $\varphi/\boldsymbol{I}$ and the relation $\varrho/\boldsymbol{I}$ satisfy the propositional function Φ?

In order to solve this problem, we consider more general propositional functions $\Phi(x, y, z, u_1, \ldots, u_k)$ of an arbitrary number of variables. Suppose that $e_1, \ldots, e_k \in P$ and let

$$A_\Phi = \{t: \Phi(F_t, f_t, R_t, e_1(t), \ldots, e_k(t))\}$$

(clearly, the set A_Φ depends not only on Φ but also on the elements $e_1, \ldots, e_k$; we do not write $e_1, \ldots, e_k$ in the symbol A_Φ in order to simplify the notation).

With this notation, the following theorems (i) – (iv) hold:

(i) $$A_{\Phi \vee \Psi} \notin \boldsymbol{I} \equiv A_\Phi \notin \boldsymbol{I} \vee A_\Psi \notin \boldsymbol{I}.$$

In fact, $A_{\Phi \vee \Psi} = A_\Phi \cup A_\Psi$; thus (see formula (11), p. 17) $A_{\Phi \vee \Psi} \in \boldsymbol{I} \equiv (A_\Phi \in \boldsymbol{I}) \wedge (A_\Psi \in \boldsymbol{I})$, and (i) follows by de Morgan's laws.

°(ii) *If Θ is the propositional function $\bigvee_{u_k} \Phi$, then*

$$A_\Theta \notin \boldsymbol{I} \equiv \bigvee_{e_k \in P} [A_\Phi \notin \boldsymbol{I}].$$

In fact, suppose that

$$A_\Theta = \{t\colon\ \Theta(F_t, f_t, R_t, e_1(t), \ldots, e_{k-1}(t))\} \notin \boldsymbol{I}.$$

For $t \in A_\Theta$ there exists $x \in F_t$ such that

$$\Phi(F_t, f_t, R_t, e_1(t), \ldots, e_{k-1}(t), x).$$

Let X_t denote the set of all these elements x, and let $X_t = F_t$ for $t \notin A_\Theta$. Let e_k be a choice function for the family consisting of all the sets X_t. We have $e_k \in P$ and

(1) $$\Phi(F_t, f_t, R_r, e_1(t), \ldots, e_k(t))$$

for all $t \in A_\Theta$. This implies $A_\Theta \subset A_\Phi$ and thus $A_\Phi \notin \boldsymbol{I}$.

Conversely, if $A_\Phi \notin \boldsymbol{I}$ then formula (1) holds for all $t \in A_\Phi$. Thus for these t

$$\Theta(F_t, f_t, R_t, e_1(t), \ldots, e_{k-1}(t)).$$

This implies that $t \in A_\Theta$. Hence $A_\Phi \subset A_\Theta$ and $A_\Theta \notin \boldsymbol{I}$.

An ideal $\boldsymbol{I}$ is said to be *prime* if for any $X \subset T$ exactly one of the conditions $A \in \boldsymbol{I}$, $T - X \in \boldsymbol{I}$ holds.

The set $\{X \subset T\colon\ x \notin X\}$ is an example of a prime ideal. In Chapter VII we shall prove that every ideal can be extended to a prime ideal.

(iii) *If $\boldsymbol{I}$ is a prime ideal and Ψ is the formula $\neg\, \Phi$, then*

$$A_\Psi \notin \boldsymbol{I} \equiv \neg (A_\Phi \notin \boldsymbol{I}).$$

In fact $A_\Psi = T - A_\Phi$.

°(iv) *If $\boldsymbol{I}$ is a prime ideal, then*

$$A_{\Phi \wedge \Psi} \notin \boldsymbol{I} \equiv (A_\Phi \notin \boldsymbol{I}) \wedge (A_\Psi \notin \boldsymbol{I});$$

moreover, if Ξ is the formula $\bigwedge_{u_k} \Phi$, then

$$A_\Xi \notin \boldsymbol{I} \equiv \bigwedge_{e_k \in P} [A_\Phi \notin \boldsymbol{I}].$$

Theorem (iv) follows from (i)–(iii).

A propositional function $\Phi(x, y, z, u_1, \ldots, u_k)$ is said to be *elementary* if it can be constructed from the propositional functions

(a) $u_i = u_j$,

(b) $y(u_i, u_j) = u_h$,

(c) $\langle u_i, u_j \rangle \in z$

by applying the operations of the propositional calculus and by applying the quantifiers $\bigvee_{u \in x}$, $\bigwedge_{u \in x}$.

The following theorem solves the problem stated above.

°THEOREM 3: *If* $\boldsymbol{I}$ *is a prime ideal,* $\Phi(x, y, z, u_1, \ldots, u_k)$ *is an elementary propositional function and* $e_1, \ldots, e_k$ *are arbitrary elements of* P*, then*[1]:

$$(2) \quad \Phi(P/\boldsymbol{I}, \varphi/\boldsymbol{I}, \varrho/\boldsymbol{I}, e_1/\boldsymbol{I}, \ldots, e_k/\boldsymbol{I}) \equiv \{t: \Phi(F_t, f_t, R_t, e_1(t), \ldots, e_k(t))\} \notin \boldsymbol{I}.$$

PROOF. If Φ is one of the propositional functions (a), (b), (c), then (2) holds. In fact, the left-hand side of (2) is equivalent to $e_i/\boldsymbol{I} = e_j/\boldsymbol{I}$ in case (a), to $\varphi/\boldsymbol{I}(e_i/\boldsymbol{I}, e_j/\boldsymbol{I}) = e_h/\boldsymbol{I}$ in case (b), and to $\langle e_i/\boldsymbol{I}, e_j/\boldsymbol{I} \rangle \in \varrho/\boldsymbol{I}$ in case (c). The right-hand side of (2) is then equivalent:

in case (a) to $\{t: e_i(t) = e_j(t)\} \notin \boldsymbol{I}$,
in case (b) to $\{t: f_t(e_i(t), e_j(t)) = e_h(t)\} \notin \boldsymbol{I}$,
in case (c) to $\{t: \langle e_i(t), e_j(t) \rangle \in R_t\} \notin \boldsymbol{I}$.

From the definitions of the set $P/\boldsymbol{I}$, the function $\varphi/\boldsymbol{I}$, and the relation $\varrho/\boldsymbol{I}$ as well as from the definition of prime ideals it follows that the left-hand and right-hand sides of (2) are equivalent.

In turn, it follows from theorems (i)–(iv) that if (2) holds for the propositional functions Φ and Ψ, then it also holds for the propositional functions arising from Φ and Ψ by applying the operations of propositional calculus and by applying the quantifiers $\bigvee_{u \in x}$ and $\bigwedge_{u \in x}$.

In this way Theorem 3 is proved.

[1]) Theorem 3 is a scheme, for each propositional function we obtain a separate theorem.

°COROLLARY 4: *If $\Phi(x,y,z)$ is an elementary propositional function, then*

$$\Phi(P/\boldsymbol{I}, \varphi/\boldsymbol{I}, \varrho/\boldsymbol{I}) \equiv \{t\colon\ \Phi(F_t, f_t, R_t)\} \notin \boldsymbol{I}.$$

This corollary follows from Theorem 3 if we assume that the propositional function does not contain the variables $u_1, \ldots, u_k$.

°COROLLARY 5: *If $\Phi(x,y,z)$ is an elementary propositional function and for every t the formula $\Phi(F_t, f_t, R_t)$ holds, then $\Phi(P/\boldsymbol{I}, \varphi/\boldsymbol{I}, \varrho/\boldsymbol{I})$.*

This corollary follows directly from the previous corollary and from the remark that if $\boldsymbol{I}$ is a prime ideal then $T \notin \boldsymbol{I}$.

Examples

In the following we suppose that $\boldsymbol{I}$ is a prime ideal in 2^T.

1. If the relations R_t are reflexive, transitive and satisfy the conditions:

$$\bigwedge_{x,y \in F_t} \{[\langle x,y\rangle \in R_t] \wedge [\langle y,x\rangle \in R_t] \rightarrow x = y\},$$

$$\bigwedge_{x,y \in F_t} [(\langle x,y\rangle \in R_t) \vee (\langle y,x\rangle \in R_t)],$$

then the relation $\varrho/\boldsymbol{I}$ satisfies the same conditions.

2. If F_t is a field with respect to the operations of addition f_t and multiplication g_t, then the set $P/\boldsymbol{I}$ is a field with respect to the operations $\varphi/\boldsymbol{I}$ and $\psi/\boldsymbol{I}$, where φ and ψ are the cartesian products of the operations f_t and g_t respectively.

Similarly, if each of the sets F_t is an ordered field with respect to the operations f_t and g_t and with respect to the order relation R_t, then $P/\boldsymbol{I}$ is an ordered field with respect to the operations $\varphi/\boldsymbol{I}$ and $\psi/\boldsymbol{I}$ and the order relation $\varrho/\boldsymbol{I}$.

These properties follow by Corollary 5 from the remark that propositional functions "X is a field under the operations D and M" and "X is a field with respect to these operations ordered by a relation R" are equivalent to elementary propositional functions $\Phi(X, D, M)$ resp. $\Phi_1(X, D, M, R)$. #

These examples show that forming the reduced direct product we can construct from a given family of models of a given system of axioms new models of the same system of axioms. Other applications of reduced direct product will be given in Chapter IX.

Exercises

1. By applying the lemma on p. 139, prove the existence of a prime ideal which contains a given ideal $\neq 2^T$.

2. Prove that if each of the sets F_t is a Boolean algebra with respect to the operations $\vee_t, \wedge_t, -_t$ and the elements $0_t, 1_t$ and if for every t the condition

$$(*) \qquad \bigwedge_x \{(x = 0_t) \vee \bigvee_{y,z} [(x = y \vee_t z) \wedge (y \neq 0_t) \wedge (z \neq 0_t)]\}$$

holds, then the set P/I is a Boolean algebra with respect to the operations $\vee/I$, $\wedge/I$, $-/I$ and the elements ξ/I, i/I, where $\vee, \wedge, -$ are the cartesian products of the operations $\vee_t, \wedge_t$ and $-_t$, respectively, and ξ, i are functions such that $\xi(t) = 0_t$ and $i(t) = 1_t$ for every t. Moreover, P/I satisfies condition (*). Show that the ordinary cartesian product of Boolean algebras satisfying (*) may fail to satisfy this condition.

§ 9. Inverse systems and their limits

Suppose we are given:

(i) an arbitrary set X;

(ii) a set T ordered (or more general, quasi-ordered) by the relation $\leqslant$;

(iii) a function $F \in (2^X)^T$, that is

$$F_t \subset X \quad \text{for every } t \in T;$$

(iv) a function $f \in \prod_{t_0 \leqslant t_1} F_{t_0}^{F_{t_1}}$, which can be written as

$$(1) \qquad f_{t_0 t_1} \in F_{t_0}^{F_{t_1}} \quad \text{or} \quad f_{t_0 t_1}\colon F_{t_1} \to F_{t_0}, \quad \text{where} \quad t_0 \leqslant t_1.$$

We assume that the function f satisfies the conditions:

$$(2) \qquad \text{if } t_0 < t_1 < t_2, \text{ then } f_{t_0 t_1} \circ f_{t_1 t_2} = f_{t_0 t_2},$$

$$(3) \qquad f_{tt} \text{ is the identity mapping for every } t \in T.$$

Then the system $U = (X, T, F, f)$ is called an *inverse system*. The subset of the cartesian product $\prod_{t \in T} F_t$ consisting of those elements φ that

$$(4) \qquad f_{t_0 t_1}[\varphi(t_1)] = \varphi(t_0)$$

is called the *inverse limit* of the system U and is denoted by

$$F_\infty \quad \text{or} \quad \underline{\mathrm{Lim}}\, U \quad \text{or} \quad \underset{t_0 < t_1}{\mathrm{Lim}} (F_t, f_{t_0 t_1}).$$

Let f_t denote the t-th coordinate of the function φ, that is, the function $f_t: F_\infty \to F_t$, defined by

(5) $$f_t(\varphi) = \varphi(t).$$

Thus we have

(6) $$f_{t_0 t_1} \circ f_{t_1} = f_{t_0}.$$

Let (X, T, F, f) and (Y, T, G, g) be two inverse systems and let h be a function $h \in \prod_{t \in T} G_t^{F_t}$, that is,

$$h_t: \ F_t \to G_t.$$

Suppose, moreover, that the following diagram is commutative:

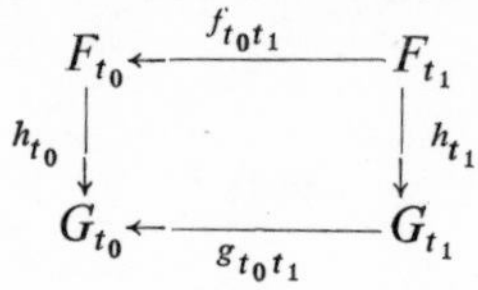

that is,

$$h_{t_0} \circ f_{t_0 t_1} = g_{t_0 t_1} \circ h_{t_1} \quad \text{if} \quad t_0 \leqslant t_1.$$

Then we can define a mapping

$$h_\infty: \ F_\infty \to G_\infty$$

in such a way that the diagram

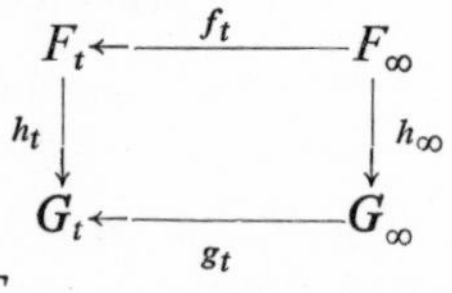

commutes for every $t \in T$.

Namely, let $\psi = h_\infty(\varphi)$ be defined for every $\varphi \in F_\infty$ by the condition

$$\psi(t) = h_t(\varphi(t)).$$

It is easy to prove that if, for every t, h_t is a one-to-one mapping of F_t onto G_t, then h_∞ is a one-to-one mapping of F_∞ onto G_∞.

Examples

1. Let the ordering relation on the set T be the identity relation. Then $F_\infty = \prod_{t \in T} F_t$.

2. Let the set T be directed, let F_t be the constant function: $F_t = X$, and let the mapping $f_{t_0 t_1}: X \to X$ be the identity mapping. Then F_∞ is the set of all constant functions $\varphi: T \to X$.

To prove this statement, we observe that if $t_0 \neq t_1$ then there exists t_2 such that $t_0 \leqslant t_2$ and $t_1 \leqslant t_2$; thus $f_{t_0t_2}[\varphi(t_2)] = \varphi(t_2)$. Hence by (4) $\varphi(t_0) = \varphi(t_2)$, and similarly $\varphi(t_1) = \varphi(t_2)$. Thus $\varphi(t_0) = \varphi(t_1)$.

3. The set Y^X of all mappings $\alpha: X \to Y$ can be represented by means of the operation of restriction $\alpha|A$ as the inverse limit of the sets Y^A where $A \subset X$. We take the set 2^X ordered by the inclusion relation as the directed set T. We define the function F by the formula $F_A = Y^A$ for $A \subset X$. Finally, we associate with each pair $A_0 \subset A_1$ the function $f_{A_0A_1}: Y^{A_1} \to Y^{A_0}$ defined by

$$f_{A_0A_1}(\alpha) = \alpha|A_0 \quad \text{where} \quad \alpha \in Y^{A_1}.$$

The role of the set X which occurs in the definition of inverse system is played here by the set S of all partial functions, that is by $\bigcup_{A \subset X} Y^A$.

Let us assign the element $\Phi(\alpha) \in \prod_A Y^A$, defined by

$$[\Phi(\alpha)]_A = \alpha|A,$$

to every element $\alpha \in Y^X$. We easily verify that $\Phi(\alpha) \in \underleftarrow{\mathrm{Lim}}(S, 2^X, F, f)$; that is,

$$\Phi: Y^X \to \underleftarrow{\mathrm{Lim}}(S, 2^X, F, f).$$

Moreover, Φ is a mapping of Y^X onto the set $\underleftarrow{\mathrm{Lim}}(S, 2^X, F, f)$. For let $\varphi \in \underleftarrow{\mathrm{Lim}}(S, 2^X, F, f)$. Then we have $\varphi_A \in Y^A$ for every $A \subset X$. Define $\alpha \in Y^X$ by the condition $\alpha(x) = \varphi_{\{x\}}(x)$. It is easy to see that $\Phi(\alpha) = \varphi$; that is, $\varphi_A(x) = \varphi_{\{x\}}(x)$ for all $x \in A$.

Finally, the mapping Φ is one-to-one. In fact, if $\alpha_1 \neq \alpha_2$, then there exists x_0 such that $\alpha_1(x_0) \neq \alpha_2(x_0)$; that is, $\alpha_1|\{x_0\} \neq \alpha_2|\{x_0\}$. Thus $[\Phi(\alpha_1)]_{\{x_0\}} \neq [\Phi(\alpha_2)]_{\{x_0\}}$ and $\Phi(\alpha_1) \neq \Phi(\alpha_2)$.

It is worth noticing that the argument above also applies when X and Y are metric spaces. In this case 2^X denotes the family of compact sets in X and Y^A denotes the family of continuous mappings $\alpha: A \to Y$.

§ 10. Infinite operations in lattices and in Boolean algebras

The theorems in the previous sections of this chapter can be considered as theorems about the lattice 2^X (see pp. 41–44). As we know, this lattice is a Boolean algebra and a complete lattice. In a natural way the question arises as to whether the theorems in § 1 can be generalized for the case of arbitrary lattices, or complete lattices, or Boolean algebras.

Suppose first that K is any ordered set and $f \in K^T$. The following theorems, analogous to Theorems 1 – 3, p. 113–115, hold:

THEOREM 1: *The least upper bound* $g = \bigvee_{t \in T} f_t$ *(resp. the greatest lower bound* $d = \bigwedge_{t \in T} f_t$*), if it exists, is the unique element of* K *satisfying the conditions*

$$\bigwedge_{t \in T} (f_t \leqslant g) \quad \text{and} \quad \bigwedge_{t \in T} (f_t \leqslant a) \to (g \leqslant a),$$

(resp.

$$\bigwedge_{t \in T} (d \leqslant f_t) \quad \text{and} \quad \bigwedge_{t \in T} (a \leqslant f_t) \to (a \leqslant d)).$$

If the least upper bound $\bigvee_{t \in T} f_t$ exists, it is called the *supremum* of the elements f_t, $t \in T$. If the greatest lower bound $\bigwedge_{t \in T} f_t$ exists, it is called the *infimum* of the elements f_t, $t \in T$.

THEOREM 2: *If* $T = \bigcup_{u \in U} H_u$ *and for every* $u \in U$ *the suprema* $\bigvee_{t \in H_u} f_t = g_u$ *exist and if the supremum* $\bigvee_{t \in T} f_t = g$ *also exists, then the supremum* $\bigvee_{u \in U} g_u$ *exists and is equal to* g *(analogously for infimum).*

THEOREM 3: *If* φ *is a permutation of the set* T *and the supremum* $\bigvee_{t \in T} f_t = g$ *exists, then the supremum* $\bigvee_{t \in T} f_{\varphi(t)}$ *also exists and is equal to* g *(analogously for infimum).*

Theorem 1 is a restatement of the definition of the least upper bound. Theorems 2 and 3 can be proved similarly as Theorems 2 and 3, pp. 114–115.

The following theorem holds for all ordered sets and is analogous to (3), p. 112.

THEOREM 4: *If the suprema* $\bigvee_{t \in T} f_t = g$ *and the infima* $\bigwedge_{t \in T} f_t = d$ *exist, then for all* $t \in T$ *we have* $d \leqslant f_t \leqslant g$.

On the other hand, formulas (4)–(11) do not have counterparts for arbitrary ordered sets.

THEOREM 5: *If the set K is a lattice, $p, q \in K^T$, and if the suprema $\bigvee_{t\in T} p_t = g_1$ and $\bigvee_{t\in T} q_t = g_2$ exist, then the supremum $\bigvee_{t\in T} (p_t \vee q_t)$ exists and is equal to $g_1 \vee g_2$ (similarly for infimum).*

PROOF. $g_1 \vee g_2 \geqslant p_t \vee q_t$ for all $t \in T$. If $\bigwedge_{t\in T} (x \geqslant p_t \vee q_t)$, then also $\bigwedge_{t\in T} (x \geqslant p_t)$, whence $x \geqslant g_1$; and similarly $x \geqslant g_2$; hence $x \geqslant g_1 \vee g_2$.

The assumption that K is a lattice has been taken in this theorem in order to ensure the existence of $p_t \vee q_t$ and $g_1 \vee g_2$.

THEOREM 6: *If K is a lattice and the suprema $\bigvee_{t\in T} f_t$ and $\bigvee_{t\in T} (a \wedge f_t)$ exist, then*

$$\bigvee_{t\in T} (a \wedge f_t) \leqslant a \wedge \bigvee_{t\in T} f_t$$

(similarly for infimum).

PROOF. For every $t \in T$ we have $a \wedge f_t \leqslant a$ and $a \wedge f_t \leqslant f_t \leqslant \bigvee_{t\in T} f_t$; thus $a \wedge f_t \leqslant a \wedge \bigvee_{t\in T} f_t$, whence the required formula follows.

The inequality sign in Theorem 6 cannot in general be replaced by the equality sign even in the case of complete lattices. However, the following theorem holds.

THEOREM 7: *If K is a Boolean algebra and the supremum $\bigvee_{t\in T} f_t$ exists, then for any $a \in K$ the supremum $\bigvee_{t\in T} (a \wedge f_t)$ exists and is identical to $a \wedge \bigvee_{t\in T} f_t$ (similarly for infimum).*

PROOF. Since $a \wedge f_t \leqslant a \wedge \bigvee_{t\in T} f_t$ for every $t \in T$, it suffices to show that if $\bigwedge_{t\in T} (a \wedge f_t \leqslant x)$, then $a \wedge \bigvee_{t\in T} f_t \leqslant x$. From the assumptions it follows that $-a \vee (a \wedge f_t) \leqslant -a \vee x$; hence $f_t \leqslant -a \vee x$ for arbitrary $t \in T$. We obtain $\bigvee_{t\in T} f_t \leqslant -a \vee x$, thus $a \wedge \bigvee_{t\in T} f_t \leqslant a \wedge (-a \vee x) \leqslant x$.

For Boolean algebras the following theorem holds (de Morgan's law).

THEOREM 8. *If the supremum* $\bigvee_{t\in T} f_t = g$ *exists, then so does the infimum* $\bigwedge_{t\in T} (-f_t)$ *and is equal to* $-g$ *(similarly with supremum and infimum interchanged).*

PROOF. Since $f_t \leqslant g$, we have $-g \leqslant -f_t$ for every $t \in T$. If $x \leqslant -f_t$ for every $t \in T$, then $f_t \leqslant -x$; hence $g \leqslant -x$ and $x \leqslant -g$, whence we obtain $\bigwedge_{t\in T} (-f_t) = -g$.

As the theorems above show, all basic theorems in § 1 can be generalized for the case of complete Boolean algebras. For non-complete Boolean algebras the theorems hold if we make the additional assumption that all the necessary suprema and infima exist. It is interesting to notice that the distributive law stated in Theorem 7 does not involve the complement sign, yet it can be proved only for Boolean algebras. The general distributive law given in Theorem 4, p. 115, is even more peculiar. We shall prove that Boolean algebras of the form 2^X are, in fact, the only Boolean algebras for which this theorem holds. First let us assume two definitions.

DEFINITION 1: A Boolean algebra K is said to be *distributive* if it is complete and, moreover, if for every set M and for every function $f: M \to K$ and for every partition of M into non-empty sets $M = \bigcup_{u\in U} T_u$ the following identity holds:

$$\bigwedge_{u\in U} \bigvee_{t\in T_u} f_t = \bigvee_{Y\in \mathbf{K}} \bigwedge_{t\in Y} f_t, \tag{1}$$

where

$$\mathbf{K} = \{Y \in 2^M : \bigwedge_{u\in U} (Y \cap T_u \neq 0)\}. \tag{2}$$

DEFINITION 2: An element a is said to be an *atom* of a Boolean algebra K provided $a \in K$, $a \neq o$ and $x < a \to x = o$. A Boolean algebra K is said to be *atomic* if for every element $x \neq o$ there is at least one atom a such that $a \leqslant x$.

THEOREM 9: *Every complete and atomic Boolean algebra K is isomorphic to the field of subsets 2^A where A is the set of atoms of K. Namely,* *there exists a one-to-one mapping Φ of K onto 2^A such that*

$$\Phi(\bigvee_{t\in T} f_t) = \bigcup_{t\in T} \Phi(f_t), \tag{3}$$

$$\Phi(\bigwedge_{t\in T} f_t) = \bigcap_{t\in T} \Phi(f_t) \tag{4}$$

for any set T and for any function $f \in K^T$ [1]).

PROOF. Let for $x \in K$

$$\Phi(x) = \{a \in A\colon\ a \leqslant x\}.$$

This formula defines a function whose domain is K and whose values are subsets of A. Clearly $x \leqslant y \to \Phi(x) \subset \Phi(y)$.

The function Φ is one-to-one. For suppose that x and y are elements of the algebra K such that $x \triangle y \neq o$. We can assume that $x-y \neq o$. By the assumption that K is atomic, there exists an atom a such that $a \leqslant x-y$. It follows from the formulas $a \wedge x \leqslant a$ and $a \wedge y \leqslant a$ that

$$a \wedge x = o \quad \text{or} \quad a \wedge x = a,$$

and

$$a \wedge y = o \quad \text{or} \quad a \wedge y = a.$$

The formulas $a \wedge x = o$ and $a \wedge y = o$ imply

$$a = a \wedge (x-y) = (a \wedge x)-(a \wedge y) = o-o = o.$$

Hence $a = o$, which contradicts the fact that a is an atom (Definition 2). Similarly, the formulas $a \wedge x = a$ and $a \wedge y = a$ imply

$$a = a \wedge (x-y) = (a \wedge x)-(a \wedge y) = a-a = o,$$

which again contradicts Definition 2.

Thus, either $a \wedge x = o$ and $a \wedge y = a$, or $a \wedge x = a$ and $a \wedge y = o$. In the former case we have a non $\leqslant x$ and $a \leqslant y$, in the latter $a \leqslant x$ and a non $\leqslant y$. Thus in both cases $\Phi(x) \neq \Phi(y)$.

Let $f \in K^T$. If $a \in \bigcup_{t\in T} \Phi(f_t)$, then there exists $t \in T$ such that $a \in \Phi(f_t)$. This implies $a \leqslant f_t \leqslant \bigvee_{t\in T} f_t$; thus $a \in \Phi(\bigvee_{t\in T} f_t)$.

[1]) See A. Tarski, *Zur Grundlegung der Boole'schen Algebra I*, Fundamenta Mathematicae **24** (1935) 197.

Hence we have proved that

$$(5)\qquad \bigcup_{t\in T}\Phi(f_t)\subset\Phi(\bigvee_{t\in T}f_t).$$

Now suppose that $a\in\Phi(\bigvee_{t\in T}f_t)$; that is, $a\leqslant\bigvee_{t\in T}f_t$. If $a\wedge f_t=o$ for every t, then we have $a=a-(a\wedge f_t)=a-f_t$; thus

$$a=\bigwedge_{t\in T}(a-f_t)=a-\bigvee_{t\in T}f_t$$

$$=a-(a\wedge\bigvee_{t\in T}f_t)=a-a=o,$$

because $a\wedge\bigvee_{t\in T}f_t=a$. But this conclusion contradicts the fact that $a\in A$. Hence there exists $t\in T$ such that $o\neq a\wedge f_t\leqslant a$. This means $a\wedge f_t=a$; thus $a\leqslant f_t$ and finally $a\in\Phi(f_t)\subset\bigcup_{t\in T}\Phi(f_t)$. We have thus proved the following inclusion

$$\Phi(\bigvee_{t\in T}f_t)\subset\bigcup_{t\in T}\Phi(f_t).$$

This by (5) implies (3).

Formula (4) can be proved even more simply. We have

$$a=\Phi(\bigwedge_{t\in T}f_t)\equiv(a\leqslant\bigwedge_{t\in T}f_t)$$

$$\equiv\bigwedge_{t\in T}(a\leqslant f_t)$$

$$\equiv\bigwedge_{t\in T}(a\in\Phi(f_t))$$

$$\equiv a\in\bigcap_{t\in T}\Phi(f_t).$$

It remains to be shown that every set $X\subset A$ can be represented as $\Phi(x)$ for some $x\in K$. For this purpose, let

$$T=X,\quad f_t=t,\quad x=\bigvee_{a\in X}f_a$$

(this union exists by the assumption that K is a complete Boolean algebra).

According to (3) we have

$$\Phi(x)=\bigcup_{a\in X}\Phi(a)=\bigcup_{a\in X}\{a\}=X,$$

because a is the unique atom included in a and hence $\Phi(a)=\{a\}$.

In this way Theorem 9 is completely proved.

THEOREM 10: *Every complete and atomic Boolean algebra K is distributive.*

PROOF. According to Theorem 9 there exists a function Φ which establishes the isomorphism between K and the field of subsets of some set A. By Theorem 4, § 1, formula (2) implies the formula

$$\bigcap_{u \in U} \bigcup_{t \in T_u} \Phi(f_t) = \bigcup_{Y \in \boldsymbol{K}} \bigcap_{t \in Y} \Phi(f_t),$$

which by (3) and (4) implies

$$\Phi(\bigwedge_{u \in U} \bigvee_{t \in T_u} f_t) = \Phi(\bigvee_{Y \in \boldsymbol{K}} \bigwedge_{t \in Y} f_t).$$

Since the function Φ is one-to-one, the formula above implies formula (1).

THEOREM 11: *If the Boolean algebra K is complete and distributive, then it is atomic* [1]).

PROOF. Suppose that K is complete and distributive but not atomic. Let a_0 be an element $\neq o$ which does not contain any atom. Let $T_u = \{u, -u\}$ for $u \in K$ and $f_t = t \wedge a_0$ for $t \in K$. Since $K = \bigcup_{u \in K} T_u$, we have equation (1), where $M = K$ and where $\boldsymbol{K}$ is defined by (2) for $M = K$. It follows from the definition of the set T_u that

$$\bigvee_{t \in T_u} f_t = f_u \vee f_{-u} = (a_0 \wedge u) \vee (a_0 \wedge -u) = a_0 \wedge (u \vee -u) = a_0,$$

hence

$$\bigwedge_{u \in U} \bigvee_{t \in T_u} f_t = a_0.$$

It follows from (1) that there exists a set $Y_0 \in \boldsymbol{K}$ such that

$$\bigwedge_{t \in Y_0} f_t \neq o.$$

Let

(6) $$b = \bigwedge_{t \in Y_0} f_t = a_0 \wedge \bigwedge_{t \in Y_0} t.$$

[1]) See A. Tarski, op. cit., p. 195.

Since a_0 contains no atom, b is not an atom. This means that there exists an element c such that

$$(7) \qquad o \neq c \leqslant b \quad \text{and} \quad c \neq b.$$

According to the definition of $\boldsymbol{K}$ (see (2)), $Y_0 \cap T_c \neq 0$; that is, either $c \in Y_0$ or $-c \in Y_0$. This implies by (6) that either $b \leqslant c$ or $b \leqslant -c$. In the former case we infer that $b = c$, in the latter case that $c \leqslant -c$. Thus either $c = b$ or $c = o$, which contradicts (7). This contradiction completes the proof.

\# *Example. The Boolean algebra* $\boldsymbol{K}$ *of regular closed sets in the plane is complete but not distributive.*

In fact, we proved in Chapter I, p. 39 that $\boldsymbol{K}$ is a Boolean algebra with respect to the operations $\bigcup$, $\odot$ and $'$. Moreover, it was shown that each element of $\boldsymbol{K}$, different from 0, contains a non-empty element distinct from itself. The Boolean algebra $\boldsymbol{K}$ is thus not atomic. From Theorems 3 and 4 given on p. 118 it follows that $\boldsymbol{K}$ is complete, from Theorem 11 it follows that $\boldsymbol{K}$ is not distributive.

This Boolean algebra $\boldsymbol{K}$ is an interesting example which shows that not all laws which hold for the algebra of sets can be transferred to the theory of Boolean algebras, even in the case of complete Boolean algebras [1]. #

Exercises

1. Prove that the equation dual to (1) also holds in atomic Boolean algebras

$$(8) \qquad \bigvee_{u \in U} \bigwedge_{t \in T_u} f_t = \bigwedge_{Y \in K} \bigvee_{t \in Y} f_t .$$

Furthermore, show that there exist complete Boolean algebras in which (8) does not hold.

[1]) For more results concerning distributivity in Boolean algebras see R. Sikorski, *Representability and distributivity of Boolean algebras*, Colloquium Mathematicum **8** (1961) 1–13.

In the present section we have dealt with the generalization of the operations of union and intersection. Other set-theoretical operations were also generalized for Boolean algebras. For instance, the operations in cylindrical algebras are generalizations of the operation of cartesian product. The theory of cylindrical algebras can be found in the book: L. Henkin, *La structure algébrique des théories mathématiques* (Paris 1955).

2. Give an example of a Brouwerian lattice K such that for some set T, for some function $f \in K^T$ and for some element $a \in K$ we have

$$a \wedge (\bigvee_{t \in T} f_t) \neq \bigvee_{t \in T} (a \wedge f_t).$$

3. Give an example of a Brouwerian lattice K such that for some set T, for some function $f \in K^T$ and for some $a \in K$ the supremum $\bigvee_{t \in T} f_t$ exists but the supremum $\bigvee_t (a \wedge f_t)$ does not exist.

§ 11. Extensions of ordered sets to complete lattices

We shall prove that every ordered set can be treated as a subsystem of a complete lattice (that is, of a lattice in which most laws of the algebra of sets hold). We shall also solve a similar problem for Boolean algebras. For this purpose, we first introduce a general notion of embedding of one system in another.

DEFINITION 1: A relational system $\langle A, R \rangle$ is said to be a *subsystem* of $\langle B, S \rangle$ if $A \subset B$ and $\bigwedge_{x, y \in A} [xRy \equiv xSy]$ (that is, $R = (A \times A) \cap S$).

DEFINITION 2: A system $\langle B, S \rangle$ is said to be an *extension* of the system $\langle A, R \rangle$ if there exists a subsystem $\langle B_1, S_1 \rangle$ of the system $\langle B, S \rangle$ isomorphic to $\langle A, R \rangle$.

In this case we also say that the system $\langle A, R \rangle$ is *embedded isomorphically* into the system $\langle B, S \rangle$ and that the function establishing the isomorphism *embeds* $\langle A, R \rangle$ in $\langle B, S \rangle$.

THEOREM 1: *Every ordered set A can be embedded isomorphically in the family of all subsets of some set (where the family is ordered by the inclusion relation). Consequently, A can be embedded in some complete and atomic Boolean algebra.*

PROOF. Let for $a \in A$

$$O(a) = \{x \colon x \leqslant a\}.$$

Because the relation $\leqslant$ is transitive, we have

$$a \leqslant b \rightarrow O(a) \subset O(b).$$

Since $a \in O(a)$, we have $O(a) \subset O(b) \rightarrow a \in O(b) \rightarrow a \leqslant b$. Hence

$$a \leqslant b \equiv O(a) \subset O(b),$$

and it follows directly that

$$O(a) = O(b) \to a = b.$$

Thus the function $a \to O(a)$ embeds A in the family of sets $O(a)$ ordered by the inclusion relation. Clearly, this family can be extended to the family 2^X, where $X = \bigcup_{a \in A} O(a)$.

In general, the extension described in Theorem 1 does not preserve supremum and infimum; that is, the equation $a = b \vee c$ does not necessarily imply $O(a) = O(b) \cup O(c)$. We shall consider whether it is possible to extend the set A to a complete lattice preserving suprema and infima.

Let the function φ embed the ordered system $\langle A, \leqslant_A \rangle$ in the ordered system $\langle B, \leqslant_B \rangle$.

DEFINITION 3: The embedding φ *preserves suprema* (resp. *infima*) if for every set T and for every function $f \in A^T$ such that the supremum $\bigvee_{t \in T} f_t$ (resp. the infimum $\bigwedge_{t \in T} f_t$) exists, the supremum $\bigvee_{t \in T} \varphi(f_t)$ also exists and

$$\varphi\Big(\bigvee_{t \in T} f_t\Big) = \bigvee_{t \in T} \varphi(f_t)$$

(resp. for infimum: $\bigwedge_{t \in T} \varphi(f_t)$ exists and

$$\varphi\Big(\bigwedge_{t \in T} f_t\Big) = \bigwedge_{t \in T} \varphi(f_t)).$$

We shall now consider a construction which will extend any ordered set to a complete lattice preserving suprema and infima. Let A be a set ordered by the relation $\leqslant$. For any set $X \subset A$, let

$$X^+ = \Big\{a \in A \colon \bigwedge_{x \in X} (x \leqslant a)\Big\}, \quad X^- = \Big\{a \in A \colon \bigwedge_{x \in X} (a \leqslant x)\Big\}.$$

The next statements follow from the definitions above:

(1) $$X \subset Y \to (X^+ \supset Y^+) \wedge (X^- \supset Y^-);$$

(2) *for any $Z \subset A$ we have $Z \subset Z^{+-}$ and $Z \subset Z^{-+}$.*

PROOF. By definition,

$$(z \in Z) \wedge (z' \in Z^+) \to (z \leqslant z'),$$

thus

$$(z \in Z) \to \bigwedge_{z' \in Z^+} (z \leqslant z') \to (z \in Z^{+-}).$$

The proof of the second part of (2) is similar.

(3) $$Z^{+-+} = Z^+ \quad \textit{and} \quad Z^{-+-} = Z^-.$$

The inclusion $Z^+ \subset Z^{+-+}$ follows from (2). If $a \in Z^{+-+}$ then $\bigwedge_{z \in Z^{+-}} (z \leqslant a)$ and therefore $\bigwedge_{z \in Z} (z \leqslant a)$ since $Z \subset Z^{+-}$. Thus $a \in Z^+$.

The proof of the second part of (3) is similar.

We now introduce the notion of a cut for ordered sets.

The pair $\langle X, Y\rangle$ is said to be a *cut* in the ordered set A if $X^+ = Y$, $Y^- = X$. The set X is called the *lower section* and Y the *upper section* of the cut.

It follows from the definition that

(4) $$(x \in X) \wedge (y \in Y) \to (x \leqslant y).$$

In fact, every element of X^+ is in relation $\geqslant$ to every element of X.

It follows from (3) that

(5) *Pairs $\langle Z^-, Z^{-+}\rangle$ and $\langle Z^{+-}, Z^+\rangle$ are cuts. Moreover, every cut can be expressed in both of these forms.*

Finally, it follows from the definition of a cut that

(6) *If $a \in A$ then the pair $\langle \{a\}^-, \{a\}^+\rangle$ is a cut.*

We can introduce an order relation between cuts:

$$\langle X, Y\rangle \leqslant \langle U, V\rangle \equiv X \subset U.$$

In view of showing that the relation $\leqslant$ is indeed an order relation, let us prove that

(7) $$\langle X, Y\rangle \leqslant \langle U, V\rangle \equiv V \subset Y.$$

PROOF. Suppose that $X \subset U$ and $v \in V$. If $x \in X$, then $x \in U = V^-$; thus $x \leqslant v$. Therefore $v \in X^+ = Y$, and finally $V \subset Y$. In a similar way we prove the opposite implication.

Let $\mathfrak{P}$ denote the family of all cuts.

(8) *$\mathfrak{P}$ is a complete lattice.*

Let $\mathfrak{L} \subset \mathfrak{P}$ and

$$S = \bigcup_{\langle X, X^+\rangle \in \mathfrak{L}} X, \qquad T = \bigcup_{\langle X^-, X\rangle \in \mathfrak{L}} X.$$

The cut $\langle S^{+-}, S^{+}\rangle$ is the supremum of $\mathfrak{L}$. In fact, $S \subset S^{+-}$ and thus $\langle X, X^{+}\rangle \leqslant \langle S^{+-}, S^{+}\rangle$ for every cut $\langle X, X^{+}\rangle \in \mathfrak{L}$. If $\langle X, X^{+}\rangle \leqslant \langle U, V\rangle$ for every $\langle X, X^{+}\rangle \in \mathfrak{L}$, then $X \subset U$ and therefore $S \subset U$. This implies $S^{+} \supset U^{+} = V$, hence $\langle S^{+-}, S^{+}\rangle \leqslant \langle U, V\rangle$.

Similarly we can prove that the cut $\langle T^{-}, T^{-+}\rangle$ is the infimum of $\mathfrak{L}$.

(9) *The function* $f(x) = \langle\{x\}^{-}, \{x\}^{+}\rangle$ *embeds* A *in* $\mathfrak{P}$ *preserving suprema and infima.*

PROOF. By definition the following equivalences hold:

$$x \leqslant y \equiv \{x\}^{-} \subset \{y\}^{-} \equiv f(x) \leqslant f(y).$$

Suppose that $x = \bigvee_{t \in T} \varphi_t$ in the set A; then $\varphi_t \leqslant x$ and therefore $f(\varphi_t) \leqslant f(x)$ for $t \in T$.

Let $\langle X, Y\rangle$ be a cut such that $f(\varphi_t) \leqslant \langle X, Y\rangle$ for $t \in T$. Then $\{\varphi_t\}^{-} \subset X$, and since $\varphi_t \in \{\varphi_t\}^{-}$, we obtain $\varphi_t \in X$. For any $y \in Y$ we have $\varphi_t \leqslant y$, thus $x \leqslant y$. This implies $x \in Y^{-} = X$, hence $\{x\}^{-} \subset X$ and $f(x) \leqslant \langle X, Y\rangle$. Thus $f(x) = \bigvee_{t} f(\varphi_t)$ in the set $\mathfrak{P}$.

The proof for infimum is similar.

The next theorem follows from (9).

THEOREM 2: *Every ordered set* A *can be extended to a complete lattice* $\mathfrak{P}$ *preserving suprema and infima*[1]).

The lattice $\mathfrak{P}$ constructed above is called the *minimal extension* of the ordered set A.

We now consider the case where A is a Boolean algebra.

First, observe that *if* Z_1 *and* Z_2 *are arbitrary subsets of an ordered set* A, *then*

(10) $$(Z_1 \cup Z_2)^{+} = Z_1^{+} \cap Z_2^{+}, \qquad (Z_1 \cup Z_2)^{-} = Z_1^{-} \cap Z_2^{-}.$$

Now let A be a lattice. We prove that *if* Y_1 *and* Y_2 *are upper sections of two cuts in* A, *then* $Y_1 \cap Y_2$ *is the set of all elements* $y_1 \vee y_2$

[1]) The method employed in the proof of Theorem 2 is due to Dedekind, who introduced the notion of a cut (in linearly ordered sets) in view of defining real numbers. See R. Dedekind, *Was sind und was sollen die Zahlen* (Braunschweig 1872). McNeille generalized this notion to arbitrary ordered sets (McNeille, *Partially ordered sets,* Transactions of the American Mathematical Society **42** (1937) 416–460). Recent results in this field are given by G. Bruns, *Darstellungen und Erweiterungen geordneter Mengen,* Crelle's Journal 209 (1962) 167–200.

where $y_i \in Y_i$ *for* $i = 1, 2$. In fact, $y_1 \vee y_2 \geqslant y_i$; thus $y_1 \vee y_2 \in Y_i$ for $i = 1, 2$. Moreover, $y \in Y_1 \cap Y_2 \to y = y \vee y$, where the first component may be understood to be an element of Y_1 and the second to be an element of Y_2.

Likewise we can prove that *if* X_1 *and* X_2 *are lower sections of two cuts in* A, *then* $X_1 \cap X_2$ *is the set of all elements of the form* $x_1 \wedge x_2$ *where* $x_i \in X_i$ *for* $i = 1, 2$.

Combining the above with formula (10) we conclude that *if* A *is a lattice and* $\langle X_1, Y_1 \rangle$, $\langle X_2, Y_2 \rangle$ *are two cuts in* A, *then*

$$(11) \qquad \begin{aligned} (X_1 \cup X_2)^+ &= Y_1 \cap Y_2 = \{y_1 \vee y_2 \colon (y_1 \in Y_1) \wedge (y_2 \in Y_2)\}, \\ (Y_1 \cup Y_2)^- &= X_1 \cap X_2 = \{x_1 \wedge x_2 \colon (x_1 \in X_1) \wedge (x_2 \in X_2)\}. \end{aligned}$$

It follows from the definitions of supremum and infimum in $\mathfrak{P}$ that for any ordered set A and for any two cuts in A we have

$$(12) \qquad \begin{aligned} \langle X_1, Y_1 \rangle \vee \langle X_2, Y_2 \rangle &= \langle (X_1 \cup X_2)^{+-}, (X_1 \cup X_2)^+ \rangle \\ &= \langle (Y_1 \cap Y_2)^-, Y_1 \cap Y_2 \rangle, \end{aligned}$$

$$(13) \qquad \begin{aligned} \langle X_1, Y_1 \rangle \wedge \langle X_2, Y_2 \rangle &= \langle (Y_1 \cup Y_2)^-, (Y_1 \cup Y_2)^{-+} \rangle \\ &= \langle X_1 \cap X_2, (X_1 \cap X_2)^+ \rangle. \end{aligned}$$

Finally, observe that *if* A *is a Boolean algebra and* $Z^* = \{-z \colon z \in Z\}$ *for any set* $Z \subset A$, *then*

(14) *if* $\langle X, Y \rangle$ *is a cut in* A, *then* $\langle Y^*, X^* \rangle$ *is also a cut in* A.

The proof of this lemma is left to the reader.

Now we shall prove the following

THEOREM 3: *The minimal extension of a Boolean algebra is a Boolean algebra.*

PROOF. Let $\mathfrak{P}$ be the minimal extension of a Boolean algebra A. It suffices to show that $\mathfrak{P}$ is a distributive lattice with zero O and with unit I and that for any cut $\langle X, Y \rangle \in \mathfrak{P}$ there exists a cut $\langle X_1, Y_1 \rangle \in \mathfrak{P}$ such that

$$(15) \qquad \langle X, Y \rangle \wedge \langle X_1, Y_1 \rangle = O, \qquad \langle X, Y \rangle \vee \langle X_1, Y_1 \rangle = I$$

(see p. 42, Theorem).

Clearly, the cut $O = \langle \{o\}, A \rangle$ is the zero of $\mathfrak{P}$ and $I = \langle A, \{i\} \rangle$ is the unit. The cut $\langle Y^*, X^* \rangle$ defined by (14) satisfies conditions (15).

In fact, the lower section of $\langle X, Y\rangle \wedge \langle Y^*, X^*\rangle$ is $X \cap Y^*$ (see formula (13)). The only element contained in $X \cap Y^*$ is o, because $a \in X \cap Y^* \to (a \in X) \wedge (-a \in Y) \to (a \leqslant -a) \to a = o$. This proves the first part of (15); the second part can be proved similarly.

It remains to show that the distributive law holds. Since the inequality $(a \wedge c) \vee (b \wedge c) \leqslant (a \vee b) \wedge c$ holds in every lattice, it suffices to show that if $\langle X_1, Y_1\rangle$, $\langle X_2, Y_2\rangle$ and $\langle U, V\rangle$ are three cuts in A, then

$$(\langle X_1, Y_1\rangle \vee \langle X_2, Y_2\rangle) \wedge \langle U, V\rangle \leqslant (\langle X_1, Y_1\rangle \wedge \langle U, V\rangle) \vee (\langle X_2, Y_2\rangle \wedge \langle U, V\rangle).$$

Applying (12) and (13), this formula can be reduced to the form

$$(Y_1 \cap Y_2)^- \cap U \subset [(X_1 \cap U)^+ \cap (X_2 \cap U)^+]^-;$$

that is, by (11) and by the definitions of Z^+ and Z^-,

$$(16) \quad \Big[(a \in U) \wedge \bigwedge_{y_1 \in Y_1, y_2 \in Y_2} (a \leqslant y_1 \vee y_2) \wedge \bigwedge_{x_1 \in X_1, x_2 \in X_2, u \in U} (b \geqslant x_1 \wedge u) \wedge (b \geqslant x_2 \wedge u)\Big] \to (a \leqslant b).$$

Suppose now that the elements a and b satisfy the antecedent of the implication (16). For arbitrary x_1 in X_1 the inequality $b \geqslant x_1 \wedge a$ holds. This implies $-a \vee b \geqslant x_1$. Since x_1 is arbitrary, we conclude that the element $y = -a \vee b$ belongs to Y_1. Similarly we prove that $y \in Y_2$. Because a satisfies the antecedent of (16), we obtain $a \leqslant y \vee y = y = -a \vee b$; hence $a \leqslant a \wedge (-a \vee b) = a \wedge b \leqslant b$. This proves (16) and thus the theorem is proved.

§ 12. Representation theory for distributive lattices

The notion of ideal [1]) is the basic concept involved in the representation theory for distributive lattices.

[1]) Instead of ideals many authors, especially in recent literature, apply *filters*, which are subsets of A satisfying the conditions dual to (1) and (2); that is:

$$(a \in I) \wedge (b \in I) \to (a \wedge b \in I) \quad \text{and} \quad (a \geqslant b) \wedge (b \in I) \to (a \in I).$$

All theorems given in the sequel can be formulated in terms of filters by substituting $\wedge$, $\vee$, $\leqslant$ for $\vee$, $\wedge$, $\geqslant$, respectively.

DEFINITION: A non-empty set $I \subset A$ is said to be an *ideal* of the distributive lattice A if

(1) $$(a \in I) \wedge (b \in I) \rightarrow (a \vee b \in I),$$

(2) $$(a \leqslant b) \wedge (b \in I) \rightarrow (a \in I).$$

An ideal I is said to be a *prime ideal* if $I \neq A$ and for $a, b \in A$,

(3) $$(a \wedge b \in I) \rightarrow [(a \in I) \vee (b \in I)].$$

Examples

1. Let $\boldsymbol{A}$ be a lattice of sets (for instance, the lattice of all subsets of an arbitrary set X) and let a be any element of the union $S(\boldsymbol{A})$. The family $\boldsymbol{I}$ of all sets $M \in \boldsymbol{A}$ which do not contain a is a prime ideal in the lattice $\boldsymbol{A}$.

2. The family of all finite sets $M \in \boldsymbol{A}$ is an ideal in $\boldsymbol{A}$.

3. If $\boldsymbol{A}$ is the family of all subsets of the set of real numbers, then the family of all sets of Lebesgue measure zero is an ideal in $\boldsymbol{A}$.

The set $\{x\colon x \leqslant a\}$ is an ideal in any lattice. This ideal is called the *principal ideal generated by a.*

We shall make use of the following general theorems concerning ideals.

(4) $$(a \vee b \in I) \rightarrow (a \in I) \wedge (b \in I).$$

In fact, $a \leqslant a \vee b$ and $b \leqslant a \vee b$. If $a \vee b \in I$, then $a \in I$ and $b \in I$ by (2).

(5) $$a \in I \rightarrow a \wedge b \in I.$$

In fact, $a \wedge b \leqslant a$.

(6) *The set $I^*(b)$ of elements x such that $x \leqslant i \vee b$ for some $i \in I$ is an ideal and $I \subset I^*(b)$, $b \in I^*(b)$.*

In fact, if $x \leqslant i_1 \vee b$ and $y \leqslant i_2 \vee b$, then $x \vee y \leqslant (i_1 \vee i_2) \vee b$; therefore $x \vee y \in I^*(b)$, because $i_1 \vee i_2 \in I$. If $x \leqslant i \vee b$ and $y \leqslant x$, then $y \leqslant i \vee b$. Thus the set $I^*(b)$ is an ideal. The conditions $I \subset I^*(b)$ and $b \in I^*(b)$ are obvious.

(7) *Let the ideals I_t, for $t \in T$, constitute a monotone family of ideals such that $a \in I_t$ and $b \notin I_t$ for every t. Then the union $I = \bigcup_t I_t$ is an ideal and $a \in I$, $b \notin I$.*

In fact, if $x \in I_{t_1}$ and $y \in I_{t_2}$, then either both elements x, y belong to I_{t_1}, or both belong to I_{t_2}. In any case, $(x \vee y) \in I$.

If $y \in I_t$ and $x \leqslant y$, then $x \in I_t$; thus $x \in I$. Hence the set I is an ideal and $a \in I$ and $b \notin I$.

(8) *If it is not true that $b \leqslant a$, then there exists an ideal I such that $a \in I$ and $b \notin I$.*

In fact, the set $\{x\colon x \leqslant a\}$ is such an ideal.

Suppose that $b \leqslant a$ is not true and let $\boldsymbol{P}_{a,b}$ be the family of those ideals which contain a but do not contain b.

(9) *If the lattice A is distributive and $b \leqslant a$ is false, then every maximal element I of the family $\boldsymbol{P}_{a,b}$ is a prime ideal.*

In fact, suppose that $x \wedge y \in I$. If $x \notin I$ then the ideal I is a proper subset of the ideal $I^*(x)$. Thus $I^*(x)$ does not belong to the family $\boldsymbol{P}_{a,b}$. Since $a \in I^*(x)$, we have $b \in I^*(x)$. Thus $b \leqslant i_1 \vee x$ for some $i_1 \in I$. Similarly we show that if $y \notin I$, then $b \leqslant i_2 \vee y$ for some $i_2 \in I$. By the distributive law for the lattice A it follows that

(i) $b = b \wedge b \leqslant (i_1 \vee x) \wedge (i_2 \vee y) = (i_1 \wedge i_2) \vee (i_1 \wedge y) \vee (x \wedge i_2) \vee (x \wedge y)$.

By (5) the elements $i_1 \wedge i_2$, $i_1 \wedge y$, and $x \wedge i_2$ belong to I and by assumption $x \wedge y$ belongs to I. Thus the element denoted by the right-hand side of (i) belongs to I. This implies by (2) that $b \in I$, which contradicts $I \in \boldsymbol{P}_{a,b}$. Hence the hypothesis that neither x nor y belongs to I leads to a contradiction. Since $b \notin I$, we have $I \neq A$. Hence I is a prime ideal.

It will be shown in Chapter VIII, p. 266, that the following theorem is a consequence of Theorems (7) and (8) (and of the axiom of choice).

°(10) *The family $\boldsymbol{P}_{a,b}$ has a maximal element, that is, there exists $I \in \boldsymbol{P}_{a,b}$ such that I is not a proper subset of any ideal belonging to $\boldsymbol{P}_{a,b}$.*

We have introduced the notions of distributive lattice, Boolean algebra, lattice of sets and field of sets. The relations among these notions are shown in the following scheme:

distributive lattice
↙ ↘
lattice of sets — Boolean algebra with 1
↘ ↙
field of sets

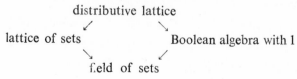

We shall prove that every distributive lattice is isomorphic to a lattice of sets and every Boolean algebra with 1 is isomorphic to a field of sets.

°THEOREM 1: *Every distributive lattice is isomorphic to a lattice of sets.*

PROOF. Let A be a distributive lattice. With each $a \in A$ we associate the family $\boldsymbol{R}(a)$ of prime ideals satisfying the condition $a \notin I$. This correspondence is one-to-one. In fact, if $a \neq b$, then either $a \leqslant b$ or $b \leqslant a$ is false. By (9) and (10) there exists a prime ideal I such that either $I \in \boldsymbol{P}_{a,b}$ or $I \in \boldsymbol{P}_{b,a}$. In other words, there exists an ideal such that either $a \in I$ and $b \notin I$ or $b \in I$ and $a \notin I$. In the first case we have $I \in \boldsymbol{R}(b)$ and $I \notin \boldsymbol{R}(a)$, in the second case $I \in \boldsymbol{R}(a)$ and $I \notin \boldsymbol{R}(b)$.

It follows from (1) and (4) that

$$\begin{aligned} I \in \boldsymbol{R}(a \vee b) &\equiv a \vee b \notin I \\ &\equiv [(a \notin I) \vee (b \notin I)] \\ &\equiv [I \in \boldsymbol{R}(a) \vee I \in \boldsymbol{R}(b)] \\ &\equiv [I \in \boldsymbol{R}(a) \cup \boldsymbol{R}(b)], \end{aligned}$$

and from (3) and (5) that

$$\begin{aligned} I \in \boldsymbol{R}(a \wedge b) &\equiv a \wedge b \notin I \\ &\equiv (a \notin I) \wedge (b \notin I) \\ &\equiv [I \in \boldsymbol{R}(a)] \wedge [I \in \boldsymbol{R}(b)] \\ &\equiv I \in \boldsymbol{R}(a) \cap \boldsymbol{R}(b); \end{aligned}$$

thus

$$\boldsymbol{R}(a \vee b) = \boldsymbol{R}(a) \cup \boldsymbol{R}(b) \quad \text{and} \quad \boldsymbol{R}(a \wedge b) = \boldsymbol{R}(a) \cap \boldsymbol{R}(b).$$

These formulas show that the class of all families $\boldsymbol{R}(a)$ is a lattice of sets isomorphic to the lattice A.

°THEOREM 2: *Every Boolean algebra is isomorphic to a field of sets.*

PROOF. If the lattice A in Theorem 1 is a Boolean algebra, then it has a zero element o and a unit element i and, moreover, for every $a \in A$ there exists an element $-a \in A$ such that $a \wedge (-a) = o$ and $a \vee (-a) = i$. Under the correspondence $a \to \boldsymbol{R}(a)$ the element o corresponds to the empty set and the element i corresponds to the whole set A. Since $A = \boldsymbol{R}(a \vee -a) = \boldsymbol{R}(a) \cup \boldsymbol{R}(-a)$ and $o = \boldsymbol{R}(a \wedge (-a)) = \boldsymbol{R}(a) \cap \boldsymbol{R}(-a)$, we have $\boldsymbol{R}(-a) = A - \boldsymbol{R}(a)$. The set of all families $\boldsymbol{R}(a)$ is not only a lattice of sets but a field of sets as well. Q.E.D.

We shall give a topological interpretation of Theorem 2. Let A be a Boolean algebra with the zero element o and the unit element i and let P be the set of all prime ideals of A. We assume each of the families $\boldsymbol{R}(a)$ to be a neighborhood of every of its elements. For any set $X \subset P$ let $I \in \overline{X}$ if every neighborhood of I contains elements of X.

°THEOREM 3. (i) *P is a compact topological space.* (ii) *The sets $\boldsymbol{R}(a)$ are both open and closed in P.* (iii) *Every set in P which is both open and closed is identical with one of the sets $\boldsymbol{R}(a)$.*

PROOF. The proof that the axioms of topology hold is left to the reader.

To prove that P is a compact space, we let $\boldsymbol{K}$ be a family of closed sets with the finite intersection property. We shall show that $\bigcap_{X \in \boldsymbol{K}} X \neq 0$.

Let $\boldsymbol{K}^*$ be the the family of all finite intersections of the form $\bigcap_{j<n} X_j$, where n is an arbitrary natural number and $X_j \in \boldsymbol{K}$. The family $\boldsymbol{K}^*$ is thus a family of closed non-empty sets.

Let

$$I = \{a \in A: \bigvee_{X \in \boldsymbol{K}^*} (\boldsymbol{R}(a) \cap X = 0)\}.$$

Clearly $a_1 \leqslant a_2 \in I \rightarrow a_1 \in I$. If $a_1, a_2 \in I$ then for some $X_1, X_2 \in \boldsymbol{K}^*$ we have $\boldsymbol{R}(a_1) \cap X_1 = 0 = \boldsymbol{R}(a_2) \cap X_2$. Thus $[\boldsymbol{R}(a_1) \cup \boldsymbol{R}(a_2)] \cap (X_1 \cap X_2) = 0$. Since $X_1 \cap X_2 \in \boldsymbol{K}^*$ and $\boldsymbol{R}(a_1) \cup \boldsymbol{R}(a_2) = \boldsymbol{R}(a_1 \vee a_2)$, we conclude that $a_1 \vee a_2 \in I$. Hence the set I is an ideal.

We show that $i \notin I$. Suppose the contrary. Then for some $X \in \boldsymbol{K}^*$ we have $\boldsymbol{R}(i) \cap X = 0$. This implies $A \cap X = 0$; that is, $X = 0$, which contradicts the hypothesis that $\boldsymbol{K}$ has the finite intersection property.

From the formula just proved and from the fact that $i \notin I$ it follows by (10) that there exists a prime ideal $I_0 \supset I$. Thus this ideal is an element of P. We shall show that $I_0 \in \bigcap_{X \in \boldsymbol{K}} X$.

Let X be an arbitrary set belonging to $\boldsymbol{K}$ and let $\boldsymbol{R}(a)$ be a neighborhood of I_0. This implies that $a \notin I_0$. Therefore $a \notin I$, which by the definition of I shows that for every $Y \in \boldsymbol{K}^*$ we have $\boldsymbol{R}(a) \cap Y \neq 0$. In particular, we have $\boldsymbol{R}(a) \cap X \neq 0$. Hence every neighborhood of I_0

has a non-empty intersection with X, and $I_0 \in \bar{X} = X$. This shows that $I_0 \in \bigcap_{X \in K} X$.

In this way part (i) of Theorem 3 is proved.

The proof of (ii) follows from the fact that the family $\boldsymbol{R}(a)$ being a neighborhood in P is open in P and its complement $P - \boldsymbol{R}(a)$ is also open, because it is equal to $\boldsymbol{R}(-a)$, which is also a neighborhood in P.

Finally, to prove (iii) suppose that X is both open and closed in P and let $\boldsymbol{L} = \{\boldsymbol{R}(a): \boldsymbol{R}(a) \subset X\}$. Since every point belonging to the open set X has at least one neighborhood $\boldsymbol{R}(a)$ which is contained in X, we have $\bigcup_{Y \in \boldsymbol{L}} Y = X$ and thus $X \cap \bigcap_{Y \in \boldsymbol{L}} (P - Y) = 0$. Hence the intersection of the family composed of the set X and the sets $P - Y$, where $Y \in \boldsymbol{L}$, is empty. Since this family consists of closed sets, it does not have the finite intersection property. This means that there exists a finite subset $\{\boldsymbol{R}(a_0), \boldsymbol{R}(a_1), \ldots, \boldsymbol{R}(a_{n-1})\}$ of $\boldsymbol{L}$ such that $X \cap \bigcap_{j<n} (P - \boldsymbol{R}(a_j)) = 0$. This implies $X = \bigcup_{j<n} \boldsymbol{R}(a_j) = \boldsymbol{R}\left(\bigvee_{j<n} a_j\right)$. Hence the set X is of the form $\boldsymbol{R}(a)$.

The space P constructed in Theorem 3 is called the *Stone space of A*.

The following corollary is a consequence of Theorem 3.

°COROLLARY 4: *Every Boolean algebra with unit is isomorphic to the field of sets which are both open and closed in a compact space* [1]).

[1]) Representation theory for Boolean algebras presented in this section is due to M. H. Stone. (M. H. Stone, *The theory of representations for Boolean algebras*, Transactions of the American Mathematical Society **40** (1936) 37–111. This theory was generalized for Boolean algebras with operators by B. Jónsson and A. Tarski (*Boolean algebras with operators*, American Journal of Mathematics **73** (1951) 891–939 and **74** (1952) 127–174).

There are a great number of publications devoted to the theory of representation for non-distributive lattices. From recent publications we mention: B. Jónsson, *On the representation of lattices*, Mathematica Scandinavica **1**(1953) 193–206; B. Jónsson, *Representations of complemented modular lattices*, Transactions of the American Mathematical Society **97** (1960), 64–94; B. Jónsson, *Representations of the relatively complemented modular lattices*, ibid. **103** (1962) 272–303; G. Grätzer, *A generalization of Stone's representation theorem for Boolean algebras*, Duke Mathematical Journal **30** (1963) 469–474.

Exercises

1. Construct a lattice of sets isomorphic to the lattice N ordered by the relation of divisibility.

2. Prove that if an ideal $I \neq A$ in a distributive lattice A is maximal (that is, if every ideal containing I is equal to either A or I), then I is a prime ideal. The converse theorem is false.

3. Prove that if A is a Boolean algebra with unit, then an ideal I is prime if and only if for arbitrary $a \in A$ either $a \in I$ or $-a \in I$.

4. Show that in a Boolean algebra with unit the notions of prime ideal and of maximal ideal are equivalent.

5. Show that the family of ideals in a distributive lattice A is, in turn, a distributive lattice with inclusion as the ordering relation.

CHAPTER V

THEORY OF CARDINAL NUMBERS

In this chapter and in the remainder of the book we shall use the axiom system Σ°[TR] (see p. 55) together with Axiom VIII formulated on p. 86. As usual, theorems not marked with the sign $^\circ$ are proved without using the axiom of choice.

§ 1. Equipollence. Cardinal numbers

We now introduce the notion of equipollence, one of the most characteristic and important notions of set theory [1]).

DEFINITION: The set A is *equipollent* to the set B if there exists a one-to-one function f with domain A and range B. We write $A \sim B$, and we say that f establishes the *equipollence of A and B*.

Examples

1. If the set A is finite, i.e., the number of its elements is a certain natural number n, then the set B is equipollent to A if and only if B contains exactly n elements. Thus the notion of equipollence is a generalization to arbitrary sets of the notion, for finite sets, of having an equal number of elements.

\# 2. Let A be the interval $a_1 < x < a_2$, B the the interval $b_1 < x < b_2$. The function

$$f(x) = \frac{b_2 - b_1}{a_2 - a_1}(x - a_1) + b_1$$

is a one-to-one correspondence from A to B. By definition, $A \sim B$.#

[1]) The notion of equipollence was first systematically investigated by G. Cantor. See *Ein Beitrag zur Mannigfaltigkeitslehre*, Journal für reine und angewandte Mathematik **84** (1878) 242–258. It had been known to B. Bolzano; see *Paradoxien des Unendlichen*, § 20 (1851).

THEOREM 1: *For arbitrary sets A, B, and C the following formulas hold:*

(1) $A \sim A, \quad (A \sim B) \to (B \sim A), \quad (A \sim B) \wedge (B \sim C) \to (A \sim C).$

Thus, *equipollence is reflexive, symmetric and transitive.*

PROOF. The function I_A (see p. 71) establishes the equipollence of A with itself. If the function f establishes the equipollence of A and B then the function f^c establishes the equipollence of B and A (see p. 70). If f establishes the equipollence of A and B and g establishes the equipollence of B and C, then the composition $g \circ f$ establishes the equipollence of A and C (see p. 71, Theorem 2).

The following formulas hold:

$$(A \times B) \sim (B \times A), \tag{2}$$

$$(A \times \{a\}) \sim A \sim A^{\{a\}}, \qquad \{a\}^A \sim \{a\}, \tag{3}$$

$$[A \times (B \times C)] \sim [(A \times B) \times C], \tag{4}$$

$$(A_1 \sim B_1) \wedge (A_2 \sim B_2) \to [(A_1 \times A_2) \sim (B_1 \times B_2)], \tag{5}$$

$$(A \sim B) \to (2^A \sim 2^B), \tag{6}$$

$$(A_1 \sim B_1) \wedge (A_2 \sim B_2) \wedge (A_1 \cap A_2 = 0 = B_1 \cap B_2) \to (A_1 \cup A_2 \sim B_1 \cup B_2), \tag{7}$$

$$Y^{X \times T} \sim (Y^X)^T, \tag{8}$$

$$(Y \times Z)^X \sim (Y^X \times Z^X), \tag{9}$$

$$(A \cap B = 0) \to (Y^{A \cup B} \sim Y^A \times Y^B). \tag{10}$$

We omit the proofs of (2)–(7), which are not difficult. On the other hand, we prove the important formulas (8)–(10).

Let $f \in Y^{X \times T}$; hence f is a function of two variables x and t, where x ranges through the set X and t through the set T and where f takes values in Y. For fixed t the function g_t (with one variable x) defined by $g_t(x) = f(x, t)$ is a function from X into Y, $g_t \in Y^X$. The function F defined by $F(t) = g_t$ associates with every $t \in T$ an element of the set Y^X, so $F \in (Y^X)^T$.

If f_1 and f_2 are distinct functions belonging to the set $Y^{X \times T}$, then the corresponding functions F_1 and F_2 are also distinct. In fact, if $f_1(x_0, t_0) \neq f_2(x_0, t_0)$ then the elements $F_1(t_0)$ and $F_2(t_0)$ of the set Y^X are distinct.

Each function $F \in (Y^X)^T$ corresponds in the manner described above to some function $f \in Y^{X \times T}$, namely, to the function f defined by $f(x, t) = g_t(x)$, where $g_t = F(t)$.

It follows that the correspondence of the function $f \in Y^{X \times T}$ to the function $F \in (Y^X)^T$ establishes the equipollence of the set $Y^{X \times T}$ with the set $(Y^X)^T$, which proves formula (8).

For the proof of (9) notice that if $f \in (Y \times Z)^X$, then $f(x)$ is, for every $x \in X$, an ordered pair $\langle g(x), h(x) \rangle$, where $g(x) \in Y$ and $h(x) \in Z$. Thus $g \in Y^X$ and $h \in Z^X$. It is easy to show that this correspondence of the function f to the pair $\langle g, h \rangle$ determines a one-to-one mapping of the set $(Y \times Z)^X$ onto the set $Y^X \times Z^X$.

Finally, to prove (10) we associate with every function $f \in Y^{A \cup B}$ the ordered pair of restricted functions $\langle f|A, f|B \rangle$. Again it is not difficult to show that this correspondence is a one-to-one mapping of the set $Y^{A \cup B}$ onto the set $Y^A \times Y^B$.

Equations (2) and (8)–(10) are particular instances of the following theorems.

THEOREM 2: (COMMUTATIVE LAW.) *Let $F \in (2^A)^X$. If φ is a permutation of the set X, then*

$$\prod_{x \in X} F_x \sim \prod_{x \in X} F_{\varphi(x)}. \tag{11}$$

PROOF. Associate with every function $f \in \prod_x F_x$ the composite function $g = f \circ \varphi$. If $f_1 \neq f_2$ then for some $x \in X$, $f_1(x) \neq f_2(x)$. Thus setting $y = \varphi^c(x)$ we obtain $f_1(\varphi(y)) \neq f_2(\varphi(y))$, that is, $g_1(y) \neq g_2(y)$. Hence the correspondence given by the equation $g = f \circ \varphi$ is one-to-one.

The function $g = f \circ \varphi$ belongs to the cartesian product $\prod_x F_{\varphi(x)}$. In fact, if $x \in X$ then $f(\varphi(x)) \in F_{\varphi(x)}$, that is, $g(x) \in F_{\varphi(x)}$.

Finally, every function belonging to the cartesian product $\prod_x F_{\varphi(x)}$ can be represented as $f \circ \varphi$ for some $f \in \prod_x F_x$. In fact, it suffices to take for f the function $g \circ \varphi^c$.

THEOREM 3: (ASSOCIATIVE LAW.) *Let $F \in (2^A)^X$. If $X = \bigcup_{y \in Y} T_y$, where* *the sets* T_y *are pairwise disjoint, then*

(12)
$$\prod_{x\in X} F_x \sim \prod_{y\in Y}\Big(\prod_{x\in T_y} F_x\Big),$$

(13)
$$A^X \sim \prod_{y\in Y}(A^{T_y}).$$

PROOF. Let $G_y = \prod_{x\in T_y} F_x$. G_y is the set of all functions f with domain T_y such that $f(x)\in F_x$ for $x\in T_y$. $\prod_{y\in Y} G_y$ consists of the functions g with domain Y such that $g(y)\in G_y$ for $y\in Y$. We denote the value $g(y)$ of the function g by g_y; g_y is a function with domain T_y such that $g_y(x)\in F_x$.

We associate with the function $g\in\prod_{y\in Y} G_y$ the function f defined by the equation

(i)
$$f(x) = g_y(x),$$

where y belongs to the set Y, and $x\in T_y$.

The domain of f is X; and for every $x\in X, f(x)\in F_x$. Thus $f\in\prod_{x\in T} F_x$.

The correspondence between the functions g and f is one-to-one. In fact, if $g^{(1)}\neq g^{(2)}$ then there exists $y\in Y$ such that $g_y^{(1)}\neq g_y^{(2)}$ and thus there exists $x\in T_y$ such that $g_y^{(1)}(x)\neq g_y^{(2)}(x)$. Hence by (i), $f^{(1)}(x) \neq f^{(2)}(x)$.

It remains to be shown that to every function $f\in\prod_{x\in T} F_x$ there corresponds a function g. For this purpose it suffices to notice that the function g defined at $y\in Y$ by the equation

$$g_y = f|T_y$$

(see p. 72) belongs to the cartesian product $\prod_y G_y$ and also satisfies (i).

To prove formula (13) it suffices to let $F_x = A$ in formula (12) for each x.

THEOREM 4: (LAW OF EXPONENTS FOR THE CARTESIAN PRODUCT.) *Let* $F\in(2^A)^T$. *For every set* H

(14)
$$\Big(\prod_{t\in T} F_t\Big)^H \sim \prod_{t\in T}(F_t^H).$$

PROOF. We define the function of two variables on the set $T\times H$ by the equation $G_{\langle t,h\rangle} = F_t$. We may represent the cartesian product in two ways as the union of disjoint sets

$$T \times H = \bigcup_{h \in H} T_h = \bigcup_{t \in T} H_t,$$

where T_h is the set of all pairs with second coordinate equal to h and H_t is the set of all pairs with first coordinate equal to t.

Applying Theorem 3 twice we obtain

$$\prod_{x \in T \times H} G_x \sim \prod_{t \in T} \Big(\prod_{x \in H_t} G_x\Big), \tag{15}$$

$$\prod_{x \in T \times H} G_x \sim \prod_{h \in H} \Big(\prod_{x \in T_h} G_x\Big). \tag{16}$$

For $x \in H_t$, $x = \langle t, h \rangle$. Thus $G_x = F_t$, which shows that

$$\prod_{x \in H_t} G_x = (F_t)^{H_t}.$$

On the other hand, since $H_t \sim H$,

$$(F_t)^{H_t} \sim F_t^H \quad \text{and} \quad \prod_{t \in T} (F_t)^{H_t} \sim \prod_{t \in T} (F_t^H).$$

Thus by (15) we get

$$\prod_{x \in T \times H} G_x \sim \prod_{t \in T} (F_t^H). \tag{17}$$

For a given h we associate the function $g \in \prod_{x \in T_h} G_x$ with the function f where $f(t) = g(t, h)$, obtaining

$$\prod_{x \in T_h} G_x \sim \prod_{t \in T} F_t.$$

Applying (16) we obtain

$$\prod_{x \in T \times H} G_x \sim \Big(\prod_{t \in T} F_t\Big)^H. \tag{18}$$

Finally (14) follows directly from (17) and (18).

If the sets A and B are equipollent, we also say that *A and B have the same power* or that they *have the same cardinal number*. Of course, in this way we neither define the power of a set nor its cardinal number, but rather we only introduce a new terminology for the old notion of equipollence [1]).

[1]) Cantor defined the cardinal number of a set A as that property which remains when we abstract from the nature and from the order of the elements of the set A. To indicate this twofold act of abstraction, Cantor introduced the symbol $\overline{\overline{A}}$ to denote the cardinal number of the set A.

The new notions are not indispensable. We may formulate all theorems of set theory so that they are statements, not about cardinal numbers or powers of sets, but rather about relationships between cardinal numbers, which can always be stated in terms of the notion of equipollence. On the other hand, many theorems can be stated more intuitively if they are formulated as theorems about cardinal numbers. For this reason it is convenient to introduce this notion.

The following theorem can be proved without difficulty.

THEOREM 5: *For the sets A and B to be equipollent it is neccessary and sufficient that the relational systems* $\langle A, A\times A\rangle$ *and* $\langle B, B\times B\rangle$ *be isomorphic.*

We shall denote by $\overline{\overline{A}}$ the relational type of the system $\langle A, A\times A\rangle$. We shall call $\overline{\overline{A}}$ the *cardinal number* or the *power* of the set A. From Theorem 5 and Axiom VIII (p. 86) we obtain the following:

THEOREM 6: *For arbitrary sets A, B the conditions* $A \sim B$ *and* $\overline{\overline{A}} = \overline{\overline{B}}$ *are equivalent.*

This theorem allows us to formulate statements about equipollence as equations involving cardinal numbers.

§ 2. Countable sets

If X is a finite set containing exactly n elements (see p. 100), then Theorem 6, §1 is satisfied if we set $\overline{\overline{X}} = n$ (see p. 102, Theorem 6). In the future we shall identify the cardinal number of a finite set of n elements with the natural number n.

The theory of cardinality for finite sets is not essentially richer than the arithmetic of the natural numbers. New notions appear when we turn to infinite sets.

DEFINITION: A set A is said to be *countable* (or *denumerable*) if it is either finite or equipollent with the set of all natural numbers.

Clearly, two arbitrary infinite countable sets are always equipollent (see §1, Theorem 1). We shall denote the cardinal number of infinite countable sets by $\mathfrak{a}$.

In Chapter III, p. 91 we defined a sequence as a function with domain equal to the set of natural numbers. From this definition it follows that a set is countable if and only if it is the range of a sequence none of whose terms are equal. Speaking somewhat figuratively, a set A is countable if its elements can be "arranged" in an infinite sequence $a_1, a_2, a_3, \ldots$.

THEOREM 1: *Every countable non-empty set is a set of terms of an infinite sequence. Conversely, the set of terms of any infinite sequence is countable and non-empty.*

PROOF. The finite set whose elements are $a_1, a_2, a_3, \ldots, a_k$ is the set of terms of the infinite sequence:

$$f(0) = a_0, \quad \ldots, \quad f(k) = a_k, \quad f(k+1) = a_k, \quad \ldots, \quad f(k+j) = a_k, \ldots$$

Every infinite countable set is by definition the set of terms of an infinite sequence.

To prove the converse we assume that X is the set of terms of an infinite sequence φ and that X is an infinite set. Let $\psi_0 = \varphi_0$ and

$$\psi_{n+1} = \varphi_m \quad \text{where} \quad m = \min_k [\bigwedge_{j \leqslant n} (\varphi_k \neq \psi_j)],$$

or

$$\psi_{n+1} = \varphi_0 \text{ if there exists no } k \text{ such that } \bigwedge_{j \leqslant n} (\psi_j \neq \varphi_k).$$

We prove by induction that for every n there exists a number k such that $\bigwedge_{j \leqslant n} (\psi_j \neq \varphi_k)$. It follows that $\bigwedge_{j \leqslant n} (\psi_{n+1} \neq \psi_j)$ and thus the sequence ψ has distinct terms. It remains to be shown that every element of the set X is a term of the sequence ψ.

For this purpose we assume that the set $\{k\colon \varphi_k \text{ is not a term of } \psi\}$ is non-empty and we let k_0 be the least element belonging to that set. Clearly $k_0 > 0$. If $i < k_0$ then φ_i is a term of ψ, say $\varphi_i = \psi_{m(i)}$. Let $m = \max_{i<k_0} m(i)$. The smallest number k such that $\bigwedge_{j \leqslant m} (\varphi_k \neq \psi_j)$ is then k_0 and thus from the definition of the sequence ψ we obtain $\psi_{m+1} = \varphi_{k_0}$, contradicting the definition of the number k_0.

In a similar manner we establish the following theorems.

THEOREM 2: *Every subset of a countable set is countable.*

THEOREM 3: *The union of two countable sets is countable.*

PROOF. Since the case where one of the given sets is empty causes no difficulty, we assume that A is the set of terms of the sequence

$$a_0, a_1, a_2, \ldots, a_n, \ldots$$

and that B is the set of terms of the sequence

$$b_0, b_1, b_2, \ldots, b_n, \ldots$$

The union of A and B is then the set of terms of the sequence

$$a_0, b_0, a_1, b_1, a_2, b_2, \ldots, a_n, b_n, \ldots,$$

and is therefore countable.

From Theorem 3 it follows by induction that the union of an arbitrary finite number of countable sets is countable.

A particular case of Theorem 3 is the following

THEOREM 4: *The union of a finite set with a countable set is countable.*

THEOREM 5: *The cartesian product of two countable sets is countable.*

PROOF. If A and B are infinite countable sets, then $A \sim N$ and $B \sim N$; and thus $A \times B \sim N \times N$. By Theorem 1, p. 170, it follows that $N \times N \sim N$, and thus $A \times B \sim N$.

If one or both of the sets A and B are finite, then $A \times B$ is equipollent to a subset of $N \times N$, that is, to a subset of N and the theorem follows by Theorem 2.

THEOREM 6: *If the set A is countable, then the set of all finite sequences with terms in A is countable.*

PROOF. The theorem follows immediately from Theorem 4, p. 98.

THEOREM 7: *If ψ is an infinite sequence whose elements are also infinite sequences, then the set X of elements x which are terms of the sequences ψ_n is countable.*

PROOF. By definition, $X = \{x : \bigvee_{mn} (x = \psi_{mn})\} = \{x : \bigvee_{p} (x = \psi_{K(p), L(p)})\}$. Thus X is the set of terms of the sequence φ defined by the equation $\varphi_p = \psi_{K(p), L(p)}$.

°THEOREM 8: *If A is a sequence whose elements are non-empty countable sets, then the union $\bigcup_n A_n$ is countable.*

PROOF. Let C_n be the set of sequences φ such that A_n is the set of terms of φ. By assumption $C_n \neq 0$ for all $n \in N$. Therefore by the axiom of choice there exists a sequence ψ such that $\psi_n \in C_n$ for each n. Thus the union $\bigcup_n A_n$ is the set of those x for which there exist $m, n \in N$ such that $x = \psi_{mn}$, which proves the theorem on the basis of Theorem 7.

REMARK: The use of the axiom of choice is neccesary for the proof of Theorem 8. For every countable set A there exists an infinite sequence containing all the elements of A among its terms. Yet there are infinitely many such sequences for a given set A and we have no way of distinguishing between them. In other words, we have no way of associating with every countable set an infinite sequence whose terms contain all the elements of the given set.

\# *Examples of countable sets*

1. *The set of integers is countable.*

In fact, it is the union $N \cup N'$ where N' is the set of integers $\leqslant 0$. Because $N \sim N'$, where the function $f(n) = -n$ establishes equipollence, both sets N and N' are countable. It follows that the set $N \cup N'$ is countable.

2. *The set of rational numbers is countable.*

Indeed, the sequence φ defined by $\varphi_p = K(p)/(L(p+1))$ contains all the non-negative rational numbers among its terms and only such numbers. Thus the set of non-negative rational numbers is countable. From this we obtain that the set of negative rationals is countable (see Example 1). Hence the set of all rationals is countable.

3. *The set of polynomials of one variable with integral coefficients is countable.*

To every polynomial with integral coefficients there corresponds the unique sequence of its coefficients. By Theorem 6 the set of all finite sequences of integers is countable.

4. *The set of algebraic numbers is countable.*

In fact, with every polynomial we may associate a finite sequence whose terms are all the roots of the polynomial. We let the first term of the sequence be that root which has the smallest modulus and among those of equal modulus that root which has the smallest argument. Similarly, we let the second term of the sequence be that root different from the first which has the smallest modulus and the smallest argument among the roots having the same modulus. In this way we define by induction the desired sequence. The countability of the set of all algebraic numbers follows now from Theorem 7.

We can obtain the same result from Theorem 8. But in this case we have to use the axiom of choice.

Exercises

1. Prove that the set of all intervals with rational endpoints (in the space of real numbers) is countable.

2. Prove that in 3-dimensional euclidean space (or more generally, in $\mathcal{E}^n$) the set of all spheres with radius of rational length and with center having rational coordinates is countable.

3. Let f be a function with field contained in the set of real numbers. We say that f has a *proper extremum* at the point a if there exists an interval P containing a such that $f(x) < f(a)$ for all $x \in P - \{a\}$ or else $f(x) > f(a)$ for all $x \in P - \{a\}$. Prove that the set of proper extrema of such a function f is at most countable.

Hint: Use Exercise 1.

Generalize the theorem to functions defined on the space $\mathcal{E}^n$ (replacing P by an n-dimensional sphere).

4. Prove that every disjoint family of intervals in the space of real numbers is countable.

Hint: Use Exercise 1.

Generalize the theorem to families of disjoint open sets in the space $\mathcal{E}^n$, using Exercise 2.

5. Let Z be a set of points in the plane. We call the point $p \in Z$ *isolated* if there exists an open circle K (i.e. without circumference) such that $\{p\} = Z \cap K$. Prove that the set of isolated points of a given set Z is countable.

Hint: Use Exercise 2.

Generalize the theorem to the space $\mathcal{E}^n$ (replacing circle by ball in the definition of isolated point).

6. Prove that every monotone discontinuous function from the set of real numbers to the set of real numbers has a countable number of points of discontinuity.

Hint: Every monotone function has both a limit from the right and a limit from the left at every point; at points of discontinuity those limits are unequal. Apply Exercise 4.

§ 3. The hierarchy of cardinal numbers

We shall prove that besides the finite cardinal numbers and the number $\mathfrak{a}$ there exists infinitely many other cardinal numbers.

For this purpose we prove the following very useful theorem.

THEOREM 1. (ON DIAGONALIZATION [1]).) *If the domain T of function F is contained in a set A and if the values of F are subsets of A, then the set*

$$Z = \{t \in T: t \notin F(t)\}$$

is not a value of the function F.

PROOF: We have to show that for every $t \in T$, $F(t) \neq Z$. From the definition of the set Z it follows that if $t \in T$, then

$$[t \in Z] \equiv [t \notin F(t)],$$

Thus if $F(t) = Z$ we obtain the contradiction:

$$(t \in Z) \equiv (t \notin Z).$$

For $A = T$ Theorem 1 has a geometrical interpretation. We may consider the set $A \times A$ represented as a square (see. p. 63, Chapter II). We let $R = \{\langle x, y \rangle: y \in F(x)\}$. The set $F(x)$ is the projection onto the vertical axis of those pairs belonging to R which have first coordinate equal to x. The set Z is the projection onto the vertical axis of those points along the diagonal of the square which do not belong to R. It is then geometrically obvious that $Z \neq F(x)$, for any $x \in A$; for if $\langle x, x \rangle \in R$, then $x \in F(x)$ but $x \notin Z$, and if $\langle x, x \rangle \notin R$, then $x \notin F(x)$ but $x \in Z$. This interpretation motivates calling Theorem 1 the *Diagonalization Theorem.*

We apply Theorem 1 to prove that there exist distinct infinite cardinal numbers.

THEOREM 2: *The set 2^A is not equipollent to A, nor to any subset of A.*

For otherwise there would exist a one-to-one function whose domain is a subset of A and whose range is the family of all subsets of A. But this contradicts Theorem 1.

THEOREM 3: *No two of the sets*

(1) $$A,\ 2^A,\ 2^{2^A},\ 2^{2^{2^A}},\ \ldots$$

are equipollent.

[1]) This theorem is due to Cantor.

PROOF. Let P_k be the kth set in sequence (1) and suppose that there exist k and l such that $k > l$ and P_k is equipollent to a subset of P_l. The set P_{k-1} is clearly equipollent to a subset of P_k, namely to the subset of singletons $\{x\}$ where $x \in P_{k-1}$. Thus the set P_{k-1} is equipollent to a subset of P_l. Repeating this argument we conclude that each of the sets $P_{k-1}, P_{k-2}, \ldots, P_{l+1}$ is equipollent to some subset of P_l, but this contradicts Theorem 2 because $P_{l+1} = 2^{P_l}$.

THEOREM 4: *Let the family A have the property*

(2) *For every $X \in A$ there exists a set $Y \in A$ which is not equipollent to any subset of X.*

Then the union $\bigcup(A)$ is not equipollent to any $X \in A$ nor to any subset of $X \in A$.

PROOF. Assume that $\bigcup(A) \sim X_1 \subset X \in A$. It follows that there exists a one-to-one function f such that $f^1(\bigcup(A)) = X_1$. By assumption (2) there is a set $Y \in A$ which is not equipollent to any subset of X. As $Y \subset \bigcup(A)$, we have $f^1(Y) \subset f^1(\bigcup(A))$; that is, $f^1(Y) \subset X_1$ and consequently $Y \sim f^1(Y) \subset X$. The contradiction shows that it is not the case that $\bigcup(A) \sim X_1$.

Theorems 3 and 4 give us some ideas of how many distinct infinite cardinal numbers exist. Starting with the set N of natural numbers which has power $\mathfrak{a}$, we can construct the sets

(3) $$N, 2^N, 2^{2^N}, 2^{2^{2^N}}, \ldots,$$

no two of which are equipollent by Theorem 3. In this way we obtain *infinitely many distinct cardinal numbers.*

By the axiom of replacement there exists the family A whose elements are exactly all the sets (3) (see p. 96). By Theorem 2 the family A satisfies condition (2); thus by Theorem 4 the union $P = \bigcup(A)$ has a cardinal number different from each of the sets (3) and from each of their subsets. Again applying Theorem 3 we obtain the sequence of sets

(4) $$P, 2^P, 2^{2^P}, 2^{2^{2^P}}, \ldots,$$

no two of which are equipollent and none of which is equipollent to any of the sets (3). We obtain in this way a new infinite quantity of distinct cardinal numbers.

We obtain still other cardinals by constructing the family $\boldsymbol{B}$ consisting of all the sets (3) and (4) and by constructing a new sequence

$$Q = \bigcup(\boldsymbol{B}),\ 2^Q, 2^{2^Q}, 2^{2^{2^Q}}, \ldots$$

We may continue this procedure indefinitely. We see that the hierarchy of distinct infinite cardinals obtained in this way is incomparably richer than the hierarchy of finite cardinals, which coincides with the natural numbers.

As a further consequence of Theorem 2 we note the following

THEOREM 5: *There exists no family of sets $\boldsymbol{U}$ which, for every set X, contains an element Y equipollent to X.*

PROOF. By Theorem 2 the set $2^{\bigcup(\boldsymbol{U})}$ is not equipollent to any subset of the set $\bigcup(\boldsymbol{U})$ and hence it is not equipollent to any of the sets Y belonging to $\boldsymbol{U}$ because $Y \in \boldsymbol{U}$ implies $Y \subset \bigcup(\boldsymbol{U})$.

THEOREM 6: *There exists no set containing all sets.*

For otherwise this set would satisfy the conditions of Theorem 5.

Theorem 6 shows again (see Chapter II, p. 61) that we cannot state as an axiom consistent with our axiom system that there exists a set composed of all elements which satisfy an arbitrary propositional function $\Phi(x)$.

Theorem 5 is also another indication of the vastness of the hierarchy of cardinal numbers, which is so "large" that it is impossible to construct a set containing at least one set of each power.

Exercises

1. Prove that the set N^N is uncountable.

Hint: If φ is a sequence of elements of N^N, then the sequence ϑ defined by $\vartheta_n = \varphi_n(n)+1$ is not a term of the sequence φ.

2. Let X be a compact space $\neq 0$ having the property: for every finite set S and for every open set $G \neq 0$ there exists an open non-empty set G^* such that $G^* \subset G$ and $\overline{G^*} \cap S = 0$. Show that $\overline{\overline{X}} \neq \mathfrak{a}$. Apply this inequality to show that the Cantor set is uncountable.

Hint: Use the axiom of choice to associate with every open set $G \neq 0$ and every finite set S an open subet $G^* = G^*(G, S) \subset G$ such that $\overline{G^*} \cap S = 0$. Assuming that φ is an infinite sequence of elements of X, let

$$G_0 = X, \quad G_{n+1} = G^*(G_n, \{\varphi_0, \ldots, \varphi_n\});$$

prove that $\bigcap_n \overline{G_n} \neq 0$.

3[1]). We say that the sequence $b_1, b_2, \ldots$ of natural numbers increases more rapidly than the sequence $a_1, a_2, \ldots,$ if $\lim\limits_{n=\infty} \dfrac{a_n}{b_n} = 0$. Prove the following statements:

(i) for every sequence there exists another sequence which increases more rapidly;

(ii) let Z be a set of sequences such that for every sequence $a_1, a_2, \ldots$ there exists a sequence $b_1, b_2, \ldots$ belonging to Z which increases more rapidly than $a_1, a_2, \ldots$; then the set Z is uncountable.

Hint: Assume $\overline{\overline{Z}} = \overline{\overline{N}}$. We then may represent the elements of Z as the rows of the table

$$\begin{array}{l} a_{1,1}, a_{1,2}, \ldots, a_{1,n}, \ldots \\ a_{2,1}, a_{2,2}, \ldots, a_{2,n}, \ldots \\ \cdots\cdots\cdots\cdots \\ a_{n,1}, a_{n,2}, \ldots, a_{n,n}, \ldots \\ \cdots\cdots\cdots\cdots \end{array}$$

Using an appropriate diagonalization argument define a sequence increasing more rapidly than every sequence in the table.

§ 4. The arithmetic of cardinal numbers

We shall define operations of addition, multiplication, and exponentiation for cardinal numbers. The definitions will be chosen so that they will coincide with the ordinary definitions for finite cardinals (that is for the natural numbers)[2]).

DEFINITION 1: The cardinal number $\mathfrak{m}$ is the *sum* of the cardinals $\mathfrak{n}_1$ and $\mathfrak{n}_2$,

$$\mathfrak{m} = \mathfrak{n}_1 + \mathfrak{n}_2,$$

if every set of power $\mathfrak{m}$ is the union of two disjoint sets, one of which has power $\mathfrak{n}_1$ and the other of which has power $\mathfrak{n}_2$.

LEMMA 1: *Given two arbitrary sets A_1 and A_2, there exist sets B_1 and B_2 such that*

$$(0) \qquad A_1 \sim B_1, \quad A_2 \sim B_2, \quad B_1 \cap B_2 = 0.$$

[1]) In connection with the problems dealt with in Exercise 3 see the book: G. H. Hardy, *Orders of infinity*, Cambridge Tracts in Mathematics and Mathematical Physics No. 12, 2nd edition (Cambridge 1924).

[2]) Basic definitions and theorems given in §4 are due to Cantor; see: *Beiträge zur Begründung der transfiniten Mengenlehre*, Math. Annalen **46** (1895) 481–512.

Choose a_1 and a_2 such that $a_1 \neq a_2$ (for instance, $a_1 = 0$, $a_2 = \{0\}$). Then, by (4), § 1, p. 170, the sets $B_1 = \{a_1\} \times A_1$ and $B_2 = \{a_2\} \times A_2$ satisfy the desired conditions.

THEOREM 2: *The sum* $\mathfrak{n}_1 + \mathfrak{n}_2$ *of any two given cardinals* $\mathfrak{n}_1$ *and* $\mathfrak{n}_2$ *always exists.*

PROOF. Assume that $\overline{\overline{A_1}} = \mathfrak{n}_1$ and $\overline{\overline{A_2}} = \mathfrak{n}_2$. Let B_1 and B_2 satisfy conditions (0). Then $B_1 \cup B_2$ is the union of two disjoint sets of power $\mathfrak{n}_1$ and $\mathfrak{n}_2$. Clearly every set equipollent to $B_1 \cup B_2$ has the same property. Thus $\overline{\overline{B_1 \cup B_2}} = \mathfrak{n}_1 + \mathfrak{n}_2$.

Moreover, we have proved that

$$\overline{\overline{A}} + \overline{\overline{B}} = \overline{\overline{A \cup B}} \quad \text{if} \quad A \cap B = 0.$$

THEOREM 3: *Addition of cardinal numbers is commutative and associative: for arbitrary cardinal numbers* $\mathfrak{n}_1, \mathfrak{n}_2$ *and* $\mathfrak{n}_3$, *we have*

(1) $$\mathfrak{n}_1 + \mathfrak{n}_2 = \mathfrak{n}_2 + \mathfrak{n}_1,$$

(2) $$\mathfrak{n}_1 + (\mathfrak{n}_2 + \mathfrak{n}_3) = (\mathfrak{n}_1 + \mathfrak{n}_2) + \mathfrak{n}_3.$$

PROOF. If $\overline{\overline{A}} = \mathfrak{n}_1 + \mathfrak{n}_2$ then $A = A_1 \cup A_2$, where $A_1 \cap A_2 = 0$, $\overline{\overline{A_1}} = \mathfrak{n}_1$ and $\overline{\overline{A_2}} = \mathfrak{n}_2$. Thus $A = A_2 \cup A_1$ and $\overline{\overline{A}} = \mathfrak{n}_2 + \mathfrak{n}_1$, which proves (1); the proof of (2) is similar.

Example. By Theorems 3 and 4, § 2, p. 175–176 we have

(3) $$\mathfrak{a} + \mathfrak{a} = \mathfrak{a}, \qquad n + \mathfrak{a} = \mathfrak{a}.$$

DEFINITION 2: The cardinal number $\mathfrak{m}$ is the *product* of $\mathfrak{n}_1$ and $\mathfrak{n}_2$, i.e.

$$\mathfrak{m} = \mathfrak{n}_1 \cdot \mathfrak{n}_2,$$

if every set of power $\mathfrak{m}$ is equipollent to the cartesian product $A_1 \times A_2$ where $\overline{\overline{A_1}} = \mathfrak{n}_1$ and $\overline{\overline{A_2}} = \mathfrak{n}_2$.

Thus

$$\overline{\overline{A_1}} \cdot \overline{\overline{A_2}} = \overline{\overline{A_1 \times A_2}}.$$

It is clear that, for arbitrary cardinals $\mathfrak{n}_1$ and $\mathfrak{n}_2$, the product $\mathfrak{n}_1 \cdot \mathfrak{n}_2$ always exists.

Definition 2 is a generalization to the case of arbitrary cardinal numbers of the usual notion of multiplication: for example, we consider the product $3 \cdot 4$ as the number of elements of a set which can be represented as three groups of four elements; that is, as the number of elements in the set $A \times B$, where A contains exactly three elements, and B four.

THEOREM 4: *Multiplication of cardinal numbers is commutative, associative, and distributive over addition*:

$$\mathfrak{n}_1 \cdot \mathfrak{n}_2 = \mathfrak{n}_2 \cdot \mathfrak{n}_1, \tag{4}$$

$$\mathfrak{n}_1 \cdot (\mathfrak{n}_2 \cdot \mathfrak{n}_3) = (\mathfrak{n}_1 \cdot \mathfrak{n}_2) \cdot \mathfrak{n}_3, \tag{5}$$

$$\mathfrak{n}_1 \cdot (\mathfrak{n}_2 + \mathfrak{n}_3) = \mathfrak{n}_1 \cdot \mathfrak{n}_2 + \mathfrak{n}_1 \cdot \mathfrak{n}_3. \tag{6}$$

PROOF. Equations (4) and (5) are immediate consequences of equations (2) and (4), § 1, p. 170. Equation (6) follows from the equations (see Chapter II. § 4, p. 63):

$$A_1 \times (A_2 \cup A_3) = (A_1 \times A_2) \cup (A_1 \times A_3),$$

$$[A_2 \cap A_3 = 0] \rightarrow [(A_1 \times A_2) \cap (A_1 \times A_3) = 0].$$

THEOREM 5: 1 *is the unit for multiplication*; *namely*,

$$\mathfrak{n} \cdot 1 = \mathfrak{n}. \tag{7}$$

The proof follows from (3), § 1, p. 170.

Example. By Theorem 5, § 2, p. 176

$$\mathfrak{a} \cdot \mathfrak{a} = \mathfrak{a}, \quad \mathfrak{a} \cdot n = \mathfrak{a}. \tag{8}$$

Denote the n-fold product $\mathfrak{m} \cdot \mathfrak{m} \cdot \ldots \cdot \mathfrak{m}$ by $\mathfrak{m}^n$. By Definition 2, $\mathfrak{m}^n$ is the power of the set of all sequences of n-elements $\langle a_1, a_2, \ldots, a_n \rangle$, where $a_1, \ldots, a_n$ are elements of a set A of power $\mathfrak{m}$. In other words (see Chapter II, §6, p. 170),

$$(\overline{\overline{A}})^n = \overline{\overline{A^n}},$$

Generalizing the example above we obtain the following definition.

DEFINITION 3: The cardinal $\mathfrak{m}$ is the *cardinal* $\mathfrak{n}$ *raised to* $\mathfrak{p}$*-th power*,

$$\mathfrak{m} = \mathfrak{n}^{\mathfrak{p}},$$

if every set of power $\mathfrak{m}$ is equipollent to the set A^B, where $\overline{\overline{A}} = \mathfrak{n}$ and $\overline{\overline{B}} = \mathfrak{p}$.

Thus

$$(\overline{\overline{A}})^{\overline{\overline{B}}} = \overline{\overline{A^B}}.$$

It is clear that for every two cardinal numbers $\mathfrak{n}$ and $\mathfrak{p}$ the cardinal $\mathfrak{n}^{\mathfrak{p}}$ always exists.

THEOREM 6: *For arbitrary cardinals* $\mathfrak{n}, \mathfrak{p}$ *and* $\mathfrak{q}$:

(9) $$\mathfrak{n}^{\mathfrak{p}+\mathfrak{q}} = \mathfrak{n}^{\mathfrak{p}} \cdot \mathfrak{n}^{\mathfrak{q}},$$

(10) $$(\mathfrak{n} \cdot \mathfrak{p})^{\mathfrak{q}} = \mathfrak{n}^{\mathfrak{q}} \cdot \mathfrak{p}^{\mathfrak{q}},$$

(11) $$(\mathfrak{n}^{\mathfrak{p}})^{\mathfrak{q}} = \mathfrak{n}^{\mathfrak{p} \cdot \mathfrak{q}},$$

(12) $$\mathfrak{n}^1 = \mathfrak{n},$$

(13) $$1^{\mathfrak{n}} = 1.$$

These equations follow directly from equations (4), (8)–(10), § 1.

THEOREM 7: *If* A *has power* $\mathfrak{m}$, *then the set* 2^A (*which consists of all subsets of* A) *has power* $2^{\mathfrak{m}}$:

$$2^{\overline{\overline{A}}} = \overline{\overline{2^A}}.$$

PROOF. $2^{\mathfrak{m}}$ is the power of the set $\{0, 1\}^A$, consisting of all functions f whose values are the numbers 0 and 1 and whose domain is the set A. Each such function is uniquely determined by the set X_f of those a for which $f(a) = 1$ (f is the characteristic function of this set, see Chapter IV, p. 122). Under this correspondence to distinct functions f_1 and f_2 correspond distinct sets X_{f_1} and X_{f_2}. Thus associating with the function $f \in \{0, 1\}^A$ the set $X_f \subset A$, we obtain a one-to-one correspondence between the sets $\{0, 1\}^A$ and 2^A.

§ 5. Inequalities between cardinal numbers. The Cantor–Bernstein theorem and its generalizations

We obtain the "less than" relation beetwen cardinal numbers from the following definition.

DEFINITION: The cardinal number $\mathfrak{m}$ is *not greater* than the cardinal number $\mathfrak{n}$,

$$\mathfrak{m} \leqslant \mathfrak{n},$$

if every set of power $\mathfrak{m}$ is equipollent to a subset of a set of power $\mathfrak{n}$.

If $\mathfrak{m} \leqslant \mathfrak{n}$ and $\mathfrak{m} \neq \mathfrak{n}$ we say that $\mathfrak{m}$ is *less* than $\mathfrak{n}$ or that $\mathfrak{n}$ is *greater* than $\mathfrak{m}$; we write $\mathfrak{m} < \mathfrak{n}$ or $\mathfrak{n} > \mathfrak{m}$.

For example,

(1) $$n < \mathfrak{a},$$

(2) $$\mathfrak{m} < 2^{\mathfrak{m}}.$$

For the proof of (2) we notice that $\mathfrak{m} \leqslant 2^{\mathfrak{m}}$, because every set A of power $\mathfrak{m}$ is equipollent to the subset of 2^A consisting of all singletons of elements of A. Moreover, $\mathfrak{m} \neq 2^{\mathfrak{m}}$ by Theorem 2, § 3.

The following theorem is an interesting consequence of the definition of inequality.

°THEOREM 1: *If f is a function defined on the set X and $f^1(X) = Y$, then $\overline{\overline{Y}} \leqslant \overline{\overline{X}}$.*

PROOF. The notion of coset of a function f (a set of all elements of X which have the same value under f) was defined in Chapter II, p. 175. Every coset is a set of the form

$$W_y = \{x \in X \colon f(x) = y\}.$$

Since all cosets are distinct and non-empty, there exi ts by the axiom of choice[1]) a set A containing exactly one element from every coset. It follows that A is equipollent to the set of all cosets of f and thus to the set $f^1(X)$. Since A is a subset of X, we conclude that $\overline{\overline{Y}} \leqslant \overline{\overline{X}}$.

Example. The projection of a plane set Q onto an arbitrary straight line has power $\leqslant \overline{\overline{Q}}$. In this case the cosets of the projection are the intersections $Q \cap L$ where L is a straight line parallel to the direction of the projection.

REMARK: We write $\mathfrak{m} \leqslant^* \mathfrak{n}$ if $\mathfrak{m} = 0$ or if every set of power $\mathfrak{m}$ is the image of every set of power $\mathfrak{n}$[2]). It is an easy consequence of Theorem 1 that $\{\mathfrak{m} \leqslant \mathfrak{n}\} \equiv \{\mathfrak{m} \leqslant^* \mathfrak{n}\}$; we saw that the proof of this

[1]) The fact that the proof of Theorem 5 requires a new axiom was pointed out by B. Levi as early as in 1902 (R. Instituto Lombardo di scienze e lettere, Rendiconti (2) **35** p. 863), before Zermelo published his axiomatic set theory with the axiom of choice.

[2]) A. Tarski has investigated the properties of $\leqslant^*$ without referring to the axiom of choice. See A. Tarski and A. Lindenbaum, *Communication sur les recherches de la théorie des ensembles,* Comptes rendus de la Société des Sciences et des Lettres de Varsovie, Classe III, **19** (1926), 299–330.

equivalence uses the axiom of choice. Without using this axiom we are not even able to prove the intuitive proposition that the conditions $\mathfrak{m} \leqslant^* \mathfrak{n}$ and $\mathfrak{n} < \mathfrak{m}$ are incompatible[1]).

The relation $\leqslant$ possesses many properties of its arithmetical counterpart.

(3) $$(\mathfrak{m} \leqslant \mathfrak{n}) \wedge (\mathfrak{n} \leqslant \mathfrak{p}) \rightarrow (\mathfrak{m} \leqslant \mathfrak{p}),$$

(4) $$(\mathfrak{m} \leqslant \mathfrak{n}) \rightarrow (\mathfrak{m}+\mathfrak{p} \leqslant \mathfrak{n}+\mathfrak{p}),$$

(5) $$(\mathfrak{m} \leqslant \mathfrak{n}) \rightarrow (\mathfrak{m}\mathfrak{p} \leqslant \mathfrak{n}\mathfrak{p}),$$

(6) $$(\mathfrak{m} \leqslant \mathfrak{n}) \rightarrow (\mathfrak{m}^{\mathfrak{p}} \leqslant \mathfrak{n}^{\mathfrak{p}}),$$

(7) $$(\mathfrak{m} \leqslant \mathfrak{n}) \rightarrow (\mathfrak{p}^{\mathfrak{m}} \leqslant \mathfrak{p}^{\mathfrak{n}}).$$

Law (3) expresses the transitivity of the relation $\leqslant$. Laws (4)–(7) express the monotonicity of addition, multiplication and exponentiation with respect to $\leqslant$.

As an example we prove (3). Let A, B and C be sets of power $\mathfrak{m}, \mathfrak{n}$ and $\mathfrak{p}$. By hypothesis, A is equipollent to a subset B_1 of B and B to a subset C_1 of C. Let f and g establish the equipollences $A \sim B_1$ and $B \sim C_1$. The composition $g \circ f$ is one-to-one and maps A onto a subset of C_1. Thus $\mathfrak{m} \leqslant \mathfrak{p}$. Q.E.D.

The laws of monotonicity do not hold for the relation $<$: for instance, $2 < \mathfrak{a}$ but $2+\mathfrak{a} = \mathfrak{a}+\mathfrak{a} = \mathfrak{a}\cdot\mathfrak{a} = 2\cdot\mathfrak{a}$; similarly, $2 < 3$, but $2^{\mathfrak{a}} = 3^{\mathfrak{a}}$ as will be shown in §6.

In the arithmetic of natural numbers the laws converse to (4)–(7) are called the cancellation laws for the relation $\leqslant$ with respect to the operations of addition, multiplication and exponentiation; these theorems hold in arithmetic provided that $p > 1$. In the arithmetic of arbitrary cardinal numbers all of the cancellation laws fail to hold: it suffices to let $\mathfrak{m} = 2$, $\mathfrak{n} = 3$ and $\mathfrak{p} = \mathfrak{a}$ to obtain a counterexample.

On the other hand, the cancellation laws with respect to addition, multiplication and exponentiation hold for the relation $<$. They follow without difficulty from the law of trichotomy which we now state but which we shall prove only in Chapter VIII.

[1]) See W. Sierpiński, *Sur une proposition qui entraîne l'existence des ensembles non mesurables,* Fundamenta Mathematicae **34**(1947) 157–162. See also A. Lévy, *On models of set theory with urelements*, Bulletin de l'Académie Polonaise des Sciences, série des sciences math., phys. et astr. **8**(1960) 463–465.

For arbitrary cardinals $\mathfrak{m}$ *and* $\mathfrak{n}$ *either* $\mathfrak{m} \leqslant \mathfrak{n}$ *or* $\mathfrak{n} \leqslant \mathfrak{m}$ [1]).

In the remainder of this section we shall treat the question of the asymmetry of the relation $<$. This problem, investigated already by Cantor but not completely solved by him, became the starting point for a number of interesting investigations regarding transformations of sets [2]).

The asymmetry of the relation $<$ is equivalent to the theorem:

(i) $$(\mathfrak{m} \leqslant \mathfrak{n}) \wedge (\mathfrak{n} \leqslant \mathfrak{m}) \rightarrow (\mathfrak{m} = \mathfrak{n}).$$

In fact, if (i) holds, then the formulas $\mathfrak{m} < \mathfrak{n}$ and $\mathfrak{n} < \mathfrak{m}$ never hold simultaneously; otherwise (i) would yield $\mathfrak{m} = \mathfrak{n}$. Conversely, if the relation $<$ is asymmetric and satisfies the antecedent of implication (i), then necessarily $\mathfrak{m} = \mathfrak{n}$, because otherwise the $\leqslant$ sings in the antecedent of the implication could be replaced by $<$, in contradiction to the assumption of the asymmetry of $<$.

To prove (i) in Σ we first prove the following more general proposition.

THEOREM 2: *If A and B are sets and f and g are one-to-one, where $f \in B^A$ and $g \in A^B$, then the sets A and B can be represented as unions of disjoint sets $A = A_1 \cup A_2$ and $B = B_1 \cup B_2$, where*

$$f^1(A_1) = B_1 \quad \textit{and} \quad g^1(B_2) = A_2.$$

PROOF. We call the element $a \in A$ *extendable* if $a \in g^1(B)$ and $g^c(a) \in f^1(A)$. For extendable a we set $a^* = f^c(g^c(a))$ and call a^* the *extension* of a.

Now we construct a maximal sequence of successive extensions starting with the element a. By $n(a)$ we denote the largest natural number

[1]) Tarski showed in his paper *Sur quelques théorèmes qui équivalent à l'axiome du choix,* Fundamenta Mathematicae **5** (1924) 147–154, that cancellation laws for $<$ are not only consequences of the law of trichotomy but that they are actually equivalent to it in the axiom system Σ[TR]. Moreover, they are equivalent to the axiom of choice as well. See Chapter VIII, §6.

[2]) S. Banach, *Un théorème sur les transformations biunivoques,* Fundamenta Mathematicae **6** (1924) 236–239.

such that there exists a sequence of $n(a)$ terms constructed by starting with a and taking successive extensions, provided that such a maximal natural number exists. Otherwise, when for every natural number k there exists such a sequence of k terms, we let $n(a) = N$. The sequence defined by

$$\varphi_0(a) = a, \quad \varphi_{j+1}(a) = \varphi_j(a)^* \text{ for } j \in n(a)$$

is the desired maximal sequence of successive extensions starting from a. For non-extendable a we have $n(a) = 1$ and $\varphi_0(a) = a$.

If $n(a)$ is finite then we let

$$s(a) = \varphi_{n(a)-1}(a).$$

We define

$$A_2 = \{a \in A: n(a) = N \vee (s(a) \in g^1(B)) \wedge (g^c(s(a)) \notin f^1(A))\}.$$

$$A_1 = A - A_2, \quad B_1 = f^1(A_1), \quad B_2 = B - B_1.$$

For the proof of the theorem it suffices to show that $g^1(B_2) = A_2$, i.e. that

(8) $$b \in B_2 \to g(b) \in A_2,$$

(9) $$A_2 \subset g^1(B_2).$$

PROOF OF (8). Assume that $b \in B_2$; that is, that $b \notin f^1(A_1)$ and let $a = g(b)$. If $b \notin f^1(A)$ then a is not extendable, $s(a) = a$, and by definition we have $a \in A_2$. If $b \in f^1(A)$ then $b \in f^1(A_2)$ and $b = f(a')$, where $a' \in A_2$. Clearly $a' = f^c(g^c(a'))$, that is $a' = a^*$; thus $a^* \in A_2$. If $n(a^*) = N$ then $n(a) = N$ and $a \in A_2$; otherwise $s(a^*) = s(a)$ and again $a \in A_2$.

PROOF OF (9). Assume that $a \in A_2$. If a is extendable then $a = g(f(a^*))$. If at the same time $n(a)$ is finite, then $s(a) = s(a^*)$ and $a^* \in A_2$. The same is true if $n(a) = N$, because then $n(a^*) = N$ as well. Thus in both cases $a^* \notin A_1$, $f(a^*) \notin f^1(A_1)$ and thus $f(a^*) \in B_2$. It follows then that $a = g(f(a^*)) \in g^1(B_2)$.

If a is not extendable, then $s(a) = a$ and by the assumption that $a \in A_2$ we obtain $a \in g^1(B)$. If a were an element of $g^1(B_1)$ then, by the definition of the set B_1, a would have the form $g(f(a'))$ and would be extendable contrary to the assumption. Thus $a \in g^1(B_2)$. Q.E.D.

As a corollary we have the *Cantor–Bernstein theorem* [1]):

THEOREM 3: *If* $\mathfrak{m} \leqslant \mathfrak{n}$ *and* $\mathfrak{n} \leqslant \mathfrak{m}$ *then* $\mathfrak{m} = \mathfrak{n}$.

PROOF. Let $\overline{\overline{A}} = \mathfrak{m}$ and $\overline{\overline{B}} = \mathfrak{n}$. Since $\mathfrak{m} \leqslant \mathfrak{n}$, there exists a one-to-one function f from A onto a subset of B. Since $\mathfrak{n} \leqslant \mathfrak{m}$, there exists, similarly, a one-to-one function g from B onto a subset of A. By Theorem 2, $A = A_1 \cup A_2$, where A_1 and A_2 are disjoint; and $B = B_1 \cup B_2$, where B_1 and B_2 are disjoint and where $f^1(A_1) = B_1$ and $g^1(B_2) = A_2$. Thus $A_1 \sim B_1$ and $A_2 \sim B_2$; hence $A \sim B$.

The Cantor–Bernstein theorem can be generalized as follows. Let R be an equivalence relation on the family 2^A and let R satisfy the following two conditions:

$$(10) \quad XRY \to \bigvee_{f \in Y^X} [(f \text{ is a one-to-one function}) \wedge \bigwedge_{Z \in X} (ZRf^1(Z))],$$

$$(11) \quad (X_1 \cap X_2 = 0 = Y_1 \cap Y_2) \wedge (X_1 R Y_1) \wedge (X_2 R Y_2) \to (X_1 \cup X_2 R Y_1 \cup Y_2).$$

THEOREM 4: *If the relation R with field* 2^A *satisfies for arbitrary subsets of A the conditions* (10) *and* (11), *and if X stands in the relation R to some subset of Y and Y stands in the relation R to some subset of X, then XRY* [2]).

PROOF. Assume that XRY_1 where $Y_1 \subset Y$, and YRX_1 where $X_1 \subset X$. From (10) it follows that there exist one-to-one functions f and g such that f maps X into Y_1 and satisfies the condition that $ZRf^1(Z)$ for every $Z \subset X$; and similarly g maps Y into X_1 and satisfies $TRg^1(T)$ for all $T \subset Y$. By Theorem 2, $X = X' \cup X''$ and $Y = Y' \cup Y''$, where $X' \cap X'' = 0$ and $Y' \cap Y'' = 0$ and where $Y' = f^1(X')$ and $X'' = g^1(Y'')$. Since $X' \subset X$, we have $X'Rf^1(X')$, that is $X'RY'$; similarly $X''RY''$. It then follows by (11) that XRY. Q.E.D.

We give two examples of relations satisfying conditions (10) and (11):

[1]) The Cantor–Bernstein theorem is also called the *Schröder–Bernstein theorem.* The first correct proof of this theorem, due to F. Bernstein, was published in the book: E. Borel, *Leçons sur la théorie des fonctions* (Paris 1898). See also J. König, Comptes Rendus de l'Académie des Sciences (Paris) **143** (1906).

[2]) Theorem 4 and the examples below are due to Banach; see his paper cited on p. 188.

1. *The relation of equipollence on subsets of A.* Theorem 4 for this relation is then identical with the Cantor–Bernstein Theorem.

2. Let $A = \mathcal{E}^n$. We call two subsets X and Y of A *equivalent by finite decomposition* if there exist a natural number k and two sequences $X_0, \ldots, X_{k-1}$ and $Y_0, \ldots, Y_{k-1}$ such that

$$X = \bigcup_{j<k} X_j, \qquad Y = \bigcup_{j<k} Y_j,$$

$$X_i \cap X_j = 0 = Y_i \cap Y_j \quad \text{for} \quad 0 \leqslant i < j < k,$$

$$X_i \text{ and } Y_i \text{ are isometric for } i < k.$$

In case X and Y are equivalent by finite decomposition we write $X \sim_{\text{fin}} Y$.

THEOREM 5: *The relation* $\sim_{\text{fin}}$ *satisfies conditions* (10) *and* (11) *and is an equivalence relation on* 2^A.

We omit the proof. #

We prove one more theorem about transformations. Like Theorem 2 it is a generalization of the Cantor–Bernstein Theorem.

THEOREM 6: (MEAN-VALUE THEOREM.) *Let A, B, C, A′ and B′ be sets such that* $A \supset C \supset B$, $A' \supset B'$, $A \sim A'$ *and* $B \sim B'$. *Then there exists a set C′ such that* $A' \supset C' \supset B'$ *and* $C \sim C'$ [1]).

PROOF. It suffices to prove the existence of a function h from A into A' satisfying the following conditions:

(12) *the restriction* $h|C$ *is one-to-one,*

(13) $$h^1(C) \supset B'.$$

In fact, if h satisfies (12) and (13), then the desired set C' is $h^1(C)$.

We define h as follows:

$$h(x) = \begin{cases} f(x) & \text{for} \quad x \in A - X, \\ g^c(x) & \text{for} \quad x \in X, \end{cases}$$

[1]) This theorem is due to A. Tarski and A. Lindenbaum. See *Communication sur les recherches de la théorie des ensembles,* Comptes rendus des séances de la Société des Sciences et des lettres de Varsovie, Classe III, **19**(1926) 299–330, Theorem 15 on p. 303.

where—for the present—X is an arbitrary subset of B and where f and g are one-to-one functions such that $f^1(A) = A'$ and $g^1(B') = B$. The function h defined in this way certainly satisfies condition (12) provided that

$$g^{-1}(X) \cap f^1(C-X) = 0. \tag{14}$$

In fact, if h satisfies (14) then $h(x') = h(x'')$ holds for no x' and x'' such that $x' \in X$ and $x'' \in C-X$.

The function h satisfies (13) if besides satisfying (14) it also satisfies

$$g^{-1}(X) \cup f^1(C-X) \supset B', \tag{15}$$

because $h^1(C) = h^1(X) \cup h^1(C-X) = g^{-1}(X) \cup f^1(C-X)$.

Both condition (14) and condition (15) hold if

$$g^1\big(B' - f^1(C-X)\big) = X. \tag{16}$$

To complete the proof it suffices to show that there exists a set $X \subset B$ satisfying (16). For this purpose we let $F(X) = g^1\big(B' - f^1(C-X)\big)$ and we notice that

$$X_1 \subset X_2 \subset B \to F(X_1) \subset F(X_2) \subset B.$$

A function F from 2^B into 2^B will be called a *monotone function on the subsets* of B if it satisfies the condition above. Therefore it suffices to prove the following lemma:

For every monotone function on the subsets of a given set B, there exists a set X such that $F(X) = X$.

We construct X as follows: let $\boldsymbol{K} = \{X \subset B\colon\ F(X) \subset X\}$. The family $\boldsymbol{K}$ is non-empty because $B \in \boldsymbol{K}$. We shall show that the condition $F(X) = X$ is satisfied by the set $X_0 = \bigcap_{X \in \boldsymbol{K}} X$.

In fact, $X \in \boldsymbol{K} \to X_0 \subset X$ and thus by monotonicity $X \in \boldsymbol{K} \to F(X_0) \subset F(X) \subset X$. It follows that $F(X_0) \subset X$ for every $X \in \boldsymbol{K}$, and hence $F(X_0) \subset \bigcap_{X \in \boldsymbol{K}} X = X_0$, so that $F(X_0) \subset X_0$. By monotonicity it follows moreover that $F\big(F(X_0)\big) \subset F(X_0)$, and thus $F(X_0) \in \boldsymbol{K}$, so $X_0 \subset F(X_0)$. We have $F(X_0) = X_0$. Q.E.D.

The Cantor–Bernstein Theorem is a consequence of Theorem 6. In fact, if $\mathfrak{m} \leqslant \mathfrak{n}$ then there exist sets X, Y such that $\overline{\overline{X}} = \mathfrak{m}$, $\overline{\overline{Y}} = \mathfrak{n}$ and

$X \subset Y$. If we assume moreover that $\mathfrak{n} \leqslant \mathfrak{m}$, then Y contains a subset Z of power $\mathfrak{m}$. Letting in Theorem 6 $A' = B' = B = Z$, $A = X$ and $C = Y$ we conclude that there exists a set C' such that $A' \supset C' \supset B'$ and $C' \sim C$. Thus $C' = Z$ and $C' \sim Y$, so $Z \sim Y$, and consequently $\mathfrak{m} = \mathfrak{n}$.

Exercises

1. We say that a cardinal number $\mathfrak{n}$ *absorbs* $\mathfrak{m}$ if $\mathfrak{m}+\mathfrak{n} = \mathfrak{n}$. Show:
(a) $\mathfrak{n}$ absorbs $\mathfrak{m}$ if and only if $\mathfrak{a}\cdot\mathfrak{m} \leqslant \mathfrak{n}$;
(b) if $\mathfrak{n}$ absorbs $\mathfrak{m}$, then every cardinal larger than $\mathfrak{n}$ absorbs $\mathfrak{m}$;
(c) $\mathfrak{n}$ absorbs $\mathfrak{m}$ if and only if $\mathfrak{n}$ absorbs $k\cdot\mathfrak{m}$ ($k \in N$);
(d) $\mathfrak{n}$ absorbs $\mathfrak{m}$ if and only if $\mathfrak{n}$ absorbs $\mathfrak{a}\cdot\mathfrak{m}$. (Tarski)

2. Without using the axiom of choice show that $\mathfrak{m} \leqslant \mathfrak{a} \equiv \mathfrak{m} \leqslant^* \mathfrak{a}$.

3. Without using the axiom of choice show that $\neg(2^{\mathfrak{m}} \leqslant^* \mathfrak{m})$. (Tarski)

4. Show that $2^{\mathfrak{m}} \geqslant \mathfrak{a} \rightarrow 2^{\mathfrak{m}} \geqslant 2^{\mathfrak{a}}$.

5. Show that the closed circle T is equivalent by finite decomposition to the union $T \cup F$, where F is an arbitrary line segment disjoint from T[1]).

§ 6. Properties of the cardinals $\mathfrak{a}$ and $\mathfrak{c}$

We introduce the following notation:

$$\mathfrak{c} = 2^{\mathfrak{a}}.$$

The cardinal $\mathfrak{c}$ is called the *power of the continuum*.

We often meet the cardinal $\mathfrak{c}$, as well as the cardinal $\mathfrak{a}$, in many parts of set theory and its applications. We shall prove several formulas concerning the numbers n (*natural numbers*), $\mathfrak{a}$ and $\mathfrak{c}$.

(1) $$\mathfrak{c} = \mathfrak{c}+\mathfrak{c}.$$

In fact (see p. 185), $\mathfrak{c}+\mathfrak{c} = 2\mathfrak{c} = 2\cdot 2^{\mathfrak{a}} = 2^{1+\mathfrak{a}} = 2^{\mathfrak{a}} = \mathfrak{c}$, because $1+\mathfrak{a} = \mathfrak{a}$.

(2) $$n < \mathfrak{a} < \mathfrak{c}.$$

The inequalities follow from equations (1) and (2), § 5, p. 186.

(3) $$n+\mathfrak{c} = \mathfrak{a}+\mathfrak{c} = \mathfrak{c}.$$

In fact, by (2) we have (see (4), § 5, p. 187)

$$\mathfrak{c} \leqslant n+\mathfrak{c} \leqslant \mathfrak{a}+\mathfrak{c} \leqslant \mathfrak{c}+\mathfrak{c},$$

[1]) For a more detailed discussion of the problems mentioned in § 5, see A. Tarski, *Cardinal Algebras* (New York, 1949), in particular Chapters 1, 2 and 17.

and by (1)

$$\mathfrak{c} \leqslant n+\mathfrak{c} \leqslant \mathfrak{a}+\mathfrak{c} \leqslant \mathfrak{c}.$$

Applying Theorem 3, § 5, p. 190 we obtain (3).

(4) $$\mathfrak{c} = \mathfrak{c}\cdot\mathfrak{c}.$$

Indeed, $\mathfrak{c} = 2^{\mathfrak{a}} = 2^{\mathfrak{a}+\mathfrak{a}} = 2^{\mathfrak{a}}\cdot 2^{\mathfrak{a}} = \mathfrak{c}\cdot\mathfrak{c}$, because $\mathfrak{a}+\mathfrak{a} = \mathfrak{a}$ (see (3), § 4, p. 183)

(5) $$n\cdot\mathfrak{c} = \mathfrak{a}\cdot\mathfrak{c} = \mathfrak{c} \qquad (\text{for } n > 0).$$

By (2) and by (5), § 4, p. 183 we have the inequalities $\mathfrak{c} \leqslant n\cdot\mathfrak{c} \leqslant \mathfrak{a}\cdot\mathfrak{c} \leqslant \mathfrak{c}\cdot\mathfrak{c}$; hence in view of (4) we obtain (5) by applying the Cantor–Bernstein Theorem.

By induction from (4) we obtain

(6) $$\mathfrak{c}^n = \mathfrak{c} \qquad (\text{for } n > 0).$$

(7) $$n^{\mathfrak{a}} = \mathfrak{a}^{\mathfrak{a}} = \mathfrak{c}^{\mathfrak{a}} = \mathfrak{c} \qquad (\text{for } n > 1).$$

In fact (see (10), p. 185),

$$\mathfrak{c} = 2^{\mathfrak{a}} \leqslant n^{\mathfrak{a}} \leqslant \mathfrak{a}^{\mathfrak{a}} \leqslant \mathfrak{c}^{\mathfrak{a}} = (2^{\mathfrak{a}})^{\mathfrak{a}} = 2^{\mathfrak{a}\cdot\mathfrak{a}} = 2^{\mathfrak{a}} = \mathfrak{c},$$

whence (7) follows by applying the Cantor–Bernstein Theorem.

The following equations concerning the number $\mathfrak{f} = 2^{\mathfrak{c}}$ are proved similarly:

(8) $$\begin{aligned} n+\mathfrak{f} &= \mathfrak{a}+\mathfrak{f} = \mathfrak{c}+\mathfrak{f} = \mathfrak{f}+\mathfrak{f} = \mathfrak{f}, \\ n\cdot\mathfrak{f} &= \mathfrak{a}\cdot\mathfrak{f} = \mathfrak{c}\cdot\mathfrak{f} = \mathfrak{f}\cdot\mathfrak{f} = \mathfrak{f} \qquad (\text{for } n > 0), \\ n^{\mathfrak{c}} &= \mathfrak{a}^{\mathfrak{c}} = \mathfrak{c}^{\mathfrak{c}} = \mathfrak{f}^{\mathfrak{c}} = \mathfrak{f} \qquad (\text{for } n > 1). \end{aligned}$$

We shall give examples of sets of powers $\mathfrak{c}$ and $2^{\mathfrak{c}}$.

THEOREM 1: *The Cantor set C has power $\mathfrak{c}$.*

PROOF. $C = \{0, 1\}^N$, so $\overline{\overline{C}} = 2^{\mathfrak{a}}$ by Theorem 7, p. 185.

THEOREM 2: *The set of all infinite sequences of natural numbers has power $\mathfrak{c}$.*

PROOF. This set is N^N. Therefore its power is $\mathfrak{a}^{\mathfrak{a}} = \mathfrak{c}$.

THEOREM 3: *The following sets have the power of the continuum:*

(a) *the set of irrational numbers in the interval* $(0, 1)$;

(b) *the set of all points in* $(0, 1)$;

(c) *the set* $\mathcal{E}$ *of all real numbers;*

(d) *the set of all points of the space* $\mathcal{E}^n$, *where n is a natural number.*

PROOF. (a) follows from the remark on p. 138 and from Theorem 2. (b) follows from the observation that the interval $(0, 1)$ is the union of the countable set of rationals in $(0, 1)$ and the set of irrationals in $(0, 1)$, which has power $\mathfrak{c}$. (c) holds because function $y = 1/2 + \frac{1}{\pi} \operatorname{arctg} x$ is one-to-one and maps the set $\mathcal{E}$ onto the interval $(0, 1)$. (d) follows from (c) and equation (6). #

THEOREM 4: *If* $\overline{\overline{A}} = \mathfrak{c}$, $\overline{\overline{B}} = \mathfrak{a}$ *and* $B \subset A$, *then* $\overline{\overline{A-B}} = \mathfrak{c}$.

PROOF. By (6) we have that $A \times A \sim A$; therefore it suffices to show that if M is a countable subset of $A \times A$, then the difference $A \times A - M$ has power $\mathfrak{c}$. The projection onto A of the points in M constitute at most a countable set, which implies that there exists an element of A which does not belong to the projection of M. The set $\{\langle a, y\rangle : y \in A\}$ is disjoint from M and has power $\mathfrak{c}$, thus the difference $A \times A - M$ has power $\geqslant \mathfrak{c}$. On the other hand, this set has power $\leqslant \mathfrak{c}$ as a subset of $A \times A$. Thus the difference $A \times A - M$ has power $\mathfrak{c}$ by the Cantor–Bernstein Theorem.

COROLLARY 5: *The set of transcendental numbers has power* $\mathfrak{c}$.

PROOF. It suffices to apply Theorem 4 to the case where A is the set $\mathcal{E}$ of real numbers and B is the set of algebraic numbers.

This corollary, proved by Cantor in 1874, was one of the first applications of set theory to concrete mathematical problems.

THEOREM 6: *The set* $\mathcal{E}^N$ *of infinite sequences of real numbers has power* $\mathfrak{c}$.

PROOF. $\overline{\overline{\mathcal{E}^N}} = \mathfrak{c}^{\mathfrak{a}} = \mathfrak{c}$ by (7).

THEOREM 7: *The set of continuous functions of one real variable has power* $\mathfrak{c}$.

PROOF. Let $r_1, r_2, \ldots, r_n, \ldots$ be an enumeration of all rational numbers. With every continuous function f of one real variable we associate the sequence of real numbers

(9) $$f(r_1), f(r_2), \ldots, f(r_n), \ldots$$

If f and g are distinct then the corresponding sequences

$$f(r_1), f(r_2), \dots, f(r_n), \dots, \qquad g(r_1), g(r_2), \dots, g(r_n), \dots$$

are also distinct. In fact, $f \neq g$ implies that $f(x) \neq g(x)$ for some x; so if r_{k_n} is a sequence of rationals converging to x, then it is not true that $f(r_{k_n}) = g(r_{k_n})$ for every n, because in that case, by the continuity of f and g, we would have

$$f(x) = \lim_{n=\infty} f(r_{k_n}) = \lim_{n=\infty} g(r_{k_n}) = g(x).$$

Thus the set of continuous functions of one real variable is equipollent to the set of sequences (2), which has power $\leqslant \mathfrak{c}$ by Theorem 4. On the other hand, the set of continuous functions has power $\geqslant \mathfrak{c}$ because it contains all constant functions. Thus by Theorem 3, § 5 we obtain Theorem 7.

THEOREM 8: *The set* $\mathcal{E}^{\mathcal{E}}$ *of all functions of one real variable has power* $2^{\mathfrak{c}}$.

PROOF. $\overline{\overline{\mathcal{E}^{\mathcal{E}}}} = \mathfrak{c}^{\mathfrak{c}} = 2^{\mathfrak{c}}$ by (8).

Exercise

Prove that the family $\boldsymbol{R}$ of closed sets of the space $\mathcal{E}$ has power $\mathfrak{c}$.

Hint: To prove that $\overline{\overline{\boldsymbol{R}}} \leqslant \mathfrak{c}$ associate with every $X \in \boldsymbol{R}$ a family of intervals with rational endpoints disjoint from X and show that the set of all such families has power $\mathfrak{c}$. The inequailty $\overline{\overline{\boldsymbol{R}}} \geqslant \mathfrak{c}$ holds because all one element sets belong to $\boldsymbol{R}$. #

§ 7. The generalized sum of cardinal numbers

Let T be an arbitrary set, $\mathfrak{f}$ a function defined on T with cardinal numbers as values. Instead of $\mathfrak{f}(x)$ we shall also write $\mathfrak{f}_x$.

Assume that the function $\mathfrak{f}$ satisfies the following condition

(W) $\begin{cases} \textit{there exists a set-valued function } F^{(0)} \textit{ defined on } T \textit{ such that} \\ \overline{\overline{F_x^{(0)}}} = \mathfrak{f}_x \textit{ for all } x \in T. \end{cases}$

Condition (W) can easily be shown to hold for many functions $\mathfrak{f}$. Such is the case, for instance, when $\mathfrak{f}$ has only finitely many distinct values. We shall show in Chapter VII, p. 268 that every $\mathfrak{f}$ satisfies condition (W), so that condition (W) does not actually affect the generality of our treatment.

° THEOREM 1: *There exists a set-valued function F defined on T such that*

(1) $$\overline{\overline{F_x}} = \mathfrak{f}_x \quad \textit{for} \quad x \in T,$$

(2) $$F_x \cap F_y = 0 \quad \textit{for} \quad x \neq y.$$

Moreover, if $F^{(1)}$ and $F^{(2)}$ both satisfy (1) *and* (2), *then*

$$\bigcup_x F_x^{(1)} \sim \bigcup_x F_x^{(2)}.$$

PROOF. For $x \in T$ let

$$F_x = F_x^{(0)} \times \{x\},$$

where $F^{(0)}$ is any function satisfying (W). If $x \neq y$ then $F_x \cap F_y = 0$, because the set F_x consists of ordered pairs with second component x and F_y of ordered pairs with second component y. Moreover, $\overline{\overline{F_x}} = \overline{\overline{F_x^{(0)}}} = \mathfrak{f}_x$. Thus F satisfies conditions (1) and (2).

Assume now that functions $F^{(1)}$ and $F^{(2)}$ satisfy conditions (1) and (2). For every $x \in T$ the set Φ_x of one-to-one functions from $F_x^{(1)}$ onto $F_x^{(2)}$ is non-empty. If $x \neq y$ then $\Phi_x \cap \Phi_y = 0$, because every function belonging to Φ_x has domain F_x and therefore is different from every function belonging to Φ_y.

By the axiom of choice it follows that there exists a set Ψ containing exactly one element in common with each of the sets Φ_x. Let φ_x be the only element of $\Psi \cap \Phi_x$; then φ_x is a one-to-one function from the set $F_x^{(1)}$ onto the set $F_x^{(2)}$.

It is now easy to show that the function $f = \bigcup_{x \in T} \varphi_x$ maps the union $\bigcup_x F_x^{(1)}$ onto $\bigcup_x F_x^{(2)}$ in a one-to-one manner. This completes the proof.

° DEFINITION: The *sum of the cardinal numbers* $\mathfrak{f}_x$ for $x \in T$ is the cardinal $\overline{\overline{\bigcup_x F_x}}$, where F is any function satisfying (1) and (2).

We denote this sum by $\sum_{x \in T} \mathfrak{f}_x$ or by $\sum \mathfrak{f}_x$:

(3) $$\sum_{x \in T} \mathfrak{f}_x = \overline{\overline{\bigcup_{x \in T} F_x}}.$$

The definition is correct since the number $\overline{\overline{\bigcup_x F_x}}$ does not depend on the choice of the function F satisfying conditions (1) and (2) and since such a function always exists. However, we cannot prove the existence of such a function without appealing to the axiom of choice, so that the definition of the sum of an arbitrary set of cardinal numbers is based upon the axiom of choice[1]).

If $T=\{1,2\}$, then $\sum\limits_{t\in T}\mathfrak{f}_t=\mathfrak{f}_1+\mathfrak{f}_2$. If $T=N$, then we shall also write

$$\mathfrak{f}_0+\mathfrak{f}_1+\mathfrak{f}_2+\mathfrak{f}_3+\ldots \quad\text{or}\quad \sum_{n=0}^{\infty}\mathfrak{f}_n$$

and speak of the sum of a series of cardinal numbers.

°THEOREM 2: (GENERALIZED COMMUTATIVE LAW.) *If φ is an arbitrary permutation of the set T, then* $\sum\mathfrak{f}_x=\sum\mathfrak{f}_{\varphi(x)}$.

For the proof it suffices to notice that

$$\sum_x\mathfrak{f}_x=\overline{\overline{\bigcup_x F_x}}=\overline{\overline{\bigcup_x F_{\varphi(x)}}}=\sum_x\mathfrak{f}_{\varphi(x)},$$

where F is any function satisfying conditions (1) and (2). The equations hold on the basis of Theorem 3, Chapter IV, § 1, p. 115 and formula (3).

°THEOREM 3: (GENERALIZED ASSOCIATIVE LAW.) *If* $T=\bigcup\limits_{y\in I}T_y$ *where the sets* T_y *are disjoint, then*

$$\sum_{x\in T}\mathfrak{f}_x=\sum_{y\in I}\Big(\sum_{x\in T_y}\mathfrak{f}_x\Big).$$

PROOF. For $y\in I$, let $\mathfrak{g}_y=\sum\limits_{x\in T_y}\mathfrak{f}_x$, that is $\mathfrak{g}_y=\overline{\overline{\bigcup\limits_{x\in T_y}F_x}}$. Then

$$\sum_{y\in I}\mathfrak{g}_y=\overline{\overline{\bigcup_{y\in I}\Big(\bigcup_{x\in T_y}F_x\Big)}}=\overline{\overline{\bigcup_{x\in T}F_x}},$$

by Theorem 2, Chapter, IV, p. 144. It follows that

$$\sum_{y\in I}\mathfrak{g}_y=\sum_{x\in T}\mathfrak{f}_x,$$

which proves Theorem 3.

[1]) The fact that the definition of the sum of an infinite sequence of cardinals requires the axiom of choice was pointed out by W. Sierpiński in the paper: *Sur l'axiome de M. Zermelo et son rôle dans la Théorie des Ensembles et Analyse,* Bulletin de l'Académie des Sciences de Cracovie, Cl. Sci. Math. et Nat., Series A (1918) 112.

°THEOREM 4: (GENERALIZED DISTRIBUTIVE LAW FOR MULTIPLICATION WITH RESPECT TO ADDITION.) *The equation*

$$(\sum_x \mathfrak{f}_x)\cdot\mathfrak{m} = \sum_x (\mathfrak{f}_x\cdot\mathfrak{m})$$

holds for every cardinal $\mathfrak{m}$.

PROOF. Let $\overline{\overline{M}} = \mathfrak{m}$. We have

$$(\sum_x \mathfrak{f}_x)\mathfrak{m} = \overline{\overline{(\bigcup_x F_x)\times M}} \quad \text{and} \quad \sum_x (\mathfrak{f}_x\cdot\mathfrak{m}) = \overline{\overline{\bigcup_x (F_x\times M)}}.$$

At the same time (see Exercise 2, Chapter IV, § 1, p. 120)

$$(\bigcup_x F_x)\times M = \bigcup_x (F_x\times M).$$

°THEOREM 5: *If* $\mathfrak{g}_x \leqslant \mathfrak{f}_x$ *for* $x\in T$, *then* $\sum_x \mathfrak{g}_x \leqslant \sum_x \mathfrak{f}_x$.

PROOF. Let $\boldsymbol{K}_x$ be the family of those $X \subset F_x$ which have power $\mathfrak{g}_x$. By assumption $\boldsymbol{K}_x \neq 0$ for every $x\in T$. It follows that there exists a function G (see Theorem 3, p. 133) such that

$$G\in\prod_{x\in T}\boldsymbol{K}_x, \quad \text{that is} \quad G_x\in\boldsymbol{K}_x.$$

Therefore $G_x\subset F_x$ and $\overline{\overline{G_x}} = \mathfrak{g}_x$. This implies

$$\bigcup_x G_x \subset \bigcup_x F_x \quad \text{and} \quad \overline{\overline{\bigcup_x G_x}} = \sum_x \mathfrak{g}_x,$$

which proves that $\sum_x \mathfrak{g}_x \leqslant \sum_x \mathfrak{f}_x$.

°THEOREM 6: *If* $S\subset T$ *then*

$$\sum_{x\in S}\mathfrak{f}_x \leqslant \sum_{x\in T}\mathfrak{f}_x.$$

PROOF. Let

$$\mathfrak{g}_x = \begin{cases}\mathfrak{f}_x & \text{for} \quad x\in S,\\ 0 & \text{for} \quad x\in T-S.\end{cases}$$

By Theorem 5,

$$\sum_{x\in T}\mathfrak{g}_x \leqslant \sum_{x\in T}\mathfrak{f}_x, \quad \text{but} \quad \sum_{x\in T}\mathfrak{g}_x = \sum_{x\in S}\mathfrak{f}_x.$$

°THEOREM 7: *If* $\mathfrak{f}_x = \mathfrak{m}$ *for all* $x\in T$, *and* $\mathfrak{n} = \overline{\overline{T}}$, *then*

$$\sum_{x\in T}\mathfrak{f}_x = \mathfrak{m}\cdot\mathfrak{n}.$$

PROOF. Let $\overline{\overline{M}} = \mathfrak{m}$. For every x there exists a one-to-one mapping f of the set F_x onto M; let Φ_x be the set of all such functions. By the axiom of choice there exists a set Ψ containing exactly one element from each of the sets Φ_x. Let f_x be the unique element of $\Psi \cap \Phi_x$.

For $t \in \bigcup\limits_x F_x$ we let

$$\varphi(t) = \langle f_x(t), x \rangle,$$

where x is the (unique) element of T such that $t \in F_x$.

The function f maps the union $\bigcup F_x$ onto $M \times T$ and is one-to-one. In fact, if

$$\varphi(t_1) = \langle f_{x_1}(t_1), x_1 \rangle \quad \text{and} \quad \varphi(t_2) = \langle f_{x_2}(t_2), x_2 \rangle,$$

then $x_1 \neq x_2$ implies $t_1 \neq t_2$, because t_1 and t_2 belong to the disjoint sets F_{x_1} and F_{x_2}. On the other hand, if $x_1 = x_2 = x$ then, since f_x is one-to-one, $\varphi(t_1) \neq \varphi(t_2)$ implies that $t_1 \neq t_2$.

Therefore $\bigcup F_x \sim M \times T$, which proves Theorem 7.

°THEOREM 8: *If* $\mathfrak{f}_x \leqslant \mathfrak{m}$ *for* $x \in T$ *and* $\mathfrak{n} = \overline{\overline{T}}$, *then* $\sum \mathfrak{f}_x \leqslant \mathfrak{m}.\mathfrak{n}$.

PROOF. Letting $\mathfrak{m}_x = \mathfrak{m}$ for $x \in T$, we have by Theorem 5 $\sum \mathfrak{f}_x \leqslant \sum \mathfrak{m}_x$, and by Theorem 7 $\sum \mathfrak{m}_x = \mathfrak{m} \cdot \mathfrak{n}$.

Examples

1. We shall calculate the sum $\sum k_n$, where k_n is a natural number and n runs through the set of natural numbers. For this purpose we notice that from Theorem 7 it follows that

(4) $\quad 1+1+1+ \ldots = 1 \cdot \mathfrak{a} = \mathfrak{a}, \quad \mathfrak{a}+\mathfrak{a}+\mathfrak{a}+ \ldots = \mathfrak{a} \cdot \mathfrak{a} = \mathfrak{a};$

since, by Theorem 5,

$$1+1+1+ \ldots \leqslant \sum_{n=1}^{\infty} k_n \leqslant \mathfrak{a}+\mathfrak{a}+\mathfrak{a}+ \ldots,$$

we have by the Cantor–Bernstein Theorem

$$\sum_{n=1}^{\infty} k_n = \mathfrak{a}.$$

In particular

$$2+2+2+ \ldots = \mathfrak{a},$$
$$1+2+3+ \ldots = \mathfrak{a},$$
$$1!+2!+3!+ \ldots = \mathfrak{a}.$$

2. It follows from equation (4) that the union of a countable number of countable sets is countable (see Theorem 8, § 2, p. 176).

3. By Theorem 7, $\mathfrak{c}+\mathfrak{c}+\mathfrak{c}+\ldots=\mathfrak{c}\cdot\mathfrak{a}=\mathfrak{c}$. Similarly, the sum $\sum_{x\in T}\mathfrak{f}_x$ where the power of T is $\mathfrak{c}$ and where each $\mathfrak{f}_x$ equals $\mathfrak{c}$ is itself equal to $\mathfrak{c}\cdot\mathfrak{c}$, that is to $\mathfrak{c}$.

§ 8. The generalized product of cardinal numbers

As before, we shall use the axiom of choice and assume that $\mathfrak{f}$ is a function having cardinal numbers as values and satisfying condition (W) given on p. 196.

° THEOREM 1: *If the functions $F^{(1)}$ and $F^{(2)}$ satisfy the condition $\overline{\overline{F_x^{(1)}}}=\mathfrak{f}_x=\overline{\overline{F_x^{(2)}}}$ for $x\in T$, then*

$$\overline{\overline{\prod_{x\in T}F_x^{(1)}}}=\overline{\overline{\prod_{x\in T}F_x^{(2)}}}.$$

PROOF. As in the proof of Theorem 1, § 7, using the axiom of choice, we show that there exists a set which for every $x\in T$ contains exactly one function φ_x which is one-to-one and maps $F_x^{(1)}$ onto $F_x^{(2)}$. With each function $f_1\in\prod_{x\in T}F_x^{(1)}$ we associate the function f_2, where

$$f_2(t)=\varphi_t(f_1(t))\quad\text{for}\quad t\in T. \tag{1}$$

Since $f_1(t)\in F_t^{(1)}$ for every $t\in T$, $\varphi_t(f_1(t))\in\varphi_t^1(F_t^{(1)})=F_t^{(2)}$, which proves that $f_2(t)\in F_t^{(2)}$, that is $f_2\in\prod_{x\in T}F_t^{(2)}$.

If $f_1'\neq f_1''$ then, for some t, $f_1'(t)\neq f_1''(t)$. Thus, since φ_t is one-to-one,

$$\varphi_t(f_1'(t))\neq\varphi_t(f_1''(t)),$$

that is $f_2'(t)\neq f_2''(t)$. Therefore the correspondence between f_1 and f_2 is one-to-one.

Finally, if $f_2\in\prod F_x^{(2)}$ then the function f_1 defined by the equation

$$f_1(t)=\varphi_t^{c}(f_2(t))$$

belongs to $\prod F_x^{(1)}$ and satisfies condition (1). Thus every function belonging to $\prod F_x^{(2)}$ corresponds to some function belonging to $\prod F_x^{(1)}$.

Thus we have proved Theorem 1. This theorem leads to the following definition.

DEFINITION: The *product of the cardinal numbers* $\mathfrak{f}_x$ is the power of the cartesian product $\prod_x F_x$, where F is an arbitrary function such that $\overline{\overline{F}}_x = \mathfrak{f}_x$; that is,

$$\prod_{x\in T} \mathfrak{f}_x = \overline{\overline{\prod_{x\in T} F_x}}, \quad \text{where} \quad \overline{\overline{F}}_x = \mathfrak{f}_x.$$

Just as for generalized sum, the use of the notion of generalized product rests upon the axiom of choice, without which we cannot prove Theorem 1 which is the basis for the definition of product.

If $T = \{1, 2\}$, then $\prod_{t\in T} \mathfrak{f}_t = \mathfrak{f}_1 \cdot \mathfrak{f}_2$. For this reason we write $\mathfrak{f}_0 \cdot \mathfrak{f}_1 \cdot \ldots$, or $\prod_{n=0}^{\infty} \mathfrak{f}_n$ when $T = N$.

From Theorems 2, 3 and 4 proved in § 1, p. 171–172 we obtain directly the *commutative, associative and distributive laws:*

$$\prod_x \mathfrak{f}_x = \prod_x \mathfrak{f}_{\varphi(x)}$$

(where φ is a permutation of T),

$$\prod_{y\in U} \Big(\prod_{x\in T_y} \mathfrak{f}_x\Big) = \prod_{x\in T} \mathfrak{f}_x$$

$\Big($where $T = \bigcup_{y\in U} T_y$ and $T_{y_1} \cap T_{y_2} = 0$ for $y_1 \neq y_2\Big)$,

$$\Big(\prod_x \mathfrak{f}_x\Big)^{\mathfrak{g}} = \prod_x \mathfrak{f}_x^{\mathfrak{g}}.$$

If all of the values of the function $\mathfrak{f}$ are identical, then multiplication coincides with exponentiation; that is,

(2) if $\mathfrak{f}_x = \mathfrak{f}_0$ for $x \in T$ and $\mathfrak{t} = \overline{\overline{T}}$, then $\prod_x \mathfrak{f}_x = \mathfrak{f}_0^{\mathfrak{t}}$.

By equation (13), Theorem 3, § 1, p. 172, we derive from the definition of sum that

(3) $$\mathfrak{f}^{\sum_y \mathfrak{t}_y} = \prod_y (\mathfrak{f}^{\mathfrak{t}_y}).$$

Finally we note without proof that

(4) $$\textit{if} \quad \mathfrak{g}_x \leqslant \mathfrak{f}_x, \quad \textit{then} \quad \prod_x \mathfrak{g}_x \leqslant \prod_x \mathfrak{f}_x,$$

analogously to Theorem 5, § 7.

Examples

1. In (2) let $f_0 = \mathfrak{a}$ and $T = N$. Since $\mathfrak{a}^{\mathfrak{a}} = \mathfrak{c}$ (see (7), § 5, p. 194), we obtain

$$\mathfrak{a}\cdot\mathfrak{a}\cdot\mathfrak{a}\cdot\ldots = \mathfrak{c}.$$

2. In (2) let $f_0 = 2$ and $T = N$. From the equation $2^{\mathfrak{a}} = \mathfrak{c}$ we have

$$2\cdot 2\cdot 2\cdot\ldots = \mathfrak{c}.$$

3. From (4) we have $2\cdot 2\cdot 2\cdot\ldots \leqslant 2\cdot 3\cdot 4\cdot 5\cdot\ldots$ and $2\cdot 3\cdot 4\cdot 5\cdot\ldots \leqslant \mathfrak{a}\cdot\mathfrak{a}\cdot\mathfrak{a}\cdot\ldots$. Thus by Theorem 3, §5, p. 190 we conclude that

$$1\cdot 2\cdot 3\cdot 4\cdot\ldots = \mathfrak{c}.$$

In the same way it can be shown that $k_1\cdot k_2\cdot k_3\cdot\ldots = \mathfrak{c}$, if for all n, $k_n > 1$.

°THEOREM 2: (J. König [1])). *If* $\mathfrak{g}_x < \mathfrak{f}_x$, *for all* $x \in T$ *then*

$$\sum_x \mathfrak{g}_x < \prod_x \mathfrak{f}_x.$$

PROOF. From the assumption that (W) holds (p. 196) it follows that there exists a function F such that $\overline{\overline{F}}_x = \mathfrak{f}_x$. We may assume, moreover, that $F_x \cap F_y = 0$ for $x \neq y$ (see Theorem 1, §7, p. 197).

Arguing as in the proof of Theorem 5, §7 we conclude that there exists a function G such that $G_x \subset F_x$ and $\overline{\overline{G}}_x = \mathfrak{g}_x$. It follows that $G_x \cap G_y = 0$ for $x \neq y$ and that $F_x - G_x \neq 0$.

We show first that

(5) $$\sum_x \mathfrak{g}_x \leqslant \prod_x \mathfrak{f}_x.$$

Let f be an arbitrary function belonging to $\prod_x (F_x - G_x)$. Such a function exists by Theorem 3, Chapter IV, p. 133. For every $a \in \bigcup_x G_x$ let

$$f_a(x) = \begin{cases} f(x) & \text{for} \quad a \notin G_x, \\ a & \text{for} \quad a \in G_x. \end{cases}$$

[1]) See J. König, *Zum Kontinuumproblem*, Mathematische Annalen **60** (1904) 177–180.

Clearly, $f_a \in \prod F_x$. If $a \neq b$ then $f_a \neq f_b$, because a and b either belong to different sets G_x, G_y and then $f_a(x) = a \in G_x$, $f_b(x) = f(x) \in F_x - G_x$, and thus $f_a(x) \neq f_b(x)$; or else a and b belong to the same set G_x and then $f_a(x) = a \neq b = f_b(x)$.

Thus the functions f_a constitute a subset of the cartesian product $\prod\limits_x F_x$ equipollent to the union $\bigcup G_x$, which proves formula (5).

It remains to show that

$$\sum_x \mathfrak{g}_x \neq \prod_x \mathfrak{f}_x. \tag{6}$$

For this purpose we observe that every set S equipollent to the union $\bigcup\limits_x G_x$ can be considered as a union of disjoint sets:

$$S = \bigcup_x H_x, \quad \text{where} \quad \overline{\overline{H}}_x = \mathfrak{g}_x.$$

Assume that $S \subset \prod\limits_x F_x$; let $h \in H_x$. Thus for every t, $h(t) \in F_t$, and in particular $h(x) \in F_x$. Hence if h ranges over the set H_x, then the elements $h(x)$ form a set K_x contained in F_x, and so (see Theorem 1, § 5, p. 186) $\overline{\overline{K}}_x \leqslant \overline{\overline{H}}_x = \mathfrak{g}_x < \overline{\overline{F}}_x$. It follows that $F_x - K_x \neq 0$ for every x, and hence $\prod\limits_x (F_x - K_x) \neq 0$.

Let $\varphi \in \prod\limits_x (F_x - K_x)$. Hence $\varphi(x) \notin K_x$, and $\varphi \notin H_x$, because $h(x) \in K_x$ for all h belonging to H_x. This implies that the function φ belongs to none of the sets H_x contained in the union S; that is, $\varphi \notin S$ and it follows that $S \neq \prod\limits_x F_x$, which proves (6).

Letting in König's theorem $\mathfrak{g}_x = 1$, $\mathfrak{f}_x = 2$, and $\mathfrak{m} = \overline{\overline{T}}$ we obtain Cantor's inequality $\mathfrak{m} < 2^{\mathfrak{m}}$ ((2), § 5, p. 186). Thus König's theorem is a generalization of this inequality.

Corollary 3: *If* $\mathfrak{m}_n < \mathfrak{m}_{n+1}$ *for* $n = 0, 1, 2 \ldots$ *and* $\mathfrak{m}_0 > 0$, *then*

$$\sum_{n=0}^{\infty} \mathfrak{m}_n < \prod_{n=0}^{\infty} \mathfrak{m}_n.$$

Proof. By König's theorem

$$\mathfrak{m}_0 + \mathfrak{m}_1 + \mathfrak{m}_2 + \ldots < \mathfrak{m}_1 \cdot \mathfrak{m}_2 \cdot \mathfrak{m}_3 \ldots,$$

whence

$$\mathfrak{m}_0+\mathfrak{m}_1+\mathfrak{m}_2+\ldots<\mathfrak{m}_0\cdot\mathfrak{m}_1\cdot\mathfrak{m}_2\ldots.$$

COROLLARY 4: *For no cardinal* $\mathfrak{n}$ *can* $\mathfrak{n}^{\mathfrak{a}}$ *be represented as the sum of an infinite strictly increasing sequence of cardinal numbers.*

PROOF. Let $\mathfrak{n}^{\mathfrak{a}}=\mathfrak{m}_0+\mathfrak{m}_1+\mathfrak{m}_2+\ldots$. Hence $\mathfrak{m}_p\leqslant\mathfrak{n}^{\mathfrak{a}}$ and (see (4), p. 203)

$$\prod_{p=0}^{\infty}\mathfrak{m}_p\leqslant(\mathfrak{n}^{\mathfrak{a}})^{\mathfrak{a}}=\mathfrak{n}^{\mathfrak{a}}=\sum_{p=0}^{\infty}\mathfrak{m}_p.$$

By Theorem 3 the sequence $\mathfrak{m}_0,\mathfrak{m}_1,\mathfrak{m}_2,\ldots$ cannot be increasing.

Thus in particular neither $\mathfrak{c}$ nor $2^{\mathfrak{c}}$ is the sum of an infinite increasing sequence. On the other hand, the number

$$\mathfrak{a}+2^{\mathfrak{a}}+2^{2^{\mathfrak{a}}}+\ldots,$$

and more generally the number

$$\mathfrak{n}+2^{\mathfrak{n}}+2^{2^{\mathfrak{n}}}+\ldots,$$

cannot be written as a single cardinal raised to the power $\mathfrak{a}$.

CHAPTER VI

LINEARLY ORDERED SETS

§ 1. Introduction

The notion of linearly ordered set was introduced in Chapter II, § 9, p. 81. A linear ordering is also called a *total*, *complete* or *simple* ordering[1]).

The types of relational systems $\langle A, R\rangle$, where R is a linear order relation, are called *order types*. The order type of the system $\langle A, R\rangle$ will usually be denoted $\overline{A}$ (although it would be more proper to denote it by $\overline{R}$).

Examples

1. For $\varphi, \psi \in N^N$ let $\varphi \leqslant \psi$ if $\varphi = \psi$ or if the least n such that $\varphi_n \neq \psi_n$ satisfies the conditions $\varphi_n < \psi_n$. The relation $\leqslant$ linearly orders the set N^N. If $A \subset N^N$, then the relation $\leqslant$ restricted to A linearly orders the set A.

\# 2. The set A consisting of all natural numbers of the form 2^n is linearly ordered by the divisibility relation, that is, by the relation

$$\big\{\langle m, n\rangle\colon\ (m \in A) \wedge (n \in A) \wedge \bigvee_k (m = kn)\big\}.$$

3. The set $N \times N$ is linearly ordered by the relation R which holds between pairs $\langle m, n\rangle$ and $\langle p, q\rangle$ if and only if $(2m+1)/2^n \leqslant (2p+1)/2^q$.

This relation is isomorphic to the relation $\leqslant$ in the set of real numbers of the form $(2m+1)/2^n$.

[1]) The notion of linearly ordered set is due to Cantor. See *Beiträge zur Begründung der transfiniten Mengenlehre,* Mathematische Annalen **46** (1895) 481–512.

4. Let $P(m)$ assert that m is an even number. The set N is linearly ordered by the relation

$$\{\langle m, n\rangle: [P(m) \wedge P(n) \wedge (m \leqslant n)] \vee [P(m) \wedge \neg P(n)] \vee [\neg P(m) \wedge \neg P(n) \wedge (n \leqslant m)]\}.$$

In this ordering every even number precedes every odd number. Of two even numbers, the smaller precedes the larger; of two odd numbers, the larger precedes the smaller.

Schematically this ordering can be illustrated by the sequence:

$$2, 4, 6, 8, 10, \ldots \quad \ldots, 9, 7, 5, 3, 1,$$

where every number preceding a number x is written to the left of x.

5. The set of complex numbers is linearly ordered by the relation

$$\{\langle x, y\rangle: [R(x) < R(y)] \vee [R(x) = R(y)] \wedge [I(x) \leqslant I(y)]\}.$$

In this ordering a number x precedes a number y if the real part $R(x)$ of the complex number x is less than the real part $R(y)$ of y. In case the real parts of x and y are equal, x precedes y if the imaginary part $I(x)$ of x is less than the imaginary part $I(y)$ of y.

6. Let $\alpha(n)$ be the number of distinct prime factors of the natural number n. The set of natural numbers is linearly ordered by the relation:

$$\{\langle x, y\rangle: [\alpha(x) < \alpha(y)] \vee [\alpha(x) = \alpha(y)] \wedge (x \leqslant y)\}.$$

7. The set of concentric circles is linearly ordered by the inclusion relation. #

Definition: An element x is said to be a *first element* of the linearly ordered set A (with respect to the relation R) if xRy for all $y \in A$. On the other hand, if yRx for all y, then x is said to be a *last element* of A (with respect to R). Generally speaking, not every set has a first or last element; but if such element exists, then it is uniquely determined.

Theorem 1: *In a finite non-empty subset X of a linearly ordered set A there is a first element and a last element.*

PROOF. The proof is by induction on the number of elements of X. If X has only one element, then the theorem is obvious. Suppose that the theorem holds for subsets with n elements. Let $X = Y \cup \{a\}$ where $a \notin Y$ and Y has n elements. Let b_1 be the first and b_2 the last element of Y. Since A is linearly ordered, either a precedes b_1 or b_1 precedes a. That element which precedes the other is clearly the first element of Y. Similarly we show that one of the elements a and b_2 is the last element of X.

In the case of linear order relations we usually speak of *similarity* of relations instead of their isomorphism. The following theorem shows that the definition of isomorphism can be simplified in the case of similarity. Namely, instead of proving that two formulas xRy and $f(x)Sf(y)$ are equivalent it suffices to prove only the implication (1) below.

THEOREM 2: *In order that two sets A and B linearly ordered respectively by relations R and S be similar it is necessary and sufficient that there exist a one-to-one function f which maps the set A onto the set B so that*

$$xRy \to f(x)Sf(y) \tag{1}$$

for all $x, y \in A$.

PROOF. Clearly it suffices to show that if $x, y \in A$ and $f(x)Sf(y)$, then xRy. Suppose the contrary: $\neg(xRy)$. Since the relation R is connected in A, we have either $x = y$ or yRx. In the first case xRy as the relation R is reflexive in A, but this contradicts the hypothesis $\neg(xRy)$. In the second case, (1) implies $f(y)Sf(x)$ and therefore $f(x) = f(y)$ because S is antisymmetric. Since f is one-to-one, we infer that $x = y$, which again contradicts $\neg(xRy)$. Hence the theorem is proved.

Similar sets are clearly equipollent. The converse theorem holds for finite sets only.

THEOREM 3: *Two finite linearly ordered equipollent sets are similar.*

PROOF. Suppose that sets A and B, linearly ordered by relations R and S, respectively, have n elements. For $n = 0$ the empty function satisfies the conditions of Theorem 2, consequently it establishes the isomorphism between the relations R and S.

Now suppose that Theorem 3 holds for sets of n elements and let A and B have $n+1$ elements. Let a be the first element of A and b the first element of B. By assumption, there exists a function f_1 which establishes similarity between the sets $A-\{a\}$ and $B-\{b\}$.

Let

$$f = f_1 \cup \{\langle a, b\rangle\}.$$

It is easy to check that f is a function which establishes similarity between A and B. In this way Theorem 3 is proved by induction.

By means of a counterexample it can be shown that Theorem 3 is false for infinite sets. For example, it fails for the set of natural numbers (se p. 207, Examples 4 and 6).

It follows from Theorem 3 that for any linearly ordered set A of n elements we can put $\overline{A} = n$.

Now we shall introduce some terminology. We say that x *precedes* y if

$$xRy \quad \text{and} \quad x \neq y.$$

In this case we write $x \prec_R y$ (or $x \prec y$ if there is no confusion about the relation R). We also write $y \succ_R x$ or $y \succ x$.

We say that y *lies between* x and z if

$$x \prec y \prec z \quad \text{or} \quad x \succ y \succ z.$$

If $x \in A$ and the set $\{y\colon x \prec y\}$ has a first element, then this element is called a *direct successor* of x (with respect to R). The last element of $\{y\colon y \prec x\}$ (if one exists) is called a *direct predecessor* of x. Each element $x \in A$ possesses at most one direct successor and at most one direct predecessor.

A proper subset X of the set A is said to be an *initial segment* (a *final segment*) if $x \in X$ implies that every element preceding x belongs to X (every element after x belongs to X).

The set $X \subset A$ is said to be an *interval* if the condition $x, y \in X$ implies that every element lying between x and y belongs to X.

Let

$$O_R(x) = \{y\colon (yRx) \wedge (y \neq x)\} = \{y\colon y \prec x\}.$$

The subscript R will sometimes be omitted.

It is easily seen that $O_R(x)$ is an initial segment. However, not every initial segment is of the form $O_R(x)$.

We say that an interval X of a linearly ordered set A *precedes* an interval Y of A if

$$(x \in X) \wedge (y \in Y) \rightarrow x \prec y.$$

Every family of disjoint intervals is linearly ordered by the relation "X precedes Y or $X = Y$".

Exercises

1. Let M be a family of subsets of a set Z such that

(i) M is a monotone family,

(ii) M is not included in any monotone family of subsets of Z different from M. Prove that the relation defined by the equivalence

$$xRy \equiv \{(x = y) \vee \bigvee_{E \in M} [(x \notin E) \wedge (y \in E)]\}$$

linearly orders the set Z. The family of final segments of this set is identical with M[1]).

2. Let M be a monotone family of subsets of a set Z. Prove that the family of all sets of the form $\bigcup_{X \in S} X$ and $\bigcap_{X \in S} X$, where $S \subset M$, is monotone.

§ 2. Dense, scattered, and continuous sets

A set A is said to be *densely ordered* by an order relation $\prec$ if for any two elements $x, y \in A$ there exists an element $z \in A$ between x and y. We say then also that A is *dense*. In a densely ordered set no element has either a direct successor or a direct predecessor. This property is characteristic for densely ordered sets. In fact, if no element of the set A has a direct predecessor and $x, y \in A$, $x \prec y$, then x cannot be the last element of the set $\{z: z \prec y\}$, for then x would be a direct predecessor of y. Thus there exists z such that $x \prec z \prec y$. Hence the set A is densely ordered.

All one-element sets, as well as the empty set, are densely ordered. All other densely ordered sets contain infinitely many elements.

A set which is not densely ordered may contain a densely ordered

[1]) See K. Kuratowski, *Sur la notion de l'ordre dans la théorie des ensembles*, Fundamenta Mathematicae **2** (1921) 161–171.

This theorem indicates the possibility of replacing the theory of linearly ordered sets by the theory of monotone families of sets.

subset. For instance, the set consisting of all positive real numbers and negative integers ordered by the relation $\leqslant$, is not densely ordered, because no element of this set lies between -2 and -1. However, this set does contain a densely ordered subset, namely, the set of positive real numbers.

A linearly ordered set which contains no infinite densely ordered subset is said to be *scattered*. For instance, the set of integers and the set composed of all fractions $1/n$ $(n = \pm 1, \pm 2, \ldots)$ are scattered if the order relation is $\leqslant$.

Every subset of a scattered set is scattered.

THEOREM 1: *If A and B are two scattered subsets of a linearly ordered set M, then the union $A \cup B$ is also scattered.*

PROOF. Suppose that there exists an infinite densely ordered subset C of the set $A \cup B$. Since $C = (C \cap A) \cup (C \cap B)$, either $C \cap A$ or $C \cap B$ is infinite. Let $C \cap A$ be infinite. Since this set is not densely ordered (as a subset of the scattered set B), there exists a pair a_1, a_2 of elements of the set $C \cap A$ such that $a_1 \prec a_2$ and such that no element of $C \cap A$ lies between a_1 and a_2. This implies that for every $x \in C$

(1) $$(a_1 \prec x \prec a_2) \rightarrow x \in B.$$

Let $B_1 = C \cap \{x\colon a_1 \prec x \prec a_2\}$. This set is infinite, for there are infinitely many elements of C between a_1 and a_2. If $x_1, x_2 \in B_1$ and $x_1 \prec x_2$, then there exists $x \in C$ lying between x_1 and x_2 thus $x \in B_1$. This implies that the set B_1 is densely ordered. By (1), $B_1 \subset B$, which means that B_1 is an infinite densely ordered subset of B. This contradicts the assumption that B is a scattered set. Hence Theorem 1 is proved.

A set X contained in a linearly ordered set A is said to be *densely ordered* in A if, for every two elements x and y of the set A, there exists an element z of X lying between x and y. For example, the set of rational numbers is densely ordered in the set of real numbers, where the order relation is $\leqslant$.

It is clear that if a set X is densely ordered in A, then the sets A and X are both densely ordered.

Of course, *two sets X and Y densely ordered in A which have neither first nor last elements are always cofinal and coinitial. If a set X is* *cofinal with Y and Y is cofinal with Z, then the sets X and Z are also cofinal.* A similar law of transitivity holds for coinitial sets.

Let $\langle X, Y\rangle$ be a cut in a linearly ordered set A. The intersection $X \cap Y$ contains at most one element. In fact, if $x, y \in X \cap Y$, then $x \preceq y$ and $y \preceq x$; thus $x = y$. If $X \cap Y = 0$, then we say that the cut $\langle X, Y\rangle$ determines a *gap* in the set A. If $X \cap Y = a$, then we say that the element *a lies in the cut* $\langle X, Y\rangle$. It can be easily shown that in this case $X = \{a\}^-$, $Y = \{a\}^+$ and $a = \bigvee_{x \in X} x = \bigwedge_{y \in Y} y$. A cut $\langle X, Y\rangle$ is said to be *proper* if $X \neq 0 \neq Y$.

A set A is said to be *continuously ordered* if no proper cut in A determines a gap in A. We also say that A is *continuous*.

If $\langle X_1, Y_1\rangle$ and $\langle X_2, Y_2\rangle$ are cuts in A, then either $X_1 \subset X_2$ or $X_2 \subset X_1$. In fact, suppose that $a \in X_1 - X_2$ and let $b \in X_2$. By connectedness, it follows that b precedes a, for in the opposite case we would have $a \in X_2$. Thus $b \in X_1$ and we obtain $X_2 \subset X_1$. This implies the following theorem.

THEOREM 2: *The minimal extension* $\mathfrak{P}$ (see p. 160) *of a linearly ordered set is continuously ordered.*

In fact, $\mathfrak{P}$ is a complete lattice and, as has been shown before, the ordering in $\mathfrak{P}$ is connected; thus it is linear. The complete linearly ordered lattice $\mathfrak{P}$ is continuously ordered, because if $\langle \mathfrak{C}_1, \mathfrak{C}_2\rangle$ is a proper cut in $\mathfrak{P}$, then the supremum of the set $\mathfrak{C}_1$ lies in this cut.

COROLLARY 3[1]): *Every linearly ordered set can be extended to a continuously ordered set (preserving suprema and infima).*

To conclude this section, we shall prove a theorem showing that the study of any order type can be reduced to the study of dense and continuous order types. For this purpose we need the notion of the ordered union of linearly ordered sets.

Let T be a set linearly ordered by the relation Q and let F and R be functions defined for $x \in T$ and such that R_x is a relation linearly ordering the set F_x. Suppose that $F_{x_1} \cap F_{x_2} = 0$ for $x_1 \neq x_2$.

THEOREM 4: *Let S be the relation which holds between two elements a and b of the union* $\bigcup_x F_x$ *if and only if either*

a and b belong to the same component F_x *and* $a R_x b$,

[1]) This corollary is due to Dedekind. See the reference on p. 160.

or

a and b belong to different components F_{x_1} *and* F_{x_2} *and* $x_1 Q x_2$.

Then the relation S linearly orders the union $\bigcup_x F_x$.

PROOF. The reflexivity of S is obvious.

If a and b belong to different components of the union $\bigcup F_x$, then either aSb or bSa, because the relation Q orders the set of indices.

On the other hand, if a and b belong to the same component F_x, then either aSb or bSa, because the relation R_x is connected in F_x. Thus the relation S is also connected.

If $a \in F_{x_1}$, $b \in F_{x_2}$, aSb and bSa, then $x_1 Q x_2$ and $x_2 Q x_1$. This implies that $x_1 = x_2$, since the relation Q is antisymmetric.

Finally, suppose that $a \in F_x$, $b \in F_y$, $c \in F_z$, aSb and bSc. These conditions imply xQy and yQz; thus xQz. If $x \neq z$, then aSc. On the other hand, if $x = z$, then we have $x = y = z$, because xQy, yQz and the relation Q is antisymmetric. By the definition of S we obtain $bR_x c$. Since the relation R_x is transitive, we obtain $aR_x c$ and thus aSc. Hence the relation S is also transitive.

Thus the relation S linearly orders the set $\bigcup F_x$.

In the following, by the *ordered union* of linearly ordered disjoint sets F_x we shall always understand the union $\bigcup_x F_x$ ordered by the relation S defined in Theorem 4. In this case the relation Q ordering the set of indices is assumed to be fixed.

We say also that $\bigcup_x F_x$ is the union of sets F_x *over the indexing set* T.

Let A be an arbitrary set, linearly ordered by the relation R. For $x, y \in A$ let $[x, y]$ denote the set of those z which equal either x or y, or which satisfy one of the conditions $x \prec z \prec y$ or $y \prec z \prec x$.

Clearly $[x, y] = [y, x]$. We shall prove that for arbitrary $x, y, z \in A$

$$[x, y] \subset [x, z] \cup [z, y]. \tag{2}$$

In fact, if $t \in [x, y]$ and $t = x$ or $t = y$, then clearly $t \in [x, z] \cup [z, y]$. If $x \prec t \prec y$ and $t = z$ or $t \prec z$, then $t \in [x, z]$. On the other hand, if $z \prec t$, then $t \in [z, y]$. Similarly, if $y \prec t \prec x$, then $t \in [x, z] \cup [z, y]$.

Let V_x be the set of all y such that the set $[x, y]$ is scattered.

Clearly $V_x \neq 0$, because $x \in V_x$.

We shall prove that the set V_x is also scattered.

Suppose that on the contrary $C \subset V_x$ and that the set C is infinite and densely ordered.

For any $c_1, c_2 \in C$ such that $c_1 \prec c_2$ we have by (2)

$$[c_1, c_2] \subset [c_1, x] \cup [c_2, x].$$

Thus the set $[c_1, c_2]$ is contained in the union of two scattered sets. By Theorem 1, p. 211 this union is scattered. But this is impossible, for between any two distinct elements of the set C there always lies at least one other element of C. Thus the assumption that V_x is not scattered leads to a contradiction.

The set V_x is an *interval in the set A*. In fact, suppose that $y, z \in V_x$ and $y \prec t \prec z$. If $x = t$ or $x \prec t$, then $[x, t] \subset [x, z]$. Thus, as a subset of the scattered set $[x, z]$, the set $[x, t]$ is also scattered. On the other hand, if $t \prec x$, then $[t, x] \subset [y, x]$. This means that the set $[t, x]$ is scattered as a subset of the scattered set $[y, x]$. It follows now that $t \in V_x$. Thus the set V_x is an interval.

If $x \neq y$, then either $V_x \cap V_y = 0$ or $V_x = V_y$. In fact, if $z \in V_x \cap V_y$, then the set $[x, y]$, as a subset of the union $[x, z] \cup [y, z]$ is scattered. It follows that if $u \in V_x$, then the set $[u, y]$ is scattered because $[u, y] \subset [u, x] \cup [x, y]$. Similarly, from $u \in V_y$ it follows that $u \in V_x$. Thus $V_x = V_y$.

Let $\mathbf{A}$ be the family of all the sets V_x. This family consists of disjoint non-empty subsets of A and is linearly ordered by the relation ϱ which holds between V_x and V_y if and only if $V_x = V_y$ or V_x precedes V_y (see p. 210).

The set A is the ordered union

$$A = \bigcup_{P \in \mathbf{A}} P,$$

where the family $\mathbf{A}$ is linearly ordered by the relation ϱ and each interval P is linearly ordered by the relation R. In fact the union $\bigcup(\mathbf{A})$ is contained in A and every element x of the set A belongs to V_x; thus every x also belongs to one component of this union.

We now prove that *the relation ϱ is a dense ordering of the family $\mathbf{A}$.* Suppose that $V_x \varrho V_y$ and $V_x \neq V_y$; that is, $V_x \cap V_y = 0$. This implies that the interval $[x, y]$ is not scattered, that is, for some z lying between x and y one of the sets $[x, z]$ and $[z, y]$, say the first, contains an infinite densely ordered set M. If m, n, p are elements of the set M such that $x \prec m \prec n \prec p \prec z$, then the sets $[x, n]$ and $[n, y]$ contain infinite densely ordered subsets. This shows that $V_x \varrho V_n \varrho V_y$ and $V_x \neq V_n \neq V_y$.

It this way we obtain the following theorem.

THEOREM 5[1]: *Every ordered set is the union of scattered sets over a densely ordered indexing set.*

Exercises

1. Give an example of an infinite set which has a first element, has no last element, and in which every element except the first has a direct predecessor. Moreover, this set should not be similar to the set of natural numbers.

2. Show that if the set X is densely ordered and if sets X_1 and X_2 are continuously ordered and contain subsets dense in themselves and similar to X, then the sets X_1 and X_2 are similar.

3. Prove that the set $\mathfrak{G}$ of those relations $R \in 2^{N^2}$ which densely order their fields is a G_δ-set (in the space 2^{N^2}).

4. Show that the union of scattered sets over a scattered indexing set is itself scattered.

5. Prove that if the sets F_x contain neither first nor last elements, and if they are infinite and densely ordered, then the union $\bigcup_{x \in T} F_x$ is densely ordered (for any ordered set T).

6. Prove that if a set T is infinite, densely ordered and $F_x \neq 0$ for each x, then the set $\bigcup_{x \in T} F_x$ contains a densely ordered subset.

7. Prove that if the union $\bigcup_{x \in T} F_x$ is continuous, then the set T has no gaps.

8. Prove that if a set T is continuously ordered and contains first and last elements and if the sets F_x are continuously ordered, then the union $\bigcup_{x \in T} F_x$ is continuously ordered. [Hausdorff]

[1]) Theorem 5 is due to Schönflies; see *Entwickelung der Mengenlehre und ihrer Anwendungen* (Leipzig–Berlin 1913) p. 184.

A detailed analysis of countable scattered order types is given by Erdös and Hajnal in the paper: *On a classification of denumerable order types...*, Fundamenta Mathematicae **51** (1962) 117–129.

§ 3. Order types ω, η and λ

We shall illustrate the notion of order type by means of examples.

Order type ω. The order type ω is the order type of the set N ordered by the relation $\leqslant$.

THEOREM 1: *A linearly ordered set A is of type ω if and only if*

(i) *A has a first element a_0,*

(ii) *every element x of the set A has a direct successor x^*,*

(iii) *if $a_0 \in X \subset A$ and if the set X contains the direct successor of every element of X, then $X = A$.*

PROOF. Conditions (i), (ii), (iii) are invariable under any transformation which preserves order. Since they are satisfied by the set of natural numbers ordered by the relation $\leqslant$, they are necessary conditions for a set A to be of type ω.

Suppose now that the set A linearly ordered by the relation R satisfies conditions (i), (ii), (iii). Let us define a function f which establishes the similarity between A and the set of natural numbers as follows:

(1) $$f(0) = a_0, \quad f(n+1) = [f(n)]^*.$$

These formulas define by induction the function f. It follows from (1) that the range of f contains a_0, and that it contains the direct successor of every of its element. Condition (iii) implies that the range of f coincides with A.

Let us prove that

(2) $$m < n \to f(m) \prec f(n).$$

It follows from (1) that formula (2) holds for $n = m+1$. If we suppose that (2) holds for some n, then (2) also holds for $n+1$. Indeed, if $f(m) \prec f(n)$, then $f(m) \prec [f(n)]^*$, because $f(n) \prec [f(n)]^*$.

It follows directly from (2) that

$$m \neq n \to f(m) \neq f(n), \quad m \leqslant n \to f(m) R f(n).$$

The first of these formulas shows that the function f is one-to-one. Together these formulas show by Theorem 2, p. 208 that the function f establishes a similarity between A and the set of natural numbers ordered by $\leqslant$.

Order type η. Before defining this type, we prove the following important theorem.

THEOREM 2: *Every two non-empty, denumerable, linearly ordered and dense sets which have neither first nor last elements are similar.*

PROOF. Let A and B be sets satisfying the assumptions of the theorem. To simplify notation, we shall use the same symbol to denote the relations ordering both sets.

It follows from the assumptions that the sets A and B are infinite. Thus there exist one-to-one sequences $a \in A^N$ and $b \in B^N$ such that $a^1(N) = A$ and $b^1(N) = B$.

Let us define by induction two permutations φ and ψ of the set N such that the mapping $f\colon a_{\varphi(n)} \to b_{\psi(n)}$ establishes a similarity between the sets A and B. For this purpose, let $\varphi(0) = \psi(0) = 0$. Now we consider two cases depending upon whether n is even or odd.

Case 1: *n even*[1]). Let

$$\varphi(n+1) = \min_k \Big[\bigwedge_{j \leqslant n} (a_k \neq a_{\varphi(j)})\Big],$$

$$\psi(n+1) = \min_k \Big(\bigwedge_{j \leqslant n} \{(b_k \neq b_{\psi(j)}) \wedge [(b_{\psi(j)} \prec b_k) \equiv (a_{\varphi(j)} \prec a_{\varphi(n+1)})]\}\Big).$$

Case 2: *n odd*. The definition is similar, but the roles of φ and ψ are interchanged.

$$\psi(n+1) = \min_k \Big[\bigwedge_{j \leqslant n} (b_k \neq b_{\psi(j)})\Big].$$

$$\varphi(n+1) = \min_k \Big(\bigwedge_{j \leqslant n} \{(a_k \neq a_{\varphi(j)}) \wedge [(a_{\varphi(j)} \prec a_k) \equiv (b_{\psi(j)} \prec b_{\psi(n+1)})]\}\Big).$$

We shall prove by induction that if $n \in N$ and $j < n$, then

(3) $$\varphi(n) \neq \varphi(j),$$

(4) $$\psi(n) \neq \psi(j),$$

(5) $$a_{\varphi(n)} \prec a_{\varphi(j)} \equiv b_{\psi(n)} \prec b_{\psi(j)}, \qquad a_{\varphi(n)} \succ a_{\varphi(j)} \equiv b_{\psi(n)} \succ b_{\psi(j)}.$$

It is clear that these formulas hold for $n = 0$. Suppose that $n_0 > 0$ and that (3)–(5) hold for $n < n_0$. Let $n_0 = n' + 1$. The proof now splits

[1]) If there exists no n such that $\Phi(n)$, then the symbol $\min_k \Phi(k)$ shall denote the number 0.

into two cases according as n' is even or n' is odd. We shall consider only the first case.

Since the set A is infinite, there exist numbers k such that $a_k \neq a_{\varphi(j)}$ for $j \leqslant n'$. By definition, $\varphi(n'+1)$ is one of these numbers k. This proves (3), for $n = n'+1 = n_0$.

To prove the remaining formulas, let

$$P = \{j \leqslant n' \colon a_{\varphi(j)} \prec a_{\varphi(n_0)}\}, \quad Q = \{j \leqslant n' \colon a_{\varphi(n_0)} \prec a_{\varphi(j)}\}.$$

Thus

$$(p \in P) \wedge (q \in Q) \rightarrow (a_{\varphi(p)} \prec a_{\varphi(q)}),$$

and since (5) holds by assumption for $n \leqslant n'$, we obtain

$$(p \in P) \wedge (q \in Q) \rightarrow (b_{\psi(p)} \prec b_{\psi(q)}).$$

Since the set B is densely ordered, the formula above shows that there exist numbers k such that $b_{\psi(p)} \prec b_k$ for every p in P and $b_k \prec b_{\psi(q)}$ for every q in Q. It follows from the definition of ψ that $\psi(n_0)$ is one of these numbers k. Thus $b_{\psi(n_0)} \neq b_{\psi(j)}$ for $j \in P \cup Q$. Moreover,

$$b_{\psi(n_0)} \prec b_{\psi(j)} \equiv (j \in Q) \equiv a_{\varphi(n_0)} \prec a_{\varphi(j)}$$

and similarly for $\succ (j \in P \cup Q)$. In this way formulas (4) and (5) are proved.

Formulas (3)–(5) show that the function $f\colon a_{\varphi(n)} \rightarrow b_{\psi(n)}$ establishes similarity between the sets $\{a_{\varphi(n)}\colon n \in N\}$ and $\{b_{\psi(n)}\colon n \in N\}$. It remains to be shown that these sets are identical with A and B respectively. In other words, we have to show that every natural number occurs in the sequences φ and ψ. We consider only the sequence φ.

Suppose on the contrary that $N - \varphi^1(N) \neq 0$ and let k_0 be the least number in this set. Clearly $k_0 > 0$. For $h < k_0$ let n_h denote the unique number such that $\varphi(n_h) = h$ and let n be an even number greater than all numbers n_h, $h < k_0$. Since $a_{k_0} \neq a_{\varphi(j)}$ for all $j \leqslant n$, and for every $h < k_0$ there exists $j \leqslant n$ such that $a_n = a_{\varphi(j)}$, namely $j = n_h$, we obtain

$$k_0 = \min_k \bigwedge_{j \leqslant n} (a_k \neq a_{\varphi(j)}).$$

This implies $k_0 = \varphi(n+1)$, which contradicts $k_0 \notin \varphi^1(N)$.

Theorem 2 is proved.

Theorem 2 shows that there exists only one type of sets which are simultaneously $\neq 0$, densely ordered, countable and without first and last elements. This type is denoted by η.

An example of an ordered set of type η is the set of rational numbers ordered by the relation $\leqslant$. # Another example is given on p. 206 (Example 3).

Sets of type η have the following property of universality:

THEOREM 3: *If* $\overline{B} = \eta$ *and* A *is any denumerable linearly ordered set, then there exists a set* $C \subset B$ *such that* A *and* C *are similar.*

PROOF. We may assume that the set A is infinite. Using the notions introduced in the proof of Theorem 2 we define the sequences φ and ψ as in Case 1. However, this time we do not confine n to even numbers only, but we let n be any natural number. Then formulas (3)–(5) are satisfied. We can prove in the same way as in Theorem 2 that $\varphi^1(N) = N$ and that the sets $\{a_{\varphi(n)}: n \in N\}$ and $\{b_{\psi(n)}: n \in N\}$ are similar. The first of these sets is equal to A and the second is contained in B. This proves the theorem [1]).

The order type λ. We precede the definition by a theorem.

THEOREM 4: *Let* A *and* B *be sets satisfying the following conditions:*

(i) *A and B are linearly and continuously ordered.*

(ii) *There exists subsets* $A_1 \subset A$ *and* $B_1 \subset B$ *dense in* A *and* B *respectively which are both coinitial and cofinal with* A *and* B *respectively.*

(iii) *The sets* A_1 *and* B_1 *are of type* η.

Then A *and* B *are similar.*

We shall only outline the proof of this theorem. By Theorem 2 there exists a function f_1 which maps A_1 onto B_1 and preserves order. It can easily be shown that the sets $X(a) = A_1 \cap \{a\}^-$ and $Y(a) = A_1 \cap \{a\}^+$

[1]) Theorems 2 and 3 are due to Cantor. In recent papers those theorems have been generalized for other relations. See: R. Fraïssé, *Sur l'extension aux relations de quelques propriétés des ordres,* Annales scientifiques de l'Ecole Normale Supérieure **71** (1954) 361–388; B. Jónsson, *Universal relational systems,* Mathematica Scandinavica **4**(1956) 194–208; B. Jónsson, *Homogeneous universal relational systems,* ibid. **8** (1960) 137–142; M. Morley and R. Vaught, *Homogeneous universal models,* ibid. **11** (1962) 37–57.

determine a proper cut in the set A_1. Hence the pair $\langle P, Q\rangle = \left\langle f_1^1(X(a)), f_1^1(Y(a))\right\rangle$ is a proper cut in the set B_1.

Let

$$\tilde{X}(a) = \{b \in B: \bigwedge_{y \in P} (b \leqslant y)\},$$

$$\tilde{Y}(a) = \{b \in B: \bigwedge_{x \in Q} (x \leqslant b)\}.$$

It can easily be shown that the pair $\langle \tilde{X}(a), \tilde{Y}(a)\rangle$ is a proper cut in the set B. Since B is continuous, there exists an element $f(a)$ lying in this cut: it is the last element of the set $\tilde{X}(a)$ and simultaneously the first element of the set $\tilde{Y}(a)$.

The mapping f satisfies the condition $a' \leqslant a'' \to f(a') \leqslant f(a'')$. In fact if $a' \leqslant a''$, then $X(a') \subset X(a'')$. Thus $f_1^1(X(a')) \subset f_1^1(X(a''))$, which proves that $\tilde{Y}(a') \supset \tilde{Y}(a'')$. Hence $f(a') \leqslant f(a'')$.

It remains to be shown that the function f is one-to-one and that it maps the set A onto the set B. For this purpose, we repeat the previous construction interchanging the roles of the sets A and B and obtain a function g mapping B into A. One can show that $f(g(b)) = b$ for every $b \in B$, which proves the theorem.

Theorem 4 enables us to admit the following definition.

A linearly ordered set A is of *type* λ if it is continuous and if it contains a subset A_1 of type η which is dense in A and which is coinitial and cofinal with A.

An example of a set of type λ is the set $\mathcal{E}$ of real numbers ordered by $\leqslant$.

REMARKS: 1. In connection with Theorem 4 we mention the *Suslin problem*. Namely, let A be a continuously ordered set without first and last elements such that every set of disjoint intervals contained in A is denumerable. Is the set A necessarily of type λ (equivalently, does A contain a dense, denumerable subset)[1])? This problem has not yet been solved.

2. Sets of types ω, η, λ are of power $\leqslant \mathfrak{c}$.

[1]) See Fundamenta Mathematicae **1**(1920) 223. S. Tennenbaum proved recently that the Suslin hypothesis is not provable within the framework of axiomatic set theory.

It has recently been shown that it is not possible to prove in Σ the existence of ordering relations for a set of power $2^{\mathfrak{c}}$.

Exercises

1. Show that every dense and infinite set contains a subset of type η.

2. Show that every infinite continuous set is of power $\geqslant \mathfrak{c}$.

3. Let $r_0, r_1, \ldots$ be an infinite sequence without repetitions consisting of all rational numbers. For $c = \sum_{j=0}^{\infty} c_j/3^j$ where $c_j = 0$ or $c_j = 2$, let $M_c = \{r_j\colon c_j = 2\}$ and let $\bar{c}$ denote the type of the set M_c ordered by the relation $\leqslant$. Prove that every denumerable order type can be represented in the form $\bar{c}$ [1]).

4. Let $C_\tau = \{c\colon \bar{c} = \tau\}$. Show that the Cantor set C is the union $\bigcup_{\tau} C_\tau$ where the union is over all denumerable order types and where the components of this union are pairwise disjoint.

5. Show that the set C_η is a G_δ-set in the space C.

6. Prove that every linearly ordered set containing a dense denumerable subset is similar to a set of real numbers (ordered by $\leqslant$).

7. Let M be a monotone family of open subsets of the real line (or generally fo the space $\mathcal{E}^n$). Prove that this family is similar to a set of real numbers (ordered by $\leqslant$).

Hint: Let $P_1, P_2, \ldots$ be a sequence of all intervals with rational endpoints. Assume that each interval occurs in this sequence infinitely many times. For a given set $G \in M$, let $k_1, k_2, \ldots$ be a sequence of all natural numbers such that $P_{k_n} \subset G$.

The function

$$t(G) = \sum_{n=1}^{\infty} \frac{1}{2^{k_n}}, \qquad t(0) = 0$$

establishes the required similarity.

§ 4. Arithmetic of order types

We can define operations on order types which are similar to certain operations in ordinary arithmetic just as we did in the case of cardinal numbers. This arithmetic of order types allows us to simplify arguments concerning linearly ordered sets.

[1]) See K. Kuratowski, Topology I, p. 36.

Inverse types. It is easy to show that *if a relation R linearly orders the set A, then so does the inverse relation* R^c (see p. 65). Of course, *the isomorphism of R and S implies the isomorphism of the inverse relations* R^c *and* S^c.

The order type of the set A ordered by R^c is said to be the *inverse* of the order type of the set A ordered by R. If the order type of A ordered by R is α, then the order type of A ordered by R^c is denoted by α^*.

It follows from the equivalence $x(R^c)^c y \equiv xRy$ that

$$(1) \qquad \alpha^{**} = \alpha.$$

Examples

1. If n is a finite order type then $n^* = n$, because every two finite equipollent sets are similar.

2. Likewise $\eta^* = \eta$ and $\lambda^* = \lambda$. On the other hand, $\omega^* \neq \omega$ because a set of type ω^* (for example, the set of negative integers) possesses a last element whereas a set of type ω has no last element.

The sum of order types. Let α and β be two order types and let A and B be two sets linearly ordered by R and S such that $\overline{A} = \alpha$, $\overline{B} = \beta$. We assume that $A \cap B = 0$. This assumption can always be satisfied, for if A and B are not disjoint, then we can replace them by the sets $A \times \{1\}$ and $B \times \{2\}$ which are similar to A and B and disjoint.

The *sum* $\alpha+\beta$ is defined by

$$\alpha+\beta = \overline{A \cup B}$$

where the set $A \cup B$ is ordered as follows: all elements of A precede all elements of B and the order in each of the sets A and B is preserved.

In particular, if α and β are finite order types, the definition of the sum $\alpha+\beta$ coincides with the definition of the sum of natural numbers.

It is easy to see that the sum $\alpha+\beta$ does not depend on the sets A and B but only upon their order types. Moreover, the following formulas clearly hold:

$$(\alpha+\beta)+\gamma = \alpha+(\beta+\gamma), \qquad \alpha+0 = \alpha = 0+\alpha.$$

On the other hand, the commutative law does not hold: for example, $\omega+1 \neq 1+\omega$. In fact, $1+\omega = \omega$ (thus $1+\omega$ is equal to the type of the set of natural numbers), whereas $\omega+1$ is the type of a set with a last element.

Product of order types. Let $\alpha = \overline{A}$, $\beta = \overline{B}$. The *product* $\alpha\cdot\beta$ of the order types α and β is defined by the formula

$$\alpha\cdot\beta = \overline{A\times B},$$

where the set $A\times B$ is ordered as follows. Let $\langle x, y\rangle$ and $\langle x_1, y_1\rangle$ be two elements of $A\times B$. Then $\langle x, y\rangle \prec \langle x_1, y_1\rangle$ if $y \prec y_1$. If $y = y_1$, then $\langle x, y\rangle \prec \langle x_1, y_1\rangle$ if $x \prec x_1$.

For example $\lambda\cdot\lambda$ or λ^2 is the order type of the set of points in the plane ordered as above.

It is easy to check that, just as for the sum, the product $\alpha\cdot\beta$ depends only upon α and β.

For finite order types, the definition given above coincides with that of multiplication of natural numbers. Moreover, we have for arbitrary order types α, β, γ the formulas:

$$(\alpha\beta)\gamma = \alpha(\beta\gamma), \qquad \alpha 1 = 1\alpha = \alpha, \qquad \alpha 0 = 0\alpha = 0.$$

Similarly as for addition, multiplication is not commutative. For example, $\omega 2 \neq 2\omega$. In fact

$$2\omega = \overline{\{1,2\}\times N} = \omega, \qquad \omega 2 = \overline{N\times\{1,2\}} = \omega+\omega.$$

The distributive law is satisfied only in the form:

$$\alpha(\beta+\gamma) = \alpha\beta+\alpha\gamma.$$

In fact, let

$$\alpha = \overline{A}, \qquad \beta = \overline{B}, \qquad \gamma = \overline{C}, \qquad B\cap C = 0.$$

Then we have (see p. 63)

$$\alpha(\beta+\gamma) = \overline{A\times(B\cup C)} = \overline{A\times B\cup A\times C}$$
$$= \overline{A\times B}\cup\overline{A\times C} = \alpha\beta+\alpha\gamma,$$

because

$$(A\times B)\cap(A\times C) = 0.$$

Exponentiation of order types in the case of a finite exponent can be defined by induction:

$$\alpha^0 = 1, \qquad \alpha^{n+1} = \alpha^n\cdot\alpha.$$

Exercises

1. Prove that $\eta+\eta = \eta$, $\lambda+1+\lambda = \lambda$, $\lambda+\lambda \neq \lambda$.

2. Using operations on the order type ω, give an example of an infinite linearly ordered set which possesses first and last elements such that every element except the first has a direct predecessor and every element except the last has a direct successor.

3. Prove that $(\alpha+\beta)^* = \beta^*+\alpha^*$.

4. Prove that $\eta^2 = \eta$.

5. Prove that $(\omega\eta)^2 = (\omega\eta+\omega)^2$, but $\omega\eta \neq \omega\eta+\omega$. [A. Davis–W. Sierpiński]

6. Prove that ω^2 is the type of the set of natural numbers ordered by the following relation: m precedes n if either m has fewer prime factors than n, or m has the same number of prime factors as n and $m \leqslant n$.

7. Prove that a set A of type λ^2 does not contain a subset which is denumerable and dense in A.

§ 5. Lexicographical ordering

The product of order types is related to lexicographical ordering. In order to define this ordering let us assume that T is a set linearly ordered by the relation Q and let each $x \in T$ be associated with a set F_x ordered by the relation R_x. We do not assume that the sets F_x are disjoint. Let

$$P = \prod_{x \in T} F_x.$$

Thus P is the set of functions f whose domain is T such that $f(x) \in F_x$ for all $x \in T$.

Two arbitrary functions f and g belonging to P determine the set

$$D(f, g) = \{x \in T: f(x) \neq g(x)\}.$$

Clearly $D(f, g) = 0$ if and only if $f = g$.

We now define a relation S in P in the following way: $f S g$ holds if and only if either $f = g$ or the set $D(f, g)$ possesses a first element x_0 and $f(x_0) R_{x_0} g(x_0)$.

This definition can be written in symbols as follows

$$f S g \equiv (f = g) \vee \bigvee_x \{(f(x) \prec_{R_x} g(x)) \wedge \bigwedge_y [(y \prec_Q x) \rightarrow (f(y) = g(y))]\}.$$

If the relation S linearly orders the cartesian product P, then this product is said to be *lexicographically ordered* (or *ordered according to the principle of first differences*).

We shall investigate the conditions under which the relation S linearly orders P.

THEOREM 1: *The relation S is reflexive, antisymmetric and transitive in P.*

PROOF. The reflexivity of S is obvious.

Suppose that both fSg and gSf. If the functions f and g are distinct, then the set $D(f,g)$ has a first element x and this element satisfies the conditions $f(x)R_x g(x)$ and $g(x)R_x f(x)$. Since, by assumption, the relation R_x orders F_x, we have $f(x) = g(x)$, which is incompatible with $x \in D(f, g)$. Thus fSg and gSf imply $f = g$. This shows that the relation S is antisymmetric.

Suppose that fSg and gSh. If $f = g$ or $g = h$ then clearly fSh. Thus we may assume that $f \neq g$ and $g \neq h$. Hence the sets $D(f,g)$ and $D(g,h)$ have first elements x and y respectively and these elements satisfy the conditions:

$$f(x) \prec_{R_x} g(x), \qquad g(y) \prec_{R_y} h(y).$$

If z precedes x and y, then $f(z) = g(z) = h(z)$. On the other hand, if z_0 is that of the elements x and y which precedes the other, then we have either $f(z_0) \prec_{R_{z_0}} g(z_0)$ and $g(z_0) = h(z_0)$ (if $x \prec_Q y$), or $f(z_0) = g(z_0)$ and $g(z_0) \prec_{R_{z_0}} h(z_0)$ (if $y \prec_Q x$), or finally $f(z_0) \prec_{R_{z_0}} h(z_0)$ and $g(z_0) \prec_{R_{z_0}} h(z_0)$ (if $x = y$). In any case $f(z_0) \prec_{R_{z_0}} h(z_0)$, which shows that z_0 is the first element of $D(f, h)$. Hence fSh and it follows that S is transitive.

REMARK: The following example shows that the relation S need not be connected.

Let T be a set of type ω^* (for instance, the set of negative integers), $F_x = \{0,1\}$ and let R_x be the relation $\leqslant$. Let f be the function whose value is 0 for even numbers and 1 for odd numbers and let $g(x) = 1 - f(x)$. Then the set $D(f,g)$ is equal to T and therefore it has no first element. Thus neither fSg and gSf.

THEOREM 2: *If $\overline{T} = n$ or $\overline{T} = \omega$, then the relation S linearly orders the set P* [1]*.*

[1]) In general, Theorem 2 holds when T is an arbitrary well ordered set. See Chapter VII.

For the proof, it suffices to show that S is connected in P. For this purpose assume that $f, g \in P$ and $f \neq g$. The set $D(f,g)$ is non-empty and therefore it has a first element x. Since R_x is connected in F_x, we infer that $f(x) R_x g(x)$ or $g(x) R_x f(x)$. This implies that fSg or gSf.

THEOREM 3: *If the sets $A_1, \ldots, A_n$ are of types $\alpha_1, \ldots, \alpha_n$, then the set $A_1 \times A_2 \times \ldots \times A_n$ lexicographically ordered is of type $\alpha_n \alpha_{n-1} \ldots \alpha_1$.*

PROOF. The proof is by induction on n. For $n = 1$ the theorem is obvious. Suppose that it holds for n and consider the product $P = A_1 \times \times A_2 \times \ldots \times A_{n+1}$ of $(n+1)$ sets, with lexicographical ordering. Let $B = A_2 \times A_3 \times \ldots \times A_{n+1}$. Ordering the set $A_1 \times B$ lexicographically we obtain a set similar to P. Hence it suffices to show that $A_1 \times B$ is of type $\alpha_{n+1} \cdot \alpha_n \cdot \ldots \cdot \alpha_2 \cdot \alpha_1$. But this follows directly from the definition of the product of types.

The definition of anti-lexicographical ordering (ordering by the principle of last differences) is similar to that of lexicographical ordering. The notion of anti-lexicographical ordering rather than that of the lexicographical ordering lies at the basis of the notion of the product of types.

\# *Examples*

1. The product $\lambda\lambda$ is the type of the set of complex numbers ordered lexicographically (where the complex number $x+iy$ is identified with the ordered pair $\langle x, y \rangle$).

2. The product $\eta\lambda$ is the type of the set of complex numbers of the form $r+iy$, where r is a rational number and y is a real number, ordered anti-lexicographically. On the other hand, the product $\lambda\eta$ is the type of the same set ordered lexicographically. These types are distinct, for a set of type $\lambda\eta$ contains continuous intervals whereas a set of type $\eta\lambda$ does not.

3. Let T be the set of natural numbers with the usual ordering, let $F_x = \{0, 1\}$ for $x \in T$, and let R_x be the relation $\leqslant$. The lexicographical ordering S is isomorphic in this case to the relation $\leqslant$ in the Cantor set C (understood as the set of real numbers of the form $\sum_{n=1}^{\infty} c_n/3^n$ where $c_n = 0$ or $c_n = 2$ for $n \in N$). In fact, associating with each function

$f \in \prod_x F_x$ the number $c_f = \sum_{n=0}^{\infty} 2f(n)/3^{n+1}$ we see that $c_f < c_g$ if and only if $f \neq g$ and, moreover, the smallest number n_0 such that $f(n_0) \neq g(n_0)$ satisfies the inequality $f(n_0) < g(n_0)$.

4. Again let $T = N$ (where the order relation is $\leqslant$) and let $F_n = N$ for $n \in N$. With each function $f \in N^N$ we associate the real number

$$r_f = \sum_{n=0}^{\infty} 2^{-(f(0)+f(1)+\ldots+f(n)+n+1)}.$$

Clearly $0 < r_f \leqslant 1$ and each real number x, $0 < x \leqslant 1$, can be represented in this form in exactly one way. In fact, if $x = \sum_{n=0}^{\infty} 2^{-\varphi(n)}$ is the binary representation of x with infinitely many digits different from 0, then the sequence φ is strictly increasing and $\varphi(0) > 0$. Assuming $f(0) = \varphi(0) - 1$ and $f(n) = \varphi(n) - \varphi(n-1) - 1$ for $n > 0$, we obtain $x = r_f$.

In order that $r_f < r_g$ it is necessary and sufficient that $f \neq g$ and that the smallest number n_0 such that $f(n_0) \neq g(n_0)$ satisfies the inequality $f(n_0) < g(n_0)$.

In this case the relation S of lexicographical ordering is similar to the relation $\leqslant$ in the set of numbers x, $0 < x \leqslant 1$. Hence the type of this relation is $\lambda + 1$. #

CHAPTER VII

WELL-ORDERED SETS

§ 1. Definitions. Principle of transfinite induction

We say that a relations R *well orders* a set X if R linearly orders X and every non-empty subset of X contains a first element (with respect to the relation R)[1].

Examples

1. Every set of type ω is well ordered.

2. The set consisting of the number 1 and of all numbers of the form $1-1/n$, $n = 1, 2, \ldots$ is well ordered by the relation $\leqslant$. The type of this set is $\omega+1$.

3. Let $\alpha(n)$ be the number of distinct prime factors of the number n. The relation

$$\{\langle xy\rangle : [\alpha(x) < \alpha(y)] \vee ([\alpha(x) = \alpha(y)] \wedge [x \leqslant y])\}$$

well orders the set of natural numbers. The type of this set is ω^2 (see Exercise 6, p. 224). #

4. The ordered union (see p. 213) $S = \bigcup_{x \in T} F_x$, where the set T and the component sets F_x are well ordered, is also well ordered.

For, let Y be a non-empty subset of S. The set of all x such that $Y \cap F_x \neq 0$ is a non empty subset of T, therefore it contains a first element x_0. Thus the intersection $Y \cap F_{x_0}$ is a non-empty subset of the

[1]) The notion of well-ordered set is due to Cantor, who introduced it first in his paper *Über unendliche lineare Punktmannigfaltigkeiten,* No. 5, Mathematische Annalen **21** (1883), § 3. It is interesting that the notion of linearly ordered set was introduced by Cantor later (in a paper published in 1895), evidently in the course of systematizing his results in the theory of well-ordered sets.

well-ordered set F_{x_0} and therefore it has a first element. This element is clearly the first element of Y.

5. The cartesian product of any finite number of well-ordered sets is itself well ordered by the relation of lexicographical ordering.

6. Every subset of a well-ordered set is also well ordered.

The following two theorems are simple consequences of the definition.

THEOREM 1: *In every well-ordered set there exists a first element. Every element except the last element (if such exists) has a direct successor.*

THEOREM 2′: *No subset of a well-ordered set is of type* ω^*.

°THEOREM 2″: *If a linearly ordered set A is not well ordered, then it contains a subset of type* ω^*.

PROOF. Let P be a non-empty subset of A which contains no first element. Let

$$Q(x) = \{y\colon (y \prec x) \wedge (y \in P)\}.$$

We have $Q(x) \neq 0$ for every $x \in P$. By Theorem 8, p.73 there exists a function f defined for every $x \in P$ such that $f(x) \in Q(x)$.

Let p_0 be any element of P. We define by induction a sequence p_1, $p_2, \ldots, p_n, \ldots$ letting $p_n = f(p_{n-1})$ for $n > 0$.

Since $f(x) \prec x$, this sequence is of type ω^*.

Theorems 2′ and 2″ imply the following.

°THEOREM 2: ***In order that a linearly ordered set be well ordered it is necessary and sufficient that it contain no subset of type*** ω^*.

THEOREM 3: ***Each initial segment of a well-ordered set A is of the form $O(x)$ for some $x \in A$.***

In fact, if x is the first element of the difference $A - X$, then $O(x) = X$ (see p. 209).

THEOREM 4: (PRINCIPLE OF TRANSFINITE INDUCTION[1]).) *If a set A is well ordered, $B \subset A$ and if for every $x \in A$ the set B satisfies the condi-*

[1]) This form of the theorem on transfinite induction was implicitly used already by Cantor; see: *Beiträge zur Begründung der transfiniten Mengenlehre,* Mathematische Annalen **49** (1897) 336–339. A clear formulation of this theorem is due to Hessenberg; see: *Grundbegriffe der Mengenlehre* (Göttingen 1906), p. 53.

tion

$$[O(x) \subset B] \rightarrow (x \in B), \tag{1}$$

then $B = A$.

PROOF. Suppose that $A - B \neq 0$. Then there exists a first element in $A - B$. This means that if $y \prec x$ then $y \notin A - B$, that is, $y \in B$. This shows that $O(x) \subset B$. Now it follows from (1) that $x \in B$, which contradicts the hypothesis that $x \notin B$.

Theorem 4 can be reformulated as follows. Let a subset B of a well-ordered set A be called *hereditary* if it satisfies condition (1). Then Theorem 4 asserts that the only hereditary subset of A is the set A itself.

For many propositional functions Φ it can be proved that the set $\{x \in A: \Phi(x)\}$ is hereditary; consequently, for such propositional functions the theorem $\bigwedge_{x \in A} \Phi(x)$ holds. This method of proving theorems of the form $\bigwedge_{x \in A} \Phi(x)$ is called the *method of transfinite induction*. Of course, this method and the method of proof by induction in ordinary arithmetics (which consists in showing that the set $\{n \in N: \Phi(n)\}$ is inductive) are analogous.

We shall use transfinite induction to prove several theorems about similarity of well-ordered sets.

Let A be a set linearly ordered by the relation R. A function f which establishes similarity between A and the set $f^1(A)$ contained in A, is said to be an *increasing function*. Such functions satisfy the condition

$$x \prec y \rightarrow f(x) \prec f(y). \tag{2}$$

THEOREM 5: *If a function f defined on a well-ordered set A is increasing, then for every x we have $x R f(x)$ (that is $x \prec f(x)$ or $x = f(x)$).*

PROOF. Let $B = \{x: x R f(x)\}$. Let $O(x) \subset B$. We show that $x \in B$. In fact, let $y \in O(x)$, that is $y \prec x$. By (2) it follows that $f(y) \prec f(x)$. Since $y \in B$, we have $y R f(y)$ and thus $y \prec f(x)$. This shows that the element $f(x)$ occurs after every element y of $O(x)$, that is, $f(x) \in A - O(x)$.

Since x is the first element of $A - O(x)$, we have $x R f(x)$ and finally $x \in B$.

Hence the set B is hereditary. Q.E.D.

COROLLARY 6: *If the well-ordered sets A and B are similar, then there exists only one function which establishes their similarity.*

PROOF. Suppose that the sets A and B are well ordered by R and S and that there exist two functions f and g establishing similarity between A and B.

The function $g^c \circ f$ is clearly increasing in A (see p. 208). By Theorem 5 we thus have $x R g^c(f(x))$ for every $x \in A$. Hence $g(x) \, S \, f(x)$. Considering $f^c \circ g$ instead of $g^c \circ f$ we have by the same argument $f(x) \, S \, g(x)$. This implies $f(x) = g(x)$, because S is antisymmetric.

COROLLARY 7: *No well-ordered set is similar to any of its initial segments.*

In fact, if the sets A and $O(x)$ were similar, then the function f establishing similarity would be increasing and would satisfy $f(x) \in O(x)$, that is $f(x) \prec x$. But this contradicts Theorem 5.

COROLLARY 8: *No two distinct initial segments of a well-ordered set are similar.*

For the proof, it suffices to apply Corollary 7 and to observe that, given two distinct initial segments one is always an initial segment of the other.

THEOREM 9[1]): *Let A and B be two well-ordered sets. Then either*

(i) *A and B are similar, or*

(ii) *the set A is similar to a segment of B, or*

(iii) *the set B is similar to a segment of A.*

PROOF. Let R and S be relations which well order A and B respectively and let

$$Z = \{x \in A: \bigvee_{y \in B} \overline{O_R(x)} = \overline{O_S(y)}\}.$$

In other words (see notation on p. 209):

$x \in Z \equiv \{$the initial segment $O_R(x)$ of A is similar to some initial segment $O_S(y)$ of $B\}$.

[1]) This theorem is due to Cantor; see Mathematische Annalen **49** (1897) 216.

By virtue of Corollary 8, for given $x \in Z$ there exists only one such segment. Thus there exists a function f defined on Z such that this segment is of the form $O_S(f(x))$.

First we show that either $Z = A$ or Z is a segment of A, that is, there exists an a in A such that $Z = O_R(a)$. In fact, let $x \prec x' \in Z$. Since $O_R(x)$ is a segment of $O_R(x')$, the function establishing similarity between $O_R(x')$ and $O_S(f(x'))$ also maps $O_R(x)$ into a segment of B. Hence $x \in Z$.

Similarly: either $f^1(Z) = B$ or else $f^1(Z)$ is a segment of B: $f^1(Z) = O_S(b)$. To show this it suffices to observe that

$$f^1(Z) = \{y \in B: \bigvee_{x \in Z} [y = f(x)]\} = \{y \in B: \bigvee_{y \in B} \overline{\overline{O_S(y)}} = \overline{\overline{O_R(x)}}\}.$$

In fact, if $O_S(y)$ is similar to a segment of A then y is of the form $f(x)$ where $x \in Z$.

Finally, observe that f establishes the similarity between Z and $f^1(Z)$. Indeed, we have just shown that $x \prec x' \in Z$ implies that $O_S(f(x))$ is a segment of $O_S(f(x'))$, therefore $f(x) \prec f(x')$.

A priori we have one of the following four possibilities:

(i) $Z = A$ and $f^1(Z) = B$,
(ii) $Z = A$ and $f^1(Z) = O_S(b)$,
(iii) $Z = O_R(a)$ and $f^1(Z) = B$,
(iv) $Z = O_R(a)$ and $f^1(Z) = O_S(b)$.

The first three possibilities correspond to those stated in the theorem. Case (iv) is impossible, because then $\overline{\overline{O_R(a)}} = \overline{\overline{O_S(b)}}$ and thus, by the definition of Z, $a \in Z$; that is, $a \in O_R(a)$, which contradicts the definition of a segment. Q.E.D.

COROLLARY 10: *If A and B are well ordered, then either $\overline{\overline{A}} \leqslant \overline{\overline{B}}$ or $\overline{\overline{B}} \leqslant \overline{\overline{A}}$. That is, powers of well-ordered sets obey the law of trichotomy.*

§ 2. Ordinal numbers

By *ordinal numbers* (or *ordinals*) we shall understand the order types of well-ordered sets [1]). Theorem 9, § 1 allows us to define a "less than"

[1]) The notion of ordinal number was introduced by Cantor. See Mathematische Annalen **21** (1883) 548. Notice that according to our definition the number 0 (the type of the empty set) is an ordinal.

relation for ordinals. This relation cannot be defined in a satisfactory way for arbitrary order types.

DEFINITION 1: We say that an ordinal α is *less* than an ordinal β if any set of type α is similar to a segment of a set of type β. We denote this relation by $\alpha < \beta$ or $\beta > \alpha$.

We write "$\alpha \leqslant \beta$" instead of "$\alpha < \beta$ or $\alpha = \beta$".

THEOREM 1: *For any ordinals α and β one and only one of the formulas $\alpha < \beta$, $\alpha = \beta$, $\alpha > \beta$ holds.*

This theorem is a direct consequence of Theorem 9, § 1.

THEOREM 2: *If α, β and γ are ordinals and if $\alpha < \beta$ and $\beta < \gamma$, then $\alpha < \gamma$.*

PROOF. Let A, B and C be sets of types α, β and γ, respectively. By assumption, the set A is similar to a segment of the set B and B is similar to a segment of C. Thus A is similar to a segment of C. Q.E.D.

The following formulas can be proved without difficulty:

$$(a \leqslant \beta) \wedge (\beta \leqslant \alpha) \rightarrow (\alpha = \beta), \qquad (\alpha \leqslant \beta) \wedge (\beta \leqslant \gamma) \rightarrow (\alpha \leqslant \gamma).$$

THEOREM 3: *If the well-ordered sets A and B are of types α and β and if the set A is similar to a subset B_1 of the set B, then $\alpha \leqslant \beta$.*

PROOF. If this were not so, then we would have $\beta < \alpha$ and then B would be similar to a segment of B_1. This contradicts Theorem 5, p. 230.

We now examine sets of ordinal numbers.

THEOREM 4: *The set $W(\alpha)$ consisting of all ordinals less than α is well ordered by relation $\leqslant$. Moreover, the type of $W(\alpha)$ is α.*

PROOF. Let A be a well-ordered set of type α. Associating the type of the segment $O(a)$ with the element $a \in A$ we infer (by the axiom of replacement) that the set $W(\alpha)$ exists and simultaneously we obtain a one-to-one mapping of A onto $W(\alpha)$. It is easily seen that following conditions are equivalent:

(i) a_1 precedes a_2 or $a_1 = a_2$,
(ii) $O(a_1)$ is a segment of $O(a_2)$ or $O(a_1) = O(a_2)$,
(iii) the type of $O(a_1)$ is not greater than the type of $O(a_2)$.

This shows that the relation $\leqslant$ indeed orders $W(\alpha)$ in type α.

THEOREM 5: *Every set of ordinals is well ordered by the relation* $\leqslant$. *In other words, in any non-empty set Z of ordinals there exists a smallest ordinal.*

PROOF. Let $\alpha \in Z$. If α is not the smallest ordinal of Z, then $Z \cap W(\alpha) \neq 0$. Then in the set $Z \cap W(\alpha)$ there exists a smallest number β, as the set $W(\alpha)$ is well ordered (see Theorem 4). At the same time β is the smallest ordinal in Z. In fact, if $\xi \in Z - W(\alpha)$ then $\xi \geqslant \alpha$; thus $\xi > \beta$.

THEOREM 6: *For every set Z of ordinals there exists an ordinal greater than all ordinals belonging to Z.*

PROOF. By the axiom of replacement there exists a set $\boldsymbol{K}$ whose elements are all the sets $W(\alpha)$ corresponding to the ordinals α belonging to Z:

$$W(\alpha) \in \boldsymbol{K} \equiv \alpha \in Z.$$

Consider the union of all sets belonging to $\boldsymbol{K}$

$$\boldsymbol{S} = \bigcup_{X \in \boldsymbol{K}} X.$$

By Theorem 5 the set S is well ordered by $\leqslant$. Let σ be its order type.

For $\alpha \in Z$ the set $W(\alpha)$ is either a segment of S or identical with S. In any case, $\alpha \leqslant \sigma$. This implies that $\alpha < \sigma + 1$ for every $\alpha \in Z$. Thus the ordinal $\sigma + 1$ is greater than every ordinal of Z.

COROLLARY 7: *There exists no set of all ordinals* [1].

COROLLARY 8: *There exists a smallest ordinal not belonging to a given set Z.*

Let $\alpha \notin Z$ (such an ordinal exists by Corollary 7). If α is not the smallest ordinal not belonging to Z, then the set $W(\alpha) - Z$ is non-empty. The smallest number in this set (see Theorem 5) is simultaneously the smallest ordinal not belonging to Z.

COROLLARY 9: *If a set Z of ordinals has the property* $(\gamma < \xi \in Z) \rightarrow (\gamma \in Z)$, *then there exists an ordinal* α *such that* $Z = W(\alpha)$.

[1]) Before set theory was axiomatized, Corollary 7 had been considered to be an antinomy. This antinomy was discovered by C. Burali-Forti. See his paper *Una questione sui numeri transfiniti*, Rendiconti del Circolo Matematico di Palermo **11** (1897) 154–164.

Namely, this ordinal α is the smallest ordinal among all ordinals not belonging to Z.

In fact, if $\xi \in Z$ then $\xi < \alpha$, because $\alpha \leqslant \xi$ would imply $\alpha \in Z$. Hence $Z \subset W(\alpha)$.

On the other hand if $\beta \in W(\alpha)$ then $\beta < \alpha$ and, by the definition of α, $\beta \in Z$. Therefore $W(\alpha) \subset Z$.

§ 3. Transfinite sequences

An ordinal is said to be a *limit ordinal* if it has no direct predecessor. Thus 0 is a limit ordinal.

THEOREM: *Each ordinal can be represented in the form $\lambda + n$ where λ is a limit ordinal and n is a finite ordinal (natural number).*

PROOF. Let α be an ordinal, A a set of type α. Every set of the form $A - O(a)$ is said to be a *remainder* of A. Clearly

$$A - O(a_1) \subset A - O(a_2) \equiv (a_1 \succ a_2) \vee (a_1 = a_2).$$

This implies that there exists no infinite increasing sequence of distinct remainders. Therefore there exists only a finite number of $m \in N$ such that there exists a remainder of power m. If n is the greatest such number and if $X - O(a)$ is a remainder of power n, then the segment $O(a)$ has no last element. Thus $\overline{O(a)}$ is the limit ordinal λ. This implies that $\alpha = \lambda + n$. Q.E.D.

By a *transfinite sequence of type* α or by an *α-sequence* we understand a function φ whose domain is $W(\alpha)$. If the values of this function (also called the *terms* of the α-sequence) are ordinals and if $\gamma < \beta < \alpha$ implies $\varphi(\gamma) < \varphi(\beta)$, then we say that this α-sequence is *increasing*.

Let φ be a λ-sequence of ordinals where λ is a limit ordinal. By Theorem 6 in § 2 there exist ordinals greater than all the ordinals $\varphi(\gamma)$ where $\gamma < \lambda$. The smallest such ordinal (see § 2, Corollary 8) is called the *limit* of the λ-sequence $\varphi(\gamma)$ for $\gamma < \lambda$ and is denoted by $\lim\limits_{\gamma<\lambda} \varphi(\gamma)$.

For example,

$$\omega = \lim_{n<\omega} n = \lim_{n<\omega} n^2.$$

We say that an ordinal λ is *cofinal* with a limit ordinal α if λ is the limit of an increasing α-sequence:

$$(1) \qquad \lambda = \lim_{\xi<\alpha} \varphi(\xi).$$

An ordinal cofinal with a limit ordinal is clearly itself a limit ordinal.

The connection between this notion and the notion of cofinality for sets is established by the following theorem.

THEOREM 2: *An ordinal λ is cofinal with the limit ordinal α if and only if $W(\lambda)$ contains a subset of type α cofinal with $W(\lambda)$.*

PROOF. Let A be a subset of $W(\lambda)$ cofinal with $W(\lambda)$ and such that $\overline{A} = \alpha$. For every ordinal $\xi < \alpha$ there exists an ordinal $\varphi(\xi)$ in A such that the set $\{\eta: (\eta \in A) \wedge (\eta < \varphi(\xi))\}$ is of type ξ. The sequence $\varphi(\xi)$ is clearly increasing and $\varphi(\xi) < \lambda$ for $\xi < \alpha$, because $\varphi(\xi) \in A \subset W(\lambda)$. If $\mu < \lambda$ then there exists an ordinal $\xi \in A$ such that $\mu < \xi$, because the sets A and $W(\lambda)$ are cofinal. Thus $\mu < \xi \leqslant \varphi(\xi)$ (see p. 230), which proves that λ is the least ordinal greater than all the ordinals $\varphi(\xi)$. This proves (1).

Suppose in turn that (1) holds. Let A be the set of all terms of φ. We have $\eta < \lambda$ for $\eta \in A$ and consequently, since λ is a limit ordinal, there exists $\xi \in W(\lambda)$ such that $\eta < \xi$. Conversely, if $\xi \in W(\lambda)$ then $\xi < \lambda$ and by the definition of limit there exists $\xi' < \alpha$ such that $\xi < \varphi(\xi')$. This means that some ordinal in A is greater than ξ. Hence the sets A and $W(\lambda)$ are cofinal.

It follows directly from the definition of limit that

$$(2) \qquad \lim_{\gamma<\lambda} \varphi(\gamma) > \varphi(\gamma) \quad \text{for} \quad \gamma < \lambda,$$

$$(3) \qquad \{\bigwedge_{\gamma<\lambda} [\mu > \varphi(\gamma)]\} \equiv \{\mu \geqslant \lim_{\gamma<\lambda} \varphi(\gamma)\}.$$

THEOREM 3: *If φ and ψ are two increasing transfinite sequences, λ is a limit ordinal and $\xi = \lim_{\gamma<\lambda} \psi(\gamma)$, then*

$$\lim_{\delta<\xi} \varphi(\delta) = \lim_{\gamma<\lambda} \varphi(\psi(\gamma)).$$

PROOF. If $\gamma < \lambda$ then by (2) $\psi(\gamma) < \xi$ and again by (2) $\varphi(\psi(\gamma)) < \lim_{\delta<\xi} \varphi(\delta)$. Applying (3) we obtain

$$(4) \qquad \lim_{\gamma<\lambda} \varphi(\psi(\gamma)) \leqslant \lim_{\delta<\xi} \varphi(\delta).$$

If $\delta < \xi$ then by (3) we infer that for some ordinal $\gamma < \lambda$ we have $\psi(\gamma) \geqslant \delta$. Since the sequence φ is increasing, $\varphi(\psi(\gamma)) \geqslant \varphi(\delta)$, and by (3) it follows that $\lim_{\gamma<\lambda} \varphi(\psi(\gamma)) > \varphi(\delta)$.

Applying (3) again we obtain

$$\lim_{\gamma<\lambda} \varphi(\psi(\gamma)) \geqslant \lim_{\delta>\xi} \varphi(\delta).$$

This together with (4) proves Theorem 3.

It follows from Theorem 3 that if a limit ordinal η is cofinal with a limit ordinal ξ and ξ is cofinal with a limit ordinal λ, then η is cofinal with λ.

We say that an α-sequence φ is *continuous* if for every limit ordinal $\lambda < \alpha$ we have

$$\varphi(\lambda) = \lim_{\gamma<\lambda} \varphi(\gamma).$$

THEOREM 4: *Let φ be an increasing continuous α-sequence. For a given ordinal $\gamma < \alpha$, let*

(5) $\quad \varkappa_\gamma = \lim_{n<\omega} \gamma_n, \quad$ *where* $\quad \gamma_0 = \gamma \quad$ *and* $\quad \gamma_{n+1} = \varphi(\gamma_n).$

Then $\varphi(\varkappa_\gamma) = \varkappa_\gamma$ (when $\varkappa_\gamma < \alpha$ and $\gamma_n < \alpha$ for $n = 1, 2, \ldots$).

PROOF. By (5) we have $\varkappa_\gamma > \gamma_{n+1} = \varphi(\gamma_n)$, and it follows by (3) that

$$\varkappa_\gamma \geqslant \lim_{n<\omega} \varphi(\gamma_n) = \varphi(\lim_{n<\omega} \gamma_n) = \varphi(\varkappa_\gamma).$$

On the other hand, $\varkappa_\gamma \leqslant \varphi(\varkappa_\gamma)$, because the sequence φ is increasing (see p. 230).

Each ordinal ξ satisfying the equation $\varphi(\xi) = \xi$ is said to be a *critical ordinal* of the sequence φ. Thus Theorem 4 states that if γ, belongs to the domain of an increasing continuous sequence φ, then there exists a critical ordinal of this sequence greater than γ, provided that this sequence is defined for sufficiently large ordinals.

Since no set contains all ordinals, there exists no transfinite sequence consisting of all ordinals. On the other hand, there exist propositional functions $\Phi(\xi, \eta)$ (for example, $\xi = \eta + 1$), of at least two free variables, such that the following holds.

For every ordinal η there exists exactly one ordinal ξ such that $\Phi(\eta, \xi)$.

Such a propositional function defines an operation on the ordinals. It is possible to define many notions and to prove many theorems about these operations, analogous to those for transfinite sequences. We here state an analogue of Theorem 4 for operations.

Let Φ be a propositional function with free variables $x, y, p_1, \ldots, p_k$. (The case $k = 0$ where Φ has exactly two free variables is not excluded.) For simplicity in the formulas below we shall not write the variables p_j explicitly. We assume that small Greek letters range over ordinal numbers.

The following abbreviations will be used:

(6) $\Pi\{\Phi\}$ is an abbreviation for $\bigwedge_x \bigvee_y \bigwedge_z [\Phi(x,z) \equiv (z = y)]$;

(7) $R\{\Phi\}$ is an abbreviation for

$$\bigwedge_\xi \bigvee_\zeta \Phi(\xi, \zeta) \wedge \bigwedge_{\xi\eta\zeta\tau} [\Phi(\xi,\eta) \wedge \Phi(\zeta,\tau) \wedge (\xi < \zeta) \rightarrow (\eta < \tau)];$$

(8) $\operatorname{Lim}_{\xi<\lambda} \{\Phi\}$ is an abbreviation for

$$\min_\mu \bigwedge_{\xi<\lambda} \bigwedge_\zeta [\Phi(\xi,\zeta) \rightarrow (\zeta < \mu)];$$

(9) $\operatorname{Cont}\{\Phi\}$ is an abbreviation for

$$\bigwedge_\lambda [(\lambda \text{ is a limit ordinal}) \rightarrow \Phi(\lambda, \operatorname{Lim}_{\xi<\lambda} \{\Phi\})].$$

The propositional function in (6) is read: Φ *defines an operation*. The propositional function $\Pi\{\Phi\}$ is equivalent to the conjunction of two propositional functions

$$\bigwedge_x \bigvee_y \Phi(x,y), \qquad \bigwedge_{x,y,z} [\Phi(x,y) \wedge \Phi(x,z) \rightarrow (y = z)].$$

This conjunction will be denoted by $\bigwedge_x \bigvee_y ! \, \Phi(x,y)$, where $\bigvee_y !$ is the quantifier "there exists exactly one y".

The propositional function in (7) is read: *the operation defined by Φ is increasing*, and in (9): *the operation defined by Φ is continuous*. Formula (8) introduces a symbol for the *limit of the operation defined by Φ*. In formula (8) the symbol $\min_\mu$ denotes 0 if there exists no ordinal μ satisfying the propositional function after the symbol $\min_\mu$.

THEOREM 5:

$$\Pi\{\Phi\} \wedge R\{\Phi\} \wedge \mathrm{Cont}\{\Phi\} \to \bigwedge_{\gamma} \bigvee_{\xi} [(\gamma < \xi) \wedge \Phi(\xi, \xi)].$$

The proof is similar to that of Theorem 4. Namely we define by induction a sequence of ordinals:

$$\gamma_0 = \gamma, \qquad \gamma_{n+1} = \min_{\zeta}(\Phi(\gamma_n, \zeta)).$$

The ordinal $\xi = \mathop{\mathrm{Lim}}_{n<\omega} \gamma_n$ it the desired ordinal.

The following theorem about operations will be used in § 4, p. 244–245.

THEOREM 6:

$$\Pi\{\Phi\} \to \bigwedge_{\alpha} \bigvee_{\varphi}! \ [(\varphi \text{ is an } \alpha\text{-sequence}) \wedge \bigwedge_{\xi<\alpha} (\Phi(\xi, \varphi_\xi))].$$

By the axiom of replacement the set $\{\langle \xi, y \rangle : (\xi < \alpha) \wedge \Phi(\xi, y)\}$ exists. This set is the required sequence. It is clear that this sequence is unique.

Theorem 6 can be written $\Pi\{\Phi\} \to \Pi\{\Psi\}$, where Ψ is the propositional function: (φ is an α-sequence) $\wedge \bigwedge_{\xi<\alpha} \Phi(\xi, \varphi_\xi)$. The unique sequence φ satisfying the condition $\Psi(\alpha, \varphi)$ is denoted by $C_\alpha\{\Phi\}$.

It should be noted that definitions (6)–(9) as well as Theorems 5 and 6 are schemes; for each propositional function Φ we obtain separate definitions and theorems.

§ 4. Definitions by transfinite induction

The theory discussed in this section is similar to the theory of inductive definitions in arithmetic of natural numbers.

THEOREM 1: (ON DEFINITIONS BY TRANSFINITE INDUCTION)[1]. *Given a set Z and an ordinal α, let Φ denote the set of all ξ-sequences for $\xi < \alpha$ with values belonging to Z. For each function $h \in Z^\Phi$ there exists one and only one transfinite sequence f defined on $\xi \leqslant \alpha$ and such that*

(1) $$f(\xi) = h[f|W(\xi)] \quad \textit{for every } \xi \leqslant \alpha.$$

[1]) A particular case of this theorem was already formulated by Cantor; see Mathematische Annalen **49** (1897) 231.

PROOF. We show first that there exists at most one sequence f satisfying condition (1). Suppose that g is a sequence defined on the set $W(\alpha+1)$ and satisfying the condition

(2) $$g(\xi) = h[g|W(\xi)] \quad \text{for every } \xi \leqslant \alpha.$$

Let $B = \{\xi\colon f(\xi) = g(\xi)\}$. If $\xi \leqslant \alpha$ and $W(\xi) \subset B$, then $f|W(\xi) = g|W(\xi)$, and by (1) and (2) $f(\xi) = g(\xi)$, that is $\xi \in B$. Thus we have shown that the condition $W(\xi) \subset B$ implies $\xi \in B$. By the principle of transfinite induction (p. 229) we infer that $W(\alpha+1) \subset B$; that is, for every $\xi \leqslant \alpha$, we have $f(\xi) = g(\xi)$. This means that the functions f and g are identical.

We now prove that there exists a function f satisfying (1).

Suppose by way of contradiction that for given α such a function does not exist. Clearly we may assume that α is the smallest ordinal with this property; otherwise we can find the smallest ordinal with this property in the set $W(\alpha)$. Thus for each $\xi < \alpha$ there exists a function f_ξ satisfying the condition

(3) $$f_\xi(\gamma) = h[f_\xi|W(\gamma)] \quad \text{for every } \gamma \leqslant \xi.$$

It follows from the part of the theorem already proved that for a given ξ there exists exactly one function f_ξ satisfying (3). We now infer that if $\gamma \leqslant \xi$ then $f_\xi|W(\gamma+1) = f_\gamma$. Hence $f_\gamma(\zeta) = f_\xi(\zeta)$ provided that $\zeta < \gamma$. This implies:

(4) $$[f_\gamma|W(\gamma)] = [f_\xi|W(\gamma)] \quad \text{for} \quad \gamma \leqslant \xi.$$

Let

(5) $$f(\xi) = f_\xi(\xi) \text{ for } \xi < \alpha \quad \text{and} \quad f(\alpha) = h(C_\alpha),$$

where C_α denotes the α-sequence such that $C_\alpha(\xi) = f_\xi(\xi)$ for $\xi < \alpha$. The function f satisfies condition (1). In fact, if $\gamma \leqslant \xi < \alpha$ then by (3), (4) and (5)

(6) $$f(\gamma) = h[f_\gamma|W(\gamma)] = h[f_\xi|W(\gamma)] = f_\xi(\gamma),$$

whence $f|W(\xi) = f_\xi|W(\xi)$ and by (3)

$$f(\xi) = h[f_\xi|W(\xi)] = h[f|W(\xi)] \quad \text{for} \quad \xi < \alpha.$$

Finally, $f(\alpha) = h[f|W(\alpha)]$, because by (5) $f|W(\alpha) = C_\alpha$.

In applications of the theorem, the function h is often defined by three formulas: the first gives the value $h(\varphi)$ for the void sequence φ

(i.e. the value $h(0)$), the second the value $h(\varphi)$ for sequences $\varphi \in Z^{\Phi}$ whose type is not a limit ordinal (i.e. is of the form $\xi+1$), the third gives the value $h(\varphi)$ for sequences whose type λ is a limit ordinal. For instance, the first formula may be of the form

$$h(0) = A,$$

the second of the form

$$h(\varphi) = F(\varphi(\xi)),$$

and the third of the form

$$h(\varphi) = G\Big(\bigcup_{\eta<\lambda}\varphi(\eta)\Big) \quad \text{or} \quad h(\varphi) = G\Big(\bigcap_{\eta<\lambda}\varphi(\eta)\Big),$$

where F and G are given functions and A is a given set.

Then the sequence f, which exists by Theorem 1, satisfies the conditions

$$\begin{cases} f(0) = A, \\ f(\xi+1) = F(f(\xi)), \\ f(\lambda) = G\Big(\bigcup_{\eta<\lambda} f(\eta)\Big) \text{ or } f(\lambda) = G\Big(\bigcap_{\eta<\lambda} f(\eta)\Big). \end{cases}$$

Usually when we apply Theorem 1 to prove the existence of f, we give only these three formulas.

Examples

\# 1. *Derivatives of order* α[1]. Let A be a subset of the real line (or, more generally, $A \subset \mathcal{E}^n$). The derivative of order α of the set A is defined by transfinite induction as follows

$$A^{(0)} = \overline{A}, \qquad A^{(\xi+1)} = A^{(\xi)c}, \qquad A^{(\lambda)} = \bigcap_{\gamma<\lambda} A^{(\gamma)},$$

where λ is a limit ordinal $\leqslant \alpha$.

In this case we have $Z = 2^{\overline{A}}$, $h(0) = \overline{A}$, $h(\varphi) = [\varphi(\xi)]^c$ if φ is of type $\xi+1$, $h(\varphi) = \bigcap_{\gamma<\lambda}\varphi(\gamma)$ if φ is of type λ. #

2. *Borel sets of type* α[2]. The family $\boldsymbol{F}_\alpha$ of Borel sets of type α is

[1]) We recall that the derivative of order 1, i.e. A^c, is the set of limit points of the set A.

[2]) Borel sets were introduced by E. Borel; see *Leçons sur la théorie des fonctions*, (Paris 1898).

defined by transfinite induction:

(i) $\boldsymbol{F}_0$ is the family of all closed subsets (of a given space),

(ii) $\boldsymbol{F}_\xi = (\bigcup_{\gamma<\xi} \boldsymbol{F}_\gamma)_\sigma$ or $\boldsymbol{F}_\xi = (\bigcup_{\gamma<\xi} \boldsymbol{F}_\gamma)_\delta$ for $0 < \xi \leqslant \alpha$,

depending on whether ξ is an even or an odd ordinal (ordinals of the form $\lambda+n$, where λ is a limit ordinal, are said to be *even* if n is even and *odd* if n is odd). See page 129 for the definitions of σ and δ.

In this case we have

$$h(0) = \boldsymbol{F}_0 \quad \text{and} \quad h(\varphi) = (\bigcup_{\gamma<\xi} \varphi(\gamma))_\sigma \quad \text{or} \quad h(\varphi) = (\bigcup_{\gamma<\xi} \varphi(\gamma))_\delta$$

depending on whether the type ξ of φ is an even or an odd ordinal.

Similarly we define the family $\boldsymbol{G}_\alpha$ by the conditions:

(iii) $\boldsymbol{G}_0$ is the family of open sets,

(iv) $\boldsymbol{G}_\xi = (\bigcup_{\gamma<\xi} \boldsymbol{G}_\gamma)_\sigma$ or $\boldsymbol{G}_\xi = (\bigcup_{\gamma<\xi} \boldsymbol{G}_\gamma)_\delta$ for $0 < \xi \leqslant \alpha$,

depending on the character of ξ (even or odd).

3. *Analytically representable functions of class* α[1]. The set of these functions is denoted by Φ_α and is defined by transfinite induction as follows:

(a) Φ_0 is the set of all real continuous functions (of a real variable),

(b) $\Phi_\xi = (\bigcup_{\gamma<\xi} \Phi_\gamma)_\lambda$ for $0 < \xi \leqslant \alpha$,

where in general Δ_λ denotes the set of all functions which are limits of convergent sequences of functions belonging to the class Δ.

In this example:

$$Z = 2^{(\mathcal{E}^{\mathcal{E}})}, \qquad h(0) = \Phi_0, \qquad h(\varphi) = (\bigcup_{\gamma<\xi} \varphi(\gamma))_\lambda,$$

where ξ is the type of the sequence φ. #

As another example of an application of Theorem 1 we prove the following theorem.

[1]) This class of functions was first investigated by R. Baire; see *Leçons sur les fonctions discontinues* (Paris 1905).

THEOREM 2: *Every limit ordinal of the form* $\lambda = \lim_{\xi<\alpha} \varphi(\xi)$ *is cofinal with some ordinal* $\gamma \leqslant \alpha$ [1]).

PROOF. According to Theorem 1, there exists an α-sequence ψ such that

(i) $\psi(\xi)$ is the smallest ordinal ζ such that $\varphi(\xi) < \zeta < \lambda$ and $\bigwedge_{\eta<\xi} \psi(\eta) < \zeta$, if such an ordinal exists;

(ii) $\psi(\xi) = \lambda$ otherwise.

We consider two cases:

I. There exists no ordinal $\xi < \alpha$ such that $\psi(\xi) = \lambda$. In this case the sequence ψ is increasing by (i) and (by induction) $\psi(\xi) > \varphi(\xi)$ for all ξ. Since λ is the smallest ordinal greater than all the $\varphi(\xi)$, we infer that $\lim_{\xi<\alpha} \psi(\xi) = \lambda$. Thus λ is cofinal with α.

II. There exist ordinals $\xi < \alpha$ such that $\psi(\xi) = \lambda$. Let γ be the smallest such ordinal, that is $\psi(\gamma) = \lambda$ and $\psi(\eta) < \lambda$ for $\eta < \gamma$. This implies that γ is a limit ordinal. In fact, would we have $\gamma = \delta + 1$ then $\psi(\delta) < \lambda$ and therefore there would exist an ordinal μ such that $\psi(\delta) < \mu < \lambda$ and $\varphi(\delta) < \mu < \lambda$, which contradicts $\psi(\gamma) = \lambda$. It follows from (i) that for $\xi_1 < \xi_2 < \gamma$ we have $\psi(\xi_1) < \psi(\xi_2)$. This means that $\psi | W(\gamma)$ is increasing. Let $\varrho = \lim_{\xi<\gamma} \psi(\xi)$. We shall show that $\varrho = \lambda$. For suppose that $\varrho < \lambda$. The ordinal ϱ is greater than all the $\psi(\eta)$ for $\eta < \gamma$ and therefore there exist ordinals $< \lambda$ greater than $\varphi(\gamma)$ and greater than $\psi(\eta)$ for $\eta < \gamma$ (namely any ordinal greater than both ϱ and $\varphi(\gamma)$ and less than λ satisfies these conditions). But this contradicts the assumption $\psi(\gamma) = \lambda$. Hence $\varrho \geqslant \lambda$. We have $\varrho \leqslant \lambda$, because $\psi(\xi) < \lambda$ for $\xi < \gamma$. Thus $\lambda = \varrho = \lim_{\xi<\gamma} \psi(\xi)$. This means that λ is cofinal with γ. Q.E.D.

It is possible to formulate for operations a theorem similar to Theorem 1. As before, let Φ be a propositional function with at least two free variables $x, y, p_1, \dots, p_k$. Let $M\{\Phi\}$ be the propositional function (with free variables $\alpha, \varphi, p_1, \dots, p_k$)

[1]) We do not suppose that the function φ is increasing.

$$(\varphi \text{ is a transfinite sequence of type } \alpha+1) \wedge \bigwedge_{\xi \leqslant \alpha} \Phi(\varphi|W(\xi), \varphi_\xi).$$

This propositional function $M\{\Phi\}$ will be read:

"φ is the inductive sequence for Φ of type $\alpha+1$".

LEMMA: $(\beta < \alpha) \wedge M\{\Phi\}(\alpha, \varphi) \rightarrow M\{\Phi\}(\beta, \varphi|W(\beta+1))$.

In fact, if φ is the inductive sequence for Φ of type $\alpha+1$, then the sequence $\psi = \varphi|W(\beta+1)$ satisfies the condition $\Phi(\psi|W(\xi), \psi_\xi)$ for every $\xi \leqslant \beta$; thus it is the inductive sequence for Φ of type $\beta+1$.

Further, let Ind $\{\Phi\}$ denote the propositional function $\bigvee_{\varphi} [M\{\Phi\} \wedge (\varphi_\alpha = a)]$; the free variables of this function are $\alpha, a, p_1, \ldots, p_k$.

We shall show that by means of Ind $\{\Phi\}$ it is possible to formulate the theorem on definitions by transfinite induction for operations. For simplicity we write Ψ instead of Ind $\{\Phi\}$ (see p. 239 for the definition of $C_\alpha\{\Psi\}$).

THEOREM 3:

(i) $\Pi\{\Phi\} \rightarrow \Pi\{\Psi\}$;

(ii) $\Pi\{\Phi\} \wedge \Psi(\alpha, a) \rightarrow \Phi(C_\alpha\{\Psi\}, a)$.

PROOF. (i) Suppose that $\Pi\{\Phi\}$ and let α be an ordinal. The consequent of implication (i) is equivalent to the conjunction of the formulas:

(7) $$\Psi(\alpha, a_1) \wedge \Psi(\alpha, a_2) \rightarrow (a_1 = a_2);$$

(8) $$\bigvee_a \Psi(\alpha, a).$$

Formula (7) follows directly from the implication

$$M\{\Phi\}(\alpha, \varphi') \wedge M\{\Phi\}(\alpha, \varphi'') \rightarrow (\varphi' = \varphi''),$$

which can be proved by showing that if $B = \{\xi \leqslant \alpha : \varphi'(\xi) = \varphi''(\xi)\}$, then $W(\xi) \subset B \rightarrow \xi \in B$ for all $\xi \leqslant \alpha$, thus $B = W(\alpha+1)$.

For the proof of formula (8), suppose by way of contradiction that there exist ordinals α such that $\bigwedge_a \neg \Psi(\alpha, a)$. Hence there exists the smallest such ordinal α. Thus for every $\beta < \alpha$ there exist an element a_β and the inductive sequence $\varphi^{(\beta)}$ for Φ of type $\beta+1$. The sequence $\varphi^{(\beta)}$ satisfies the conditions $\Phi(\varphi^{(\beta)}|W(\xi), \varphi^{(\beta)}_\xi)$ for $\xi \leqslant \beta$ and

$\varphi_\beta^{(\beta)} = a_\beta$. By part (i) of Theorem 3 $\varphi^{(\beta)}$ as well as a_β are uniquely determined. It follows from the lemma that $\varphi^{(\beta)}|W(\xi+1) = \varphi^{(\xi)}$ for $\xi \leqslant \beta$ and thus $a_\xi = \varphi_\xi^{(\xi)} = \varphi_\xi^{(\beta)}$ for $\xi \leqslant \beta$.

The sequence $\bar{\varphi}$ of type α defined by $\bar{\varphi}_\beta = \varphi^{(\beta)}(\beta) = a_\beta$ for $\beta < \alpha$ satisfies the condition $\bar{\varphi}|W(\beta) = \varphi^{(\beta)}|W(\beta)$ for every $\beta < \alpha$, and therefore it also satisfies the condition $\bigwedge_{\beta<\alpha} \Phi(\bar{\varphi}|W(\beta), \bar{\varphi}_\beta)$. Let a be the unique element such that $\Phi(\bar{\varphi}, a)$. The sequence φ^* such that $\varphi_\xi^* = \bar{\varphi}_\xi$ for $\xi < \alpha$ and such that $\varphi_\alpha^* = a$ is of type $\alpha+1$ and is the inductive sequence for Φ, that is $M\{\Phi\}(\varphi^*, a)$. Since $\varphi_\alpha = a$, we now obtain $\Psi(\alpha, a)$ which contradicts the hypothesis.

Part (i) of the theorem is thus proved.

To prove (ii), suppose that $\Pi\{\Phi\}$ and $\Psi(\alpha, a)$. Thus there exists a sequence φ of type $\alpha+1$ such that $M\{\Phi\}(\alpha, \varphi)$ and $\varphi_\alpha = a$.

It suffices to show that $\varphi = C_\alpha\{\Psi\}$ or that $\Psi\{\xi, \varphi_\xi\}$ for every $\xi \leqslant \alpha$. But this follows directly from the lemma and from the uniqueness of inductive sequences.

Theorem 3 is a theorem scheme: for each propositional function Φ we obtain a separate theorem.

Examples

1. Let $\Phi = \Phi(C, Y, P)$ be the following propositional function:

$$[(C \text{ is not a transfinite sequence}) \wedge (Y = 0)] \vee$$
$$[(C \text{ is a sequence of type } 0) \wedge (Y = P)] \vee$$
$$[(C \text{ is a sequence of type } \gamma+1) \wedge (Y = 2^{C_\xi})] \vee$$
$$[(C \text{ is a sequence of type } \lambda \text{ where } \lambda \text{ is a limit ordinal}) \wedge (Y = \bigcup_{\xi<\lambda} C_\xi)].$$

Clearly $\bigwedge_C \bigvee_Y ! \, \Phi(C, Y, P)$. Applying the scheme described in Theorem 3 we obtain the propositional function $\mathrm{Ind}\{\Phi\}$ with free variables α, P, Y such that $\bigwedge_\alpha \bigvee_Y ! \, \mathrm{Ind}\{\Phi\}(\alpha, Y, P)$. The unique Y satisfying the condition $\mathrm{Ind}\{\Phi\}(\alpha, Y, P)$ is denoted by $R_\alpha(P)$. The following formulas are consequences of Theorem 3:

$$(9) \qquad R_0(P) = P, \qquad R_{\xi+1}(P) = 2^{R_\xi(P)}, \qquad R_\lambda(P) = \bigcup_{\xi<\lambda} R_\xi(P).$$

When $P = 0$ we write R_α instead of $R_\alpha(P)$. This set is called the *family of sets of rank at most* α[1]. These sets will be examined more closely in § 7, Chapter VIII.

2. Let $\Phi = \Phi(C, y, p)$ be the following propositional function:

$$\{[(C \text{ is not a transfinite sequence of ordinals}) \vee (p \text{ is not an ordinal})] \wedge (y = 0)\} \vee [(C = 0) \wedge (y = 1)] \vee$$
$$\{[(\text{the type of } C \text{ is of the form } \gamma + 1) \wedge (y = C_\gamma \cdot p)] \vee [(\text{the type of } C \text{ is a limit ordinal } \lambda) \wedge (y = \lim_{\xi < \gamma} C_\xi)]\}.$$

Clearly $\bigwedge_C \bigvee_y ! \, \Phi(C, y, p)$, that is $\Pi\{\Phi\}$. Applying the scheme of Theorem 3 to this propositional function we obtain the propositional function $\mathrm{Ind}\{\Phi\}$ such that $\bigwedge_\alpha \bigvee_y ! \, \mathrm{Ind}\{\Phi\}(\alpha, y, p)$. Let π^α denote the unique ordinal y such that $\mathrm{Ind}\{\Phi\}(\alpha. y, \pi)$. We now obtain the formulas

$$\pi^0 = 1, \qquad \pi^{\gamma+1} = \pi^\gamma \cdot \pi, \qquad \pi^\lambda = \lim_{\xi < \lambda} \pi^\xi.$$

Exercises

1. Show that it is possible to obtain Theorem 1 from Theorem 3 by an appropriate choice of the propositional function.

2. Construct a propositional function φ which defines an operation $\alpha \to \mathfrak{a}_\alpha$ from ordinals to cardinals in such a way that

$$\mathfrak{a}_0 = \mathfrak{a}, \qquad \mathfrak{a}_{\gamma+1} = 2^{\mathfrak{a}_\gamma}, \qquad \mathfrak{a}_\lambda = \sum_{\xi < \lambda} \mathfrak{a}_\xi.$$

§ 5. Ordinal arithmetic[2]

The following theorem is a direct consequence of the definitions given in Chapter VI, p. 222–223

THEOREM 1: *The sum and the product of two ordinal numbers are ordinal numbers.*

[1] This notion of rank is virtually due to Russell. He called objects that are not sets the objects of type 0, objects whose all elements are of type n—the sets of type $n+1$. Russell considered only finite types and "homogeneous" sets, i.e. sets whose elements are all of the same type. See B. Russell and A. N. Whitehead, *Principia Mathematica*, 2nd edition (Cambridge 1925).

[2] Definitions and theorems given in §§ 5–7 are due to Cantor; see Mathematische Annalen **21** (1873).

By means of Example 4, p. 228 we obtain the following

THEOREM 2: *The ordered sum of ordinal numbers, where the indexing set is well ordered, is itself an ordinal number.*

The first part of Theorem 1 follows from Theorem 2, by letting the indexing set be a two-element set. Similarly, assuming that the indexing set is of type β and that all components are equal to α, we conclude that $\alpha\beta$ is an ordinal. We shall prove some arithmetic laws for the ordinal addition and multiplication.

THE FIRST MONOTONIC LAW FOR ADDITION:

(1) $$(\alpha < \beta) \rightarrow (\gamma+\alpha < \gamma+\beta).$$

PROOF. Let $\overline{C} = \gamma$, $\overline{B} = \beta$ and $B \cap C = 0$. Since $\alpha < \beta$, the set B contains a segment A of type α. The ordered sum $C \cup A$, which is of type $\gamma+\alpha$, is a segment of $C \cup B$, which is of type $\gamma+\beta$. Thus $\gamma+\alpha < \gamma+\beta$.

It follows from (1) (for $\alpha = 0$) that

(2) $$(\beta > 0) \rightarrow (\gamma+\beta > \gamma).$$

Thus the sum of two ordinals different from 0 is greater than the first component.

THE SECOND MONOTONIC LAW FOR ADDITION:

(3) $$(\alpha \leqslant \beta) \rightarrow (\alpha+\gamma \leqslant \beta+\gamma).$$

In fact, assuming that $\overline{A} = \alpha$, $\overline{B} = \beta$, $\overline{C} = \gamma$, $A \subset B$, $B \cap C = 0$ and applying Theorem 3, p. 233 to the ordered unions $A \cup C$ and $B \cup C$, we obtain (3).

In particular, it follows from (3) that

(4) $$\beta+\gamma \geqslant \gamma.$$

Thus the sum of two ordinals is not less than the second component. On the other hand, from $1+\omega = \omega$ we see that the sum does not need to be greater than the second component (although the first component is not zero).

THEOREM 3: *If $\alpha \geqslant \beta$ then there exists exactly one ordinal γ such that $\alpha = \beta+\gamma$.*

PROOF. Let $\overline{A} = \alpha$, let B be a segment of A of type β and let $\gamma = \overline{A-B}$. Clearly, $\alpha = \beta+\gamma$. To prove the uniqueness of γ suppose that $\beta+\gamma_1 = \beta+\gamma_2$. By (1) this implies that $\gamma_1 \not< \gamma_2$ and $\gamma_2 \not< \gamma_1$. Thus $\gamma_1 = \gamma_2$ by Theorem 1, p. 233.

It follows from Theorem 3 and formula (2) that the inequality $\alpha \geqslant \beta$ is a necessary and sufficient condition for the equation $\alpha = \beta+x$ to be solvable.

On the other hand, the equation $\alpha = x+\beta$ is not always solvable, for example we have $\omega \neq x+2$ for every ordinal x.

In connection with Theorem 3 we introduce the following definition.

The *difference of the ordinals* α *and* β ($\alpha \geqslant \beta$) is defined to be the unique ordinal γ such that $\alpha = \beta+\gamma$. This ordinal is denoted by $\alpha-\beta$. Thus

(5) $$\alpha = \beta+(\alpha-\beta).$$

For instance, $\omega-n = \omega$, because $n+\omega = \omega$. Similarly $\omega^2-\omega = \omega^2$, because $\omega+\omega^2 = \omega^2$.

THE MONOTONIC LAWS FOR ORDINAL SUBTRACTION:

(6) $$(\alpha > \alpha_1) \rightarrow (\alpha-\beta > \alpha_1-\beta),$$

(7) $$(\beta > \beta_1) \rightarrow (\alpha-\beta \leqslant \alpha-\beta_1).$$

In order for the subtraction to be performable we assume in (6) that $\alpha_1 \geqslant \beta$ and in (7) that $\alpha \geqslant \beta$.

PROOF. For the purpose of obtaining a contradiction, suppose that $\alpha-\beta \leqslant \alpha_1-\beta$. From formulas (5) and (1) it follows that $\alpha = \beta+(\alpha-\beta) \leqslant \beta+(\alpha_1-\beta) = \alpha_1$, which contradicts the assumption $\alpha > \alpha_1$.

Similarly, assume that $\alpha-\beta > \alpha-\beta_1$; then it follows from (5) and (1) that $\alpha = \beta+(\alpha-\beta) > \beta+(\alpha-\beta_1)$. This contradicts $\beta > \beta_1$, because $\beta > \beta_1$ implies by (3) that $\beta+(\alpha-\beta_1) \geqslant \beta_1+(\alpha-\beta_1) = \alpha$ and consequently we would obtain $\alpha > \alpha$.

The identity $\omega-2 = \omega-3 = \omega$ shows that the symbol $\leqslant$ in (7) cannot in general be replaced by $<$.

THE FIRST MONOTONIC LAW FOR ORDINAL MULTIPLICATION:

(8) $$(\alpha < \beta) \rightarrow (\gamma\alpha < \gamma\beta) \quad \text{for} \quad \gamma > 0.$$

In fact, $\gamma\beta$ is the type of the cartesian product $C\times B$ ordered antilexicographically, where $\overline{B} = \beta$ and $\overline{C} = \gamma$. Let $\overline{A} = \alpha$ and let A be a segment of B. The cartesian product $C\times A$ ordered antilexicographically is a segment of $C\times B$. Q.E.D.

THE SECOND MONOTONIC LAW FOR ORDINAL MULTIPLICATION:

$$(\alpha \leqslant \beta) \to (\alpha\gamma \leqslant \beta\gamma). \tag{9}$$

To prove (9), we consider sets A, B, C of types α, β, γ respectively, and we assume that $A \subset B$. Thus $A \times C \subset B \times C$ which proves (9).

It follows from the identity $1 \cdot \omega = 2 \cdot \omega$ that the symbol $\leqslant$ in (9) cannot be replaced by $<$.

LEFT DISTRIBUTIVITY OF ORDINAL MULTIPLICATION WITH RESPECT TO ORDINAL SUBTRACTION:

$$\alpha(\beta - \gamma) = \alpha\beta - \alpha\gamma \quad \text{for} \quad \beta \geqslant \gamma. \tag{10}$$

PROOF. Since multiplication is left-distributive over addition (see p. 223), we have by (5) $\alpha\beta = \alpha[\gamma + (\beta - \gamma)] = \alpha\gamma + \alpha(\beta - \gamma)$. This implies (10) by the definition of subtraction.

We now prove a theorem about division of ordinal numbers.

THEOREM 4: *If β is an ordinal > 0, then for each ordinal α there exist ordinals γ and ϱ such that*

$$\alpha = \beta\gamma + \varrho \quad \textit{and} \quad \varrho < \beta. \tag{11}$$

The ordinals γ and ϱ are then uniquely determined.

PROOF. Since $1 \leqslant \beta$, we have by (9) $\alpha \leqslant \beta\alpha$. If $\alpha = \beta\alpha$, then it suffices to let $\gamma = \alpha$ and $\varrho = 0$. Therefore suppose that $\alpha < \beta\alpha$. The product $\beta\alpha$ is the type of the set $B \times A$ where $\overline{B} = \beta$, $\overline{A} = \alpha$. It follows from the hypothesis $\alpha < \beta\alpha$ that the set $B \times A$ contains a segment $O(\langle b, a \rangle)$ of type α. Since

$$\langle y, x \rangle \in O(\langle b, a \rangle) \equiv \{(x \prec a) \vee [(x = a) \wedge (y \prec b)]\},$$

we have

$$O(\langle b, a \rangle) = \big(B \times O_A(a)\big) \cup \big(O_B(b) \times \{a\}\big),$$

where every element belonging to the first component precedes every element belonging to the second component. Since the first component is of type $\beta \cdot \overline{O_A(a)} = \beta\gamma$ and the second of type $\overline{O_B(b)} = \varrho$, we have $\alpha = \beta\gamma + \varrho$ where $\gamma < \alpha$, $\varrho < \beta$. In this way we have proved that there exist ordinals γ and ϱ satisfying conditions (11).

To prove uniqueness, suppose that

$$\beta\gamma + \varrho = \beta\gamma_1 + \varrho_1, \quad \varrho < \beta, \quad \varrho_1 < \beta. \tag{12}$$

Let $\gamma > \gamma_1$. Then $\gamma = \gamma_1 + (\gamma - \gamma_1)$ and

(13) $$\beta\gamma + \varrho = \beta[\gamma_1 + (\gamma - \gamma_1)] + \varrho = \beta\gamma_1 + \beta(\gamma - \gamma_1) + \varrho.$$

Since $\gamma - \gamma_1 \geqslant 1$, we have by (8)

(14) $$\beta(\gamma - \gamma_1) \geqslant \beta.$$

It follows from (12) and (13) that

$$\beta\gamma_1 + \varrho_1 \geqslant \beta\gamma_1 + \beta(\gamma - \gamma_1),$$

whence by (14)

(15) $$\beta\gamma_1 + \varrho_1 \geqslant \beta\gamma_1 + \beta.$$

As $\beta > \varrho_1$, we obtain by (1) $\beta\gamma_1 + \beta > \beta\gamma_1 + \varrho_1$. But this is impossible, because (15) implies $\beta\gamma_1 + \varrho_1 > \beta\gamma_1 + \varrho_1$. Thus the hypothesis $\gamma > \gamma_1$ leads to a contradiction. Similarly it can be shown that $\gamma_1 > \gamma$ does not hold. Hence $\gamma = \gamma_1$.

This formula and (12) imply that $\beta\gamma + \varrho = \beta\gamma + \varrho_1$; by (1) this formula implies $\varrho = \varrho_1$.

Thus Theorem 4 is completely proved.

The ordinal γ in (11) is called the *quotient* and ϱ the *remainder*.

The following theorem is a consequence of Theorem 4.

THEOREM 5: (THE EUCLIDEAN ALGORITHM FOR ORDINAL NUMBERS.) *For any two ordinals α_0 and α_1 different from* 0, *there exist a natural number n and sequences $\alpha_2, \ldots, \alpha_n, \beta_1, \ldots, \beta_n$ such that $\alpha_1 > \alpha_2 > \ldots > \alpha_n > 0$ and*

$$\alpha_0 = \alpha_1\beta_1 + \alpha_2, \quad \alpha_1 = \alpha_2\beta_2 + \alpha_3, \ldots,$$
$$\alpha_{n-2} = \alpha_{n-1}\beta_{n-1} + \alpha_n, \quad \alpha_{n-1} = \alpha_n\beta_n.$$

PROOF. According to Theorem 4 and to the theorem on inductive definitions, there exist infinite sequences φ and ψ such that

$$\varphi_0 = \alpha_0, \quad \varphi_1 = \alpha_1, \quad \psi_0 = \psi_1 = 1$$

and, for $j > 1$,

$$\varphi_{j-1} = \varphi_j\psi_{j+1} + \varphi_{j+1}$$

and

$$\varphi_{j-1} < \varphi_j \quad \text{if} \quad \varphi_j \neq 0,$$
$$\varphi_{j+1} = \psi_{j+1} = 0 \quad \text{if} \quad \varphi_j = 0.$$

Since there exists no infinite decreasing sequence of ordinals, all terms of φ from a certain term on are equal to 0. Let $n' = \min_j (\varphi_j = 0)$. Clearly, $n' > 0$, because by assumption φ_0 and φ_1 are $\neq 0$. To prove the theorem it suffices to let $n = n'-1$, $\alpha_j = \varphi_j$ for $2 \leqslant j < n'$ and $\beta_j = \psi_{j+1}$ for $1 \leqslant j < n'$.

Now we shall prove several formulas concerning the operation of taking limits (p. 235). We assume that λ is a limit ordinal and that φ is an increasing λ-sequence. Then we have

$$\lim_{\xi<\lambda}[\alpha+\varphi(\xi)] = \alpha+\lim_{\xi<\lambda}\varphi(\xi). \tag{16}$$

Proof. Let $\beta = \lim_{\xi<\lambda}\varphi(\xi)$. If $\xi < \lambda$, then $\varphi(\xi) < \beta$ and therefore $\alpha+\varphi(\xi) < \alpha+\beta$. Let $\zeta < \alpha+\beta$; we shall prove that there exists $\xi < \lambda$ such that $\zeta < \alpha+\varphi(\xi)$. If $\zeta < \alpha$, then $\zeta < \alpha+\varphi(0)$; on the other hand, if $\zeta \geqslant \alpha$, then $\zeta = \alpha+(\zeta-\alpha)$ and $\zeta-\alpha < (\alpha+\beta)-\alpha \leqslant \beta$. It follows that for some $\xi < \lambda$ we have $\zeta-\alpha < \varphi(\xi)$, thus $\zeta < \alpha+\varphi(\xi)$. Hence the ordinal $\alpha+\beta$ is the smallest ordinal greater than all ordinals $\alpha+\varphi(\xi)$ for $\xi < \lambda$. This proves (16).

$$\lim_{\xi<\lambda}[\alpha\cdot\varphi(\xi)] = \alpha\cdot\lim_{\xi<\lambda}\varphi(\xi). \tag{17}$$

Proof. We may clearly suppose that $\alpha \neq 0$. Let $\beta = \lim_{\xi<\lambda}\varphi(\xi)$. For $\xi < \lambda$ we have $\varphi(\xi) < \beta$, thus $\alpha\cdot\varphi(\xi) < \alpha\cdot\beta$. Let $\zeta < \alpha\cdot\beta$. By Theorem 4 there exist ordinals γ and ϱ such that $\zeta = \alpha\gamma+\varrho < \alpha\beta$ and $\varrho < \alpha$. If $\gamma \geqslant \beta$ then we have $\zeta \geqslant \alpha\beta+\varrho \geqslant \alpha\beta$, which contradicts the hypothesis. Thus $\gamma < \beta$, which implies that for some $\xi < \lambda$ we have $\gamma \leqslant \varphi(\xi)$. Hence

$$\zeta \leqslant \alpha\cdot\varphi(\xi)+\varrho \leqslant \alpha\cdot\varphi(\xi)+\alpha = \alpha\cdot[\varphi(\xi)+1],$$

and

$$\zeta \leqslant \alpha\cdot\varphi(\xi+1),$$

because the function φ is increasing by assumption. Since λ is a limit ordinal, we have $\xi+1 < \lambda$ and the formula $\zeta \leqslant \alpha\cdot\varphi(\xi+1)$ shows that ζ is not greater than some ordinal of the form $\alpha\cdot\varphi(\eta)$ where $\eta \leqslant \lambda$. Thus the ordinal $\alpha\beta$ is the smallest ordinal greater than all ordinals $\alpha\cdot\varphi(\eta)$ for $\eta < \lambda$. This proves (17).

Remarks. Assuming $\varphi(\xi) = \xi$, we infer from (1) and (16) that *the function $s(\xi) = \alpha+\xi$ is increasing and continuous (on the set $W(\beta)$ for* *every* β). It follows from (8) and (17) that the function $p(\xi) = \alpha\cdot\xi$ possesses the same property. Theorem 4, § 3, p. 237 implies that there exist critical ordinals for the function s and for the function p. A critical ordinal for the function s is $\xi = \alpha\cdot\omega$, and, more generally, every ordinal of the form $\alpha\cdot\omega+\varrho$ where ϱ is an arbitary ordinal. In fact,

$$s(\alpha\cdot\omega+\varrho) = \alpha+\alpha\cdot\omega+\varrho = \alpha(1+\omega)+\varrho = \alpha\cdot\omega+\varrho.$$

One of the critical ordinals for the function p is $\lim\limits_{n<\omega} \alpha^n$, where $\alpha^n = \underbrace{\alpha\cdot\alpha\ldots\alpha}_{n}$. All critical ordinals for the function p will be determined in the following section.

Exercises [1])

1. Determine whether $\lim[\varphi(\xi)+\psi(\xi)] = \lim\varphi(\xi)+\lim\psi(\xi)$ holds.

2. Determine whether $\lim[\varphi(\xi)]\cdot\alpha = [\lim\varphi(\xi)\cdot\alpha]$ holds.

3. Prove that if $\alpha_1+\beta_1 = \alpha+\beta$ and $\beta_1 > \beta$, then $\alpha_1 < \alpha$.

4. Show that for every ordinal α there exists a finite number of ordinals β such that the equation $\alpha = \xi+\beta$ is solvable for ξ (each such ordinal is called a *remainder* of α).

5. Show that if a sequence φ is increasing, $\alpha = \lim\limits_{\xi<\lambda}\varphi(\xi)$ and if $\alpha = \varphi(\xi)+\varrho(\xi)$, then there exists an ordinal $\mu < \lambda$ such that $\varrho(\xi)$ is constant for $\mu < \xi < \lambda$ and ihs constant is equal to the smallest remainder of α [2]).

§ 6. Ordinal exponentiation

The operation of *ordinal exponentiation* is defined by transfinite induction as follows:

(1) $$\gamma^0 = 1,$$

(2) $$\gamma^{\xi+1} = \gamma^\xi\cdot\gamma,$$

(3) $$\gamma^\lambda = \lim_{\xi<\lambda}\gamma^\xi,$$

where λ is a limit ordinal.

[1]) More material related to the exercises can be found in Sierpiński's books; in particular see *Cardinal and Ordinal Numbers*, 2nd edition (Warszawa 1964).

[2]) See A. Hoborski, Fundamenta Mathematicae **2** (1921) 193.

We say that γ^α is the *power* of γ, γ is the *base* and α the *exponent*. It follows from the definition that if $\gamma \geqslant 1$, then

(4) $$\alpha < \beta \rightarrow \gamma^\alpha < \gamma^\beta.$$

We shall prove that

(5) $$\gamma^{\xi+\eta} = \gamma^\xi \cdot \gamma^\eta.$$

PROOF. Given an ordinal ξ, let B denote the set of those $\zeta \in W(\eta+1)$ for which $\gamma^{\xi+\zeta} = \gamma^\xi \cdot \gamma^\zeta$. We shall show that if $\zeta \leqslant \eta$, then

(*) $$W(\zeta) \subset B \rightarrow \zeta \in B.$$

In fact, the following three cases are possible: (i) $\zeta = 0$, (ii) ζ is not a limit ordinal; (iii) ζ is a limit ordinal > 0. In case (i), $\zeta \in B$, because $\gamma^{\xi+0} = \gamma^\xi = \gamma^\xi \cdot 1 = \gamma^\xi \cdot \gamma^0$. In case (ii), $\zeta = \zeta_1 + 1$ where $\zeta_1 \in W(\zeta)$; thus, by assumption, $\zeta_1 \in B$. Hence we have $\gamma^{\xi+\zeta_1} = \gamma^\xi \cdot \gamma^{\zeta_1}$ and therefore

$$\gamma^{\xi+\zeta} = \gamma^{\xi+(\zeta_1+1)} = \gamma^{(\xi+\zeta_1)+1} = \gamma^{\xi+\zeta_1} \cdot \gamma = (\gamma^\xi \cdot \gamma^{\zeta_1})\, \gamma = \gamma^\xi (\gamma^{\zeta_1} \cdot \gamma)$$
$$= \gamma^\xi \cdot \gamma^{\zeta_1+1} = \gamma^\xi \cdot \gamma^\zeta,$$

which shows that $\zeta \in B$. Finally, in case (iii), $\xi + \zeta$ is a limit ordinal, thus

$$\gamma^{\xi+\zeta} = \lim_{\alpha < \xi+\zeta} \gamma^\alpha.$$

Applying Theorem 3, p. 236 to the functions $\varphi(\alpha) = \gamma^\alpha$ and $\psi(\alpha) = \xi + \alpha$ we infer that

$$\lim_{\alpha < \xi+\zeta} \gamma^\alpha = \lim_{\alpha<\zeta} \gamma^{\xi+\alpha}, \qquad \gamma^{\xi+\zeta} = \lim_{\alpha<\zeta} \gamma^{\xi+\alpha}.$$

Since for $\alpha < \zeta$ we have $\alpha \in W(\zeta)$, it follows that $\alpha \in B$, i.e. $\gamma^{\xi+\alpha} = \gamma^\xi \cdot \gamma^\alpha$. Thus

$$\gamma^{\xi+\zeta} = \lim_{\alpha<\zeta} (\gamma^\xi \cdot \gamma^\alpha) = \gamma^\xi \lim_{\alpha<\zeta} \gamma^\alpha = \gamma^\xi \cdot \gamma^\zeta,$$

which implies that $\zeta \in B$.

Hence implication (*) is proved. By induction it follows that $B = W(\eta+1)$. Thus $\eta \in B$, which proves (5).

(6) $$(\gamma^\xi)^\eta = \gamma^{\xi\eta}.$$

The proof is analogous to that of (5). Let B denote the set of those $\zeta \in W(\eta+1)$ for which $(\gamma^\xi)^\zeta = \gamma^{\xi\zeta}$. It suffices to show that implication (*) holds. As previously we consider cases (i), (ii), and (iii). In case

(i) we have $\zeta \in B$, because $(\gamma^\xi)^0 = 1 = \gamma^0 = \gamma^{\xi 0}$. In case (ii) we have $\zeta = \zeta_1 + 1$, where ζ_1 satisfies the condition $(\gamma^\xi)^{\zeta_1} = \gamma^{\xi\zeta_1}$. This formula in turn implies

$$(\gamma^\xi)^\zeta = (\gamma^\xi)^{\zeta_1+1} = (\gamma^\xi)^{\zeta_1}\gamma^\xi = \gamma^{\xi\zeta_1}\gamma^\xi = \gamma^{\xi\zeta_1+\xi} = \gamma^{\xi(\zeta_1+1)} = \gamma^{\xi\zeta},$$

which shows that $\zeta \in B$. Finally, if ζ is a limit ordinal > 0, then

$$(\gamma^\xi)^\zeta = \lim_{\alpha<\zeta} (\gamma^\xi)^\alpha = \lim_{\alpha<\zeta} \gamma^{\xi\alpha}.$$

Since Theorem 3, § 2, p. 236 implies that

$$\lim_{\alpha<\zeta} \gamma^{\xi\alpha} = \lim_{\eta<\xi\zeta} \gamma^\eta = \gamma^{\xi\zeta},$$

we have $\zeta \in B$. Hence formula (6) is proved.

(7) $$\gamma > 1 \rightarrow \gamma^\xi \geqslant \xi.$$

This formula follows from (4) by Theorem 5, p. 230.

The operation of ordinal exponentiation allows us to find all critical ordinals of the function $p(\xi) = \alpha \cdot \xi$ (compare p. 252). Namely, these critical ordinals are all ordinals of the form $\alpha^{\omega+\sigma}$ where σ is any ordinal. In fact,

$$p(\alpha^{\omega+\sigma}) = \alpha \cdot \alpha^{\omega+\sigma} = \alpha^{1+(\omega+\sigma)} = \alpha^{(1+\omega)+\sigma} = \alpha^{\omega+\sigma},$$

The function $f(\xi) = \gamma^\xi$ is—according to (3) and (4)—increasing and continuous (on every set $W(\alpha)$). Thus this function possesses critical ordinals by Theorem 5, p. 239. According to this theorem, those critical ordinals can be obtained as the limits of the sequences α_n where α_0 is an arbitrary ordinal and $\alpha^{n+1} = \gamma^{\alpha_n}$.

For example, assuming that $\gamma = \omega$, $\alpha_0 = 1$ we have

$$\alpha_1 = \omega, \quad \alpha_2 = \omega^\omega, \quad \alpha_3 = \omega^{\omega^\omega}, \quad \ldots$$

The limit of this sequence,

$$\varepsilon = \lim_{n<\omega} \alpha_n,$$

is the smallest critical ordinal of the function ω^ξ, i.e. the smallest ordinal satisfying the equality

(8) $$\omega^\varepsilon = \varepsilon.$$

Such ordinals ε are called *epsilon-ordinals*.

Exercises

1. Let λ be a limit ordinal. Show that if the function φ is continuous on the set $W(\lambda)$ and satisfies the conditions $\varphi(0) = 1$, $\varphi(1) = \gamma$, $\varphi(\alpha+\beta) = \varphi(\alpha)\cdot\varphi(\beta)$ for $\alpha, \beta, \alpha+\beta < \lambda$, then $\varphi(\xi) = \gamma^{\xi}$ for $\xi < \lambda$.

2. Show that if $\omega^{\xi} = \alpha+\beta$ and $\beta \neq 0$, then $\beta = \omega^{\xi}$.

3. Show that for every ordinal α there exists an epsilon-ordinal greater than α.

§ 7. Expansions of ordinal numbers for an arbitrary base

The operation of ordinal exponentiation can be used in order to represent ordinal numbers in the form similar to decimal expansion of natural numbers. For this purpose, we shall first prove the following theorem.

THEOREM 1: *If $\gamma > 1$ and $1 \leqslant \alpha < \gamma^{\xi}$, then there exist ordinals η, β and ϱ such that*

$$\alpha = \gamma^{\eta}\cdot\beta+\varrho, \quad 0 \leqslant \eta < \xi, \quad \beta < \gamma \quad \textit{and} \quad \varrho < \gamma^{\eta}.$$

PROOF. Let ζ be the smallest ordinal such that $\alpha < \gamma^{\zeta}$. Clearly $0 < \zeta \leqslant \xi$. If ζ were a limit ordinal, then we would have $\gamma^{\zeta} = \lim_{\lambda<\zeta} \gamma^{\lambda}$ and $\gamma^{\lambda} \leqslant \alpha$ for $\lambda < \zeta$. This implies $\gamma^{\zeta} \leqslant \alpha$, which contradicts the definition of ζ. Thus $\zeta = \eta+1$, where

$$0 \leqslant \eta < \xi, \quad \gamma^{\eta} \leqslant \alpha < \gamma^{\eta+1}.$$

By virtue of Theorem 4, § 5 (p. 249) there exist ordinals β and ϱ such that

$$\alpha = \gamma^{\eta}\cdot\beta+\varrho, \quad \varrho < \gamma^{\eta}.$$

If $\beta \geqslant \gamma$ then we would have $\alpha \geqslant \gamma^{\eta}\cdot\gamma+\varrho \geqslant \gamma^{\eta+1}$. Therefore $\beta < \gamma$ and the ordinals β, η and ϱ satisfy the theorem.

THEOREM 2: *If $\gamma > 1$ and $1 \leqslant \alpha < \gamma^{\eta}$, then there exist a natural number n and sequences $\beta_1, \beta_2, \ldots, \beta_n$ and $\eta_1, \eta_2, \ldots, \eta_n$ such that*

$$(1) \qquad \alpha = \gamma^{\eta_1}\beta_1+\gamma^{\eta_2}\beta_2+ \ldots +\gamma^{\eta_n}\beta_n,$$

$$(2) \quad \eta > \eta_1 > \eta_2 > \ldots > \eta_n, \quad 0 \leqslant \beta_i < \gamma \quad \textit{for} \quad i = 1, 2, \ldots, n.$$

The proof is almost a repetition of that of Theorem 5, p. 250. Namely, we define by induction three sequences φ, ψ, ϑ such that

$$\varphi_0 = \alpha, \quad \psi_0 = \min_{\xi}(\alpha < \gamma^{\xi}), \quad \vartheta_0 = 0,$$

$$\varphi_j = \gamma^{\psi_{j+1}}\vartheta_{j+1} + \varphi_{j+1} \quad \text{and} \quad \varphi_{j+1} < \gamma^{\psi_{j+1}}, \quad \psi_{j+1} < \psi_j, \ \vartheta_{j+1} < \gamma$$

if $\varphi_j \neq 0$, and

$$\varphi_{j+1} = \psi_{j+1} = \vartheta_{j+1} = 0$$

if $\varphi_j = 0$.

The existence of these sequences follows from the theorem on definition by induction (see p. 239) and from Theorem 1. Clearly $\varphi_j = 0$ from a j on.

Now we let $n^* = \min_j(\varphi_j = 0)$, $n = n^* - 1$ and $\eta_j = \psi_j$, $\beta_j = \vartheta_j$ for $1 \leqslant j < n^*$.

Formula (1) for ordinals β_j and η_j satisfying condition (2) is called the *expansion of an ordinal number* α *for the base* γ. The ordinals β_j are called *digits* and the ordinals η_i *exponents* of this expansion. If $\gamma = \omega$, then the digits are natural numbers.

Examples

$\alpha = \omega^2 + \omega \cdot 5 + 9$ is the expansion of the ordinal α for the base ω. To expand the same ordinal for the base 2 it suffices to notice that $\omega = \lim_{n<\omega} 2^n = 2^{\omega}$, thus

$$\omega^2 = (2^{\omega})^2 = 2^{\omega \cdot 2} \quad \text{and} \quad \omega \cdot 5 = 2^{\omega+2} + 2^{\omega}.$$

Therefore

$$\omega^2 + \omega \cdot 5 + 9 = 2^{\omega \cdot 2} + 2^{\omega+2} + 2^{\omega} + 2^3 + 2^0.$$

In a similar way we obtain

$$\omega^{\omega} = 2^{\omega^2}.$$

For epsilon-ordinals, the expansion for the base ω is $\varepsilon = \omega^{\varepsilon}$. Thus an epsilon-ordinal ε cannot be represented in the form (1) for $\gamma = \omega$ with exponents smaller than ε.

Two ordinals represented in the form (1) can be compared with respect to their magnitude by means of the following theorem.

THEOREM 3: *If* $\eta > \xi_1 > \ldots > \xi_p$ *and* $\gamma > \vartheta_n$ *for* $n \leqslant p$, *then*

$$\gamma^{\eta} > \gamma^{\xi_1}\vartheta_1 + \gamma^{\xi_2}\vartheta_2 + \ldots + \gamma^{\xi_p}\vartheta_p.$$

PROOF. From the assumption it follows that $\eta \geqslant \xi_1+1$ and $\gamma-\vartheta_1 > 0$. This implies

$$\gamma^{\eta} \geqslant \gamma^{\xi_1}\gamma = \gamma^{\xi_1}\vartheta_1+\gamma^{\xi_1}(\gamma-\vartheta_1) \geqslant \gamma^{\xi_1}\vartheta_1+\gamma^{\xi_1}.$$

Since $\gamma^{\xi_1} \geqslant \gamma^{\xi_2}\gamma$, we have $\gamma^{\xi_1} \geqslant \gamma^{\xi_2}\vartheta_2+\gamma^{\xi_2}$. Thus

$$\gamma^{\eta} \geqslant \gamma^{\xi_1}\vartheta_1+\gamma^{\xi_2}\vartheta_2+\gamma^{\xi_2}.$$

Repeating this operation, after p steps we obtain the inequality

$$\gamma^{\eta} \geqslant \gamma^{\xi_1}\vartheta_1+\gamma^{\xi_2}\vartheta_2+ \dots +\gamma^{\xi_p}\vartheta_p+\gamma^{\xi_p},$$

from which the required inequality follows directly (since $\gamma^{\xi_p} > 0$).

THEOREM 4: *If*

$$\alpha = \gamma^{\eta_1}\beta_1+ \dots +\gamma^{\eta_{i-1}}\beta_{i-1}+\gamma^{\eta_i}\beta_i+ \dots +\gamma^{\eta_n}\beta_n,$$

$$\zeta = \gamma^{\eta_1}\beta_1+ \dots +\gamma^{\eta_{i-1}}\beta_{i-1}+\gamma^{\xi_i}\vartheta_i+ \dots +\gamma^{\xi_p}\vartheta_p,$$

where

$$\eta_1 > \eta_2 > \dots > \eta_n, \qquad \eta_{i-1} > \xi_i > \dots > \xi_p,$$

$$0 < \beta_1, \dots, \beta_n < \gamma, \qquad 0 < \vartheta_i, \dots, \vartheta_p < \gamma,$$

and $\gamma^{\eta_i}\beta_i \neq \gamma^{\xi_i}\vartheta_i$, *then*

$$(\alpha > \zeta) \equiv [(\eta_i > \xi_i) \vee (\eta_i = \xi_i) \wedge (\beta_i > \vartheta_i)].$$

PROOF. Suppose that $\eta_i > \xi_i$. It follows from Theorem 3 that

$$\gamma^{\eta_i}\beta_i+ \dots +\gamma^{\eta_n}\beta_n \geqslant \gamma^{\eta_i} > \gamma^{\xi_i}\vartheta_i+\gamma^{\xi_{i+1}}\vartheta_{i+1}+ \dots +\gamma^{\xi_p}\vartheta_p,$$

therefore $\alpha > \zeta$, because by (1), p. 247 we have

$$\alpha = \gamma^{\eta_1}\beta_1+ \dots +\gamma^{\eta_{i-1}}\beta_{i-1}+\gamma^{\eta_i}\beta_i+ \dots +\gamma^{\eta_n}\beta_n$$
$$> \gamma^{\eta_1}\beta_1+ \dots +\gamma^{\eta_{i-1}}\beta_{i-1}+\gamma^{\xi_i}\vartheta_i+ \dots +\gamma^{\xi_p}\vartheta_p = \zeta.$$

In turn, suppose that $\eta_i = \xi_i$ and $\beta_i > \vartheta_i$. It follows from Theorem 3 that

$$\gamma^{\eta_i}(\beta_i-\vartheta_i) \geqslant \gamma^{\eta_i} > \gamma^{\xi_{i+1}}\vartheta_{i+1}+ \dots +\gamma^{\xi_p}\vartheta_p.$$

This implies

$$\gamma^{\eta_i}\vartheta_i+\gamma^{\eta_i}(\beta_i-\vartheta_i) > \gamma^{\xi_i}\vartheta_i+\gamma^{\xi_{i+1}}\vartheta_{i+1}+ \dots +\gamma^{\xi_p}\vartheta_p,$$

or

$$\gamma^{\eta_i}\beta_i > \gamma^{\xi_i}\vartheta_i+\gamma^{\xi_{i+1}}\vartheta_{i+1}+ \dots +\gamma^{\xi_p}\vartheta_p.$$

Therefore we have

$$\gamma^{\eta_i}\beta_i+ \dots +\gamma^{\eta_n}\beta_n > \gamma^{\xi_i}\vartheta_i+ \dots +\gamma^{\xi_p}\vartheta_p$$

which shows that $\alpha > \zeta$.

Finally, if either $\eta_i < \xi_i$ or $\eta_i = \xi_i$ and $\beta_i < \vartheta_i$, then applying an analogous reasoning we obtain the inequality $\alpha < \zeta$. This concludes the proof of Theorem 4.

Theorem 4 shows that expansions of ordinals possess properties analogous to those of expansions of natural numbers. In both cases, comparing the magnitudes of two numbers, we consider the first non-identical components of their expansions and we compare the exponents. In case the exponents are equal, we compare their coefficients.

THEOREM 5: *For a given base, every ordinal number can be represented in the form* (1) *in exactly one way.*

PROOF. In fact, by virtue of Theorem 4, if

$$\gamma^{\eta_1}\beta_1 + \ldots + \gamma^{\eta_n}\beta_n = \gamma^{\xi_1}\vartheta_1 + \ldots + \gamma^{\xi_p}\vartheta_p$$

(where $\eta_1 > \eta_2 > \ldots > \eta_n$, $\xi_1 > \xi_2 > \ldots > \xi_p$, $0 < \beta_1, \ldots, \beta_n < \gamma$, $0 < \vartheta_1, \ldots, \vartheta_p < \gamma$), then $n = p$ and $\eta_k = \xi_k$, $\beta_k = \vartheta_k$ for $k \leqslant n$.

Theorem 4 allows us to establish a connection between the notion of power of ordinal numbers defined in § 6, and the notion of lexicographical ordering introduced in § 5, Chapter VI.

THEOREM 6: *The power γ^η is the order type of the set of those functions belonging to the lexicographically ordered set $W(\gamma)^{W(\eta)}$ which have values $\neq 0$ only for a finite number of arguments.*

PROOF. According to Theorem 4, § 2, p. 233 $\gamma^\eta = \overline{W(\gamma^\eta)}$. To each ordinal $\alpha \in W(\gamma^\eta)$ there corresponds a unique expansion

$$\gamma^{\eta_1}\beta_1 + \gamma^{\eta_2}\beta_2 + \ldots + \gamma^{\eta_n}\beta_n,$$

where $\eta > \eta_1 > \eta_2 > \ldots > \eta_n$ and $0 < \beta_1, \ldots, \beta_n < \gamma$. In turn, this expansion can be associated with the function $f_\alpha \in W(\gamma)^{W(\eta)}$ defined as follows

$$f_\alpha(\eta_i) = \beta_i \quad \text{for} \quad i = 1, 2, \ldots, n,$$

$$f_\alpha(\xi) = 0 \quad \text{for} \quad \xi \neq \eta_1, \eta_2, \ldots, \eta_n.$$

Conversely, each function $g \in W(\gamma)^{W(\eta)}$ which assumes values different from 0 only for a finite number of arguments can be associated with the ordinal $\alpha \in W(\gamma^\eta)$ such that $g = f_\alpha$.

Finally, it follows from Theorem 4 that f_α precedes f_ζ in the lexicographical ordering of the set $W(\gamma)^{W(\eta)}$ if and only if $\alpha < \zeta$.

As another application of expansion (1), we shall establish a characteristic property of powers of the ordinal ω.

DEFINITION: An ordinal ϱ is said to be a *remainder* of an ordinal α if $\varrho \neq 0$ and there exists an ordinal σ such that $\alpha = \sigma + \varrho$.

THEOREM 7: *In order that every remainder of an ordinal α be equal to α it is neccessary and sufficient that the ordinal α be a power of the ordinal ω.*

PROOF. If every remainder of the ordinal α equals α, then in the expansion

$$\alpha = \omega^{\eta_1}\beta_1 + \omega^{\eta_2}\beta_2 + \ldots + \omega^{\eta_n}\beta_n$$

we have $n = 1$ and $\beta_1 = 1$, i.e. $\alpha = \omega^{\eta_1}$.

Suppose that $\alpha = \omega^{\beta}$ and let ϱ be a remainder of α. Thus for a certain σ we have

$$(3) \qquad \alpha = \sigma + \varrho \quad \text{and} \quad \sigma < \alpha, \quad \text{i.e.} \quad \sigma < \omega^{\beta}.$$

Let us expand σ for the base ω:

$$\sigma = \omega^{\eta} n + \omega^{\eta_1} n_1 + \ldots + \omega^{\eta_k} n_k.$$

We have $\eta < \beta$, i.e. $\eta + 1 \leqslant \beta$. Let $\tau = \omega^{\beta} - \omega^{\eta+1}$. We obtain

$$\begin{aligned}\omega^{\beta} \leqslant \sigma + \omega^{\beta} \leqslant \omega^{\eta}(n+1) + \omega^{\beta} &= \omega^{\eta}(n+1) + \omega^{\eta+1} + \tau \\ = \omega^{\eta}(n+1+\omega) + \tau = \omega^{\eta}\cdot\omega + \tau &= \omega^{\eta+1} + \tau = \omega^{\beta}\end{aligned}$$

and we infer that $\omega^{\beta} = \sigma + \omega^{\beta}$, that is, $\alpha = \sigma + \alpha$. According to (3), $\sigma + \varrho = \sigma + \alpha$, which shows that $\varrho = \alpha$. Q.E.D.

Using expansions for the base ω we can define two operations on ordinals, called *natural addition* and *natural multiplication*[1]). These operations have more properties in common with operations of addition and multiplication of natural numbers than the operations of ordinal addition and multiplication considered before.

In order to define these operation let us consider two ordinals

$$\alpha = \omega^{\eta_1} n_1 + \omega^{\eta_2} n_2 + \ldots + \omega^{\eta_k} n_k,$$

$$\beta = \omega^{\zeta_1} m_1 + \omega^{\zeta_2} m_2 + \ldots + \omega^{\zeta_l} m_l.$$

Upon completing these expansions by powers of ω with the coeffi-

[1]) G. Hessenberg, *Grundbegriffe der Mengenlehre* (Göttingen 1906), pp. 591–594.

cients 0, we obtain expansions with the same powers of ω:

$$\alpha = \omega^{\xi_1}p_1+\omega^{\xi_2}p_2+\ldots+\omega^{\xi_h}p_h, \tag{4}$$

$$\beta = \omega^{\xi_1}q_1+\omega^{\xi_2}q_2+\ldots+\omega^{\xi_h}q_h. \tag{5}$$

The *natural sum* of α and β is defined to be

$$\alpha(+)\beta = \omega^{\xi_1}(p_1+q_1)+\omega^{\xi_2}(p_2+q_2)+\ldots+\omega^{\xi_h}(p_h+q_h).$$

The *natural product* $\alpha(\cdot)\beta$ is defined to be the ordinal arising by formal multiplication of the expansions (4) and (5) as though they were polynomials in ω: multiplying two powers of ω we take the natural sum of the exponents and the terms obtained in this way are ordered according to their magnitude.

Natural addition and natural multiplication are *commutative*.

Examples

1. A natural sum may be different from the ordinary sum, for instance:

$$[\omega^2+\omega+1](+)[\omega^3+\omega] = \omega^3+\omega^2+\omega\cdot 2+1,$$

$$[\omega^2+\omega+1]+[\omega^3+\omega] = \omega^3+\omega.$$

2. $[\omega^2+\omega+1](\cdot)[\omega^3+\omega] = \omega^5+\omega^4+\omega^3\cdot 2+\omega^2+\omega.$

3. $[\omega^{\omega+1}+\omega^{\omega}+1](\cdot)[\omega^{\omega+1}+\omega^{\omega}+\omega]$

$$= \omega^{\omega\cdot 2+2}+\omega^{\omega\cdot 2+1}\cdot 2+\omega^{\omega\cdot 2}+\omega^{\omega+2}+\omega^{\omega+1}\cdot 2+\omega^{\omega}+\omega.$$

4. Expansions (4) and (5) can be rewritten as

$$\alpha = \omega^{\xi_1}p_1(+)\omega^{\xi_2}p_2(+)\ldots(+)\omega^{\xi_h}p_h,$$

$$\beta = \omega^{\xi_1}q_1(+)\omega^{\xi_2}q_2(+)\ldots(+)\omega^{\xi_h}q_h.$$

Exercises

1. Show that the sum $\alpha(+)\beta$ is an increasing function with respect to α as well as with respect to β.

2. Show that for every ordinal γ there exist at most finitely many pairs α, β such that $\alpha(+)\beta = \gamma$.

3. Prove that if $\xi < \omega^{\omega^\alpha}$ and $\eta < \omega^{\omega^\alpha}$, then $\xi\cdot\eta < \omega^{\omega^\alpha}$.

Conversely if an ordinal ζ satisfies the condition

(6) $$(\xi < \zeta)\cdot(\eta < \zeta) \rightarrow (\xi\cdot\eta < \zeta),$$

then there exists an α such that $\zeta = \omega^{\omega^{\alpha}}$.

REMARK: The ordinals ζ satisfying (6) for all ξ, η are called the *principal ordinals of multiplication* [1]).

§ 8. The well-ordering theorem

Well-ordered sets owe their importance mainly to the fact that for each set there exists a relation which well orders it. This theorem, called the *well-ordering theorem* or *Zermelo's Theorem* [2]) is equivalent to the axiom of choice on the basis of the axioms Σ[TR]. In this section we shall prove this equivalence and formulate several theorems equivalent to Zermelo's theorem. Some applications of these theorems will also be given.

THEOREM 1: *If A is any set such that there exists a choice function for the family $2^A - \{0\}$, then there exists a relation well ordering A.*

PROOF. Let f be a choice function for the family $2^A - \{0\}$; we can extend this function to the whole family 2^A letting $f(0) = p$ where p is any fixed element which does not belong to A.

Now let C denote the family of relations $R \subset A \times A$ well ordering their field. In virtue of the axiom of replacement, there exists a set consisting of all ordinals $\overline{R}$ where $R \in C$. Let α be the smallest ordinal greater than every ordinal $\overline{R}$ of this set.

According to the theorem on definition by induction, there exists a transfinite sequence φ of type α such that

$$\varphi_\xi = f(A - \{\varphi_\eta : \eta < \xi\}).$$

If $\varphi_\xi \neq p$ then $\varphi_\xi \in A - \{\varphi_\eta : \eta < \xi\}$ and $\varphi_\xi \neq \varphi_\eta$ for $\eta < \xi$. If for all $\xi < \alpha$ we had $\varphi_\xi \neq p$, then there would exist a transfinite sequence of type α with distinct terms belonging to A. This implies that there exists a relation well ordering a subset of A into type α. But this contradicts

[1]) Principal ordinals for other operations were defined and investigated by E. Jacobstahl; see Mathematische Annalen **66** (1907) 149.

[2]) This theorem was first proved by E. Zermelo in his paper *Beweis dass jede Menge wohlgeordnet werden kann*, Mathematische Annalen **59** (1904) 514-516.

the definition of α. Therefore there exists the smallest ordinal β such that $\varphi_\beta = p$. This implies that $A = \{\varphi_\eta : \eta < \beta\}$, thus A is the set of all terms of a transfinite sequence of type β whose all terms are distinct. Consequently there exists a relation well ordering the set A into type β. Q.E.D.

REMARK: In the proof above we used only ordinals of the form $\overline{R}$ where $R \subset A \times A$ and the ordinal α. It is therefore easy to reformulate the proof in such a way as to eliminate the notion of an ordinal. We simply replace $\overline{R}$ by the family of all relations $S \subset A \times A$ which are similar to R and α by the family of all well-ordering relations $R \subset A \times A$. The proof thus modified can be based on axioms Σ and is independent of the axiom of replacement[1]).

Another method of eliminating ordinal numbers consists in replacing them by the so-called *von Neumann's ordinals* to be discussed in §9. The proof of Theorem 1 obtained by this modification is also based only on the axioms Σ but this time with the axiom of replacement.

The converse to Theorem 1 is also true:

THEOREM 2: *If there exists a relation well ordering a set A, then there exists a choice function for the family $2^A - \{0\}$.*

In fact, for $X \in 2^A - \{0\}$ we define $f(X)$ to be the first element of X in the given well-ordering.

The following corollary is a direct consequence of Theorem 1.

°COROLLARY 3: *For every set A there exists a relation well ordering A.*

Now we shall formulate the so-called *maximum principle*, which is often used in place of the well-ordering theorem.

Let A be an ordered set. We say that A is a *closed set* if for every linearly ordered subset B of A the supremum $\bigvee_{x \in B} x$ exists in A. An element x is said to be *maximal* if there is no $y \in A$ such that $y > x$.

[1]) Such a proof can be found in many books; see for example A. A. Fraenkel, *Abstract Set Theory* (Amsterdam 1953), pp. 309-315.

THEOREM 4: *If A is an ordered closed set and there exists a choice function for the family $2^A - \{0\}$, then there exists a maximal element in A*[1].

PROOF. As in the proof of Theorem 1, we extend f by letting $f(0) = p$ where p is any element not belonging to A. Let α be the ordinal defined in the proof of Theorem 1. By theorem on transfinite induction there exists a sequence φ of type α such that

$$\varphi_\xi = f(\{x \in A: x > \bigvee_{\eta<\xi} \varphi_\eta\}),$$

where the symbol after the sign f denotes the empty set if not all φ_η, $\eta < \xi$, belong to A or if the supremum $\bigvee_{\eta<\xi} \varphi_\eta$ does not exist.

Since A is closed, we see that if $\varphi_\xi \neq p$, then $\varphi_\eta \neq p$ for every ordinal $\eta < \xi$ and the supremum $k = \bigvee_{\eta<\xi} \varphi_\eta$ exists and is $< \varphi_\xi$. If we had $\varphi_\xi \neq p$ for every $\xi < \alpha$, then there would exist a transfinite sequence of type α with distinct terms belonging to A. But this contradicts the definition of α. Consequently, there exist ordinals ξ such that $\varphi_\xi = p$. If β is the smallest such ordinal, then there is no $x \in A$ such that $x > \bigvee_{\xi<\beta} \varphi_\xi$. Hence the supremum $\bigvee_{\xi<\beta} \varphi_\xi$ is a maximal element of A. Q.E.D.

°COROLLARY 5: (The so-called ZORN MAXIMUM PRINCIPLE.) *In every closed, ordered set there exists a maximal element.*

The following theorem is a special case of Theorem 4.

THEOREM 6: *If A is a family of sets with the following property*

$$(*) \qquad (\bigcup_{X \in B} X) \in A \text{ for every monotonic family } B \subset A$$

and if there exists a choice function for the family $2^A - \{0\}$, then there exists a maximal element in A[2].

[1]) M. Zorn, *A remark on method in transfinite algebra,* Bulletin of the American Mathematical Society **41** (1935) 667–670. See also the next reference.

[2]) Theorem 6 was proved by K. Kuratowski in his paper *Une méthode d'élimination des nombres transfinis des raisonnements mathématiques,* Fundamenta Mathematicae **3** (1922) 89.

For the proof it suffices to notice that the family $\boldsymbol{A}$ is ordered by the inclusion relation and the union $\bigcup_{X \in \boldsymbol{B}} X$ is the supremum of $\boldsymbol{B}$.

Theorems 4 and 6 show that the existence of maximal elements follows from the axiom of choice. We now show that, conversely, the axiom of choice follows from the existence of maximal elements.

THEOREM 7: *If for every family of sets $\boldsymbol{A}$ satisfying condition* $(*)$ *there exists a maximal element, then for every family $\boldsymbol{Z}$ of non-empty sets there exists a choice function.*

PROOF. Let $\boldsymbol{A}$ be a family of functions f such that

(i) The domain of f is a family $\boldsymbol{C}_f \subset \boldsymbol{Z}$.

(ii) $f(X) \in X$ for all $X \in \boldsymbol{C}_f$.

Let us recall that a function f with domain $\boldsymbol{C}_f$ is the set of pairs $\langle X, f(X) \rangle$ where $X \in \boldsymbol{C}_f$. Thus the formula $f_1 \subset f_2$ means that $\boldsymbol{C}_{f_1} \subset \boldsymbol{C}_{f_2}$ and $f_1(X) = f_2(X)$ for all $X \in \boldsymbol{C}_{f_1}$:

$$(1) \qquad f_1 \subset f_2 \equiv \Big\{ (\boldsymbol{C}_{f_1} \subset \boldsymbol{C}_{f_2}) \wedge \bigwedge_{X \in \boldsymbol{C}_{f_1}} [f_1(X) = f_2(X)] \Big\},$$

that is, the function f_2 is an extension of the function f_1.

We shall show that the family $\boldsymbol{A}$ satisfies condition $(*)$.

For this purpose, suppose that $\boldsymbol{B}$ is a monotonic family included in $\boldsymbol{A}$ and let F denote the union $\bigcup \boldsymbol{B}$. The elements of the set F, are pairs of the form $\langle X, y \rangle$ where $X \in \boldsymbol{Z}$. In fact, each component f of the union F is a set of such pairs. If $\langle X, y_1 \rangle \in F$ and $\langle X, y_2 \rangle \in F$, then there exist f_1 and f_2 such that $\langle X, y_1 \rangle \in f_1 \in \boldsymbol{B}$ and $\langle X, y_2 \rangle \in f_2 \in \boldsymbol{B}$. This implies that $y_1 = f_1(X)$ and $y_2 = f_2(X)$.

Since the family $\boldsymbol{B}$ is monotone, we have either $f_1 \subset f_2$ or $f_2 \subset f_1$. By (1) we infer that in both cases, $y_1 = f_1(X) = f_2(X) = y_2$.

Thus the set F satisfies the condition

$$[\langle X, y_1 \rangle \in F] \wedge [\langle X, y_2 \rangle \in F] \rightarrow (y_1 = y_2),$$

i.e., F is a function. The domain of this function is $\bigcup_{f \in \boldsymbol{B}} \boldsymbol{C}_f$, i.e. a family included in $\boldsymbol{Z}$.

If $\langle X, y \rangle \in F$ then there exists a function $f \in \boldsymbol{B}$ such that $\langle X, y \rangle \in f$. This implies that $y = f(X)$; hence $y = F(X) = f(X) \in X$. Therefore the function F belongs to the family $\boldsymbol{A}$. This shows that this family satisfies condition $(*)$.

By assumption there exists a maximal element f_0 in the family $\boldsymbol{A}$. We shall show that $\boldsymbol{C}_{f_0} = \boldsymbol{Z}$. Suppose the contrary. Then there exists an element X of the difference $\boldsymbol{Z} - \boldsymbol{C}_{f_0}$ which is a non-empty set. Thus there also exists an element $x \in X$. Letting $f = f_0 \cup \{\langle X, x\rangle\}$, we obtain $f_0 \subset f$, $f_0 \neq f$ and $f \in \boldsymbol{A}$. But this contradicts the hypothesis that f_0 is a maximal element in $\boldsymbol{A}$.

Hence the function f_0 satisfies the condition $f_0(X) \in X$ for all $X \in \boldsymbol{Z}$. Q.E.D.

Applications

1. *Extension of an order to a linear order.*

° THEOREM 8: *For every relation R_0 ordering the set A there exists a relation linearly ordering A which contains R_0.*

PROOF. Let $\boldsymbol{K}$ be the family of relations ordering A and containing R_0. It can easily be shown that this family satisfies condition (*) of Theorem 6, therefore it contains a maximal element R.

We shall show that R is the required extension of R_0 to a linear order. Since R is by definition an order, it suffices to show that the relation R is connected. Suppose on the contrary that there exist elements $a, b \in A$ such that $\neg(a\,R\,b) \wedge \neg(b\,R\,a)$. We shall show that the relation

$$R' = R \cup \{\langle x, y\rangle : (x\,R\,a) \wedge (b\,R\,y)\} = R \cup S$$

orders A. This will provide a contradiction since $R' \supset R$ and $R' \neq R$.

Clearly $x\,R'x$ for every $x \in A$. To show that the relation R' is transitive, suppose that $x\,R'y$ and $y\,R'z$. One of the following cases holds:

(i) $(x\,R\,y) \wedge (y\,R\,z)$;

(ii) $(x\,R\,y) \wedge (y\,R\,a) \wedge (b\,R\,z)$;

(iii) $(x\,R\,a) \wedge (b\,R\,y) \wedge (y\,R\,z)$;

(iv) $(x\,R\,a) \wedge (b\,R\,y) \wedge (y\,R\,a) \vee (b\,R\,z)$.

Case (iv) is impossible: it implies $b\,R\,a$, which contradics the hypothesis. In case (i) we obtain $x\,R\,z$ since R is transitive. Therefore we also have $x\,R'z$. In cases (ii) and (iii) we obtain $(x\,R\,a) \wedge (b\,R\,z)$ by the transitivity of R, thus $x\,S\,z$ and, consequently, $x\,R'z$. This shows that R' is transitive.

Finally, in order to prove that R' is antisymmetric, suppose that $xR'y$ and $yR'x$. We now have the cases analogous to (i)–(iv) where z is replaced by x. Cases (ii)–(iv) are impossible, case (i) implies $x = y$. Thus Theorem 8 is proved.

° 2. Let A be a distributive lattice and I_0 its ideal not containing an element b (see p. 163). The family of all ideals $I \supset I_0$ of the lattice A not containing the element b satisfies condition (*) of Theorem 6. Therefore there exist maximal elements of this family. In particular, there exist maximal elements in the family $\boldsymbol{P}_{a.b}$ of those ideals which contain a but which do not contain b (provided that a non$\geqslant b$, (see p. 164).

If, in particular, A is a lattice with unit i and I is an ideal different from A (hence I does not contain i), then there exists at least one maximal ideal different from A and containing I. Such an ideal is prime (see p. 168, Exercise 2).

° 3. Let $\overline{\overline{A}} = \mathfrak{m} \geqslant \mathfrak{a}_0$ and let $\boldsymbol{M}$ be a family of a power $\leqslant \mathfrak{m}$ such that each element of $\boldsymbol{M}$ is a subset of A and has the power $\mathfrak{m}$. Then there is a set Z such that

$$(2) \quad Z \subset A, \quad \overline{\overline{Z}} = \mathfrak{m}, \quad \overline{\overline{A-Z}} = \mathfrak{m}$$

$$\text{and} \quad Z \cap X \neq 0 \neq X - Z \quad \text{for every } X \in \boldsymbol{M}.$$

Proof. In virtue of the well-ordering theorem there is a smallest ordinal α such that there exists a sequence of type α without repetitions composed of all the elements of A. Let x_ξ denote the ξth term of this sequence and let M_ξ be the ξth term of a sequence of type α (not necessarily without repetitions) which contains all the elements of $\boldsymbol{M}$.

We define by transfinite induction two sequences p and q of type α. Namely p_ξ is the first term x_ν belonging to $M_\xi - S_\xi$, and q_ξ is the first term x_μ belonging to $(M_\xi - \{p_\xi\}) - S_\xi$ where

$$S_\xi = \{p_\eta \colon \eta < \xi\} \cup \{q_\eta \colon \eta < \xi\}.$$

The elements p_ξ and q_ξ exist, because the set S_ξ is of power $< \mathfrak{m}$ and M_ξ is of power $\mathfrak{m}$.

The set Z consisting of all p_ξ where $\xi < \alpha$ satisfies condition (2).

The theorem above has an interesting topological application[1]). Let $A = \mathcal{E}$ (thus $\mathfrak{m} = \mathfrak{c}$) and let $\boldsymbol{M}$ be a family of non-empty perfect sets (a *perfect set* is a set identical with its derivative). Such sets are of power $\mathfrak{c}$[2]). Hence there is a set Z which has a point in common with every perfect subset of the set $\mathcal{E}$ and whose complement possesses the same property.

It can be proved that such a set is non-measurable in the sense of Lebesgue. #

4. Let X be an arbitrary set, $\boldsymbol{R}^*$ a family contained in 2^X. We shall prove that *the set A of all families $\boldsymbol{R}$ with the finite intersection property satisfying the condition $\boldsymbol{R}^* \subset \boldsymbol{R} \subset 2^X$ possesses property* $(\check{*})$ (see p. 139).

Suppose that $B \subset A$ and that the set B is linearly ordered by inclusion. We shall show that $\bigcup_{\boldsymbol{R} \in B} \boldsymbol{R} \in A$. Clearly, it suffices to show that this union possesses the finite intersection property. Let $n \in N$ and $X_i \in B$ for $i < n$. For each i there is a family $\boldsymbol{R}_i \in B$ such that $X_i \in \boldsymbol{R}_i$. Since B is linearly ordered, one of these families, say $\boldsymbol{R}_0$, contains all the remaining families. This implies $X_i \in \boldsymbol{R}_0$ for $i < n$ and since $\boldsymbol{R}_0$ has the finite intersection property, we obtain $\bigcap_i X_i \neq 0$. Q.E.D.

° It follows from Theorem 6 that *for every family $\boldsymbol{R}_0 \subset 2^X$ with the finite intersection property there is a maximal family $\boldsymbol{R}$ with the finite intersection property such that $\boldsymbol{R} \subset 2^X$ and $\boldsymbol{R}$ contains $\boldsymbol{R}_0$.*

5. *Hamel's basis*[3]). A set $X \subset \mathcal{E}$ is said to be *independent* if for any finite sequence $x_0, x_1, \ldots, x_{n-1}$ of distinct elements of X the equation $r_0 x_0 + r_1 x_1 + \ldots + r_{n-1} x_{n-1} = 0$ is satisfied by rational numbers $r_0, \ldots, r_{n-1}$ if and only if all these numbers are equal to 0. An example of an independent set is $\{\sqrt{2}, \sqrt{3}\}$.

[1]) See F. Bernstein, *Zur Theorie der trigonometrischen Reihen*, Leipziger Berichte **60** (1908) 329.

[2]) See K. Kuratowski, *Topology I*, p. 514 (Warszawa 1966).

[3]) G. Hamel, *Eine Basis aller Zahlen und die unstetigen Lősungen der Funktionalgleichung $f(x+y) = f(x)+f(y)$*, Mathematische Annalen **60** (1908), 459–462.

It is easy to show that if $\boldsymbol{B}$ is a monotone family of independent sets, then $\bigcup_{X \in \boldsymbol{B}} X$ is also an independent set. By Theorem 6 this implies

°THEOREM 9: *There exists a maximal independent set.*

Such a set is called a *Hamel basis* for $\mathcal{E}$.

If H is a Hamel basis, then every number $x \neq 0$ can be uniquely represented in the form

$$x = \sum_{i<n} r_i b_i, \tag{3}$$

where $n \in N$, b_i are distinct elements of the basis and r_i rational coefficients different from 0. For if there existed a number x not having such a representation, then the set $H \cup \{x\}$ would be independent, contrary to the assumption that H is maximal. On the other hand, if there were two representations $\sum_{i<n} r'_i b'_i = \sum_{j<m} r''_j b''_j$, then the elements of the set $\{b'_0, \ldots, b'_{n-1}, b''_0, \ldots, b''_{m-1}\}$ would not be independent.

° COROLLARY 10: *There exist non-continuous functions of the real variable x satisfying for all x, y the equation*

$$f(x+y) = f(x)+f(y).$$

In fact, let H be a Hamel basis and let $x_0 \in H$. Denoting by $f(x)$ the number r_0 such that in the expansion (3) x_0 occurs with the coefficient r_0 we obtain the required function. This function is not continuous, because it takes only rational values and is not constant. #

The theory given in this section enables us to prove the theorem mentioned on p. 196.

° THEOREM 11: *If $\mathfrak{f}$ is a function defined on the set T whose values are cardinal numbers, then there exists a function F defined on T such that $\overline{\overline{F_t}} = \mathfrak{f}_t$ for every $t \in T$.*

PROOF. Let $t \in T$. Since $\mathfrak{f}_t$ is a cardinal, there exists a set X such that $\mathfrak{f}_t = \overline{\overline{X}}$. According to Corollary 3 there exist an ordinal α and a relation R such that R orders X into type α. Let α_t be the smallest ordinal with this property. Now we define the function F by $F_t = W(\alpha_t)$.

Exercises

1. A family A of sets is said to be *inductive* if it has the following properties:

(i) if $X \in A$, then every finite set $Y \subset X$ belongs to A,
(ii) if every finite set $Y \subset X$ belongs to A, then $X \in A$.

Show (without the axiom of choice) that the maximum principle is equivalent to the theorem: every inductive family possesses a maximal element [1]).

2. Show (without the axiom of choice) that the maximum principle is equivalent to the following theorem: every linearly ordered subset Z of an ordered set A (that is, a set with the property $x, y \in Z \to [(x \leqslant y) \vee (y \leqslant x)]$ is contained in the maximal linearly ordered set included in A [2]).

3. Show (without the axiom of choice) that the maximum principle is equivalent to the following theorem: for every family $\boldsymbol{F}$ of non-empty sets there exists a maximal family of disjoint sets contained in $\boldsymbol{F}$ [3]).

§ 9. Von Neumann's method of elimination of ordinal numbers

In this section our exposition is based exclusively on the axioms of Σ.

We shall show that it is possible to define sets possessing exactly the same properties as ordinal numbers. We shall establish a one-to-one correspondence between those sets and types of well-ordering relations.

DEFINITION [4]): A set A is said to be an *ordinal number in the sense of von Neumann* (briefly: a *VN ordinal*) if it has the following properties:

1. *Every element of A is a set.*
2. *If $X \in A$ then $X \subset A$.*
3. *If X, $Y \in A$ then $X = Y$ or $X \in Y$ or $Y \in X$.*
4. *If $0 \neq B \subset A$ then there exists an X such that $X \in B$ and $X \cap B = 0$.*

[1]) This formulation of the maximum principle was given by Teichmüller in the paper *Braucht der Algebraiker das Auswahlaxiom?*, Deutsche Mathematik **4** (1939) 567–577. This paper also gives other forms of the maximum principle.

[2]) Garrett Birkhoff, *Lattice Theory*, Second Edition (New York 1948), p. 42.

[3]) R. L. Vaught, *On the equivalence of the axiom of choice and a maximal principle*, Bulletin of the American Mathematical Society **58** (1952) 66.

A great number of other theorems equivalent to the maximum principle, as well as many applications of the axiom of choice and Zermelo's theorem, can be found in the book: W. Sierpiński, *Cardinal and ordinal numbers* (Warszawa 1965). See also H. Rubin and J. Rubin, *Equivalents of the axiom of choice* (Amsterdam 1963).

[4]) J. v. Neumann, *Zur Einführung der transfiniten Zahlen*, Acta Litt. Ac. Scientiarum r. Univ. Hung. Franc. Joseph., Sectio sc. math. **1** (1923) 199–208.

Examples of VN ordinals:

(i) the empty set $N_0 = 0$,

(ii) the set $N_1 = \{0\}$,

(iii) the set $N_2 = \{0, \{0\}\} = \{N_0, N_1\}$,

(iv) the set $N_3 = \{N_0, N_1, N_2\}$,

(v) the set $N_\omega = \{N_0, N_1, N_2, \ldots\}$,

(vi) the set $N_{\omega+1} = N_\omega + \{N_\omega\}$.

We prove several properties of *VN* ordinals.

5. *If A is a VN ordinal then there exists no finite sequence of sets $X_1, \ldots, X_k$ such that $X_k \in X_1 \in X_2 \in \ldots \in X_{k-1} \in X_k \in A$.*

PROOF. Suppose that there exist sets $X_1, \ldots, X_k$ with this property. Let $B = \{X_1, \ldots, X_k\}$. Since $X_k \in A$, we have $X_k \subset A$ by 2 and thus $X_{k-1} \in A$. By the same argument, $X_{k-2} \in A$ and so forth. Therefore all the sets $X_1, \ldots, X_k$ belong to A and consequently $B \subset A$. None of the sets X_i satisfies condition 3. In fact, for $i > 1$ we have $X_{i-1} \in X_i \cap B$ and for $i = 1$ we have $X_k \in X_1 \cap B$. Q.E.D.

6. *If A is a VN ordinal and $M \in A$, then M is also a VN ordinal.*

PROOF. We prove that M satisfies 1–4.

(i) If $X \in M$, then we also have $X \in A$ because 2 implies $M \subset A$, and thus X is a set.

(ii) Suppose that $X \in M$ and $Y \in X$. We have

$$Y \in X \in M \in A,$$

which in view of the inclusion $M \subset A$ implies that $Y \in X \in A$; consequently $Y \in A$ by 2. According to 3 we have either $Y = M$ or $M \in Y$ or $Y \in M$. In the first case we obtain

$$M \in X \in M \in A,$$

and in the second

$$M \in Y \in X \in M \in A,$$

which contradicts Theorem 5. Thus $Y \in M$. As Y is arbitrary we infer that $X \subset M$. Therefore the set M satisfies condition 2.

(iii) If X, $Y \in M$, then X, $Y \in A$ because $M \subset A$. Thus 3 implies that either $X = Y$ or $X \in Y$ or $Y \in X$.

(iv) Suppose that $0 \neq B \subset M$. The set B is thus a non-empty subset of A and in view of 4 it contains an element X such that $X \cap B = 0$. This shows that M itself satisfies condition 4.

7. *If A and B are VN ordinals, then*

$$(A \in B) \equiv (A \subset B) \wedge (A \neq B).$$

PROOF. If $A \in B$, then $A \subset B$ by 2 and $A \neq B$ since otherwise we would have $B \in B$, contrary to 5. Suppose that $A \neq B$ and $A \subset B$. The set $B-A$ is therefore a non-empty subset of B and according to 4 there exists a set $X \in B-A$ such that $X \cap (B-A) = 0$. Now it suffices to show that $X = A$, because $X = A$ together with $X \in B$ imply $A \in B$, which proves the theorem.

The condition $X \in B$ implies $X \subset B$. Since $X \cap (B-A) = 0$, we get $X-A = 0$, that is, $X \subset A$. Suppose that $A-X \neq 0$. Hence there exists a set Y such that $Y \in A-X$ and $Y \cap A-X = 0$. Since $A-X \subset B$, we infer that $Y \in B$, and according to 3 we have either $Y \in X$ or $X \in Y$ or $X = Y$. But $Y \in X$ is impossible, for $Y \in A-X$; similarly $X \in Y$ is not the case, because it would imply $X \notin A-X$, that is (in view of $X \in A$) $X \in X \in A$, contrary to 5; finally, we cannot have $X = Y$ since $Y \in A$ and $X \in B-A$.

Hence we have proved that $A-X = 0$, i.e. $A \subset X$, which shows that $A = X$.

8. *Each VN ordinal is well ordered by the inclusion relation.*

PROOF. It suffices to show that if A is a VN ordinal, then
(a) the inclusion relation is connected in A;
(b) every non-empty subset of A has a first element.
Now (a) follows from 3, 6 and 7; and (b) follows from 4 and 7.

9. *If A and B are VN ordinals, then $A \cap B$ is also a VN ordinal.*

PROOF. We show that $A \cap B$ satisfies conditions 1–4.

(i) From $X \in A \cap B$ it follows that $X \in A$; thus X is a set.

(ii) From $X \in A \cap B$ it follows that $X \in A$ and $X \in B$; hence $X \subset A$; $X \subset B$ and consequently $X \subset A \cap B$.

(iii) From $X, Y \in A \cap B$ it follows that $X, Y \in A$; thus $X = Y$ or $X \in Y$ or $Y \in X$.

(iv) From $0 \neq M \subset A \cap B$ it follows that $0 \neq M \subset A$; hence there exists an X such that $X \in M$ and $X \cap M = 0$.

10. *If A and B are VN ordinals, then either $A \subset B$ or $B \subset A$.*

PROOF. In fact, suppose that $A \neq A \cap B \neq B$. From 9 and 7 it follows that $A \cap B \in A$ and $A \cap B \in B$. This implies $A \cap B \in A \cap B$, which contradicts 5 because $A \cap B$ is a VN ordinal. Hence $A = A \cap B$ or $B = A \cap B$.

11. *If A and B are distinct VN ordinals, then either A is a segment of B or B is a segment of A. Consequently, these sets are not similar (with respect to the inclusion relation).*

PROOF. Suppose that $A \neq B$; by 10 we have either $A \subset B$ or $B \subset A$. Suppose that the former holds. It follows from 7 that $A \in B$, which shows that the elements of A precede (in the set B) the element A. Hence the set A is a segment of B, consequently it cannot be similar to B (see Corollary 7, p. 231).

12. *For every relation R well ordering its field there exists exactly one VN ordinal ordered by the inclusion relation similarly to R.*

PROOF. Let Z be the field of the relation R and H the set of those $z \in Z$ for which there exists exactly one VN ordinal N_z satisfying the condition: N_z is ordered by the inclusion relation similarly to the segment $O(z)$ of the set Z; in this case we write $N_z \sim O(z)$.

Suppose that $O(x) \subset H$. We shall show that $x \in H$. By 11 there exists at most one VN ordinal similar to $O(x)$. Hence it suffices to show that there exists at least one such VN ordinal.

Let

$$N_x = \{X: \bigvee_z (z \prec x) \wedge (X = N_z)\}.$$

We are going to show that N_x is a VN ordinal. In fact, condition 1 clearly holds.

If $N_z \in N_x$ and $Y \in N_z$, then Y is a VN ordinal. Moreover, since $Y \in N_z \sim O(z)$, we see by 11 that Y is similar to a segment of N_z; hence Y is similar to a segment $O(t)$ of the set $O(z)$. Since $t \prec z \prec x$, we obtain $t \in O(x)$ and, consequently, $t \in H$ and $Y \sim N_t$. In view of 11 this implies $Y = N_t$ and finally $Y \in N_x$, because $N_t \in N_x$. Thus $N_z \subset N_x$; that is, N_x satisfies condition 2.

Condition 3 follows directly from 10 and 7.

Now let B be a non-empty set contained in N_x and let z_0 be the smallest element of Z such that $N_{z_0} \in B$. If there were $Y \in N_{z_0}$ such that $Y \in B$, then we would have $Y = N_z$ where $z \prec z_0$, which contradics the definition of z_0.

Hence the set N_x is a VN ordinal. If $z_1 \prec z_2 \prec x$, then $N_{z_1} \sim O(z_1)$ and $N_{z_2} \sim O(z_2)$. Thus N_{z_1} is similar to a segment of N_{z_2}. This implies by 11 that $N_{z_1} \subset N_{z_2}$ and $N_{z_1} \neq N_{z_2}$. Therefore $N_x \sim O(x)$, which proves that $x \in H$.

By induction we now infer that $H = Z$. The set

$$N^* = \{X: \bigvee_x (x \in Z) \wedge (X = N_x)\}$$

is a VN ordinal ordered similarly to Z. The proof is analogous to that carried out for the set N_x.

It follows from properties 12, 11, 8 that VN ordinals indeed satisfy all the requirements for ordinal numbers.

In connection with the reasoning just given it is worth mentioning that in the proof of property 12 we made essential use of the axiom of replacement. Without this axiom the existence of the sets N_x and N^* could not be proved.

CHAPTER VIII

ALEPHS AND RELATED TOPICS

In this chapter we shall discuss application of the theory of well-orderings to the arithmetic of cardinal numbers.

§ 1. Ordinal numbers of power $\mathfrak{a}$ [1]

The cardinal number of an ordinal ξ is the power of any set ordered in type ξ. We denote this cardinal number by $\overline{\xi}$.

Thus

$$\overline{\xi} = \overline{\overline{W(\xi)}}.$$

Ordinals of power $\mathfrak{a}$ can be treated as the types of well-ordered sets of natural numbers. This fact implies the following theorem.

THEOREM 1: *All ordinals of power* $\mathfrak{a}$ *form a set.*

DEFINITION 1: The smallest ordinal greater than every ordinal of power $\mathfrak{a}$ will be denoted by Ω.

The existence of the ordinal Ω follows from Corollary 8, p. 234.

THEOREM 2: $(\xi < \Omega) \equiv (\overline{\xi} \leqslant \mathfrak{a})$.

PROOF. If $\overline{\xi} \leqslant \mathfrak{a}$, then $\xi < \Omega$ by Definition 1. Conversely, if $\xi < \Omega$, then there exists an ordinal ζ such that $\xi \leqslant \zeta$ and $\overline{\zeta} = \mathfrak{a}$, thus $\overline{\xi} \leqslant \overline{\zeta} = \mathfrak{a}$.

DEFINITION 2 [2]: $\aleph_1 = \overline{\Omega}$, i.e. $\aleph_1 = \overline{\overline{W(\Omega)}}$.

In Theorem 2, letting $\xi = \Omega$ we obtain $\aleph_1$ non-$\leqslant \mathfrak{a}$. On the other hand, $\mathfrak{a} \leqslant \aleph_1$ and thus we have the following corollary.

[1]) Called by Cantor *numbers of the second class*. According to Cantor, the first class consists of finite numbers.

[2]) ℵ is the Hebrew letter aleph.

COROLLARY 3: $\aleph_1 > \mathfrak{a}$.

It follows that the set of ordinals ξ such that $\overline{\xi} \leqslant \mathfrak{a}$, that is, the set $W(\Omega)$, is uncountable.

THEOREM 4: *If* $\mathfrak{m} < \aleph_1$ *then* $\mathfrak{m} \leqslant \mathfrak{a}$.

In other words, *there is no cardinal which lies between* $\mathfrak{a}$ *and* $\aleph_1$.

PROOF. Let $\mathfrak{m} < \aleph_1$. Then there exists a set $M \subset W(\Omega)$ such that $\overline{\overline{M}} = \mathfrak{m}$. Let $\overline{M} = \xi$. Thus $\xi \leqslant \Omega$. Moreover, $\xi \neq \Omega$ as otherwise $\overline{\xi} = \overline{\Omega}$ and $\mathfrak{m} = \aleph_1$. Therefore, $\xi < \Omega$ and thus by Theorem 2, $\xi \leqslant \mathfrak{a}$ and thus $\mathfrak{m} \leqslant \mathfrak{a}$. Q.E.D.

The following form of the induction principle holds for ordinals $\xi < \Omega$.

THEOREM 5: *Let the set A of ordinals satisfy the conditions*:

(1) $$0 \in A,$$

(2) $$\xi \in A \rightarrow (\xi+1) \in A,$$

(3) *if* φ *is an increasing sequence and if* $\varphi(n) \in A$ *for* $n \in N$, *then*
$$[\lim_n \varphi(n)] \in A.$$

Then $W(\Omega) \subset A$.

PROOF. Suppose that the theorem does not hold. Let α be the least ordinal such that $\alpha < \Omega$ and $\alpha \notin A$. From (1) it follows that $\alpha \neq 0$. If α is not a limit ordinal, then $\alpha = \xi+1$ for a ξ in A, whence by (2) $\xi+1 \in A$, and $\alpha \in A$, contrary to the definition of α. It remains to examine the case where α is a limit ordinal.

Since $\overline{\alpha} \leqslant \mathfrak{a}$, there exists a relation R which well orders the set N of natural numbers into type α.

We define a sequence $k_0, k_1, \ldots$ of natural numbers by induction: let k_0 be the first element of the set N with respect to the relation R and let k_{n+1} be the least number $k > k_n$ such that $\overline{O_R(k_n)} < \overline{O_R(k)}$ (where $O_R(k)$ denotes, as usual, the segment of N determined by k). Such a number k exists because α is a limit ordinal.

Let $\varphi(n) = \overline{O_R(k_n)}$. Thus $\varphi(n) < \varphi(n+1)$. Moreover, $\overline{\varphi(n)} < \alpha$ for $n = 0, 1, 2, \ldots$, because $O_R(k_n)$ is a segment of a set of type α. If $\xi < \alpha$ then there exists a number m such that $\overline{O_R(m)} = \xi$. Since the sequence $k_0, k_1, \ldots$ is increasing, it follows that for some n, $O_R(m) \subset O_R(k_n)$, whence $\xi \leqslant \varphi(n)$. Hence $\alpha = \lim_{n<\omega} \varphi(n)$. On the other hand, $\varphi(n) < \alpha$ implies $\varphi(n) \in A$ for $n = 0, 1, 2, \ldots$ and thus by (3), $\alpha \in A$. But this contradicts the definition of α.

Clearly the set $W(\Omega)$ satisfies conditions (1) and (2). In fact, a more general theorem holds for $W(\Omega)$.

THEOREM 6: *If* $\xi < \Omega$ *and* $\eta < \Omega$, *then* $\xi + \eta < \Omega$ *and* $\xi \cdot \eta < \Omega$.

For $\overline{\xi+\eta} = \bar{\xi} + \bar{\eta}$ and $\overline{\xi \cdot \eta} = \bar{\xi} \cdot \bar{\eta}$; since $\bar{\xi} \leqslant \mathfrak{a}$ and $\bar{\eta} \leqslant \mathfrak{a}$, $\mathfrak{a} + \mathfrak{a} = \mathfrak{a} = \mathfrak{a} \cdot \mathfrak{a}$, it follows that $\overline{\xi+\eta} \leqslant \mathfrak{a}$ and $\overline{\xi \cdot \eta} \leqslant \mathfrak{a}$.

Using the axiom of choice we shall show that the set $W(\Omega)$ satisfies condition (3).

°THEOREM 7: *If* $\varphi(1) < \varphi(2) < \ldots$ *and* $\varphi(n) < \Omega$, *then* $\lim_{n<\omega} \varphi(n) < \Omega$.

PROOF. Let $\alpha = \lim_{n<\omega} \varphi(n)$. Then $W(\alpha) = \bigcup_n W(\varphi(n))$. The set $W(\alpha)$, being a countable union of countable sets, is countable (see p. 176). Thus $\alpha < \Omega$.

Application. Let $\boldsymbol{F}_\alpha$ be the set defined on p. 242.

°THEOREM 8: *The family* $\boldsymbol{F}_\Omega$ *is identical with the family* $\boldsymbol{B}$ *of Borel sets* (*i.e. the least* σ*-additive and* σ*-multiplicative family containing all closed sets*).

PROOF. By transfinite induction with respect to α it is easy to show that for every α (in particular for $\alpha = \Omega$), $\boldsymbol{F}_\alpha \subset \boldsymbol{B}$. It remains to show that the family $\boldsymbol{F}_\Omega$ is σ-additive and σ-multiplicative. For this purpose let X be a sequence of sets such that $X_n \in \boldsymbol{F}_\Omega$ for all n. Thus for all n there is an ordinal α_n such that $X_n \in \boldsymbol{F}_{\alpha_n}$; we may assume that α_n is the least ordinal greater than α_{n-1} such that $X_n \in \boldsymbol{F}_{\alpha_n}$. By Theorem 7 it follows that there exists β such that $\alpha_n < \beta < \Omega$ for every n, moreover, we may assume that β is, for instance, odd. Then

$$\bigcup X_n \in \Big(\bigcup_{\gamma<\beta} \boldsymbol{F}_\gamma\Big)_\sigma = \boldsymbol{F}_{\beta+1} \subset \boldsymbol{F}_\Omega \quad \text{and} \quad \bigcap X_n \in \Big(\bigcup_{\gamma<\beta+1} \boldsymbol{F}_\gamma\Big)_\sigma = \boldsymbol{F}_{\beta+2} \subset \boldsymbol{F}_\Omega .$$

Q.E.D.

Exercises

1. Prove (without using the axiom of choice) that if $\alpha < \Omega$ and $\beta < \Omega$, then $\alpha^\beta < \Omega$.

\# **2.** Let Φ_α be the family of analytically representable functions of class α (see p. 242). Prove that the union $\bigcup_{\alpha<\Omega} \Phi_\alpha$ is the least family of real functions such that

(i) every continuous function belongs to the family,

(ii) if f_n belongs to the family for $n \in N$ and if $f(x) = \lim_{n\to\infty} f_n(x)$ for every x, then f belongs to the family.

Discuss the role played by the axiom of choice in the proof of this theorem.

3. If $\{X_\alpha\}_{\alpha<\Omega}$ is a sequence of type Ω of closed subsets of the space $\mathcal{E}$ or N^N and if $X_\alpha \supset X_{\alpha+1}$ for all $\alpha < \Omega$, then there exists an ordinal $\beta < \Omega$ such that $X_\alpha = X_\beta$ for all $\alpha \geqslant \beta$.

Hint: Denote by $N_0, N_1, N_2, \ldots$ a sequence whose terms constitute an open subbase of the space. Associate with the ordinal α where $X_\alpha \neq X_{\alpha+1}$ the least number m such that $N_m \cap X_\alpha \neq 0 = N_m - X_{\alpha+1}$ and show that with distinct α are associated distinct natural numbers.

4. Prove that if A is an arbitrary subset of $\mathcal{E}$ (or of N^N), then for every transfinite sequence of derivatives of A (see p. 241) there exists a term $A^{(\beta)}$ such that $A^{(\beta)} = A^{(\alpha)}$ for all $\alpha \geqslant \beta$, where $\beta < \Omega$.

Hint: Notice that all derivatives $A^{(\alpha)}$ are closed sets and apply Exercise 3.

5. Prove the following theorem of Cantor-Bendixson: Every set $A \subset \mathcal{E}$ (or $A \subset N^N$) is the union of a perfect set and of a countable set.

Hint: Show that the difference $A - A'$ is a countable set (see Exercise 5, p. 178). #

6. Show that $2^{2^{\mathfrak{a}}} \geqslant \aleph_1$ without using the axiom of choice.

Hint: The set $2^{N\times N}$ is the union $Z \cup \bigcup_{\xi<\Omega} Z_\xi$, where Z_ξ is the set of relations well-ordering their fields in type ξ and where Z is the set of relations which are not well-orderings.

§ 2. The cardinal $\aleph(\mathfrak{m})$. Hartogs' aleph

We now generalize the construction carried out in § 1 for the cardinal $\mathfrak{a}$ to the case of an arbitrary cardinal $\mathfrak{m}$.

THEOREM 1: *For every cardinal* $\mathfrak{m}$ *there exists a set*

$$Z(\mathfrak{m}) = \{\xi \colon \overline{\overline{\xi}} \leqslant \mathfrak{m}\}.$$

PROOF. Let $\overline{\overline{A}} = \mathfrak{m}$. Every relation R whose field is contained in A is a subset of $A \times A$, that is, $R \subset 2^{A\times A}$. Therefore there exists a set $\boldsymbol{R}$ of all relations $R \subset 2^{A\times A}$ which well order their fields.

Associate with every relation $R \in \boldsymbol{R}$ its type. By the axiom of replacement we obtain the set $Z(\mathfrak{m})$ of ordinals such that

$$\xi \in Z(\mathfrak{m}) \to \overline{\overline{\xi}} \leqslant \mathfrak{m}.$$

Conversely, if $\overline{\xi} \leqslant \mathfrak{m}$, then there exists a relation R ordering a subset of A in type ξ. Thus $\xi \in Z(\mathfrak{m})$. Q.E.D.

THEOREM 2: *If* $\xi \in Z(\mathfrak{m})$, *then* $W(\xi) \subset Z(\mathfrak{m})$.

For $\eta < \xi$ implies that $\overline{\eta} \leqslant \overline{\xi}$.

DEFINITION: $\aleph(\mathfrak{m}) = \overline{\overline{Z(\mathfrak{m})}}$.

By this definition we have correlated with every cardinal $\mathfrak{m}$ an aleph $\overline{\overline{Z(\mathfrak{m})}}$. This operation is referred to as Hartogs' aleph function [1]).

THEOREM 3: $\aleph(\mathfrak{m})$ non $\leqslant \mathfrak{m}$.

PROOF. The set $Z(\mathfrak{m})$, as a set of ordinals, is well ordered by the relation $\leqslant$ (see p. 234). Let $\xi = \overline{Z(\mathfrak{m})}$. Suppose that $\aleph(\mathfrak{m}) \leqslant \mathfrak{m}$, that is $\overline{\xi} \leqslant \mathfrak{m}$. Then $\xi \in Z(\mathfrak{m})$ and thus by Theorem 2 the set $W(\xi)$ is a segment of $Z(\mathfrak{m})$. But this is impossible because by Theorem 4, p. 233 $\overline{W(\xi)} = \xi = \overline{Z(\mathfrak{m})}$, and no set is similar to its segment (p. 231).

COROLLARY 4: $\mathfrak{m} < \mathfrak{m} + \aleph(\mathfrak{m})$.

The inequality $\leqslant$ is obvious and equation is impossible as it implies that $\aleph(\mathfrak{m}) \leqslant \mathfrak{m}$.

THEOREM 5: *If there exists an ordinal* ξ *of power* $\mathfrak{m}$, *then* $\aleph(\mathfrak{m}) > \mathfrak{m}$.

PROOF. By Theorem 2, $W(\xi) \subset Z(\mathfrak{m})$ and thus $\aleph(\mathfrak{m}) \geqslant \overline{\xi} = \mathfrak{m}$; hence by Theorem 3, $\aleph(\mathfrak{m}) > \mathfrak{m}$.

THEOREM 6: *For every set* X *of ordinal numbers there exists an ordinal* α *such that* $\overline{\xi} < \overline{\alpha}$ *for every* $\xi \in X$.

PROOF. Let $S = \bigcup_{\xi \in X} W(\xi)$, $\mathfrak{m} = \overline{\overline{S}}$ and $\alpha = \overline{Z(\mathfrak{m})}$. Since $\xi = \overline{W(\xi)}$ and $W(\xi) \subset S$ for every $\xi \in X$, we have by Theorem 5,

$$\overline{\xi} = \overline{\overline{W(\xi)}} \leqslant \overline{\overline{S}} = \mathfrak{m} < \aleph(\mathfrak{m}) = \overline{\overline{Z(\mathfrak{m})}} = \overline{\alpha}.$$

THEOREM 7: $\aleph(\mathfrak{m}) < 2^{\aleph(\mathfrak{m})} \leqslant 2^{2^{\mathfrak{m}^2}}$.

PROOF. Let $\overline{\overline{A}} = \mathfrak{m}$ and let $\boldsymbol{X}$ be the family of those relations $R \subset A \times A$ which well order their fields. Clearly, $\boldsymbol{X} \subset 2^{A \times A}$. The set $\boldsymbol{X}$ is the dis-

[1]) F. Hartogs, *Über das Problem der Wohlordnung*, Math Ann. **76** (1915) 442. Theorems 3 and 5 are due to Hartogs.

joint union

(2)
$$X = \bigcup_{\alpha \in Z(\mathfrak{m})} X_\alpha$$

where X_α is the subfamily of X consisting of relations of type α. To every subset $Y \subset Z(\mathfrak{m})$ there corresponds in a one-to-one manner the union $\bigcup_{\alpha \in Y} X_\alpha = F(Y) \subset X$, therefore the family of subsets Y is of power $\leqslant 2^{\overline{\overline{X}}} = 2^{2^{\mathfrak{m}^2}}$. Thus $2^{\aleph(\mathfrak{m})} \leqslant 2^{2^{\mathfrak{m}^2}}$. Q.E.D.

Exercises

1. Using the axiom of choice show that

(3)
$$\aleph(\mathfrak{m}) \leqslant 2^{\mathfrak{m}^2}.$$

Hint: From the axiom of choice it follows that there exists a set T, containing exactly one element from each of the sets X_α (see formula (2)).

From the identity $\mathfrak{m}^2 = \mathfrak{m}$ which we shall prove in § 6, p. 292, we conclude a stronger inequality, namely

$$\aleph(\mathfrak{m}) \leqslant 2^{\mathfrak{m}}.$$

2. In the definition of the set $Z(\mathfrak{m})$ and of the cardinal $\aleph(\mathfrak{m})$ replace the relation $\leqslant$ by $\leqslant^*$ (see p. 186) and prove for so defined $\aleph^*(\mathfrak{m})$ the theorems analogous to Theorems 3–5. [Lindenbaum]

§ 3. Initial ordinals

The ordinal φ is said to be an *initial ordinal* if φ is the least ordinal ξ such that $\overline{\xi} = \overline{\varphi}$; that is:

(1)
$$\gamma < \varphi \rightarrow \overline{\gamma} < \overline{\varphi}.$$

For example, the ordinals ω and Ω are initial ordinals. We shall also denote these ordinals respectively by ω_0 and ω_1 in agreement with the notation for initial ordinals which we shall introduce in this section.

THEOREM 1: *For every infinite cardinal* $\mathfrak{m}$, *the type* φ *of the set* $Z(\mathfrak{m})$ (*that is, of the set of all ordinals of power* $\leqslant \mathfrak{m}$) *is an initial ordinal.*

Since $\xi < \gamma \in Z(\mathfrak{m})$ implies $\xi \in Z(\mathfrak{m})$, it follows that (see p. 234) $Z(\mathfrak{m}) = W(\varphi)$. On the other hand, since $\varphi \notin W(\varphi)$, we have $\varphi \notin Z(\mathfrak{m})$, whence $\overline{\varphi}$ non $\leqslant \mathfrak{m}$. From $\mathfrak{m} \geqslant \overline{\gamma}$ it follows $\overline{\varphi} > \overline{\gamma}$; thus (1) holds.

The proof of the following more general theorem is similar.

THEOREM 2: *If* $\mathfrak{m}$ *is a function defined in a set* X *and* $\mathfrak{m}_x \geqslant \mathfrak{a}$ *for every* $x \in X$, *then the ordinal* $\overline{\bigcup_{x \in X} Z(\mathfrak{m}_x)}$ *is an initial ordinal.*

For a given initial ordinal φ we shall denote by $P(\varphi)$ the set of all initial ordinals $\psi < \varphi$ and we let

(2) $$\iota(\varphi) = \overline{P(\varphi)}.$$

DEFINITION 1: The ordinal $\iota(\varphi)$ is said to be the *index* of the initial ordinal φ.

Clearly $\iota(\omega) = 0$, and $\iota(\Omega) = 1$.

THEOREM 3: *If* ψ *and* φ *are initial ordinals and if* $\psi < \varphi$, *then* $\iota(\psi) < \iota(\varphi)$.

PROOF. By assumption, $\psi \in P(\varphi)$, and it follows that $P(\psi)$ is a segment of the set $P(\varphi)$; thus $\overline{P(\psi)} < \overline{P(\varphi)}$.

THEOREM 4: *To distinct initial ordinals there correspond distinct indices.*

Theorem 4 follows from Theorem 3.

THEOREM 5: *Every ordinal* α *is the index of some initial ordinal.*

PROOF. Suppose that α is the index of no initial ordinal. Assume, moreover, that α is the least ordinal having this property. We shall show that these assumptions lead to a contradiction with Theorems 1 and 2.

In fact, if $\alpha = \beta+1$ then let ψ be such that $\iota(\psi) = \beta$, and let $\varphi = \overline{Z(\overline{\psi})}$. By Theorem 1, φ is an initial ordinal; moreover:

$$W(\varphi) = Z(\overline{\psi}) = W(\psi) \cup \{\gamma\colon (\overline{\gamma} = \overline{\psi})\}, \quad \text{whence} \quad P(\varphi) = P(\psi) \cup \{\psi\}.$$

Thus $\iota(\varphi) = \iota(\psi)+1 = \alpha$.

It remains to consider the case where α is a limit ordinal > 0. By assumption, to every $\xi < \alpha$ there corresponds exactly one ordinal ψ_ξ (by Theorem 4) such that $\iota(\psi_\xi) = \xi$. Let $\varphi = \overline{\bigcup_{\xi<\alpha} Z(\overline{\psi}_\xi)}$. By Theorem 2, φ is an initial ordinal. Moreover, $\psi_\xi \in P(\varphi)$ for $\xi < \alpha$. Finally, if $\psi \in P(\varphi)$, then $\psi \in Z(\overline{\psi}_\xi)$ for some $\xi < \alpha$ and thus $\psi < \psi_{\xi+1}$, which by Theorem 3 implies $\iota(\psi) < \xi+1 < \alpha$, therefore ψ coincides with one of the ordinals ψ_ξ, $\xi < \alpha$. Thus $\overline{P(\varphi)} = \alpha$, that is, $\iota(\varphi) = \alpha$.

On the basis of Theorem 5 we have the following definition.

DEFINITION 2: Let ω_α denote the initial ordinal whose index is equal to α; that is, $\iota(\omega_\alpha) = \alpha$.

In this way we have associated with every ordinal an initial ordinal. Every initial ordinal is associated with its index and distinct initial ordinals are associated with distinct indices.

It is easy to check that the following theorems hold.

THEOREM 6: $(\alpha < \beta) \equiv (\omega_\alpha < \omega_\beta) \equiv (\overline{\omega}_\alpha < \overline{\omega}_\beta)$.

THEOREM 7: $Z(\overline{\omega}_\alpha) = W(\omega_{\alpha+1})$, *in other words*, $\aleph(\overline{\omega}_\alpha) = \overline{\omega}_{\alpha+1}$, *and* $\bigcup_{\xi<\lambda} Z(\overline{\omega}_\xi) = W(\omega_\lambda)$, *when* λ *is a limit ordinal.*

THEOREM 8: *If* λ *is a limit ordinal, then* $\omega_\lambda = \lim_{\xi<\lambda} \omega_\xi$.

Thus the function ω_ξ is continuous, and it follows that the ordinal ω_λ is cofinal with λ.

THEOREM 9: *Every initial ordinal is of the form* ω^γ *for some* γ.

PROOF. Assume that $\alpha > 0$ and that

$$\omega_\alpha = \omega^{\gamma_1}\cdot n_1 + \omega^{\gamma_2}\cdot n_2 + \ldots + \omega^{\gamma_k}\cdot n_k, \quad \text{where} \quad \gamma_1 > \gamma_2 > \ldots > \gamma_k.$$

By Theorem 4, p. 257 it follows that

$$\omega^{\gamma_1} \leqslant \omega_\alpha < \omega^{\gamma_1}(n_1+1). \tag{3}$$

Since $\gamma_1 \neq 0$, $\gamma_1 = 1+\delta$ for some δ; thus

$$\omega^{\gamma_1}\cdot(n_1+1) = \omega^{1+\delta}\cdot(n_1+1) = \omega\cdot\omega^\delta(n_1+1).$$

The power of the ordinal $\xi\eta$ equals the power of $\eta\xi$, because one is the power of the set $W(\xi)\times W(\eta)$ and the other is the power of the set $W(\eta)\times W(\xi)$. Therefore

$$\overline{\omega^{\gamma_1}(n_1+1)} = \overline{(n_1+1)\omega\cdot\omega^\delta} = \overline{\omega\cdot\omega^\delta} = \overline{\omega^{\gamma_1}},$$

and by (3) we have $\overline{\omega^{\gamma_1}} \leqslant \overline{\omega_\alpha}$. Since $\omega^{\gamma_1} \leqslant \omega_\alpha$, it follows by (1)

$$\omega_\alpha = \omega^{\gamma_1},$$

since ω_α is initial.

THEOREM 10: *Every limit ordinal* $\lambda \neq 0$ *is cofinal with an initial ordinal* α, *where* α *is the least ordinal among ordinals cofinal with* λ.

PROOF. We shall prove that the least ordinal α cofinal with λ is an initial ordinal. Let $\gamma < \alpha$. It suffices to show that $\overline{\gamma} \neq \overline{\alpha}$ (see formula (1)). Suppose on the contrary that $\overline{\gamma} = \overline{\alpha}$. Then there exists a sequence φ of type γ whose values are exactly all ordinals $\xi < \alpha$; thus $\alpha = \lim\limits_{\zeta<\gamma} \varphi(\zeta)$. It follows then by Theorem 2, p. 243 that the ordinal α is cofinal with some $\beta \leqslant \gamma$. Thus λ is cofinal with β, which contradicts the definition of α.

For every limit ordinal α we shall denote by $cf(\alpha)$ the least ξ such that α is cofinal with ω_ξ. Thus, for example,

$$cf(\omega) = 0, \quad cf(\Omega) = 1, \quad cf(\omega_\omega) = 0, \quad cf(\omega_\Omega) = 1.$$

Clearly, for every limit ordinal α we have

$$(4) \qquad cf(\omega_\alpha) \leqslant \alpha \quad \text{and} \quad cf(\alpha) \leqslant \alpha,$$

since $\alpha \leqslant \omega_\alpha$ and thus α is cofinal with ω_ξ for some $\xi \leqslant \alpha$. In § 4 we shall prove that, for every ordinal α,

$$°(5) \qquad cf(\omega_{\alpha+1}) = \alpha + 1$$

(see p. 285).

§ 4. Alephs and their arithmetic

Every cardinal number of an infinite well-ordered set, that is, any power of an ordinal $\geqslant \omega$ (see § 1, p. 274) is called an *aleph*.

The axiom of choice implies that every infinite cardinal is an aleph (see Corollary 3, p. 262). However, many theorems about alephs do not require the use of the axiom of choice; in particular, the law of trichotomy (see p. 232) holds for alephs.

For every ordinal α, let

$$\aleph_\alpha = \overline{\omega_\alpha}, \quad \text{i.e.} \quad \aleph_\alpha = \overline{\overline{W(\omega_\alpha)}}.$$

In particular $\aleph_0 = \mathfrak{a}$, $\aleph_1 = \overline{\Omega}$ (see Definition 2, p. 274). By Theorem 7, p. 281 we have

$$(0) \qquad \aleph(\aleph_\alpha) = \aleph_{\alpha+1}.$$

THEOREM 1: *If* $\alpha < \beta$ *then* $\aleph_\alpha < \aleph_\beta$.

Theorem 1 is an immediate consequence of Theorem 6, p. 281.

THEOREM 2: *If* $\mathfrak{m} \leqslant \aleph_\alpha$, *then* $\mathfrak{m}$ *is an aleph.*

For $\mathfrak{m}$ is then the power of a subset of a well-ordered set.

THEOREM 3: *The cardinal* $\aleph_{\alpha+1}$ *is the direct successor of* $\aleph_\alpha$; *that is, there exists no cardinal* $\mathfrak{m}$ *such that* $\aleph_\alpha < \mathfrak{m} < \aleph_{\alpha+1}$.

PROOF. If $\mathfrak{m} < \aleph_{\alpha+1}$ then $\mathfrak{m}$ is the power of a subset of the set $W(\omega_{\alpha+1})$, and thus is the power of well-ordered set. Thus $\mathfrak{m}$ is an aleph: $\mathfrak{m} = \aleph_\beta$ and by Theorem 1, $\aleph_\alpha < \mathfrak{m} < \aleph_{\alpha+1}$ implies that $\alpha < \beta < \alpha+1$, which is impossible.

The proof of Theorem 4 is similar.

THEOREM 4: *If* α *is a limit ordinal and if* $\aleph_\xi < \mathfrak{m}$ *for every* $\xi < \alpha$, *then* $\mathfrak{m} \nless \aleph_\alpha$.

Theorems 3 and 4 imply that the hierarchy of alephs is in a certain sense complete: it cannot be enriched by the introduction of new cardinals comparable with the alephs.

THEOREM 5[1]: $\aleph_\alpha^2 = \aleph_\alpha$ *for every* α.

PROOF. Let $\xi < \omega_\alpha$ and $\eta < \omega_\alpha$ where $\xi \neq 0$ or $\eta \neq 0$. Expanding the numbers ξ and η at the base ω (see Theorem 5, p. 258) and adding whenever necessary terms with coefficient 0, we can represent ξ and η uniquely in the form:

$$(1)\qquad \begin{aligned} \xi &= \omega^{\gamma_1}\cdot m_1 + \omega^{\gamma_2}\cdot m_2 + \ldots + \omega^{\gamma_k}\cdot m_k, \\ \eta &= \omega^{\gamma_1}\cdot n_1 + \omega^{\gamma_2}\cdot n_2 + \ldots + \omega^{\gamma_k}\cdot n_k, \end{aligned}$$

where $\gamma_1 > \gamma_2 > \ldots > \gamma_k$ and for all $i \leqslant k$ either $m_i > 0$ or $n_i > 0$.

By Theorem 9, p. 281, ω_α is of the form ω^λ. Since $\xi < \omega_\alpha$ and $\eta < \omega_\alpha$, it follows by (1) that (see p. 257) $\lambda > \gamma_1$.

Let $\Phi(0,0) = 0$ and let

$$(2)\qquad \Phi(\xi,\eta) = \omega^{\gamma_1}\cdot J(m_1,n_1) + \ldots + \omega^{\gamma_k}\cdot J(m_k,n_k).$$

In this way we have associated with every pair of ordinals ξ, η smaller than ω_α an ordinal $\Phi(\xi,\eta)$ which is smaller than ω_α (since $\gamma_1 < \lambda$). We prove that

$$(3)\qquad [\Phi(\xi,\eta) = \Phi(\zeta,\tau)] \rightarrow (\xi = \zeta) \wedge (\eta = \tau).$$

[1]) This theorem was first proved by G. Hessenberg; see *Grundbegriffe der Mengenlehre*, p. 593 (Göttingen 1906).

This formula is obvious in the case where $\Phi(\xi,\eta) = 0 = \Phi(\zeta,\tau)$, for then $\xi = \eta = 0 = \zeta = \tau$, so suppose that $\Phi(\xi,\eta) = \Phi(\zeta,\tau) > 0$. Then $\xi > 0$ or $\eta > 0$ and $\zeta > 0$ or $\tau > 0$.

Let ζ and τ be represented as

$$\zeta = \omega^{\delta_1}\cdot p_1+\omega^{\delta_2}\cdot p_2+\ldots+\omega^{\delta_h}\cdot p_h,$$

(4)

$$\tau = \omega^{\delta_1}\cdot q_1+\omega^{\delta_2}\cdot q_2+\ldots+\omega^{\delta_h}\cdot q_h,$$

where for every $i \leqslant h$ either $p_i > 0$ or $q_i > 0$. Then

(5) $$\Phi(\zeta,\tau) = \omega^{\delta_1}\cdot J(p_1,q_1)+\ldots+\omega^{\delta_h}\cdot J(p_h,q_h).$$

Since all coefficients in the expansions (2) and (5) are positive and since expansion at the base ω is unique (see p. 258), it follows that

$$k = h, \quad \gamma_i = \delta_i \quad \text{and} \quad J(m_i,n_i) = J(p_i,q_i) \quad \text{for} \quad i = 1,2,\ldots,k.$$

Thus $m_i = p_i$ and $n_i = q_i$ for $i \leqslant k$ and hence by (1) and (4), $\xi = \zeta$ and $\eta = \tau$. Thus (3) holds.

Finally, every $\vartheta < \omega_\alpha$ is a value of the function Φ. For assume $\vartheta = \omega^{\gamma_1}\cdot r_1+\omega^{\gamma_2}\cdot r_2+\ldots+\omega^{\gamma_k}\cdot r_k$, where $r_1, r_2, \ldots, r_k$ are positive; it suffices to take as ξ and η the ordinals (1) where $m_i = K(r_i)$ and $n_i = L(r_i)$ for $i = 1,2,\ldots,k$. If $\vartheta = 0$ it suffices to let $\xi = \eta = 0$.

Therefore the function Φ establishes a one-to-one correspondence between elements of the set $W(\omega_\alpha)$ and ordered pairs of elements of $W(\omega_\alpha)$. Thus the sets $W(\omega_\alpha)$ and $W(\omega_\alpha)\times W(\omega_\alpha)$ are equipollent. Q.E.D.

COROLLARY 6: $\aleph_\alpha+\aleph_\beta = \aleph_{\max(\alpha,\beta)} = \aleph_\alpha\cdot\aleph_\beta$, *where* $\max(\alpha,\beta) = \alpha$ *if* $\alpha \geqslant \beta$ *and* $\max(\alpha,\beta) = \beta$ *if* $\beta \geqslant \alpha$.

PROOF. Assume that $\max(\alpha,\beta) = \alpha$. Then $\aleph_\alpha \leqslant \aleph_\beta$ and

$$\aleph_\alpha \leqslant \aleph_\alpha+\aleph_\beta \leqslant \aleph_\alpha+\aleph_\alpha = 2\aleph_\alpha \leqslant \aleph_\alpha\cdot\aleph_\alpha = \aleph_\alpha,$$

$$\aleph_\alpha \leqslant \aleph_\alpha\cdot\aleph_\beta \leqslant \aleph_\alpha\cdot\aleph_\alpha = \aleph_\alpha,$$

whence the desired identities follow by the Cantor–Bernstein Theorem (p. 190).

THEOREM 7: $\overline{\overline{W(\omega_{\alpha+1})-W(\omega_\alpha)}} = \aleph_{\alpha+1}$.

PROOF. Let $W(\omega_{\alpha+1}) = A$ and $W(\omega_\alpha) = B$. The difference $A-B$ is a well-ordered set and thus its cardinal number is an aleph, which we shall denote by $\aleph_\gamma$. The identity $A = (A-B)\cup B$ implies that $\aleph_{\alpha+1}$

$= \aleph_\gamma + \aleph_\alpha = \aleph_{\max(\gamma,\alpha)}$, thus $\alpha+1 = \max(\gamma, \alpha)$. As $\alpha < \alpha+1$, it follows that $\gamma = \alpha+1$.

°LEMMA 8: $\overline{\overline{\bigcup_{t\in T} F_t}} \leqslant \sum_{t \in T} \overline{\overline{F}}_t$, *where F is any function whose values are sets.*

For

$$(6) \qquad \sum_{t\in T} \overline{\overline{F}}_t = \overline{\overline{\{\langle t, x\rangle : \ (t \in T) \wedge (x \in F_t)\}}};$$

on the other hand, the set $\bigcup_{t \in T} F_t$ can be obtained from the set $\{\langle t, x\rangle : \ (t \in T) \wedge (x \in F_t)\}$ by the mapping f defined by the formula $f(\langle t, x\rangle) = x$, and thus it has power less than or equal to that of the latter (see Theorem 1, p. 186).

°THEOREM 9: $cf(\omega_{\alpha+1}) = \alpha+1$.

Let $\beta = cf(\omega_{\alpha+1})$. Then the ordinal ω_β is cofinal with $\omega_{\alpha+1}$ and there exists a transfinite sequence φ of type ω_β whose limit is $\omega_{\alpha+1}$. It follows that if $\xi < \omega_{\alpha+1}$, then there exists an ordinal $\zeta < \omega_\beta$ such that $\xi < \varphi(\zeta)$ or, in other words,

$$(7) \qquad W(\omega_{\alpha+1}) \subset \bigcup_{\zeta<\omega_\beta} W(\varphi(\zeta)).$$

Because $\overline{\overline{W(\omega_\beta)}} = \aleph_\beta$, and because for all $\zeta < \omega_\beta$ we have

$$\overline{\overline{W(\varphi(\zeta))}} < \aleph_{\alpha+1}, \quad \text{that is} \quad \overline{\overline{W(\varphi(\zeta))}} \leqslant \aleph_\alpha,$$

it follows by (7), the lemma and Theorem 8, p. 200 that

$$\aleph_{\alpha+1} = \overline{\overline{W(\omega_{\alpha+1})}} \leqslant \overline{\overline{\bigcup_{\zeta<\omega_\beta} W(\varphi(\zeta))}} \leqslant \sum_{\zeta<\omega_\beta} \overline{\overline{W(\varphi(\zeta))}} \leqslant \aleph_\beta \cdot \aleph_\alpha = \aleph_{\max(\alpha,\beta)}.$$

Thus $\alpha+1 \leqslant \max(\alpha, \beta)$ and $\alpha+1 \leqslant \beta$. At the same time (see (4), p. 282) $cf(\omega_{\alpha+1}) \leqslant \alpha+1$, that is $\beta \leqslant \alpha+1$, and thus $\beta = \alpha+1$.

°THEOREM 10: *For arbitrary* α,

$$(8) \qquad \sum_{\xi\leqslant\alpha} \aleph_\xi = \aleph_\alpha.$$

PROOF. Since $(\xi \leqslant \alpha) \rightarrow (\aleph_\xi \leqslant \aleph_\alpha)$ and

$$\overline{\overline{\{\xi : \ \xi \leqslant \alpha\}}} \leqslant \aleph_\alpha,$$

it follows by Theorem 8, p. 282 that

$$\sum_{\xi\leqslant\alpha} \aleph_\xi \leqslant \aleph_\alpha \cdot \aleph_\alpha = \aleph_\alpha,$$

which implies (8), because

$$\aleph_\alpha \leqslant \sum_{\xi \leqslant \alpha} \aleph_\xi$$

°THEOREM 11: *If* $\alpha = \beta+1$, *then*

$$\sum_{\xi<\alpha} \aleph_\xi = \aleph_\beta. \tag{9}$$

On the other hand, if α *is a limit ordinal* > 0, *then*

$$\sum_{\xi<\alpha} \aleph_\xi = \aleph_\alpha. \tag{10}$$

PROOF. Let $\alpha = \beta+1$. Then $(\xi < \alpha) \equiv (\xi \leqslant \beta)$ and by (8)

$$\sum_{\xi<\alpha} \aleph_\xi = \sum_{\xi\leqslant\beta} \aleph_\xi = \aleph_\beta.$$

Suppose that α is a limit ordinal; then

$$W(\omega_\alpha) = \bigcup_{\xi<\alpha} W(\omega_\xi);$$

hence (by Lemma 8)

$$\aleph_\alpha = \overline{\overline{W(\omega_\alpha)}} = \overline{\overline{\bigcup_{\xi<\alpha} W(\omega_\xi)}} \leqslant \sum_{\xi<\alpha} \overline{\overline{W(\omega_\xi)}} = \sum_{\xi<\alpha} \aleph_\xi,$$

which implies (10), because by (8)

$$\sum_{\xi<\alpha} \aleph_\xi \leqslant \aleph_\alpha.$$

The following more general theorem can be proved in a similar manner.

°THEOREM 12. *If* α *is a limit ordinal,* φ *is a transfinite increasing sequence of type* α *and* $\lambda = \lim_{\xi<\alpha} \varphi(\xi)$, *then*

$$\sum_{\xi<\alpha} \aleph_{\varphi(\xi)} = \aleph_\lambda.$$

Remark. It is interesting to note that the aleph $\aleph_1$ and more generally, the aleph $\aleph_n$ can be defined without appealing to the notions of ordinal or cardinal numbers. In order to formulate the appropriate theorem, we introduce the following definition: set A contained in the cartesian product $X^n = X \times X \times \ldots \times X$ is *finite in the direction of the k-th axis* provided that for every element $(x_1, \ldots, x_{k-1}, x_{k+1}, \ldots, x_n)$ belonging to X^{n-1} the set

$$\{x_k\colon (x_1, \ldots, x_{k-1}, x_k, x_{k+1}, \ldots, x_n) \in A\}$$

is finite (more figuratively: every straight line parallel to the kth axis intersects A in a finite number of points).

The following theorem holds [1]):

A neccesary and sufficient condition for the set X to be of power $\leqslant \aleph_n$ (n finite $\geqslant 0$) is that the set X^{n+2} be representable as a union $A_1 \cup \ldots \cup A_{n+2}$, where A_k is finite in the direction of the k-th axis.

§ 5. The exponentiation of alephs

First of all we make note of the following elementary theorem.

THEOREM 1: *If $\alpha \leqslant \beta$, then $\aleph_\alpha^{\aleph_\beta} = 2^{\aleph_\beta}$.*

PROOF. From the inequality $2 < \aleph_\alpha < 2^{\aleph_\alpha}$ and from the laws of exponentiation for cardinal numbers (p. 185 and p. 187) we obtain

$$2^{\aleph_\beta} \leqslant \aleph_\alpha^{\aleph_\beta} \leqslant 2^{\aleph_\alpha \cdot \aleph_\beta} = 2^{\aleph_\beta},$$

which implies the desired equality.

°THEOREM 2: (THE HAUSDORFF RECURSION FORMULA [2]).)

$$\aleph_{\alpha+1}^{\aleph_\beta} = \aleph_\alpha^{\aleph_\beta} \cdot \aleph_{\alpha+1}.$$

PROOF. We shall examine two cases.

Case I: $\alpha+1 \leqslant \beta$. Then by Theorem 1 we have

$$\aleph_{\alpha+1}^{\aleph_\beta} = 2^{\aleph_\beta} = \aleph_\alpha^{\aleph_\beta}. \tag{2}$$

[1]) This theorem is due to W. Sierpiński (*Sur quelques propositions concernant la puissance du continu*, Fund. Math. **38** (1951), 1–13). See also K. Kuratowski, *Sur une caractérisation des alephs*, ibid. 14–17. A further generalization is given by R. Sikorski, *A characterization of alephs*, ibid. 18–22.

[2]) F. Hausdorff, *Der Potenzbegriff in der Mengenlehre*, Jahresberichte der Deutschen Mathematiker Vereinigung **13** (1904) 570.

On the other hand, since $\aleph_{\alpha+1} \leqslant \aleph_\beta < 2^{\aleph_\beta}$, we also have

$$(3) \qquad \aleph_\alpha^{\aleph_\beta} \cdot \aleph_{\alpha+1} = 2^{\aleph_\beta} \cdot \aleph_{\alpha+1} \leqslant 2^{\aleph_\beta} \cdot 2^{\aleph_\beta} = 2^{\aleph_\beta + \aleph_\beta} = 2^{\aleph_\beta}.$$

By (2) and (3) it follows that

$$\aleph_{\alpha+1}^{\aleph_\beta} = 2^{\aleph_\beta} = \aleph_\alpha^{\aleph_\beta} \leqslant \aleph_\alpha^{\aleph_\beta} \cdot \aleph_{\alpha+1} \leqslant 2^{\aleph_\beta} = \aleph_{\alpha+1}^{\aleph_\beta},$$

which implies (1).

Case II: $\beta < \alpha+1$. In this case,

$$(4) \qquad \aleph_\alpha^{\aleph_\beta} \cdot \aleph_{\alpha+1} \leqslant \aleph_{\alpha+1}^{\aleph_\beta} \cdot \aleph_{\alpha+1} = \aleph_{\alpha+1}^{\aleph_\beta+1} = \aleph_{\alpha+1}^{\aleph_\beta}.$$

It remains to show that the opposite inequality also holds. For this purpose we consider the set $W(\omega_{\alpha+1})^{W(\omega_\beta)}$, that is, the set of all transfinite sequences of type ω_β whose terms are less than $\omega_{\alpha+1}$. We shall show that

$$(5) \qquad W(\omega_{\alpha+1})^{W(\omega_\beta)} \subset \bigcup_{\xi < \omega_{\alpha+1}} W(\xi)^{W(\omega_\beta)}.$$

For if φ is a transfinite sequence of type $\omega_\beta < \omega_{\alpha+1}$, then (see Theorem 9, p. 285) the set of its term is not cofinal with $W(\omega_{\alpha+1})$. Thus there exists an ordinal $\xi < \omega_{\alpha+1}$ for which $W(\xi)$ contains all the terms of the sequence φ; hence $\varphi \in W(\xi)^{W(\omega_\beta)}$. Thus inclusion (5) holds.

As $\overline{\overline{W(\xi)}} = \overline{\xi} \leqslant \aleph_\alpha$ for $\xi < \omega_{\alpha+1}$, it follows that $\overline{\overline{W(\xi)^{W(\omega_\beta)}}} \leqslant \aleph_\alpha^{\aleph_\beta}$.

Therefore from (5), by Lemma 8, p. 285 and by Theorem 8, p. 200 we obtain

$$\aleph_{\alpha+1}^{\aleph_\beta} = \overline{\overline{W(\omega_{\alpha+1})^{W(\omega_\beta)}}} \leqslant \overline{\overline{\bigcup_{\xi<\omega_{\alpha+1}} W(\xi)^{W(\omega_\beta)}}} \leqslant \sum_{\xi<\omega_{\alpha+1}} \overline{\overline{W(\xi)^{W(\omega_\beta)}}} \leqslant \aleph_\alpha^{\aleph_\beta} \cdot \aleph_{\alpha+1},$$

which together with (4) proves (1).

°THEOREM 3. (THE TARSKI RECURSION FORMULA[1]).) *If φ is an increasing sequence of a limit type α and $\lambda = \lim_{\xi<\alpha} \varphi(\xi)$ and $\beta < cf(\alpha)$*, then $\aleph_\lambda^{\aleph_\beta} = \sum_{\xi<\alpha} \aleph_{\varphi(\xi)}^{\aleph_\beta}$, *in particular*, $\aleph_\alpha^{\aleph_\beta} = \sum_{\xi<\alpha} \aleph_\xi^{\aleph_\beta}$ *for every limit ordinal α and for every $\beta < cf(\alpha)$.*

[1]) A. Tarski, *Quelques théorèmes sur les alephs*, Fundamenta Mathematicae **7** (1925) 7.

PROOF. By assumption, $cf(\lambda) = cf(\alpha)$. Thus no transfinite sequence of type ω_β with values in $W(\lambda)$ is convergent to λ, hence for every such sequence there exists $\xi < \alpha$ such that this sequence belongs to $W(\varphi(\xi))^{W(\omega_\beta)}$. Therefore

$$W(\lambda)^{W(\omega_\beta)} \subset \bigcup_{\xi<\alpha} W(\varphi(\xi))^{W(\omega_\beta)},$$

which implies that

$$\aleph_\lambda^{\aleph_\beta} \leqslant \sum_{\xi<\alpha} \aleph_{\varphi(\xi)}^{\aleph_\beta}.$$

The opposite inequality follows from the remark that $\aleph_\lambda \geqslant \bar{\alpha}$, which implies that

$$\aleph_\lambda^{\aleph_\beta} = \aleph_\lambda \cdot \aleph_\lambda^{\aleph_\beta} \geqslant \bar{\alpha}\, \aleph_\lambda^{\aleph_\beta} \geqslant \aleph_\lambda^{\aleph_\beta} \geqslant \sum_{\xi<\alpha} \aleph_{\varphi(\xi)}^{\aleph_\beta}.$$

°THEOREM 4: (THE GENERALIZED HAUSDORFF FORMULA.) *For finite n,*

(8) $$\aleph_{\alpha+n}^{\aleph_\beta} = \aleph_\alpha^{\aleph_\beta} \cdot \aleph_{\alpha+n}.$$

PROOF. For $n = 1$, (8) coincides with (1). Assume that (8) holds for a particular n. Replacing in (1) α by $\alpha+n$ we obtain

$$\aleph_{\alpha+n+1}^{\aleph_\beta} = \aleph_{\alpha+n}^{\aleph_\beta} \cdot \aleph_{\alpha+n+1},$$

thus by the induction hypothesis and by Corollary 6, p. 284 it follows that

$$\aleph_{\alpha+n+1}^{\aleph_\beta} = \aleph_\alpha^{\aleph_\beta} \cdot \aleph_{\alpha+n} \cdot \aleph_{\alpha+n+1} = \aleph_\alpha^{\aleph_\beta} \cdot \aleph_{\alpha+n+1}.$$

Thus (8) holds for $n+1$, and hence it holds for arbitrary finite n.

Setting $\alpha = 0$ in (8) and using Theorem 1 we obtain the following theorem.

°THEOREM 5: (THE BERNSTEIN FORMULA[1]).) *For finite n*

(9) $$\aleph_n^{\aleph_\beta} = 2^{\aleph_\beta} \cdot \aleph_n.$$

Examples

1. (9) implies that

$$\aleph_1^{\aleph_0} = 2^{\aleph_0} \cdot \aleph_1.$$

[1]) F. Bernstein, *Untersuchungen aus der Mengenlehre*, Mathematische Annalen **61** (1905) 150.

More results concerning exponentiation of alephs are given by Heinz Bachman, *Transfinite Zahlen. Ergebnisse der Mathematik und ihrer Grenzgebiete*, (Berlin 1955), pp. 143–155.

2. Theorem 1 implies that

$$\aleph_0^{\aleph_1} = 2^{\aleph_1}.$$

3. In formula (6) let $\alpha = \omega_1 = \Omega$, $\beta = 0$. Since $cf(\omega_1) = 1$, the hypotheses of Theorem 3 are satisfied and we conclude that

$$\aleph_\Omega^{\aleph_0} = \sum_{\xi<\Omega} \aleph_\xi^{\aleph_0}.$$

We now give a theorem in the proof of which we shall use König's theorem (p. 203):

°THEOREM 6: *If α is a limit ordinal and $\beta \geqslant cf(\alpha)$, then for every cardinal* $\mathfrak{m}$

(10) $$\aleph_\alpha \neq \mathfrak{m}^{\aleph_\beta}.$$

PROOF. Let $\xi = cf(\alpha)$. Then the ordinal ω_ξ is cofinal with α; that is, there exists an increasing sequence φ of type ω_ξ such that

$$\lim_{\zeta<\omega_\xi} \varphi(\zeta) = \alpha.$$

By applying Theorem 12, p. 286 it follows that

(11) $$\aleph_\alpha = \sum_{\zeta<\omega_\xi} \aleph_{\varphi(\zeta)}.$$

By König's theorem we have

(12) $$\sum_{\zeta<\omega_\xi} \aleph_{\varphi(\zeta)} < \prod_{\zeta<\omega_\xi} \aleph_{\varphi(\zeta)}.$$

On the other hand, since $\aleph_{\varphi(\zeta)} < \aleph_\alpha$ and $\overline{\omega}_\zeta = \aleph_\zeta \leqslant \aleph_\beta$, we obtain

(13) $$\prod_{\zeta<\omega_\xi} \aleph_{\varphi(\zeta)} \leqslant \aleph_\alpha^{\aleph_\beta}.$$

Formulas (11), (12) and (13) imply that

(14) $$\aleph_\alpha < \aleph_\alpha^{\aleph_\beta}.$$

If there existed a cardinal $\mathfrak{m}$ such that $\aleph_\alpha = \mathfrak{m}^{\aleph_\beta}$, then we would have

$$\aleph_\alpha^{\aleph_\beta} = \mathfrak{m}^{\aleph_\beta \aleph_\beta} = \mathfrak{m}^{\aleph_\beta} = \aleph_\alpha,$$

contrary to (14).

We conclude that (10) holds.

°COROLLARY 7: *If $\beta \geqslant cf(\alpha)$, then $\aleph_\alpha < \aleph_\alpha^{\aleph_\beta}$.*

From Theorem 6 it follows, in particular, that for no $\mathfrak{m}$ and β do the equations $\aleph_\omega = \mathfrak{m}^{\aleph_\beta}$, $\aleph_{\omega_\omega} = \mathfrak{m}^{\aleph_\beta}$, $\aleph_\varepsilon = \mathfrak{m}^{\aleph_\beta}$ hold (see p. 254 for the definition of ε); for (see p. 282) $cf(\omega) = cf(\omega_\omega) = cf(\varepsilon) = 0$.

It also follows from Theorem 6 that if $\aleph_{\omega_n} = \mathfrak{m}^{\aleph_\beta}$, then β can assume only one of the values $0, 1, \ldots, n-1$. In fact, $cf(\omega_n) = n$, and thus for $\beta \geqslant n$ the equation $\aleph_{\omega_n} = \mathfrak{m}^{\aleph_\beta}$ does not hold.

COROLLARY 8: $\aleph_\omega \neq 2^{\aleph_0}$.

For $\aleph_\omega = 2^{\aleph_0}$ implies that $\aleph_\omega^{\aleph_0} = 2^{\aleph_0 \cdot \aleph_0} = 2^{\aleph_0} = \aleph_\omega$, whereas by Corollary 7 we have $\aleph_\omega^{\aleph_0} > \aleph_\omega$.

We shall conclude this section by evaluating the power of the set

$$P_\mathfrak{n}(M) = \{X \subset M \colon \overline{\overline{X}} = \mathfrak{n}\}, \qquad \text{where} \qquad \overline{\overline{M}} = \mathfrak{m}.$$

For $\mathfrak{m}$ and $\mathfrak{n}$ finite the power of $P_\mathfrak{n}(M)$ is $\binom{\mathfrak{m}}{\mathfrak{n}}$.

°THEOREM 9: *If M is an infinite set of power $\mathfrak{m}$ and if $\mathfrak{n} \leqslant \overline{\overline{M}}$, then $P_\mathfrak{n}(M)$ has power $\mathfrak{m}^\mathfrak{n}$.*

PROOF. Let Z be a fixed set of power $\mathfrak{n}$. To every $X \in P_\mathfrak{n}(M)$ there corresponds in a one-to-one manner a non-empty family $C(X)$ of functions $f \in M^Z$ such that $f^1(Z) = X$; clearly $C(X') \cap C(X'') = 0$ for $X' \neq X''$. By applying the axiom of choice we conclude that the power of $P_\mathfrak{n}(M)$ is not greater that $\overline{\overline{M^Z}} = \mathfrak{m}^\mathfrak{n}$.

Conversely, to every function $f \in M^Z$ there corresponds the set $A_f = \{\langle z, f(z)\rangle \colon (z \in Z)\}$. This set has power $\mathfrak{n}$, because the set Z has power $\mathfrak{n}$. Moreover, $A_f \subset Z \times M$ and the set $Z \times M$ has power $\mathfrak{n} \cdot \mathfrak{m} = \mathfrak{m}$. If $f' \neq f''$ and, for example, $f'(z_0) \neq f''(z_0)$, then $A_{f'} \neq A_{f''}$, as $\langle z_0, f'(z_0)\rangle \in A_{f'} - A_{f''}$. It follows that the set $P_\mathfrak{n}(Z \times M)$ has power $\geqslant \mathfrak{m}^\mathfrak{n}$ and thus $P_\mathfrak{n}(M)$ has power $\geqslant \mathfrak{m}^\mathfrak{n}$ for the sets $P_\mathfrak{n}(Z \times M)$ and $P_\mathfrak{n}(M)$ are equipollent.

°COROLLARY 10: *If $\overline{\overline{M}} = \mathfrak{m} \geqslant \mathfrak{a}$, then the set $\{X \subset M \colon \overline{\overline{X}} < \mathfrak{m}\}$ has power $\sum_{\mathfrak{x} < \mathfrak{m}} \mathfrak{m}^\mathfrak{x}$.*

§ 6. Equivalence of certain statements about cardinal numbers and the axiom of choice

From the well-ordering theorem and thus indirectly from the axiom of choice (see p. 262) it follows that every cardinal is an aleph. Thus the laws of arithmetic for cardinal numbers coincide with those for alephs and we have the following theorem.

°THEOREM 1:

(1) $$\bigwedge_{\mathfrak{m},\, \mathfrak{n} \notin N} [(\mathfrak{m} \leqslant \mathfrak{n}) \vee (\mathfrak{n} \leqslant \mathfrak{m})] \qquad (\textit{law of trichotomy}),$$

(2) $$\bigwedge_{\mathfrak{m} \notin N} [\mathfrak{m}^2 = \mathfrak{m}],$$

(3) $$\bigwedge_{\mathfrak{m},\, \mathfrak{n} \notin N} [(\mathfrak{m} \cdot \mathfrak{n} = \mathfrak{m} + \mathfrak{n} = \mathfrak{m}) \vee (\mathfrak{m} \cdot \mathfrak{n} = \mathfrak{m} + \mathfrak{n} = \mathfrak{n})],$$

(4) $$\bigwedge_{\mathfrak{m},\, \mathfrak{n} \notin N} [(\mathfrak{m}^2 = \mathfrak{n}^2) \rightarrow (\mathfrak{m} = \mathfrak{n})],$$

(5) $$\bigwedge_{\mathfrak{m},\, \mathfrak{n},\, \mathfrak{p},\, \mathfrak{q} \notin N} [(\mathfrak{m} < \mathfrak{n}) \wedge (\mathfrak{p} < \mathfrak{q}) \rightarrow (\mathfrak{m} + \mathfrak{p} < \mathfrak{n} + \mathfrak{q})],$$

(6) $$\bigwedge_{\mathfrak{m},\, \mathfrak{n},\, \mathfrak{p},\, \mathfrak{q} \notin N} [(\mathfrak{m} < \mathfrak{n}) \wedge (\mathfrak{p} < \mathfrak{q}) \rightarrow (\mathfrak{m} \cdot \mathfrak{p} < \mathfrak{n} \cdot \mathfrak{q})],$$

(7) $$\bigwedge_{\mathfrak{m},\, \mathfrak{n},\, \mathfrak{p} \notin N} [(\mathfrak{m} + \mathfrak{p} < \mathfrak{n} + \mathfrak{p}) \rightarrow (\mathfrak{m} < \mathfrak{n})],$$

(8) $$\bigwedge_{\mathfrak{m},\, \mathfrak{n},\, \mathfrak{p} \notin N} [(\mathfrak{m} \cdot \mathfrak{p} < \mathfrak{n} \cdot \mathfrak{p}) \rightarrow \mathfrak{m} < \mathfrak{n}].$$

Seemingly each of the laws (1)–(8) is a special consequence of the axiom of choice. We shall show, however, that each of these laws in conjunction with the axioms Σ[TR] and VIII implies the axiom of choice.

THEOREM 2[1]): *If for every pair of infinite cardinals* $\mathfrak{m}$ *and* $\mathfrak{n}$ *either* $\mathfrak{m} \leqslant \mathfrak{n}$ *or* $\mathfrak{n} \leqslant \mathfrak{m}$, *then there exists a choice function for every family o non-empty sets.*

PROOF. Let X be an arbitrary infinite set and let $\mathfrak{m} = \overline{\overline{X}}$. By assumption either $\mathfrak{m} \leqslant \aleph(\mathfrak{m})$ or $\aleph(\mathfrak{m}) \leqslant \mathfrak{m}$. The second case is impossible by Theorem 3, p. 278; in the first case $\mathfrak{m}$ is an aleph and thus there exists a relation well ordering X. Therefore the hypothesis of the theorem implies the well-ordering theorem, and thus the existence of the desired choice function (see p. 262).

REMARK: Theorem 2 can be expressed more concisely: formula (1)

[1]) This theorem was first proved by F. Hartogs; see his paper cited on p. 278.

for all infinite $\mathfrak{m}$ and $\mathfrak{n}$ implies the axiom of choice. We shall employ this sort of abbreviated language; in the statements of other theorems the word "implies" will be taken to denote the existence of a proof which does not use the axiom of choice.

LEMMA 3: $(3) \to (2) \to (4)$.

In fact, if $\mathfrak{m} \notin N$, then by (3), $\mathfrak{m}^2 = \mathfrak{m}$. If $\mathfrak{m}, \mathfrak{n} \notin N$, then by (2) $\mathfrak{m}^2 = \mathfrak{m}$ and $\mathfrak{n}^2 = \mathfrak{n}$, whence $\mathfrak{m}^2 = \mathfrak{n}^2 \to \mathfrak{m} = \mathfrak{n}$.

LEMMA 4: *If* $\mathfrak{p} \notin N$ and $\mathfrak{p} \cdot \aleph(\mathfrak{p}) = \mathfrak{p} + \aleph(\mathfrak{p})$, *then* $\mathfrak{p}$ *is an aleph*[1]).

PROOF. Let $\overline{\overline{A}} = \mathfrak{p}$, $\overline{\overline{B}} = \aleph(\mathfrak{p})$. By hypothesis there exists a partition $A \times B = P \cup Q$ into two disjoint sets P and Q such that $\overline{\overline{P}} = \mathfrak{p}$, $\overline{\overline{Q}} = \aleph(\mathfrak{p})$; thus $\overline{\overline{Q}}$ is an aleph and there exists a relation well ordering Q.

There are, a priori, two possibilities.

I. There exists $a \in A$ such that $\{a\} \times B \subset P$. However, since $\overline{\overline{\{a\} \times B}} = \aleph(\mathfrak{p})$, it would then follow that $\aleph(\mathfrak{p}) \leqslant \mathfrak{p}$ contrary to Theorem 3, p. 278. Thus case I is impossible.

II. For every $a \in A$, $(\{a\} \times B) \cap Q \neq 0$. As there exists a relation well ordering Q, there exists a function which associates with every $a \in A$ the earliest element $q(a)$ of $(\{a\} \times B) \cap Q$. Moreover, as $q(a)$ is of the form $\langle a, b \rangle$ where $b \in B$, it follows that $q(a') \neq q(a'')$ for $a' \neq a''$. Thus the function q establishes a one-to-one mapping of A onto a subset of Q; hence $\overline{\overline{A}} \leqslant \overline{\overline{Q}}$ and $\overline{\overline{A}}$ is an aleph. Q.E.D.

THEOREM 5: (4) *implies the axiom of choice.*

PROOF. Let $\mathfrak{k}$ be an arbitrary infinite cardinal. Let $\mathfrak{p} = \mathfrak{k}^{\aleph_0}$, $\mathfrak{m} = \mathfrak{p} + \aleph(\mathfrak{p})$ and $\mathfrak{n} = \mathfrak{p} \cdot \aleph(\mathfrak{p})$. Clearly

$$\mathfrak{p}^2 = (\mathfrak{k}^{\aleph_0})^2 = \mathfrak{k}^{\aleph_0} = \mathfrak{p},$$

which implies that $\mathfrak{p} \leqslant \mathfrak{p}+1 \leqslant \mathfrak{p} \cdot \mathfrak{p} = \mathfrak{p}^2 = \mathfrak{p}$ and thus

$$\mathfrak{p} + 1 = \mathfrak{p}.$$

Since $2\aleph(\mathfrak{p}) = \aleph(\mathfrak{p}) = \aleph(\mathfrak{p}) + 1 = [\aleph(\mathfrak{p})]^2$, we obtain from these for-

[1]) This lemma as well as Theorems 3–7 are due to A. Tarski. See his paper: *Sur quelques théorèmes qui equivalent à l'axiome du choix*, Fundamenta Math. **5** (1924) 147–154.

mulas that

$$\begin{aligned}
\mathfrak{m}^2 &= [\mathfrak{p}+\aleph(\mathfrak{p})]^2 \\
&= \mathfrak{p}^2+2\mathfrak{p}\cdot\aleph(\mathfrak{p})+[\aleph(\mathfrak{p})]^2 \\
&= \mathfrak{p}+\mathfrak{p}\,[\aleph(\mathfrak{p})2]+\aleph(\mathfrak{p}) \\
&= \mathfrak{p}+\mathfrak{p}\cdot\aleph(\mathfrak{p})+\aleph(\mathfrak{p}) \\
&= \mathfrak{p}\,[1+\aleph(\mathfrak{p})]+\aleph(\mathfrak{p}) \\
&= \mathfrak{p}\cdot\aleph(\mathfrak{p})+\aleph(\mathfrak{p}) \\
&= (\mathfrak{p}+1)\aleph(\mathfrak{p}) \\
&= \mathfrak{p}\cdot\aleph(\mathfrak{p}) \\
&= \mathfrak{p}^2[\aleph(\mathfrak{p})]^2 \\
&= \mathfrak{n}^2.
\end{aligned}$$

Thus by (4) we have $\mathfrak{m} = \mathfrak{n}$, that is, $\mathfrak{p}+\aleph(\mathfrak{p}) = \mathfrak{p}\cdot\aleph(\mathfrak{p})$, and thus $\mathfrak{p}$ is an aleph by Lemma 3. Since $\mathfrak{k} \leqslant \mathfrak{p}$, $\mathfrak{k}$ is also an aleph. Q.E.D.

COROLLARY 6: *Each of the formulas* (2) *and* (3) *implies the axiom of choice.*

THEOREM 7: *Each of the formulas* (5) *and* (6) *implies the axiom of choice.*

PROOF. Let $\mathfrak{k}$ be an infinite cardinal. Clearly

$$\mathfrak{k} \leqslant \mathfrak{k}+\aleph(\mathfrak{k}) \quad \text{and} \quad \aleph(\mathfrak{k}) \leqslant \mathfrak{k}+\aleph(\mathfrak{k}).$$

If the strict inequality were to hold in both of these formulas, then by (5) we would obtain the false inequality $\mathfrak{k}+\aleph(\mathfrak{k}) < \mathfrak{k}+\aleph(\mathfrak{k})$. Thus either $\mathfrak{k} = \mathfrak{k}+\aleph(\mathfrak{k})$ or $\aleph(\mathfrak{k}) = \mathfrak{k}+\aleph(\mathfrak{k})$. But the first equation implies $\mathfrak{k} \geqslant \aleph(\mathfrak{k})$ which contradicts Theorem 3, p. 278. Thus the second equation holds, which implies $\mathfrak{k} \leqslant \aleph(\mathfrak{k})$ and thus $\mathfrak{k}$ is an aleph. It follows that (5) implies the axiom of choice.

The proof of the second part of the theorem is similar, except that instead of $\mathfrak{k}+\aleph(\mathfrak{k})$ we examine the product $\mathfrak{k}\cdot\aleph(\mathfrak{k})$.

THEOREM 8: *Each of the formulas* (7) *and* (8) *implies the axiom of choice.*

PROOF. Let $\mathfrak{k}$ be an arbitrary infinite cardinal. Let $\mathfrak{m} = \aleph_0\cdot\mathfrak{k}$; then $\mathfrak{m}+\mathfrak{m} = \mathfrak{m}$. Now let $\mathfrak{n} = \aleph(\mathfrak{m})$ and $\mathfrak{p} = \mathfrak{m}$. Hence $\mathfrak{m}+\mathfrak{p} = \mathfrak{m}$ and

$\mathfrak{n}+\mathfrak{p} = \mathfrak{m}+\aleph(\mathfrak{m})$, which implies that $\mathfrak{m}+\mathfrak{p} \leqslant \mathfrak{n}+\mathfrak{p}$. If the equation $\mathfrak{m}+\mathfrak{p} = \mathfrak{n}+\mathfrak{p}$ were true, then the inequality $\mathfrak{m} \geqslant \aleph(\mathfrak{m})$ would also be true, in contradiction to Theorem 3, p. 278. Hence $\mathfrak{m}+\mathfrak{p} < \mathfrak{n}+\mathfrak{p}$ and by (7) $\mathfrak{m} < \mathfrak{n}$, that is $\mathfrak{m} < \aleph(\mathfrak{m})$. Thus $\mathfrak{k} < \aleph(\mathfrak{m})$, which implies that $\mathfrak{k}$ is an aleph.

The proof of the second part of the theorem is similar; we replace $\mathfrak{m}$ by $\mathfrak{k}^{\aleph_0}$ and discuss the products $\mathfrak{m}\cdot\mathfrak{p}$ and $\mathfrak{n}\cdot\mathfrak{p}$ instead of the sums $\mathfrak{m}+\mathfrak{p}$, $\mathfrak{n}\cdot\mathfrak{p}$ [1]).

It is not known whether the formula

$$\bigwedge_{\mathfrak{m}\notin N} [\mathfrak{m}+\mathfrak{m} = \mathfrak{m}]$$

is equivalent to the axiom of choice in the system of axioms Σ[TR] and VIII.

From Theorem 1 (proved with the axiom of choice) it follows that for every infinite cardinal $\mathfrak{m}$ and for $n \in N$, $\mathfrak{m}^n < 2^{\mathfrak{m}}$. Specker has shown that the weaker theorem $\mathfrak{m}^n$non-$\geqslant 2^{\mathfrak{m}}$ can be proved without the axiom of choice. We shall use this fact in Chapter IX, p. 333.

THEOREM 9 [2]): *If* $\mathfrak{m}$ *is infinite and* $n \in N$, *then* $\mathfrak{m}^n$ *non-*$\geqslant 2^{\mathfrak{m}}$.

PROOF. Assume that $\overline{\overline{A}} = \mathfrak{m}$ and that there exists a one-to-one function F mapping 2^A into A^n. We shall show that there exists a function f which associates with every transfinite sequence φ of distinct elements of A an element of A which is not a term of φ.

The theorem then follows from the existence of such a function f as follows: Let α be the least ordinal of power $\aleph(\mathfrak{m})$. By theorem on inductive definitions there exists an α-sequence ψ such that $\psi_\xi = f(\psi|\xi)$ for $\xi < \alpha$. By construction, ψ_ξ is not a term of $\psi|\xi$ and thus $\psi_\xi \neq \psi_\eta$ for $\xi \neq \eta$. We conclude that $\overline{\overline{A}} \geqslant \overline{\alpha} = \aleph(\mathfrak{m})$ in contradiction to Theorem 3, p. 278.

It now remains to construct the function f. For this purpose we

[1]) A detailed discussion of the theorems about cardinal numbers equivalent to the axiom of choice is given in the book: H. Rubin and J. Rubin, *Equivalents of the axiom of choice* (Amsterdam 1963). Most of these theorems are due to Tarski.

[2]) See E. Specker, *Verallgemeinerte Kontinuumhypothese und das Auswahlaxiom.* Archiv der Mathematik **5** (1954) 332–337.

choose an integer $k_0 > 1$ such that $2^{k_0} > k_0^n$ and k_0 distinct elements of A: $a_0, \ldots, a_{k_0-1}$. If $\varphi = \langle\varphi_0, \ldots, \varphi_{k-1}\rangle$ with $k < k_0$, then we put $f(\varphi) = a_j$ where $j = \min_i (a_i \neq \varphi_s$ for $s<k)$. Assume now that $\varphi = \langle\varphi_0, \ldots, \varphi_{k-1}\rangle$ with $k \geqslant k_0$ distinct terms. Denote by $S(\varphi)$ the set $\{\varphi_0, \ldots, \varphi_{k-1}\}$. There are 2^k subsets of $S(\varphi)$; we may represent them as $\{\varphi_i: i \in Z\} = S(\varphi, Z)$ where Z is contained in $\{0, 1, \ldots, k-1\}$. By the definition of F each $F(S(\varphi, Z))$ is an n-termed sequence. Since there are only k^n sequences in A^n whose terms are elements of $S(\varphi)$ and since $2^k > k^n$, we infer that there is at least one Z such that not all terms of $F(S(\varphi, Z))$ belong to $S(\varphi)$. We order sets Z similarly to the lexicographical ordering of their characteristic functions and choose the first Z_0 with the property stated above. Now we define $f(\varphi)$ as the first term of $F(S(\varphi, Z_0))$ which does not belong to $S(\varphi)$.

Finally assume that the type of φ is an infinite ordinal α. Since $\overline{\alpha}$ is an aleph, there exists a one-to-one mapping of the set $W(\alpha)$ onto the set $W(\alpha)^n$. Let the ordinal $\xi < \alpha$ correspond to the sequence $\langle\xi^{(0)}, \ldots, \xi^{(n-1)}\rangle$ under this mapping.

Let $H_\xi = 0$ if $\langle\varphi_{\xi^{(0)}}, \ldots, \varphi_{\xi^{(n-1)}}\rangle$ does not belong to the set of values of the function F, let $H_\xi = F^c\langle\varphi_{\xi^{(0)}}, \ldots, \varphi_{\xi^{(n-1)}}\rangle$ otherwise, and let $X_0 = \{\varphi_\xi: \varphi_\xi \notin H_\xi\}$, $\langle a_0, \ldots, a_{n-1}\rangle = F(X_0)$. If all of the elements a_j were terms of φ, then for some $\xi_0 < \alpha$ we would have $\langle a_0, \ldots, a_{n-1}\rangle = \langle\varphi_{\xi_0^{(0)}}, \ldots, \varphi_{\xi_0^{(n-1)}}\rangle$; thus this sequence would belong to the set of values of F, which implies that $H_{\xi_0} = X_0$ and $\varphi_{\xi_0} \in X_0 \equiv \varphi_{\xi_0} \in H_{\xi_0}$. On the other hand, from the definition of the set X_0 it follows that $\varphi_\xi \in X_0 \equiv \varphi_\xi \notin H_{\xi_0}$ for every ξ. Thus some a_j is not a term of φ and it suffices to set $f(\varphi) = a_j$ where j is the least index such that a_j has this property.

COROLLARY 10: *If* $\mathfrak{m}$ *is an infinite cardinal then* $\mathfrak{m}+1 < 2^{\mathfrak{m}}$.

PROOF. From the fact that $2^{\mathfrak{m}} > \mathfrak{m}$ it follows that $2^{\mathfrak{m}} \geqslant \mathfrak{m}+1$. If $\mathfrak{m}+1 = 2^{\mathfrak{m}}$ then, since $\mathfrak{m}^2 \geqslant \mathfrak{m}\cdot 2 \geqslant \mathfrak{m}+1$, we would conclude that $\mathfrak{m}^2 \geqslant 2^{\mathfrak{m}}$, contrary to Theorem 9.

Exercises

1. Derive the Cantor inequality $\mathfrak{m} < 2^{\mathfrak{m}}$ and its strengthened version $\mathfrak{k}\cdot\mathfrak{m} < 2^{\mathfrak{m}}$ (for finite $\mathfrak{k}$ and infinite $\mathfrak{m}$) from Theorem 9. [Specker]

2. Prove that the following formulas are equivalent to the axiom of choice:

(a) $$\bigwedge_{\mathfrak{m},\mathfrak{n}\notin N} [(\mathfrak{m}+\mathfrak{n} = \mathfrak{m}) \vee (\mathfrak{m}+\mathfrak{n} = \mathfrak{n})],$$

(b)
$$\bigwedge_{\mathfrak{m},\mathfrak{n}\notin N} [(\mathfrak{m}\cdot\mathfrak{n} = \mathfrak{m}) \vee (\mathfrak{m}\cdot\mathfrak{n} = \mathfrak{n})].$$
[Leśniewski]

3. Prove that the following formula is equivalent to the axiom of choice:
$$\bigwedge_{\mathfrak{m},\mathfrak{n}\notin N} [(\mathfrak{m} \leqslant^* \mathfrak{n}) \vee (\mathfrak{n} \leqslant^* \mathfrak{m})]$$
(the relation $\leqslant^*$ is defined on p. 186). [Lindenbaum]

Hint: Replace $\aleph(\mathfrak{m})$ by $\aleph^*(\mathfrak{m})$ (defined in Exercise 2, p. 279) in the proof of Hartogs' theorem.

4. Prove that the following formula is equivalent to the axiom of choice:
$$\bigwedge_{\mathfrak{m},\mathfrak{p},\mathfrak{q}\notin N} [(\mathfrak{m}^{\mathfrak{p}} < \mathfrak{m}^{\mathfrak{q}}) \to (\mathfrak{p} < \mathfrak{q})].$$
[Tarski]

Hint: Let $\mathfrak{m} = 2^{(\mathfrak{p}^{\aleph_0})}$, $\mathfrak{q} = \aleph(\mathfrak{m})$ and show that $\mathfrak{m}^{\mathfrak{p}} = \mathfrak{m} < \mathfrak{m}^{\mathfrak{q}}$ and that the formula $\mathfrak{m}^{\mathfrak{p}} = \mathfrak{m}^{\mathfrak{q}}$ would imply $\mathfrak{m} \geqslant \aleph(\mathfrak{m})$.

§ 7. The exponential hierarchy of cardinal numbers

In § 4 it was shown that addition and multiplication of alephs is an entirely straightforward matter which reduces to the comparison of alephs. The theory of addition and multiplication of arbitrary cardinals has the same banal character provided that we accept the axiom of choice. Moreover, as was shown in § 6, even very specialized laws of cardinal arithmetic imply the axiom of choice.

On the other hand, as was indicated in § 5, the exponentiation of alephs is not simple even assuming the axiom of choice. In this section we shall consider certain cardinals for which the laws of exponentiation are relatively simple. In the next chapter we shall examine the hypothesis according to which all cardinal numbers belong to this class.

The sets R_α satisfying the following inductive definition were defined already on p. 246:
$$R_0 = 0, \quad R_{\alpha+1} = 2^{R_\alpha}, \quad R_\lambda = \bigcup_{\xi<\lambda} R_\xi \quad (\lambda \text{ a limit ordinal}).$$

Let $\mathfrak{a}_\xi = \overline{\overline{R}}_{\omega+\xi}$. The cardinals $\mathfrak{a}_\xi$ constitute the exponential hierarchy of cardinals.

In order to derive arithmetic laws for these cardinals we must first establish several properties of the sets R_α.

THEOREM 1: (a) $R_\alpha \subset R_\beta$ *for* $\alpha < \beta$; (b) $X \in R_\beta \to X \subset R_\beta$.

PROOF. The proof is by induction with respect to β. It suffices to show that if $\beta_0 \geqslant 0$, and if the theorem holds for all $\beta < \beta_0$, then it also holds for β_0.

The case $\beta_0 = 0$ is obvious. If $\beta_0 = \beta + 1$ and $\alpha < \beta_0$, then $\alpha \leqslant \beta$ and thus by assumption $R_\alpha \subset R_\beta$ and from (b) we obtain $R_\beta \subset R_{\beta+1}$. If β_0 is a limit ordinal and $\alpha < \beta_0$, then $R_\alpha \subset R_{\beta_0}$ because R_{β_0} is the union of all R_ξ for $\xi < \beta_0$. Part (a) is proved.

Assume now that $X \in R_{\beta_0}$; then $\beta_0 \neq 0$ and β_0 either has the form $\beta + 1$ or else it is a limit ordinal. In the first case $X \in 2^{R_\beta}$, that is, $X \subset R_\beta$ and thus $X \subset R_{\beta_0}$ by (a) proved above. If β_0 is a limit ordinal, then there exists $\beta < \beta_0$ such that $X \in R_\beta$ and thus, by assumption, $X \subset R_\beta$ and by (a), $X \in R_{\beta_0}$. Thus part (b) holds.

THEOREM 2: $R_\alpha \times R_\alpha \subset R_{\alpha+2}$.

PROOF. The elements of $R_\alpha \times R_\alpha$ are pairs $\langle X, Y \rangle$ where $X, Y \in R_\alpha$. As $\{X, Y\} \subset R_\alpha$ and $\{X\} \subset R_\alpha$, thus $\{X, Y\} \in R_{\alpha+1}$ and $\{X\} \in R_{\alpha+1}$. It now follows that $\{\{X\}, \{X, Y\}\} \subset R_{\alpha+1}$, and thus $\{\{X\}, \{X, Y\}\} \in R_{\alpha+2}$. Q.E.D.

THEOREM 3: *If* α *is a limit ordinal then* $R_\alpha \times R_\alpha \subset R_\alpha$.

The proof is analogous to that of Theorem 2.

THEOREM 4: $R_\alpha \supset N_\alpha$, *where* N_α *is the* α*-th VN ordinal.*

PROOF. For $\alpha = 0$, $R_\alpha = N_\alpha = 0$. If $R_\alpha \supset N_\alpha$ then $N_\alpha \in 2^{R_\alpha} = R_{\alpha+1}$ and thus $\{N_\alpha\} \subset R_{\alpha+1}$. As $N_\alpha \subset R_\alpha$, it follows that $N_\alpha \cup \{N_\alpha\} \subset R_{\alpha+1}$ whence $N_{\alpha+1} \subset R_{\alpha+1}$. If α is a limit ordinal, and if the theorem holds for $\xi < \alpha$, then since $N_\alpha \subset \bigcup_{\xi<\alpha} N_\xi$, $N_\alpha \subset \bigcup_{\xi<\alpha} R_\xi = R_\alpha$.

THEOREM 5: $\overline{\overline{R_n}} = 2^n$ *for* $n < \omega$; $\mathfrak{a}_0 = \aleph_0$.

PROOF. The first part of the theorem follows from the definitions by induction.

To prove the second part of the theorem it suffices to prove that there exists a one-to-one mapping ν_n of the set R_n into N where ν_{n+1} is an extension of ν_n.

Define ν_0 by $\nu(0) = 0$; for $X \in R_{n+1}$ let $\nu_{n+1}(X) = \nu_n(X)$ if $X \in R_n$;

if $X \in R_{n+1} - R_n$ then let $\nu_{n+1}(X) = \sum_{j<k} 2^{\nu_n(Y_j)}$, where $Y_0, Y_1, \ldots, Y_{k-1}$ are the elements of X ordered so that $\nu_n(Y_{j-1}) < \nu_n(Y_j)$ for $1 < j < k$. It is easy to show that the functions ν_n are one-to-one and that ν_{n+1} is an extension of ν_n.

THEOREM 6: $\mathfrak{a}_{\alpha+1} = 2^{\mathfrak{a}_\alpha}$; $\mathfrak{a}_\alpha < \mathfrak{a}_\beta$ *for* $\alpha < \beta$.

The theorem follows from the definitions and from Theorem 1.

THEOREM 7: $\mathfrak{a}_\alpha^2 = \mathfrak{a}_\alpha$.

PROOF. The theorem is obvious for $\alpha = 0$. If it holds for the ordinal β, and if $\alpha = \beta + 1$, then it also holds for the ordinal α, because $\mathfrak{a}_\alpha = \overline{\overline{R_{\beta+1}}} = 2^{\mathfrak{a}_\beta}$; and thus $\mathfrak{a}_\alpha^2 = 2^{\mathfrak{a}_\beta + \mathfrak{a}_\beta}$, which implies that $\mathfrak{a}_\alpha^2 = \mathfrak{a}_\alpha$ as $\mathfrak{a}_\beta \leqslant \mathfrak{a}_\beta + \mathfrak{a}_\beta \leqslant \mathfrak{a}_\beta^2 = \mathfrak{a}_\beta$. Finally, if α is a limit ordinal, then by Theorem 3 it follows that $\mathfrak{a}_\alpha^2 \leqslant \mathfrak{a}_\alpha$; and because $\mathfrak{a}_\alpha^2 \geqslant \mathfrak{a}_\alpha$, we conclude that $\mathfrak{a}_\alpha^2 = \mathfrak{a}_\alpha$.

COROLLARY 8: $\mathfrak{a}_\alpha + \mathfrak{a}_\beta = \mathfrak{a}_\alpha \mathfrak{a}_\beta = \mathfrak{a}_{\max(\alpha,\beta)}$.

The corollary follows from Theorem 7 with a proof similar to that of the analogous theorem for alephs (see p. 284).

°THEOREM 9: *If* α *is a limit ordinal then*

$$\mathfrak{a}_\alpha = \sum_{\xi<\alpha} \mathfrak{a}_\xi .$$

PROOF. On the one hand,

$$\overline{\overline{\bigcup_{\xi<\alpha} R_\xi}} \leqslant \sum_{\xi<\alpha} \overline{\overline{R_\xi}} = \sum_{\xi<\alpha} \mathfrak{a}_\xi .$$

On the other, $\mathfrak{a}_\alpha = \mathfrak{a}_\alpha \cdot \mathfrak{a}_\alpha \geqslant \mathfrak{a}_\alpha \cdot \overline{\alpha}$ by Theorem 4, since $\overline{\overline{N_\alpha}} = \overline{\alpha}$. But since $\mathfrak{a}_\alpha \cdot \overline{\alpha} \geqslant \sum_{\xi<\alpha} \mathfrak{a}_\xi$, the desired equation follows by the Cantor–Bernstein theorem.

REMARK. The axiom of choice is used in this theorem because the very definition of the infinite sum of cardinal numbers demands the use of this axiom.

We shall now establish several laws concerning exponentiation of the cardinals $\mathfrak{a}_\xi$.

THEOREM 10: *If* $\alpha \leqslant \beta$ *then* $\mathfrak{a}_\alpha^{\mathfrak{a}_\beta} = \mathfrak{a}_{\beta+1}$.

PROOF. $\mathfrak{a}_{\beta+1} = 2^{\mathfrak{a}_\beta} \leqslant \mathfrak{a}_\alpha^{\mathfrak{a}_\beta} < (2^{\mathfrak{a}_\alpha})^{\mathfrak{a}_\beta} = 2^{\mathfrak{a}_\alpha \mathfrak{a}_\beta} = 2^{\mathfrak{a}_\beta} = \mathfrak{a}_{\beta+1}$.

THEOREM 11: *If* $\alpha+1>\beta$ *then* $\mathfrak{a}_{\alpha+1}^{\mathfrak{a}_\beta}=\mathfrak{a}_{\alpha+1}$.

PROOF. $\mathfrak{a}_{\alpha+1}^{\mathfrak{a}_\beta}=2^{\mathfrak{a}_\alpha\mathfrak{a}_\beta}=2^{\mathfrak{a}_\alpha}=\mathfrak{a}_{\alpha+1}$.

We lack a full description for powers of $\mathfrak{a}_\xi$ in the case of the power $\mathfrak{a}_\alpha^{\mathfrak{a}_\beta}$, where α is a limit ordinal and $\beta<\alpha$. It turns out that it is not possible to prove any simple formula for such powers. Certain fragmentary results in this area are collected in Theorem 18 below. First we shall establish certain relations between the hierarchy of alephs and the exponential hierarchy.

°THEOREM 12: *If* λ *is a limit ordinal* $\geqslant 0$, *then*

(1) $$\aleph_{\lambda+n}\leqslant\mathfrak{a}_{\lambda+n}\quad \textit{for}\quad n=0,1,2,\ldots$$

PROOF. Suppose that there are numbers λ and n for which the inequality (1) does not hold. Among them there exists a least one, say λ_0; there also exists a least ordinal n_0 such that for $\lambda=\lambda_0$ and $n=n_0$ the inequality (1) does not hold.

The case where $\lambda_0=0$ and $n_0=0$ is impossible since $\aleph_0=\mathfrak{a}=\mathfrak{a}_0$.

We shall show that $n_0=0$. For if $n_0=n_1+1$, then by the definition of n_0 it follows that

$$\aleph_{\lambda_0+n_1}\leqslant\mathfrak{a}_{\lambda_0+n_1},$$

which by (3), p. 279, implies that

$$\aleph(\aleph_{\lambda_0+n_1})\leqslant 2^{\mathfrak{a}_{\lambda_0+n_1}},$$

and thus

$$\aleph(\aleph_{\lambda_0+n_1})\leqslant\mathfrak{a}_{\lambda_0+n_1+1}=\mathfrak{a}_{\lambda_0+n_0}.$$

But since $\aleph(\aleph_{\lambda_0+n_1})=\aleph_{\lambda_0+n_1+1}=\aleph_{\lambda_0+n_0}$ (see p. 282), we infer that

$$\aleph_{\lambda_0+n_0}\leqslant\mathfrak{a}_{\lambda_0+n_0},$$

which contradicts the choice of n_0. Thus the assumption that $n_0\neq 0$ leads to a contradiction.

Every ordinal $\xi<\lambda_0$ can be represented in the form $\gamma+n$ where γ is a limit ordinal less than λ_0 (see Theorem 1, p. 235). Thus by the choice of λ_0 we have

$$\aleph_\xi=\aleph_{\gamma+n}\leqslant\mathfrak{a}_{\gamma+n}<\mathfrak{a}_{\lambda_0},$$

which implies that

$$\sum_{\xi<\lambda_0}\aleph_\xi\leqslant\overline{\overline{\lambda}}_0\cdot\mathfrak{a}_{\lambda_0},$$

and thus by Theorems 4 and 8,

$$\sum_{\xi<\lambda_0} \aleph_\xi \leqslant \mathfrak{a}_{\lambda_0}^2 = \mathfrak{a}_{\lambda_0}.$$

Finally since $\aleph_{\lambda_0} = \sum_{\xi<\lambda_0} \aleph_\xi$, we conclude that $\aleph_{\lambda_0} \leqslant \mathfrak{a}_{\lambda_0}$, in contradiction to the definition of λ_0. Thus the assumption that there exist numbers λ and n for which (1) does not hold leads to a contradiction.

Theorem 12 provides an estimation of alephs "from above" by means of the exponential hierarchy. No estimation of the numbers $\mathfrak{a}_\xi$ by means of alephs is possible, even for $\xi = 1$.

The well-ordering theorem implies that for every ordinal α there exists an ordinal $\pi(\alpha)$ such that $\mathfrak{a}_\alpha = \aleph_{\pi(\alpha)}$. The axioms of set theory yield only fragmentary information about the ordinals $\pi(\alpha)$. The following theorem is obvious.

°THEOREM 13: $\alpha < \beta \rightarrow \pi(\alpha) < \pi(\beta)$.

°THEOREM 14: *The function π is continuous (on every set of the form $W(\alpha)$).*

PROOF. Let α be a limit ordinal and let $\lambda = \lim_{\xi<\alpha} \pi(\xi)$. Applying Theorem 12, p. 286 we obtain

$$\aleph_\lambda = \sum_{\xi<\alpha} \aleph_{\pi(\xi)} = \sum_{\xi<\alpha} \mathfrak{a}_\xi = \mathfrak{a}_\alpha,$$

and thus $\lambda = \pi(\alpha)$.

The following is an easy corollary of Theorem 14.

°COROLLARY 15: *If α is a non-zero limit ordinal, then $cf(\alpha) \leqslant \pi(\alpha)$.*

PROOF. Let $cf(\alpha) = \delta$ and let φ be an increasing sequence of type ω_δ such that $\alpha = \lim_{\xi<\omega_\delta} \varphi(\xi)$. Then

$$\pi(\alpha) = \lim_{\xi<\omega_\delta} \pi(\varphi(\xi)) = \lim_{\xi<\omega_\delta} \psi(\xi),$$

where the composite sequence $\psi = \pi \circ \varphi$ is increasing. Thus $\pi(\alpha) \geqslant \omega_\delta \geqslant \delta$.

°THEOREM 16: *If $\pi(\gamma+1)$ is not a limit ordinal, then $\pi(\gamma+1) > \gamma$; if $\pi(\gamma+1)$ is a limit ordinal, then $cf(\pi(\gamma+1)) > \gamma$.*

PROOF. The first part of the theorem is obvious since the function π is increasing.

Assume that $\pi(\gamma+1)$ is a limit ordinal and that $\delta = cf(\pi(\gamma+1))$. If $\delta \leqslant \gamma$ were true then by Corollary 7, p. 290 $\aleph_{\pi(\gamma+1)} < \aleph_{\pi(\gamma+1)}^{\aleph_\gamma}$ would also be true, that is

$$\mathfrak{a}_{\gamma+1} < \mathfrak{a}_{\gamma+1}^{\aleph_\gamma} = 2^{\mathfrak{a}_\gamma \aleph_\gamma} = 2^{\mathfrak{a}_\gamma} = \mathfrak{a}_{\gamma+1},$$

which is impossible. Thus $\delta > \gamma$. Q.E.D.

Using the ordinals $\pi(\alpha)$ we are now able to evaluate the power $\mathfrak{a}_\alpha^{\aleph_\beta}$ where α is a limit ordinal.

THEOREM 17: *If $\alpha > 0$ is a limit ordinal, then*

$$\mathfrak{a}_\alpha^{\aleph_\beta} = \begin{cases} \mathfrak{a}_\alpha & \text{if} \quad \beta < cf(\alpha), \\ \mathfrak{a}_{\alpha+1} & \text{if} \quad cf(\alpha) \leqslant \beta \leqslant \pi(\alpha). \end{cases}$$

PROOF. Assume that $\beta < cf(\alpha)$. Clearly it suffices to show that $\mathfrak{a}_\alpha^{\aleph_\beta} \leqslant \mathfrak{a}_\alpha$. By Theorem 3, p. 288,

$$\aleph_{\pi(\alpha)}^{\aleph_\beta} = \sum_{\xi<\alpha} \aleph_{\pi(\xi)}^{\aleph_\beta} \leqslant \sum_{\xi<\alpha} \aleph_{\pi(\xi+1)}^{\aleph_\beta}.$$

The last sum can be separated into two sums $\sum'$ and $\sum''$ where in the first sum ξ is such that $\pi(\xi+1) \leqslant \beta$ and in the second such that $\beta < \pi(\xi+1)$. From Theorem 1, p. 287 it follows that the ξth component of the sum $\sum'$ is equal to $2^{\aleph_\beta}$; and as $\aleph_\beta \leqslant \mathfrak{a}_\beta < \mathfrak{a}_{cf(\alpha)} \leqslant \mathfrak{a}_\alpha$, we have

$$\textstyle\sum' \leqslant \overline{\beta} \cdot \mathfrak{a}_\alpha \leqslant \mathfrak{a}_\beta \cdot \mathfrak{a}_\alpha = \mathfrak{a}_\alpha.$$

The ξth component of the second sum $= \mathfrak{a}_{\xi+1}^{\aleph_\beta} = 2^{\mathfrak{a}_\xi \aleph_\beta} \leqslant 2^{\mathfrak{a}_\xi \mathfrak{a}_{\xi+1}} = \mathfrak{a}_{\xi+2}$, because $\aleph_\beta < \aleph_{\pi(\xi+1)} = \mathfrak{a}_{\xi+1}$. Thus

$$\textstyle\sum'' \leqslant \sum_{\xi<\alpha} \mathfrak{a}_{\xi+2} \leqslant \mathfrak{a}_\alpha \overline{\alpha} = \mathfrak{a}_\alpha.$$

It follows that

$$\mathfrak{a}_\alpha^{\aleph_\beta} \leqslant \mathfrak{a}_\alpha + \mathfrak{a}_\alpha = \mathfrak{a}_\alpha.$$

Assume now that φ is an increasing sequence of type $\omega_{cf(\alpha)} = \gamma$ convergent to α and that $cf(\alpha) \leqslant \beta \leqslant \pi(\alpha)$. Then

$$\mathfrak{a}_\alpha^{\aleph_\beta} \leqslant \mathfrak{a}_\alpha^{\aleph_{\pi(\alpha)}} = \mathfrak{a}_\alpha^{\mathfrak{a}_\alpha} \leqslant 2^{\mathfrak{a}_\alpha^2} = \mathfrak{a}_{\alpha+1}.$$

On the other hand,

$$\mathfrak{a}_{\alpha+1} = 2^{\mathfrak{a}_\alpha} = 2^{\aleph_{\pi(\alpha)}} = 2^{\sum_{\xi<\gamma} \aleph_{\pi(\varphi_\xi)}}$$

$$= \prod_{\xi<\gamma} 2^{\aleph_{\pi(\varphi_\xi)}} = \prod_{\xi<\gamma} \mathfrak{a}_{\varphi_\xi+1} \leqslant \mathfrak{a}_\alpha^{\bar{\bar{\gamma}}} = \mathfrak{a}_\alpha^{\aleph_{cf(\alpha)}} \leqslant \mathfrak{a}_\alpha^{\aleph_\beta},$$

which proves Theorem 17.

°COROLLARY 18: *If α is a limit ordinal then*

$$\mathfrak{a}_\alpha^{\mathfrak{a}_\beta} = \begin{cases} \mathfrak{a}_\alpha & \text{if} \quad \pi(\beta) < cf(\alpha), \\ \mathfrak{a}_{\alpha+1} & \text{if} \quad cf(\alpha) \leqslant \pi(\beta) \leqslant \pi(\alpha), \\ \mathfrak{a}_{\beta+1} & \text{if} \quad \beta \leqslant \alpha. \end{cases}$$

Corollary 18 shows that the difficulty in giving general formulas for the powers $\mathfrak{a}_\alpha^{\mathfrak{a}_\beta}$ is caused by the lack of knowledge about the values of the function π.

§ 8. Miscellaneous problems of power associated with Boolean algebras

We shall illustrate how one calculates the cardinality of a set by solving the problem of the cardinality of the set of prime ideals of a complete atomic Boolean algebra. As we know such an algebra is isomorphic with the field 2^Y of all subsets of some set Y (see p. 152). We shall assume that $\bar{\bar{Y}} = \mathfrak{m}$ and that $\mathfrak{m}$ is infinite.

°THEOREM 1: *The field of sets 2^Y contains $2^{2^{\mathfrak{m}}}$ prime ideals* [1]).

First we reduce the proof to the following lemma:

°LEMMA 1: *There exists a family $S \subset 2^Y$ of power $2^{\mathfrak{m}}$ such that every finite subfamily $S_1 \subset S$ is independent* (see p. 22).

With every function $f \in \{0, 1\}^S$ we associate the family

$$S(f) = \{Z: [[(Z \in S) \wedge (f(Z) = 0)] \vee [(Y - Z \in S) \wedge (f(Z) = 1)]]\}.$$

It is clear that distinct functions are associated with distinct families.

If k is a natural number > 0, and if $Z_i \in S(f)$ for $i < k$, then $\bigcup_{i<k} Z_i \neq Y$. Indeed, assume for example that $Z_i \in S$ for $i < p$ and

[1]) This theorem was first proved (for $\mathfrak{m} = \aleph_0$) by G. Fichtenholz and L. Kantorovitch, Studia Mathematica **5** (1935) 69–99. A simpler proof was given by F. Hausdorff, *Über zwei Sätze von G. Fichtenholz und L. Kantorovitch*, Studia Mathematica **6** (1936). Tarski's papers: *Sur les classes d'ensembles closes par rapport à certaines opérations élémentaires*, Fundamenta Mathematicae **16** (1930) 181–304 and *Ideale in vollständigen Mengenkörpern*, ibid. **32** (1939) 45–63 contain an extensive discussion of similar problems.

that $Y-Z_i \in S$ for $p \leqslant i < k$. If the equation $\bigcup_{i<k} Z_i = Y$ were true, then letting $W_i = Y-Z_i$ for $p \leqslant i < k$ we would have $\bigcap_{i<p} (Y-Z_i) \cap \bigcap_{p \leqslant i<k} W_i = 0$, contradicting the fact that the family composed of the sets $Z_0, \ldots, Z_{p-1}$ and $W_p, \ldots, W_{k-1}$ is independent.

Let $I(f)$ be the family composed of sets $Z \subset Y$ having the following property: there exists a finite number of sets $Z_1, \ldots, Z_n \in S(f)$ such that $Z \subset Z_1 \cup \ldots \cup Z_n$. It is clear that

$$Z' \subset Z \in I(f) \rightarrow Z' \in I(f)$$

and that

$$(Z \in I(f)) \wedge (Z' \in I(f)) \rightarrow (Z \cup Z' \in I(f)).$$

Thus the family $I(f)$ is an ideal. Since no finite sum $Z_1 \cup \ldots \cup Z_n$ of elements of $S(f)$ is equal to Y, it follows that $Y \notin I(f)$. Finally by definition we have $S(f) \subset I(f)$.

By 2, p. 266 there exists a maximal (and thus a prime) ideal $J(f)$ containing $I(f)$ (see Exercises 2, p. 168).

If $f_1 \neq f_2$, then $J(f_1) \neq J(f_2)$. If for example $f_1(Z) = 0$ and $f_2(Z) = 1$, then $Z \in S(f_1) \subset J(f_1)$ and $Y-Z \in S(f_2) \subset J(f_2)$ and thus the ideals $J(f_1)$ and $J(f_2)$ are distinct, because otherwise $Y = Z \cup (Y-Z) \in J(f_1)$ in contradiction to the definition of prime ideal. Thus the set of all prime ideals is at least of the same power as the set of all functions $f \in \{0, 1\}^S$, that is, at least of power $2^{2^{\mathfrak{m}}}$. On the other hand, every prime ideal is contained in the family 2^Y and thus the set of all prime ideals has at most power $2^{2^{\mathfrak{m}}}$.

It remains to prove the lemma. For this purpose we shall accomplish a series of reductions.

Let X be an arbitrary set and let R be a family of subsets of X. We shall say that R is

(a) *independent*,

(b) *weakly independent*,

(c) *very weakly independent*,

if respectively

(a) every finite subfamily $R_1 \subset R$ is independent,

(b) $M - \bigcup_{i<k} M_i \neq 0$ for arbitrary distinct $M, M_0, \ldots, M_{k-1} \in R$, $(k = 0, 1, 2, \ldots)$,

(c) $M_1 - M_2 \neq 0$ for arbitrary distinct $M_1, M_2 \in \boldsymbol{R}$.

We say that the *cardinal* $\mathfrak{m}$ *satisfies condition* (A), (B), or (C) provided there exists a set X of power $\mathfrak{m}$ and a family $\boldsymbol{R} \subset 2^X$ of power $2^{\mathfrak{m}}$ satisfying the condition (a), (b), or (c), respectively.

It is clear that if $\mathfrak{m}$ satisfies condition (A), then for every set X of power $\mathfrak{m}$ there exists a strongly independent family $\boldsymbol{R} \subset 2^X$ of power $2^{\mathfrak{m}}$. Similar theorems hold for conditions (B) and (C).

The lemma above is equivalent to the statement that every infinite cardinal $\mathfrak{m}$ satisfies condition (A).

We now show that conditions (A), (B), (C) are mutually equivalent. The implications (A) → (B) → (C) are obvious. Thus it suffices to show that

(1) $$(B) \to (A),$$

(2) $$(C) \to (B).$$

The scheme of proof of (1) and (2) is as follows: we assume that there is a set X of power $\mathfrak{m}$ and a family $\boldsymbol{R} \subset 2^X$ of power $2^{\mathfrak{m}}$ satisfying condition (b) (respectively (c)) and we then construct a set K of the same power $\mathfrak{m}$ as well as a family $\boldsymbol{S} \subset 2^K$ of power $2^{\mathfrak{m}}$ satisfying condition (a) (respectively (b)).

PROOF OF (1). Let X be a set of power $\mathfrak{m}$ and $\boldsymbol{R}$ a weakly independent family of power $2^{\mathfrak{m}}$ consisting of subsets of X. Let $\boldsymbol{K}$ denote the family of all finite subsets of X. Clearly $\boldsymbol{K} = \bigcup_n \boldsymbol{K}_n$, where $\boldsymbol{K}_n$ is the family of all subsets of X which contain exactly n elements. Moreover, $\overline{\overline{\boldsymbol{K}_n}} = \mathfrak{m}^n = \mathfrak{m}$ (see p. 291), and thus $\overline{\overline{\boldsymbol{K}}} = \mathfrak{m} \cdot \mathfrak{a} = \mathfrak{m}$.

For $T \in \boldsymbol{R}$, let

$$X(T) = \{Z \in \boldsymbol{K} \colon Z \cap T \neq 0\},$$

and denote by $\boldsymbol{S}$ the family of all subsets of $\boldsymbol{K}$ having the form $X(T)$.

We shall prove that every finite family $\{X(T_1), \ldots, X(T_k)\}$, where $T_1, \ldots, T_k$ are distinct elements of $\boldsymbol{R}$, is independent. We shall show, for example, that the set

$$X(T_1) \cap \ldots \cap X(T_p) \cap [\boldsymbol{K} - X(T_{p+1})] \cap \ldots \cap [\boldsymbol{K} - X(T_k)]$$

is non-empty.

Indeed, from the assumption that $\boldsymbol{R}$ is weakly independent it follows that $T_j - \bigcup_{i=p+1}^{k} T_i \neq 0$ for $j = 1, 2, \ldots, p$. If x_j is an element of this difference, then the set $\{x_1, \ldots, x_p\}$ clearly belongs to $\boldsymbol{X}(T_j)$ and to $\boldsymbol{K} - \boldsymbol{X}(T_i)$ for $j = 1, \ldots, p$, $i = p+1, \ldots, k$.

From the independence proved above it follows in particular that $\boldsymbol{X}(T) \neq \boldsymbol{X}(T')$ for $T \neq T'$. Therefore $\boldsymbol{S}$ is a family of power $2^{\mathfrak{m}}$ consisting of subsets of $\boldsymbol{K}$ and every finite subfamily $\boldsymbol{S}_1 \subset \boldsymbol{S}$ is independent; that is, the family $\boldsymbol{S}$ satisfies condition (a).

PROOF OF (2). Let X be a set of power $\mathfrak{m}$ and let $\boldsymbol{R}$ be a very weakly independent family of power $2^{\mathfrak{m}}$ consisting of subsets of $\boldsymbol{X}$. For every set Z let $Z' = \bigcup_{n \in N} Z^n$; thus Z' is the family of all finite sequences whose terms belong to Z.

Let $K = X'$; clearly $K = \bigcup_{n \in N} X^n$ and as $\overline{\overline{X^n}} = \mathfrak{m}^n = \mathfrak{m}$ it follows that $\overline{\overline{K}} = \mathfrak{m} \cdot \mathfrak{a} = \mathfrak{m}$. Let $\boldsymbol{S} = \{M' \colon M \in \boldsymbol{R}\}$; clearly $\boldsymbol{S}$ is a family of subsets of K and $\overline{\overline{\boldsymbol{S}}} = \overline{\overline{\boldsymbol{R}}} = 2^{\mathfrak{m}}$ since the mapping $M \to M'$ is one-to-one.

We shall now show that the family $\boldsymbol{S}$ is weakly independent. Let $M, M_0, \ldots, M_{k-1}$ be distinct elements of $\boldsymbol{R}$ and assume that $M' \subset \bigcup_{i<k} M_i'$. From the assumption it follows that $M - M_i \neq 0$ for $i < k$; let $x_i \in M - M_i$ for $i < k$. Thus the k-term sequence $\langle x_0, \ldots, x_{k-1} \rangle$ belongs to M' but does not belong to M_i' because its ith term does not belong to M_i. Consequently, we have a contradiction which proves that the family $\boldsymbol{S}$ is weakly independent.

PROOF OF THE LEMMA. Let X and X' be two disjoint sets of power $\mathfrak{m}$ and let a one-to-one function f map X onto X'. For $M \subset X$ let $M^* = M \cup [X' - f^1(M)]$. Let $\boldsymbol{S}$ be the family of all sets M^*. The family $\boldsymbol{S}$ consists of subsets of the union $K = X \cup X'$, where $\overline{\overline{K}} = \mathfrak{m} + \mathfrak{m} = \mathfrak{m}$ and $\overline{\overline{\boldsymbol{S}}} = 2^{\mathfrak{m}}$ because the mapping $M \to M^*$ is one-to-one.

If $M_1 \neq M_2$ and $M_1, M_2 \subset X$, then $M_1^* \neq M_2^*$. For $x \in M_1 - M_2$ implies that $x \in M_1^* - M_2^*$ whereas $x \in M_2 - M_1$ implies that $f(x) \in M_1^* - M_2^*$. Thus $\boldsymbol{S}$ is very weakly independent, which proves that the cardinal $\mathfrak{m}$ has property (C); hence, by (1) and (2), $\mathfrak{m}$ also has property (A). This completes the proof of the lemma.

Exercises

1. Prove that if a Boolean algebra is finite and has 2^n elements, then it contains exactly n prime ideals.

Hint: Every prime ideal has the form $\{x: x \wedge a = o\}$, where a is an atom.

2. The Boolean algebra K with unit of infinite power $\mathfrak{m}$ contains at least 1 and at most $2^{\mathfrak{m}}$ prime non-principal ideals.

Hint: Let a_t denote any element of K such that the ideal $\{x: x \leqslant a_t\}$ is prime; then there exists a proper ideal I containing all elements $-a_t$.

3. Construct countable Boolean algebras with resp. $n, \mathfrak{a}$ and $2^{\mathfrak{a}}$ prime, non-principal ideals (where $n \in N$).

4. We say that a subset X of the Boolean algebra K is a *base* for the ideal I if (1) $X \subset I$, (2) for every $a \in I$ there exist finitely many $x_1, \ldots, x_n$ elements of X such that $a \leqslant x_1 \vee x_2 \vee \ldots \vee x_n$ and (3) no proper subset of X satisfies conditions (1) and (2).

Prove that an ideal is principal if and only if it has a one element base.

5. If $K = 2^N$ and I is a non-principal prime ideal, then no base for I is countable.

CHAPTER IX

INACCESSIBLE CARDINALS. THE CONTINUUM HYPOTHESIS

In this chapter we shall deal with two rather unrelated topics. First we shall discuss certain properties of the so-called *inaccessible cardinal numbers.* As we shall see, these cardinals are situated immensely high in the hierarchy of cardinal numbers. Although we can examine the properties of inaccesible ordinals within the framework of the system Σ°[TR], the existence of such numbers cannot be deduced from these axioms. In fact, each proposition regarding the existence of an innaccessible number demands its own axiom.

The second topic to be discussed is the *continuum hypothesis* and several of its consequences. This hypothesis, formulated by Cantor, concerns the relationship between the exponential hierarchy and the hierarchy of alephs. It has been shown that this hypothesis is independent of the axioms Σ°[TR], VIII. Opinions vary among mathematicians as to whether this hypothesis should be rejected or accepted as a new axiom of set theory.

The motive for treating these two topics in one chapter is that they give some idea of the nature of propositions indecidable in the axiomatic system of set theory.

§ 1. Inaccessible cardinals

On p. 279 we defined initial ordinals as numbers of the form ω_α. We shall now divide initial ordinals into *regular* and *singular* ones. The ordinal ω_α is singular if it is cofinal with an ordinal smaller than itself, that is, if there exists a sequence φ of type β, where β is a limit ordinal $< \omega_\alpha$, such that $\lim_{\xi<\beta} \varphi_\xi = \omega_\alpha$. An ordinal ω_α is *regular* if it is not singular.

°THEOREM 1: *The ordinal* $\omega_{\alpha+1}$ *is regular for every* α.

PROOF. If $\omega_{\alpha+1} = \lim_{\xi<\beta} \varphi_\xi$ where β is a limit ordinal $< \omega_{\alpha+1}$, then by letting $\gamma = cf(\beta)$ we would have $\gamma < \alpha+1$ and $cf(\omega_{\alpha+1}) \leqslant \gamma \leqslant \alpha$ contrary to Theorem 9 on p. 285.

The initial ordinal ω_α is called *weakly inaccessible* if it is regular and if the index α is a limit ordinal. For example, the ordinal ω is weakly inaccessible. On the other hand, the numbers ω_ω, ω_Ω, ω_{ω_ω} are not regular and thus are not weakly inaccessible.

THEOREM 2: *If* $\alpha > 0$, *then the ordinal* ω_α *is weakly inaccessible if and only if* $\alpha = \omega_\alpha = cf(\alpha)$.

PROOF. Assume that $\alpha > 0$ and that ω_α is weakly inaccessible. The ordinal α is then a limit ordinal $\neq 0$; let $\gamma = cf(\alpha)$. If $\alpha < \omega_\alpha$ then, since $\omega_\alpha = \lim_{\xi<\alpha} \omega_\xi$, it follows that ω_α is not regular. Thus $\alpha = \omega_\alpha$ since $\beta \leqslant \omega_\beta$ for all β.

Let $\gamma = cf(\alpha)$. By the definition of γ there is an increasing sequence φ of type ω_γ such that $\alpha = \lim_{\xi<\omega_\gamma} \varphi(\xi)$, thus $\omega_\alpha = \lim_{\xi<\omega_\gamma} \omega_{\varphi(\xi)}$; if $\gamma < \alpha$ then ω_α would not be regular.

Conversely, assume that $\alpha = \omega_\alpha = cf(\alpha) > 0$. Thus α is a limit ordinal and to show that ω_α is weakly inaccessible it suffices to show that it is regular. Assume thus that β is a limit ordinal $\leqslant \omega_\alpha$ and that $\omega_\alpha = \lim_{\xi<\beta} \varphi(\xi)$. If $\gamma = cf(\beta)$ then β is the limit of an increasing sequence ψ of type ω_γ. Thus $\omega_\alpha = \lim_{\xi<\omega_\gamma} \varphi(\psi(\xi))$ and $cf(\alpha) \leqslant \gamma$. On the other hand, $\gamma \leqslant \omega_\gamma$ and $\omega_\gamma \leqslant \beta$, because $\psi(\xi) \geqslant \xi$ for $\xi < \omega_\gamma$. Thus we have the inequality $cf(\alpha) \leqslant \gamma \leqslant \omega_\gamma \leqslant \beta \leqslant \omega_\alpha$; hence from our initial assumptions it follows that $\alpha = \beta$. Thus ω_α is cofinal with no ordinal $< \omega_\alpha$. Q.E.D.

REMARK: The equation $\alpha = \omega_\alpha$ does not characterize inaccessible ordinals. In fact, if β is a sequence of type ω defined inductively by the formulas $\beta_0 = 0$, $\beta_{n+1} = \omega_{\beta_n}$ then the ordinal $\alpha = \lim_n \beta_n$ satisfies the equation $\alpha = \omega_\alpha$ (see p. 237), but ω_α is not regular since $cf(\alpha) = 0$. See also exercise 3, p. 314.

We now introduce the notion of weakly and strongly inaccessible cardinals.

The cardinal $\mathfrak{m}$ is *weakly inaccessible* if it is an aleph, $\mathfrak{m} = \aleph_\alpha$ and if ω_α is a weakly inaccessible ordinal[1]).

We shall characterize weakly inaccessible cardinals in terms of the theory of cardinal numbers.

°THEOREM 3: *The cardinal* $\mathfrak{m}$ *is weakly inaccessible if and only if it is infinite and satisfies the conditions:*

(i) *if* $\mathfrak{n} < \mathfrak{m}$, *then there exists a* $\mathfrak{p}$ *such that* $\mathfrak{n} < \mathfrak{p} < \mathfrak{m}$; *and*

(ii) *if* I *is a set of power* $< \mathfrak{m}$ *and* $\mathfrak{f}$ *a function whose values are cardinals* $< \mathfrak{m}$, *then* $\sum_{x \in I} \mathfrak{f}_x < \mathfrak{m}$.

PROOF. Let $\mathfrak{m} = \aleph_\alpha$ be a weakly inaccessible cardinal. Then α is a limit ordinal, which proves condition (i). Let I be a set and $\mathfrak{f}$ a function satisfying the antecedent of the implication (ii). We can assume that $I = W(\omega_\lambda)$, where $\lambda < \alpha$ and that $\mathfrak{f}_x = \aleph_{\varphi(x)}$, where $\varphi(x) < \alpha$ for $x < \omega_\lambda$.

If there exists a largest ordinal among the ordinals $\varphi(x)$, say μ, then

$$\sum_{x<\omega_\lambda} \aleph_{\varphi(x)} \leqslant \aleph_\lambda \aleph_\mu = \aleph_{\max(\lambda,\mu)} < \aleph_\alpha.$$

Otherwise letting $\mu = \lim_{x<\omega_\lambda} \varphi(x)$ we have $\mu < \alpha$ by the assumption of inaccessibility, thus again

$$\sum_{x<\omega_\lambda} \aleph_{\varphi(x)} \leqslant \aleph_\lambda \aleph_\mu < \aleph_\alpha.$$

Thus in either case $\sum_{x\in I} \mathfrak{f}_x < \mathfrak{m}$, which proves that condition (ii) holds.

Conversely, assume that $\mathfrak{m}$ is an infinite cardinal satisfying conditions (i) and (ii). Let $\mathfrak{m} = \aleph_\alpha$. By (i) it follows that α is a limit ordinal. If ω_α were not regular then there would exist a limit ordinal $\beta < \omega_\alpha$ and an increasing sequence φ of type β such that $\omega_\alpha = \lim_{\xi<\beta} \varphi(\xi)$. Letting

$$I = W(\beta) \quad \text{and} \quad \mathfrak{f}_\xi = \overline{\overline{W(\omega_{\varphi(\xi+1)}) - W(\omega_{\varphi(\xi)})}} \quad \text{for} \quad \xi \in I$$

we obtain (see pp. 284–286)

$$\aleph_\alpha = \sum_{\xi\in I} \mathfrak{f}_\xi,$$

in contradiction to (ii). Thus Theorem 3 is proved.

[1]) This notion was first introduced by F. Hausdorff in his paper *Grundzüge einer Theorie der geordneten Mengen*, Mathematische Annalen **65** (1908) 443.

The cardinal $\mathfrak{m}$ is *strongly inaccessible*[1]) if it is weakly inaccessible and satisfies the formula

(iii) $\mathfrak{n} < \mathfrak{m} \rightarrow 2^{\mathfrak{n}} < \mathfrak{m}$.

Clearly condition (iii) implies (i).

The existence of weakly inaccessible cardinals which are not strongly inaccessible presents a problem which is not decidable on the basis of the accepted axioms. The generalized continuum hypothesis, which we shall treat in § 6, implies that every weakly inaccessible cardinal is also strongly inaccessible.

°THEOREM 4. *The cardinal* $\mathfrak{m} = \aleph_\alpha$ *is strongly inaccessible if and only if it is weakly inaccessible and* $\pi(\alpha) = \alpha$ (see p. 301 for the definition of the operation π).

PROOF. If $\mathfrak{m}$ is weakly inaccessible and $\pi(\alpha) = \alpha$, then $\mathfrak{n} < \mathfrak{m}$ implies that $\mathfrak{n} < \aleph_0$ or $\mathfrak{n} = \aleph_\beta$ for some $\beta < \alpha$. In the first case clearly $2^{\mathfrak{n}} < \mathfrak{m}$, in the second case $2^{\mathfrak{n}} \leqslant 2^{\mathfrak{a}_\beta} = \mathfrak{a}_{\beta+1} = \aleph_{\pi(\beta+1)}$; since π is strictly increasing (see p. 301), it follows that $2^{\mathfrak{n}} < \aleph_{\pi(\alpha)} = \aleph_\alpha = \mathfrak{m}$. Thus $\mathfrak{m}$ satisfies (iii) and hence is strongly inaccessible.

Conversely, if $\mathfrak{m}$ is strongly inaccessible and if $\alpha = 0$, then it is clear that $\pi(\alpha) = \alpha$. On the other hand, if $\alpha \neq 0$ then α is a limit ordinal and thus $\alpha = \lim_{\beta<\alpha} \beta$. Since the operation π is monotonic and continuous (p. 301), we have $\pi(\alpha) = \lim_{\beta<\alpha} \pi(\beta)$. It follows from (iii) that $\beta < \alpha \rightarrow \aleph_{\pi(\beta)} < \aleph_\alpha$ and thus $\pi(\beta) < \alpha$ for $\beta < \alpha$, hence $\lim_{\beta<\alpha} \pi(\beta) = \alpha$. Therefore $\pi(\alpha) = \alpha$. Q.E.D.

°THEOREM 5[2]): *In order that* $\mathfrak{m} = \aleph_\alpha$ *be strongly inaccessible it is neccessary and sufficient that* $\mathfrak{m}$ *satisfy the condition* (iii) *and*

(iv) $$\sum_{x<\mathfrak{m}} \mathfrak{m}^x = \mathfrak{m}.$$

[1]) This notion was first introduced by A. Tarski. See his paper *Über unerreichbare Kardinalzahlen*, Fundamenta Mathematicae **30** (1938) 68–89, reference 1) on page 87. The first publication using this notion was the paper of W. Sierpiński and A. Tarski, *Sur une propriété caractéristique des nombres inaccessibles*, Fundamenta Mathematicae **15** (1930) 292–300. An equivalent definition of strongly inaccessible cardinals was also given by E. Zermelo, *Über Grenzzahlen und Mengenbereiche*, Fundamenta Mathematicae **16** (1930) 29–47.

[2]) Theorems 5 and 6 are given in Tarski's paper cited above.

Proof. Assume that $\mathfrak{m} = \aleph_\alpha$ is strongly inaccessible. It suffices to show that $\mathfrak{m}$ satisfies (iv). Moreover, we may assume that $\mathfrak{m} > \aleph_0$ and thus, by Theorem 2, that $\alpha = \omega_\alpha = cf(\alpha)$. Let $\mathfrak{x} < \mathfrak{m}$. Either $\mathfrak{x}$ is finite or $\mathfrak{x} = \aleph_\xi$ where $\xi < \alpha$. In the former case it is clear that $\mathfrak{m}^{\mathfrak{x}} = \mathfrak{m}$. In the latter we apply Corollary 18, p. 303 and Theorem 4, p. 311. From $\alpha = cf(\alpha)$ we obtain $\xi < cf(\alpha)$ and thus

$$\mathfrak{m}^{\mathfrak{x}} = \aleph_\alpha^{\aleph_\xi} = \mathfrak{a}_\alpha^{\aleph_\xi} = \mathfrak{a}_\alpha = \aleph_\alpha = \mathfrak{m}.$$

Hence $\mathfrak{m}^{\mathfrak{x}} = \mathfrak{m}$ for all $\mathfrak{x} < \mathfrak{m}$ and thus

$$\sum_{\mathfrak{x}<\mathfrak{m}} \mathfrak{m}^{\mathfrak{x}} = \mathfrak{m} \cdot \mathfrak{m} = \mathfrak{m},$$

which proves (iv).

Conversely, assume that $\mathfrak{m}$ is a cardinal number and that conditions (iii) and (iv) are satisfied. We have to show that $\mathfrak{m}$ is strongly inaccessible, that is, that conditions (i), (ii) and (iii) are satisfied. Because condition (iii) is satisfied by assumption and because (iii) implies (i), it remains to show that (ii) is satisfied. Thus let $\mathfrak{f}$ be a transfinite sequence of cardinals less than $\mathfrak{m}$ and let $\mathfrak{f}$ be of type ω_β where $\beta < \alpha$. Applying König's theorem (p. 203) we obtain

$$\sum_{\gamma<\omega_\beta} \mathfrak{f}_\gamma < \mathfrak{m}^{\aleph_\beta} \leqslant \sum_{\mathfrak{x}<\mathfrak{m}} \mathfrak{m}^{\mathfrak{x}} = \mathfrak{m},$$

which proves (ii).

°Theorem 6: *Let $\mathfrak{m}$ and $\mathfrak{n}$ be cardinal numbers and $\mathfrak{m} \geqslant \aleph_0$. The cardinal $\mathfrak{m}$ is strongly inaccessible and larger than $\mathfrak{n}$ if and only if there exists a family $\boldsymbol{R}$ of power $\mathfrak{m}$ such that:*

(1) *There exists a set A of power $\geqslant \mathfrak{n}$ such that $A \in \boldsymbol{R}$,*

(2) $$x \in Y \in \boldsymbol{R} \rightarrow (x \text{ is a set}) \wedge (x \subset \boldsymbol{R}),$$

(3) $$X \in \boldsymbol{R} \rightarrow 2^X \in \boldsymbol{R},$$

(4) $$(X \subset \boldsymbol{R}) \wedge \bigwedge_{f \subset \boldsymbol{R} \times \boldsymbol{R}} [(f \in \boldsymbol{R}^X) \rightarrow (f^1(X) \neq \boldsymbol{R})] \rightarrow (X \in \boldsymbol{R}).$$

Proof. Assume that $\mathfrak{m} = \aleph_\alpha$ is strongly inaccessible and that $\mathfrak{m} > \mathfrak{n}$. If $\alpha = 0$ then the desired family is clearly R_ω (see p. 297). Assume that $\alpha \neq 0$; we shall show that the family R_α satisfies all of the desired conditions.

The family R_α has power $\mathfrak{m}$ because $\omega + \alpha = \alpha$, and thus $\mathfrak{a}_\alpha = \overline{\overline{R_{\omega+\alpha}}} = \overline{\overline{R_\alpha}}$, and $\mathfrak{a}_\alpha = \aleph_\alpha$ by Theorem 4, p. 311.

Clearly condition (1) is satisfied if $\mathfrak{n} < \aleph_0$. If $\mathfrak{n} = \aleph_\beta$, where $\beta < \alpha$ then $\overline{\overline{R_{\omega+\beta}}} = \mathfrak{a}_\beta$ implies that $R_{\omega+\beta}$ contains a subset of power $\aleph_\beta$ (see p. 300). However, since $\omega+\beta < \omega+\alpha = \alpha$, we have $R_{\omega+\beta} \in R_{\omega+\beta+1} \subset R_\alpha$, and thus some element of R_α has power $\geqslant \mathfrak{n}$. Thus (1) is satisfied.

If $X \in Y \in R_\alpha$, then $X \in R_\alpha$ as was shown on p. 298; thus (2) holds. Condition (3) follows from Theorem 1, p. 298 because $X \in R_\alpha \to \bigvee_{\beta<\alpha} (X \in R_\beta)$, and $X \in R_\beta \to 2^X \subset R_\beta \to 2^X \in R_{\beta+1} \subset R_\alpha$.

Finally to prove (4), assume that $X \subset R_\alpha$ and that there does not exist a function mapping X onto R_α. For every $Y \in X$ there is the least ordinal $\eta(Y)$ such that $Y \in R_{\eta(Y)}$. If the set of all such $\eta(Y)$ were cofinal with α, then there would exist an increasing sequence of type $\omega_{cf(\alpha)}$ convergent to α whose terms are ordinals of the form $\eta(Y)$. Since $cf(\alpha) = \alpha = \omega_\alpha$, the set of terms of the sequence would have power $\mathfrak{m} = \aleph_\alpha$. Thus we would obtain $\overline{\overline{X}} \geqslant \mathfrak{m} = \aleph_\alpha = \mathfrak{a}_\alpha = \overline{\overline{R_{\omega+\alpha}}} = \overline{\overline{R_\alpha}}$. And then there would exist a function mapping X onto R_α in contradiction with the assumption. Thus we have shown that there exists an ordinal $\gamma < \alpha$ such that $\eta(Y) < \gamma$ for every $Y \in X$, that is $X \subset R_\gamma$, $X \in R_{\gamma+1}$ and $X \in R_\alpha$.

Assume now that $\boldsymbol{R}$ is a family satisfying (1)–(4) and let $\mathfrak{m} = \overline{\overline{\boldsymbol{R}}}$. From (1) and (2) it follows that $\mathfrak{m} > \mathfrak{n}$. From (3) it follows that $\mathfrak{m}$ satisfies (iii) and thus (i). It remains to show that $\mathfrak{m}$ satisfies (ii). For this purpose notice that (4) implies that every subset of $\boldsymbol{R}$ of power less than $\mathfrak{m}$ belongs to $\boldsymbol{R}$. Conditions (2) and (3) imply that every element of $\boldsymbol{R}$ is a set of power $< \overline{\overline{\boldsymbol{R}}} = \mathfrak{m}$ contained in $\boldsymbol{R}$. Thus $\boldsymbol{R}$ is identical with the family of its subsets of power $< \mathfrak{m}$. Applying Corollary 10, p. 291 we conclude that $\sum_{\mathfrak{x}<\mathfrak{m}} \mathfrak{m}^{\mathfrak{x}} = \mathfrak{m}$ and thus by Theorem 5, p. 311 $\mathfrak{m}$ is strongly inaccessible.

Exercises

1. Let $S_\alpha(X)$ and $P_\alpha(X)$ be respectively the families of unions and intersections of less than $\aleph_\alpha$ sets belonging to X. Prove that if ω_α is strongly inaccessible then

$$S_\alpha(P_\alpha(X)) = P_\alpha(S_\alpha(X)). \qquad \text{[Sierpiński–Tarski]}$$

2. Show that the infinite cardinal $\mathfrak{m}$ is strongly inaccessible if and only if for every function $\mathfrak{f}$ whose values are cardinal numbers $< \mathfrak{m}$ and whose domain I has power $< \mathfrak{m}$ the formula $\prod_{x\in I} \mathfrak{f}_x < \mathfrak{m}$ holds. [Tarski]

3. Show that a cardinal $\mathfrak{m} = \aleph_\alpha$ is weakly inaccessible and greater than $\aleph_0$ if and only if α is a limit ordinal and $cf(\alpha) = \alpha$.

Hint: If β is an increasing sequence of type $\omega_{cf(\alpha)}$ such that $\alpha = \lim\limits_{\xi<\omega_{cf(\alpha)}} \beta_\xi$, then $\alpha > \beta_\xi \geqslant \xi$ for $\xi < \omega_{cf(\alpha)}$ and thus $\alpha \geqslant \omega_{cf(\alpha)} = \omega_\alpha$.

§ 2. Classification of inaccessible cardinals[1])

The strongly inaccessible cardinal $\aleph_\alpha$ is said to be *inaccessible of class* 1 if the set of strongly inaccessible cardinals $\aleph_\beta < \aleph_\alpha$ is ordered by $\leqslant$ in type α. The cardinal $\aleph_\alpha$ is called *inaccessible of class* 2 if the set of cardinals $\aleph_\beta < \aleph_\alpha$ which are inaccessible of class 1 is ordered by $\leqslant$ in type α. Clearly in a similar manner we can define inaccessible cardinals of class 3, 4 and so forth.

We shall define the ξth cardinal of the class η. We shall say that α is the *ξ-th cardinal of the class* η (in symbols $M(\xi, \eta, \alpha)$) if there exists an infinite sequence φ of type $\eta+1$ such that

(i) φ_0 is the set of all strongly inaccessible cardinals $\leqslant \aleph_\alpha$;

(ii) if $\zeta \leqslant \eta$ then $\varphi_{\zeta+1}$ is the set of all cardinals $\aleph_\beta < \aleph_\alpha$ such that $\aleph_\beta \in \varphi_\zeta$ and such that the type of the set $\{\aleph_\gamma \in \varphi_\zeta\colon \gamma < \beta\}$ is equal to β;

(iii) if $\lambda < \eta+1$ is a limit ordinal then $\varphi_\lambda = \bigcap\limits_{\zeta<\lambda} \varphi_\zeta$;

(iv) $\{\aleph_\beta \in \varphi_\eta\colon \beta < \alpha\}$ has type ξ;

(v) $\aleph_\alpha \in \varphi_\eta$.

The cardinal $\aleph_\alpha$ *is inaccessible of class* η if there exists $\xi \leqslant \alpha$ such that $M(\xi, \eta, \alpha)$.

The proof that the definition above coincides with that given earlier for the cases $\eta = 1, 2, 3, \ldots$ is left to the reader.

Hyper-inaccessible cardinals, also introduced by Mahlo, are defined in a different manner.

In order to explain the principle behind the classification of hyper-inaccessible cardinals assume that $\aleph_\alpha$ is the first strongly inaccessible aleph. Then $\alpha = \lim\limits_{\xi<\alpha} \xi$ where none of the alephs $\aleph_\xi$ is inaccessible.

[1]) The idea of this classification is due to P. Mahlo. See *Über lineare transfinite Mengen*. Leipziger Berichte, math.-phys. Klasse **63** (1911), pp. 187–225. Mahlo's paper is concerned with weakly inaccessible cardinals.

Thus α can be represented as the limit of an increasing continuous infinite sequence ψ of type $\tau \leqslant \alpha$ such that each of the alephs $\aleph_{\psi(\xi)}$, $\xi < \tau$ is accessible. Clearly such a representation can also be given for the second strongly inaccessible cardinal, the third, etc.

We shall call the strongly inaccessible cardinal $\aleph_\alpha$ *hyper-inaccessible of type* 0 if for every increasing continuous sequence of ordinals φ of type $\beta \leqslant \alpha$ such that $\lim_{\xi<\beta} \varphi_\xi = \alpha$ at least one of the cardinals $\aleph_{\varphi_\xi}$, $\xi < \beta$ is strongly inaccessible.

Replacing the words "strongly inaccessible" at the end of the definition above by the words "hyper-inaccessible of type 0" we obtain the definition of the *hyper-inaccessible cardinals of type* 1. Similarly as for inaccessible cardinals of class η we can define *hyper-inaccessible cardinals of type* ξ where ξ is an arbitrary ordinal.

Exercise

1. Show that the first inaccessible cardinal of class 1 is not hyper-inaccessible. *Hint*: Consider the sequence of critical numbers for the operation defined by the formula $\omega_\xi = \eta$.

§ 3. Measurability of cardinal numbers

Abstract measure theory arose in connection with the theory of measure for subsets of the Euclidean plane. The discussion which evolved around this problem[1]) led to the formulation of a new hypothesis regarding the existence of certain cardinal numbers. It is interesting to note that this hypothesis is incomparably stronger than the existential hypotheses associated with the classification of Mahlo.

DEFINITION. The cardinal $\mathfrak{m}$ is said to be *measurable* if for every set A of power $\mathfrak{m}$ the Boolean ring 2^A contains a σ-additive prime ideal I such that $\bigcup_{Y \in I} Y = A$.

The following theorem gives an equivalent formulation of this definition.

[1]) This problem was formulated by S. Banach. See S. Banach and K. Kuratowski, *Sur une généralisation du problème de la mesure*, Fundamenta Mathematicae **15** (1929) 127–131.

THEOREM 1: *For a cardinal* $\mathfrak{m}$ *to be measurable it is necessary and sufficient that there exist a set* A *of power* $\mathfrak{m}$ *and a function defined on all elements of the family* 2^A *having values* 0 *or* 1 *and having the following properties*:

(i) $f(A) = 1$,

(ii) $f(\{a\}) = 0$ *for* $a \in A$,

(iii) *if* X_n *is a sequence of disjoint subsets of* A *then*

$$f\Big(\bigcup_{n=0}^{\infty} X_n\Big) = \sum_{n=0}^{\infty} f(X_n).$$

PROOF. Let I be a σ-additive prime ideal in 2^A such that $\bigcup_{Y \in I} Y = A$ and let $f(X) = 0$ or 1 depending on whether $X \in I$ or $X \notin I$. Equation (i) follows from the fact that $A \notin I$ (see p. 163), equation (ii) from the fact that each singleton $\{a\}$ is contained in some $Y \in I$. If X_n is a sequence of disjoint subsets of A and $X_n \in I$ for all n, then $\bigcup X_n \in I$ by the σ-additivity of I and we get (iii) since $f(X_n) = 0$ for every n. If, for some n_0, $X_{n_0} \notin I$, then $A - X_{n_0} \in I$ because $X_{n_0} \cap (A - X_{n_0}) = 0 \in I$. From $X_{n_0} \cap X_n = 0$ it follows that $X_n \in I$ for $n \neq n_0$. Since $\bigcup_{n=0}^{\infty} X_n \notin I$, both the left and the right-hand sides of equation (iii) are equal to 1.

Conversely, assume that f is a function satisfying (i)–(iii) and let $I = \{X \subset A: f(X) = 0\}$. From (i) it follows that $A \notin I$ and thus $I \neq 2^A$. If $Y \subset X \in I$, then $f(Y) = 0$ since $0 = f(X) = f(Y \cup (X - Y)) = f(Y) + f(X - Y)$ and thus $f(Y) = 0$. If $X_1 \in I$ and $X_2 \in I$, then

$$\begin{aligned} f(X_1 \cup X_2) &= f((X_1 - X_2) \cup (X_2 - X_1) \cup (X_1 \cap X_2)) \\ &= f(X_1 - X_2) + f(X_2 - X_1) + f(X_1 \cap X_2) = 0, \end{aligned}$$

because each of the sets $X_1 - X_2$, $X_2 - X_1$, $X_1 \cap X_2$ belongs to I. Thus I is an ideal.

Let $Z \notin I$. In order to show that I is a prime ideal we have to show that $A - Z \in I$. But $A = Z \cup (A - Z)$ and thus by (iii) $f(A) = f(Z) + f(A - Z)$ and hence $f(A - Z) = 0$, i.e. $A - Z \in I$.

From (ii) it follows that

$$\bigcup_{Y \in I} Y \supset \bigcup_{a \in A} \{a\} = A.$$

It remains to be shown that the ideal $\boldsymbol{I}$ is σ-additive. For this purpose assume that $X_n \in \boldsymbol{I}$ for $n \in N$. Since

$$\bigcup_{n=0}^{\infty} X_n = \bigcup_{n=0}^{\infty} (X_n - \bigcup_{k<n} X_k) = \bigcup_{n=0}^{\infty} X'_n,$$

and because each of the sets X'_n belongs to $\boldsymbol{I}$ and $X'_n \cap X'_m = 0$ for $n \neq m$, it follows by (iii) that

$$f(\bigcup_{n=0}^{\infty} X'_n) = \sum_{n=0}^{\infty} f(X'_n) = 0$$

and thus

$$\bigcup_{n=0}^{\infty} X'_n \in \boldsymbol{I}, \qquad \text{that is} \qquad \bigcup_{n=0}^{\infty} X_n \in \boldsymbol{I}.$$

A function satisfying conditions (ii) and (iii) is said to be a *σ-additive, zero-one measure* defined on A. If in addition the function satisfies condition (i), then it is said to be *non-trivial*. In the sequel we shall speak simply of a measure defined on A instead of "σ-additive zero-one measure" since we shall not consider any other kind of measure. If $\boldsymbol{I}$ is an ideal in 2^A and all elements of a set $X \notin \boldsymbol{I}$ have some property W, then we say that *almost all* elements of A have the property W. Similarly, if a function is defined on a set $X \notin \boldsymbol{I}$, then we say that it is defined *almost everywhere*.

THEOREM 2: *If* $\mathfrak{n} \leqslant \mathfrak{m}$ *and* $\mathfrak{m}$ *is non-measurable, then* $\mathfrak{n}$ *is non-measurable.*

PROOF. Let $A \subset B$, $\overline{\overline{A}} = \mathfrak{n}$, $\overline{\overline{B}} = \mathfrak{m}$ and let f be a measure on A. Extending f to 2^B by the formula $g(X) = f(A \cap X)$ we obtain a measure on B. By assumption g is a trivial measure and thus $g(B) = 0$ and $g(X) = 0$ for all $X \subset B$. Hence $g(A) = f(A) = 0$.

The cardinal $\aleph_0$ is clearly non-measurable. Thus by Theorem 2 the non-measurable cardinals form a "segment" in the class of all infinite cardinals. The following theorems are intended to provide some information about the extent of this segment.

The ideal $\boldsymbol{I}$ is said to be $\mathfrak{m}$-*additive* if for every family $\boldsymbol{R} \subset \boldsymbol{I}$ of power $\mathfrak{m}$, $\bigcup_{Y \in \boldsymbol{R}} Y \in \boldsymbol{I}$.

°THEOREM 3[1]). *If $\boldsymbol{I}$ is a σ-additive prime ideal in 2^A such that* $\bigcup_{Y\in \boldsymbol{I}} Y = A$ *and if* $\mathfrak{m}$ *is a non-measurable cardinal then* $\boldsymbol{I}$ *is* $\mathfrak{m}$*-additive.*

PROOF. Let $\overline{\overline{M}} = \mathfrak{m}$ and let $F \in \boldsymbol{I}^M$; we have to show that $\bigcup_{m\in M} F(m) \in \boldsymbol{I}$. We assume, temporarily, that $F(m_1) \cap F(m_2) = 0$ for $m_1 \neq m_2$. We define the family $\boldsymbol{J} \subset 2^M$ by $Z \in \boldsymbol{J} \equiv \bigcup_{m\in Z} F(m) \in \boldsymbol{I}$. The family $\boldsymbol{J}$ is an ideal in 2^M. Indeed, if $Z_1 \in \boldsymbol{J}$ and $Z_2 \in \boldsymbol{J}$ then $\bigcup_{m\in Z_1} F(m) \cup \bigcup_{m\in Z_2} F(m) \in \boldsymbol{I}$ and thus $\bigcup_{m\in Z_1\cup Z_2} F(m) \in \boldsymbol{I}$, whence $Z_1 \cup Z_2 \in \boldsymbol{J}$. If $Z_1 \subset Z_2 \in \boldsymbol{J}$ then

$$\bigcup_{m\in Z_1} F(m) \subset \bigcup_{m\in Z_2} F(m) \in \boldsymbol{I},$$

and thus

$$\bigcup_{m\in Z_1} F(m) \in \boldsymbol{I} \quad \text{and} \quad Z_1 \in \boldsymbol{J}.$$

We now show that $(Z_1 \cap Z_2 = 0) \to [(Z_1 \in \boldsymbol{J}) \vee (Z_2 \in \boldsymbol{J})]$. Let $Z_1 \cap Z_2 = 0$. By the assumption that $F(m_1) \cap F(m_2) = 0$ for $m_1 \neq m_2$, it follows that $[\bigcup_{m\in Z_1} F(m)] \cap [\bigcup_{m\in Z_2} F(m)] = 0 \in \boldsymbol{I}$; thus one of the sets $\bigcup_{m\in Z_i} F(m)$, $i = 1, 2$, belongs to $\boldsymbol{I}$ and hence one of the sets Z_i, $i = 1, 2$, belongs to $\boldsymbol{J}$.

The ideal $\boldsymbol{J}$ is σ-additive. For if $Z_n \in \boldsymbol{J}$ for $n \in N$, then $\bigcup_{m\in Z_n} F(m) \in \boldsymbol{I}$ for $n \in N$ and thus $\bigcup_{n\in N} \bigcup_{m\in Z_n} F(m) \in \boldsymbol{I}$, whence $\bigcup_n Z_n \in \boldsymbol{J}$.

Finally, we show that $\bigcup_{Y\in \boldsymbol{J}} Y = M$. For $F(m) \in \boldsymbol{I}$ by assumption, therefore $\bigcup_{n\in\{m\}} F(n) \in \boldsymbol{I}$, which implies that $\{m\} \in \boldsymbol{J}$. Since $M = \bigcup_{m\in M} \{m\} \subset \bigcup_{Y\in \boldsymbol{J}} Y$, it follows that $\bigcup_{Y\in \boldsymbol{J}} Y = M$.

If the ideal $\boldsymbol{J}$ were different from 2^M then it would be a prime σ-additive ideal satisfying the condition $\bigcup_{Y\in \boldsymbol{J}} Y = M$ and thus $\overline{\overline{M}}$ would be measurable, contrary to our assumption. Thus $M \in \boldsymbol{J}$ and $\bigcup_{m\in M} F(m) \in \boldsymbol{I}$.

[1]) S. Ulam, *Zur Masstheorie in der allgemeinen Mengenlehre,* Fundamenta Mathematicae **16** (1930) 140–150.

The general case, where we do not assume that $F(m_1) \cap F(m_2) = 0$ for $m_1 \neq m_2$, is reduced to the case just considered as follows.

Let $\leqslant$ well order M and let $F'(m) = F(m) - \bigcup_{n<m} F(n)$. Then $F'(m_1) \cap F'(m_2) = 0$ for $m_1 \neq m_2$. Thus $\bigcup_{m \in M} F'(m) \in \boldsymbol{I}$, which proves the theorem, because $\bigcup_{m \in M} F'(m) = \bigcup_{m \in M} F(m)$.

°COROLLARY 4: *If $\overline{\overline{M}}$ is non-measurable, $\mathfrak{f}$ is a function defined on M such that $\mathfrak{f}_m$ is a non-measurable cardinal for all $m \in M$, then $\sum_{m \in M} \mathfrak{f}_m$ is a non-measurable cardinal.*

PROOF. If $\overline{\overline{A}} = \sum_{m \in M} \mathfrak{f}_m$ then $A = \bigcup_{m \in M} A_m$ where $\overline{\overline{A_m}} = \mathfrak{f}_m$ and $A_{m_1} \cap A_{m_2} = 0$ for $m_1 \neq m_2$. Restricting to A_m the measure f defined on A we obtain a measure on A_m and thus this measure must be trivial. Thus $f(A_m) = 0$ for $m \in M$ and by Theorem 3 it follows that $f(A) = 0$.

°THEOREM 5[1]): *If $\mathfrak{m}$ is a non-measurable cardinal, then $2^{\mathfrak{m}}$ is also a non-measurable cardinal.*

PROOF. Assume that $2^{\mathfrak{m}}$ is measurable and let $\mathfrak{m} = \aleph_\alpha$, $A = \{0, 1\}^{W(\omega_\alpha)}$. Thus A is the set of sequences of type ω_α whose terms are 0 or 1. Let $\boldsymbol{I}$ be a σ-additive prime ideal in 2^A such that $\bigcup_{Y \in \boldsymbol{I}} Y = A$.

For every $\xi < \omega_\alpha$ we have $A = A_\xi^{(0)} \cap A_\xi^{(1)}$ where $A_\xi^{(i)} = \{\varphi \in A : \varphi_\xi = i\}$. Clearly $A_\xi^{(0)} \cap A_\xi^{(1)} = 0$ and thus exactly one of the sets $A_\xi^{(0)}$, $A_\xi^{(1)}$ belongs to the ideal $\boldsymbol{I}$. Let i_ξ be that of the numbers 0 or 1 for which $A_\xi^{(i_\xi)} \in \boldsymbol{I}$.

By Theorem 3 it follows that $\bigcup_{\xi < \omega_\alpha} A_\xi^{(i_\xi)} \in \boldsymbol{I}$ and thus $\bigcap_{\xi < \omega_\alpha} A_\xi^{(1-i_\xi)} \notin \boldsymbol{I}$. On the other hand, it is easy to check that this intersection contains exactly one element, namely the sequence φ such that $\varphi_\xi = 1 - i_\xi$ for $\xi < \omega_\alpha$. Thus we obtain a contradiction since every one-element set belongs to $\boldsymbol{I}$.

°COROLLARY 6: *Every cardinal less than the first strongly inaccessible cardinal is non-measurable*[2]).

The corollary follows directly from Corollary 4 and Theorem 5.

[1]) See S. Ulam, op. cit., Theorem 1, p. 146.

[2]) This is a result of S. Ulam and A. Tarski. See S. Ulam, op. cit., p. 150.

§ 4. The non-measurability of the first inaccessible aleph

The problem of the measurability of the first inaccessible cardinal proved to be more difficult than the problems discussed in the preceding section. The first results concerning this problem were obtained by Hanf and Tarski in 1960[1]). The method discovered by Tarski allowed him to establish the non-measurability of many inaccessible cardinals[2]) but it has not provided a solution to the question as to whether there exists at least one measurable cardinal.

In this section we shall sketch the simplest of Tarski's results[3]).

°THEOREM 1: *The first strongly inaccessible cardinal is non-measurable.*

PROOF. Let $\mathfrak{m} = \aleph_\nu$ be the first strongly inaccessible cardinal. Assume that there exists a prime σ-additive ideal $\boldsymbol{I}$ in $W(\nu)$ such that $\bigcup_{Y \in \boldsymbol{I}} Y = W(\nu)$. Consider the set K of all ordinals ω_α, $\alpha < \nu$ and let $\boldsymbol{Z} = K^{W(\nu)}$ be the set of sequences of type ν, whose terms are these ordinals. Finally, let $\boldsymbol{Z}/\boldsymbol{I}$ be the cartesian product $K^{W(\nu)}$ reduced mod $\boldsymbol{I}$ (see p. 142). Thus the elements $\boldsymbol{Z}/\boldsymbol{I}$ are equivalence classes of sequences $\varphi \in \boldsymbol{Z}$, where φ is equivalent to ψ if $\varphi_\xi = \psi_\xi$ for almost all ξ. We denote by φ^* the class of all sequences equivalent to φ.

The set $\boldsymbol{Z}/\boldsymbol{I}$ is ordered by the relation $\precsim$ defined by the formula

$$\varphi^* \precsim \psi^* \equiv \overline{\{\xi\colon \varphi_\xi > \psi_\xi\}} \in \boldsymbol{I}$$

(see p. 143). We shall show that the relation $\precsim$ is a well-ordering. In fact, assume that there is a sequence $\varphi^{(n)}$ $(n \in \overline{N})$ of elements of $\boldsymbol{Z}$ such that $\varphi^{(n+1)*} \precsim \varphi^{(n)*}$ for $n \in N$. Thus for every $n \in N$ there is a set $X_n \in \boldsymbol{I}$ such that $\varphi_\xi^{(n+1)} < \varphi_\xi^{(n)}$ for $\xi \notin X_n$. From the σ-additivity of the ideal it follows that $\bigcap X_n = X \notin \boldsymbol{I}$ and thus $\varphi_\xi^{(n+1)} < \varphi_\xi^{(n)}$ for all $n \in N$ and for all $\xi \in X$. For fixed $\xi_0 \notin X$ we then obtain a strictly decreasing sequence of ordinals, which is not possible.

[1]) A. Tarski, *Some problems and results relevant to the foundations of set theory.* Proceedings of the 1960 International Congress for Logic, Methodology and Philosophy of Science (Stanford 1962) 125–135.

[2]) A. Tarski and J. H. Keisler, *From accessible to inaccessible cardinals,* Fundamenta Mathematicae **53** (1964) 117–199.

[3]) This proof is due to J. H. Keisler; see his paper *Some applications of the theory of models to set theory.* Proceedings of the 1960 International Congress for Logic, Methodology and Philosophy of Science (Stanford 1962) 80–86.

We shall denote the class containing the constant sequence (the sequence defined for $\xi < \nu$ by the equation $\varphi_\xi = \omega_\alpha$) by the symbol ω_α^*. These classes form a proper segment of the set $\boldsymbol{Z}/\boldsymbol{I}$. In fact, if $\varphi^* \precsim \omega_\alpha^*$ then there exists a set $X \in \boldsymbol{I}$ such that $\varphi_\xi \leqslant \omega_\alpha$ for all $\xi \notin X$. Let $X_\beta = \{\xi: (\xi \in W(\nu) - X) \vee (\varphi_\xi = \omega_\beta)\}$. The sets $X_\beta, \beta < \alpha$, form a family of power $\overline{\alpha} < \overline{\nu} = \mathfrak{m}$; if all these sets X_β belonged to the ideal $\boldsymbol{I}$ then by Theorem 3 $\bigcup_{\beta<\alpha} X_\beta \in \boldsymbol{I}$ and thus $W(\nu) = X \cup \bigcup_{\beta<\alpha} X_\beta \in \boldsymbol{I}$ which contradicts the assumption about $\boldsymbol{I}$. Thus, for some $\beta < \alpha, X_\beta \notin \boldsymbol{I}$. It then follows that for almost all ξ, $\varphi_\xi = \omega_\beta$ and consequently $\varphi^* = \omega_\beta^*$.

Thus the classes ω_α^* form a segment of the set $\boldsymbol{Z}/\boldsymbol{I}$. In order to show that this segment is proper, we consider the function φ_0 defined by $\varphi_0(\xi) = \omega_\xi$ for $\xi < \nu$. Clearly, $\{\xi: \varphi_0(\xi) < \omega_\alpha\} = W(\alpha)$. Thus if $\varphi_0^* \precsim \omega_\alpha^*$, then the set $W(\nu) - W(\alpha)$ belongs to $\boldsymbol{I}$. By a method similar to that used above we show that this assumption leads to a contradiction. Namely, we consider the family of power $\overline{\alpha} < \mathfrak{m}$ composed of sets $\{\xi\}$ where $\xi < \alpha$ and of the set $W(\nu) - W(\alpha)$. Because all of these sets belong to $\boldsymbol{I}$, by Theorem 3 their union also belongs to $\boldsymbol{I}$, contrary to the assumption that $W(\nu) \notin \boldsymbol{I}$.

Let φ be a sequence such that φ^* is the first element of $\boldsymbol{Z}/\boldsymbol{I}$ following the classes $\omega_\alpha^*, \alpha < \nu$. We shall examine the function φ and show that its existence leads to a contradiction.

First of all we remark that the set $\{\xi: \varphi_\xi = \omega\}$ belongs to $\boldsymbol{I}$ since $\varphi^* \succ \omega^*$. Using the well-ordering theorem we infer that for every ϱ there exists exactly one ordinal $q(\varrho)$ such that $2^{\aleph_\varrho} = \aleph_{q(\varrho)}$.

Let P be the set of ordinals $\xi < \nu$ having the property

$$(\varphi_\xi = \omega) \vee (\text{there exists } \varrho \text{ such that } \omega_\varrho < \varphi_\xi \leqslant \omega_{q(\varrho)}).$$

If $\xi \in P$ and $\varphi_\xi \neq \omega$ then by $\varrho(\xi)$ we denote the least ordinal such that

$$\omega_{\varrho(\xi)} < \varphi_\xi \leqslant \omega_{q(\varrho(\xi))}.$$

If $\varphi_\xi = \omega$, we put $\varrho(\xi) = 0$.

Case I. $P \notin \boldsymbol{I}$. We define a sequence ψ by letting $\psi_\xi = \omega_{\varrho(\xi)}$ for $\xi \in P$ and $\psi_\xi = 0$ for $\xi \notin P$. For almost all ξ, $\psi_\xi < \varphi_\xi$ and consequently $\psi^* \precsim \varphi^*$. This implies that there exists $\beta < \nu$ such that $\psi_\xi = \omega_\beta$ for almost all ξ. Thus $\varrho(\xi) = \beta$ for almost all ξ and hence $\omega_{q(\varrho(\xi))} = \omega_{q(\beta)}$

and $\varphi_\xi \leqslant \omega_{q(\beta)}$, which implies that $\varphi^* \precsim (\omega_{q(\beta)})^*$. On the other hand, $q(\beta) < \nu$ since $\aleph_\nu$ is inaccessible and we have a contradiction with the definition of φ^*.

Case II. $P \in \boldsymbol{I}$. For almost all ξ, we have $\varphi_\xi \neq \omega$ and

$$\bigwedge_\varrho [(\omega_\varrho < \varphi_\xi) \to (\omega_{q(\varrho)} < \varphi_\xi)]. \tag{1}$$

For $\xi \notin P$ let $\varphi_\xi = \omega_{\zeta(\xi)}$. From (1) we obtain $\zeta(\xi) > 0$ and

$$\varrho < \zeta(\xi) \to q(\varrho) < \zeta(\xi) \tag{2}$$

and thus $\zeta(\xi)$ is a limit ordinal and $\zeta(\xi) = \lim\limits_{\varrho < \zeta(\xi)} q(\varrho)$.

We define a sequence ψ by

$$\psi_\xi = \begin{cases} cf(\zeta(\xi)) & \text{for} \quad \xi \notin P, \\ 0 & \text{for} \quad \xi \in P. \end{cases}$$

If $\psi_\xi = \zeta(\xi)$ for some $\xi \notin P$, then the ordinal $\zeta(\xi)$ would be strongly inaccessible (see Exercise 3, p. 314) in contradiction to $\zeta(\xi) \leqslant \varphi_\xi < \nu$. Consequently $\psi_\xi < \zeta(\xi)$ for almost all ξ and $\omega_{\psi_\xi} < \varphi_\xi$, and thus the sequence $\vartheta_\xi = \omega_{\psi_\xi}$ has the property that $\vartheta^* \prec \varphi^*$. Thus there exists $\beta < \nu$ such that $\vartheta_\xi = \omega_\beta$ for almost all ξ, that is, $\psi_\xi = \beta$. Let X be the set of ξ for which $\psi_\xi = \beta$. In the sequel, ξ will always denote an element of X.

As has been shown above, the ordinal $\zeta(\xi)$ is the limit of an infinite sequence of type $\omega_\beta < \nu$. Using the axiom of choice we associate with every ordinal $\xi \in X$ an increasing sequence $\alpha^{(\xi)}$ of type ω_β such that its terms belong to K and $\varphi_\xi = \lim\limits_{\eta < \omega_\beta} \alpha_\eta^{(\xi)}$.

For fixed $\eta < \omega_\beta$ the sequence τ defined by

$$\tau_\xi = \alpha_\eta^{(\xi)} \quad \text{for} \quad \xi \in X \qquad \text{and} \qquad \tau_\xi = 0 \quad \text{for} \quad \xi \notin X$$

satisfies for all $\xi \in X$ the inequality $\tau_\xi < \varphi_\xi$, thus $\tau^* \prec \varphi^*$. It follows that there exists an ordinal $\alpha_\eta < \nu$ such that for almost all ξ

$$\alpha_\eta^{(\xi)} = \alpha_\eta. \tag{3}$$

Let X_η be the set of those $\xi < \nu$ which satisfy (3). Then $W(\nu) - X_\eta \in \boldsymbol{I}$ for all $\eta < \omega_\beta$; since $\omega_\beta < \nu$ and $\aleph_\beta$ is non-measurable, we obtain

$$\bigcup_{\eta < \omega_\beta} (W(\nu) - X_\eta) \in \boldsymbol{I}.$$

Thus

$$X_0 = \bigcap_{\eta<\omega_\beta} X_\eta \notin \boldsymbol{I}.$$

Equation (3) then holds for every η and for every $\xi \in X_0$.

A sequence of type $\omega_\beta < \nu$ of ordinals α_η less than ν cannot be convergent to ν because $cf(\nu) = \nu$. Thus there exists an ordinal ω_γ such that $\alpha_\eta < \omega_\gamma < \nu$ for all $\eta < \omega_\beta$; hence by (3)

$$\varphi_\xi = \lim_{\eta<\omega_\beta} \alpha_\eta^{(\xi)} = \lim_{\eta<\omega_\beta} \alpha_\eta \leqslant \omega_\gamma$$

for all $\xi \in X_0$. We conclude that $\varphi^* \precsim (\omega_\gamma)^*$, but this contradicts the definition of φ.

This completes the proof of Theorem 7.

By a method similar to that used in the proof of Theorem 7 it can be shown that many other inaccessible cardinals are also non-measurable. For example, the first hyper-inaccessible cardinal and the first hyper-inaccessible cardinal of type 1 are non-measurable.

It is not known whether the hypothesis:

There exist measurable cardinals

is consistent with the axioms of set theory.

If this hypothesis will prove to be consistent, then it will be an extremely strong existential proposition asserting the existence of large cardinal numbers.

Properties of non-measurable cardinals often play a role in abstract algebra and topology [1]). We prove below a theorem indicating their significance for the notion of compactness. Let $\mathfrak{m}$ be an infinite cardinal number.

Definition: The topological space X is said to be $\mathfrak{m}$-*compact* if every family $\boldsymbol{R}$ of open sets which covers X (that is, $X = \bigcup_{Y \in \boldsymbol{R}} Y$) contains a subfamily $\boldsymbol{R}_1 \subset \boldsymbol{R}$ of power $< \mathfrak{m}$ which also covers X.

[1]) A detailed discussion of these applications can be found in a paper of H. J. Keisler and A. Tarski, *From accessible to inaccessible cardinals,* Fundamenta Mathematicae **53** (1964) 225–308.

An example of an $\mathfrak{m}$-compact space is any space of power $< \mathfrak{m}$ with the discrete topology (i.e. such that every singleton $\{x\}$ is open).

The notion of $\mathfrak{m}$-compactness coincides with the ordinary notion of compactness when $\mathfrak{m} = \aleph_0$. The Tychonoff theorem (see p. 139) states that the cartesian product of an arbitrary number of $\aleph_0$-compact spaces is itself $\aleph_0$-compact. We shall show in the following theorem that this property of the cardinal $\aleph_0$ is exceptional.

THEOREM 2: *If* $\mathfrak{m}$ *is a non-measurable cardinal and* $\mathfrak{m} > \aleph_0$, *then there exists a cartesian product of subset of* N *(with the discrete topology) which is not* $\mathfrak{m}$*-compact.*

LEMMA 3: *If the space* X *is* $\mathfrak{m}$*-compact, then there exists an accumulation point for every set* $Y \subset X$ *of power* $\mathfrak{m}$, *that is such a point* x *that for every non-empty open set* V *containing* x *the intersection* $Y \cap V$ *is infinite.*

Otherwise it would be possible to cover the space X with a family $\boldsymbol{R}$ of open sets such that for all $V \in \boldsymbol{R}$ the set $Y \cap V$ is finite. Then there would also exist a family of power $< \mathfrak{m}$ with this property, but this implies $\overline{\overline{Y}} \leqslant \mathfrak{m} \cdot \aleph_0 = \mathfrak{m}$.

PROOF OF THEOREM 2. Let $\mathfrak{m}$ be a non-measurable cardinal and let M be a set of power $\mathfrak{m}$. Let $I = N^M$ and let $T = \prod \varphi^1(M)$ with φ ranging over I. Then the elements of T are functions g mapping I into N and the neighborhood of g determined by the elements $\varphi_1, \ldots, \varphi_k \in I$ consists of functions g' such that $g'(\varphi_j) = g(\varphi_j)$ for $j \leqslant k$. All neighborhoods of this form constitute a base for the space T.

For arbitrary $m \in M$, let g_m be the function defined on the set I by the equation $g_m(\varphi) = \varphi(m)$. It is clear that $g_m \in T$ and that $g_{m'} \neq g_{m''}$ for $m' \neq m''$. Thus the set Y consisting of all functions g_m has power $\mathfrak{m}$. We shall show that if there were an accumulation point a of Y then there would exist a σ-additive prime ideal $\boldsymbol{J}$ of subsets of M such that $\bigcup_{Z \in \boldsymbol{J}} Z = M$. Because we assume that $\mathfrak{m}$ is non-measurable, it follows that the set Y does not have accumulation points, which by Lemma 3 completes the proof of the theorem.

Therefore, assume that a is an accumulation point of Y and let $Z_\varphi = \{m \in M: \varphi(m) \neq a(\varphi)\}$ for $\varphi \in I$. Let $\boldsymbol{J}$ be the family consisting of all the sets Z_φ.

Every subset Z of the set M can be represented in the form $\{m \in M: \varphi_0(m) = 0\}$, where $\varphi_0 \in \{0, 1\}^M \subset I$. It follows that $Z = Z_{\varphi_0}$ if $a(\varphi_0) \neq 0$ and $Z = M - Z_{\varphi_0}$ if $a(\varphi_0) = 0$. Thus for arbitrary $Z \subset M$ either $Z \in \boldsymbol{J}$ or $M - Z \in \boldsymbol{J}$.

Examine now the neighborhood of a determined by $\varphi_1, \ldots, \varphi_k$. By assumption this neighborhood contains infinitely many functions g_m $(m \in M)$, that is, there exist infinitely many elements m such that $g_m(\varphi_i) = a(\varphi_i)$; equivalently, $\varphi_i(m) = a(\varphi_i)$ and thus $m \notin Z_{\varphi_i}$. In other words, the set $\bigcap_{i \leqslant k} (M - Z_{\varphi_i})$ is infinite for arbitrary $\varphi_1, \ldots, \varphi_k$.

It follows that every subset of the set Z_φ belongs to $\boldsymbol{J}$. For otherwise for some ψ we would have the inclusion $M - Z_\psi \subset Z_\varphi$ and thus the intersection $(M - Z_\varphi) \cap (M - Z_\psi)$ would be empty. Similarly, for arbitrary φ and ψ, $Z_\varphi \cup Z_\psi \in \boldsymbol{J}$, since otherwise $Z_\varphi \cup Z_\psi = M - Z_\vartheta$ for some ϑ, and then $(M - Z_\varphi) \cap (M - Z_\psi) \cap (M - Z_\vartheta) = 0$. Finally $M \notin \boldsymbol{J}$ since $M = Z_\varphi$ would imply that $M - Z_\varphi = 0$. Thus $\boldsymbol{J}$ is a prime ideal in the ring of subsets of M.

It remains to show that $\boldsymbol{J}$ is σ-additive. Assume that $\bigcup_{i=1}^{\infty} Z_{\varphi_i} \notin \boldsymbol{J}$. The complement of this union is of the form Z_{φ_0}; thus $\bigcup_{i \in N} Z_{\varphi_i} = M$. Let $\xi(m) = \min_{i \in N} (m \in Z_{\varphi_i})$. Then $\xi \in N^M = I$ and $a(\xi)$ is a natural number n. From the definition of ξ it follows that $(\xi(m) = n) \equiv (\xi(m) = a(\xi)) \to (m \in Z_{\varphi_n})$ and thus $(m \notin Z_\xi) \to (m \in Z_{\varphi_n})$; hence $(M - Z_{\varphi_n}) \cap (M - Z_\xi) = 0$ in contradiction to the property of the sets Z_φ proved above. Thus $\bigcup_{i=1}^{\infty} Z_{\varphi_i} \in \boldsymbol{J}$. Q.E.D.

The fact that the cartesian product of $\mathfrak{m}$-compact spaces need not be $\mathfrak{m}$-compact has several algebraic consequences[1]).

The problem whether it is consistent to assume that there exists a

[1]) See J. Łoś, *Linear equations and pure subgroups*, Bulletin de l'Académie Polonaise des Sciences. Série des Sciences Math. et Phys. **7** (1959) 13–18; A. Ehrenfeucht and J. Łoś, *Sur les produits cartésiens des groupes cycliques*, ibid. **2** (1954) 261–263. Cf. also J. Mycielski, α *incompactness of* N^α and *Two remarks on Tychonoff product theorem*, ibid. **12**(1964) 437–441, and the paper of Keisler–Tarski quoted on p, 323.

cardinal $\mathfrak{m} > \aleph_0$ such that the cartesian product of $\mathfrak{m}$-compact spaces is always $\mathfrak{m}$-compact has not been solved. Moreover, it is not known whether the least such number would coincide with the least measurable cardinal[1]).

§ 5. The axiomatic introduction of inaccessible cardinals

It can be shown that the existence of inaccessible cardinals cannot be deduced from the axioms Σ°[TR] of set theory. On the other hand, it is possible to strengthen this system by new axioms guaranteeing the existence of inaccessible cardinals.

AXIOM OF TARSKI[2]). *For every set M there exists a family $\boldsymbol{R}$ of sets such that*

(i) $M \in \boldsymbol{R}$,

(ii) $X \in Y \wedge Y \in \boldsymbol{R} \to X \in \boldsymbol{R}$,

(iii) $X \in \boldsymbol{R} \to 2^X \in \boldsymbol{R}$,

(iv) $(X \subset \boldsymbol{R}) \wedge \bigwedge_{f \in \boldsymbol{R}^X} (f^1(X) \neq \boldsymbol{R}) \to X \in \boldsymbol{R}$.

°THEOREM 1: *Tarski's Axiom implies that for every cardinal* $\mathfrak{m}$ *there exists a strongly inaccessible cardinal* $> \mathfrak{m}$.

Indeed, such a cardinal is $\overline{\overline{\boldsymbol{R}}}$ where $\boldsymbol{R}$ is any family satisfying (i)–(iv), where $\overline{\overline{M}} = \mathfrak{m}$.

We shall write In(α) instead of: there exists a family $\boldsymbol{R}$ of power $\aleph_\alpha$ satisfying (ii)–(iv).

Tarski's Axiom does not allow us to conclude the existence of cardinals of the first Mahlo class and thus of cardinals of higher classes. Lévy[3]) has formulated an axiom scheme from which we can deduce the existence of such cardinals.

[1]) In connection with this problem see J. Łoś, *Some properties of inaccessible numbers* in *Infinitistic Methods* (Warszawa 1960), pp. 21–23; D. Monk and D. Scott, *Additions to some results of Erdös and Tarski,* Fundamenta Mathematicae **53** (1964) 335–343 and the paper of Keisler and Tarski cited on p. 323, in particular Theorems 2.30 and 5.11.

[2]) See the paper cited on p. 311.

[3]) A. Lévy, *Axiom schemata of strong infinity in axiomatic set theory,* Pacific Journal of Mathematics **10** (1960) 223–238.

LÉVY'S SCHEME:

$$\Pi\{\Phi\} \wedge R\{\Phi\} \wedge \text{Cont}\ \{\Phi\} \to \bigvee_{\alpha, \beta} [\Phi(\alpha,\beta) \wedge \text{In}\,(\beta)];$$

(Π, R, Cont are defined on p. 238).

Lévy's scheme states that every increasing and continuous operation defined for all ordinals has for at least one argument α a value β such that $\aleph_\beta$ is strongly inaccessible.

Tarski's axiom follows from Lévy's scheme. Namely, letting Φ be the propositional function $\mu+\xi = \zeta$ we conclude from Lévy's scheme that for arbitrary μ there exists an inaccessible cardinal $> \overline{\mu}$.

Using Lévy's scheme we can prove the following theorem.

°THEOREM 2: *There exist cardinals of the first Mahlo class.*

PROOF. Let Φ be the following propositional function with free variables x and y:

$$[(x \text{ is not an infinite increasing sequence of ordinal numbers}) \wedge \wedge (y = 0)] \vee$$

$$\vee \big\{(x \text{ is an infinite increasing sequence of ordinals}) \wedge \wedge [(\text{the type } \alpha \text{ of the sequence } x \text{ is a limit ordinal}) \wedge \wedge (y = \lim_{\xi<\alpha} x_\xi)] \vee \big[(\text{the type } \alpha \text{ of the sequence is of the form } \beta+1) \wedge \wedge \{y = \min_\zeta [(\zeta > x_\beta) \wedge \text{In}(\zeta)]\}\big]\big\}.$$

From Tarski's axiom, which is a consequence of Lévy's scheme, it follows that $\bigwedge_x \bigvee_y ! \Phi(x,y)$, that is, Φ defines an operation. Using the construction described on p. 244 we obtain a propositional function Ind $\{\Phi\}$, which we shall abbreviate as Ψ, such that

$$\Pi\{\Psi\}, \qquad \Psi(\alpha, a) \to \Phi(C_\alpha\{\Psi\}, a).$$

Denote by μ_α the unique ordinal β such that $\Psi(\alpha,\beta)$. Then we have $\Phi(\mu|W(\xi), \mu_\xi)$ for every ordinal ξ; thus by induction with respect to ξ and by the definition of Φ we infer that

$$\mu_\xi < \mu_\eta \quad \text{for} \quad \xi < \eta,$$

$$\mu_\lambda = \lim_{\xi<\lambda} \mu_\xi \quad \text{if } \lambda \text{ is a limit ordinal},$$

$$\mu_{\alpha+1} = \min_\zeta [(\zeta > \mu_\alpha) \wedge \text{In}\,(\zeta)].$$

Thus we may define the operation $\xi \to \mu_\xi$ as follows: $\mu_{\xi+1}$ is the least ordinal $\alpha > \mu_\xi$ such that $\aleph_\alpha$ is strongly inaccessible; if λ is a limit ordinal, then $\mu_\lambda = \lim_{\xi<\lambda} \mu_\xi$.

Now apply Lévy's axiom scheme to the propositional function $\Theta(\xi, \eta)$ defined by $\eta = \mu_{\omega_\xi}$. Clearly $\Pi\{\Theta\} \wedge R\{\Theta\} \wedge \mathrm{Cont}\{\Theta\}$ and thus there exists an ordinal α such that $\mathrm{In}(\mu_{\omega_\alpha})$, that is, such that $\aleph_{\mu_{\omega_\alpha}} = \mathfrak{m}$ is strongly inaccessible. This cardinal belongs to the first Mahlo class. Indeed, $cf(\mu_{\omega_\alpha}) = cf(\alpha)$, because μ_{ω_α} is cofinal with α. Since $\mathfrak{m}$ is inaccessible, $cf(\alpha) = \mu_{\omega_\alpha}$. The set of ordinals $\xi < \mu_{\omega_\alpha}$ such that $\mathrm{In}(\xi)$ is clearly of type $\leqslant \mu_\alpha$; on the other hand, this set contains all ordinals of the form $\mu_{\omega_{\zeta+1}}$ where $\zeta < \alpha$ and thus its type is $\geqslant \alpha \geqslant cf(\alpha) = \mu_{\omega_\alpha}$. Thus this set has the type μ_{ω_α} and it follows that $\aleph_{\mu_{\omega_\alpha}}$ belongs to the first Mahlo class.

Similarly we can deduce from Lévy's axiom scheme the existence of cardinals of an arbitrary Mahlo class. On the other hand, this axiom scheme is not sufficient to conclude the existence of hyper-inaccessible cardinals. Lévy has formulated another axiom scheme from which we can deduce the existence of arbitrary large hyper-inaccessible cardinals[1]). Undoubtedly the process of adding new axioms which guarantee the existence of larger and larger cardinals can be extended without limitation.

§ 6. The continuum hypothesis

Cantor conjectured that the cardinals $\aleph_1$ and $\mathfrak{a}_1$ are identical. This conjecture, referred to as the *continuum hypothesis,* has been proved to be independent of the axioms of set theory.

The continuum hypothesis is a particular case of the *generalized continuum hypothesis*, according to which the *hierarchy of alephs is identical with the exponential hierarchy*:

(1) $$\mathfrak{a}_\alpha = \aleph_\alpha \quad \text{for all ordinals } \alpha.$$

This hypothesis is also independent of the axioms of set theory. We shall denote the generalized continuum hypothesis by (H).

°THEOREM 1: *In the system consisting of axioms* Σ°[TR] *and* VIII, *the hypothesis* (H) *is equivalent to*:

[1]) See the paper cited on p. 326.

(C) *If* $\mathfrak{m}$ *is any cardinal number then there exists no cardinal* $\mathfrak{x}$ *such that* $\mathfrak{m} < \mathfrak{x} < 2^{\mathfrak{m}}$.

PROOF. If $\mathfrak{m} = \aleph_\alpha$ then (H) implies that

$$2^{\mathfrak{m}} = 2^{\aleph_\alpha} = 2^{\mathfrak{a}_\alpha} = \mathfrak{a}_{\alpha+1} = \aleph_{\alpha+1},$$

and thus no cardinal lies between $\mathfrak{m}$ and $2^{\mathfrak{m}}$. Suppose now that there is no cardinal between $\mathfrak{m}$ and $2^{\mathfrak{m}}$. We shall prove by induction that (1) holds. For $\alpha = 0$, (1) is obvious. If (1) holds for an α, then it also holds for $\alpha+1$ since

$$\mathfrak{a}_{\alpha+1} = 2^{\mathfrak{a}_\alpha} \geqslant \aleph_{\alpha+1} > \aleph_\alpha = \mathfrak{a}_\alpha;$$

and if $\mathfrak{a}_{\alpha+1} \neq \aleph_{\alpha+1}$, then $\aleph_{\alpha+1}$ would lie between $2^{\mathfrak{a}_\alpha}$ and $\mathfrak{a}_\alpha$. Finally, if (1) holds for all $\xi < \lambda$ where λ is a limit ordinal, then

$$\mathfrak{a}_\lambda = \sum_{\alpha<\lambda} \mathfrak{a}_\alpha = \sum_{\alpha<\lambda} \aleph_\alpha = \aleph_\lambda.$$

The generalized continuum hypothesis implies a simplification of the laws of exponentiation of cardinal numbers.

°THEOREM 2: (H) *implies*:

(a) $\pi(\alpha) = \alpha$ *for all* α,

(b) *if* α *is a limit ordinal and* $\beta < \alpha$, *then*

$$\mathfrak{a}_\alpha^{\mathfrak{a}_\beta} = \begin{cases} \mathfrak{a}_\alpha & \text{for} \quad \beta < cf(\alpha), \\ \mathfrak{a}_{\alpha+1} & \text{for} \quad cf(\alpha) \leqslant \beta \leqslant \alpha. \end{cases}$$

PROOF. Clearly $\pi(0) = 0$. If $\pi(\alpha) = \alpha$, then $\aleph_{\pi(\alpha+1)} = \mathfrak{a}_{\alpha+1}$ by definition and thus by (H) $\aleph_{\pi(\alpha+1)} = \aleph_{\alpha+1}$, which implies that $\pi(\alpha+1) = \alpha+1$. Finally, if λ is a limit ordinal and if $\pi(\alpha) = \alpha$ for all $\alpha < \lambda$, then

$$\aleph_{\pi(\lambda)} = \sum_{\xi<\lambda} \aleph_{\pi(\xi)} = \sum_{\xi<\lambda} \aleph_\xi = \aleph_\lambda$$

and thus $\pi(\lambda) = \lambda$.

Formula (b) is a consequence of (a) and of Theorem 17, p. 302.

°THEOREM 3: (H) *implies that if*

$$s_{\alpha,\beta} = \sum_{\xi<\beta} \mathfrak{a}_\alpha^{\mathfrak{a}_\xi},$$

then

(i) $s_{\alpha,\delta+1} = \mathfrak{a}_{\alpha}^{\mathfrak{a}_{\delta}}$,

(ii) $s_{\gamma+1,\beta} = \mathfrak{a}_{\gamma+1}$ *if* $\beta < \gamma+1$, β *is a limit ordinal,*

(iii) $s_{\gamma+1,\beta} = \mathfrak{a}_{\beta}$ *if* $\beta > \gamma+1$, β *is a limit ordinal,*

(iv) $s_{\alpha,\beta} = \mathfrak{a}_{\alpha}$ *if* α *and* β *are limit ordinals and* $\beta < cf(\alpha)$,

(v) $s_{\alpha,\beta} = \mathfrak{a}_{\alpha+1}$ *if* α *and* β *are limit ordinals and* $cf(\alpha) < \beta \leqslant \alpha$,

(vi) $s_{\alpha,\beta} = \mathfrak{a}_{\beta}$ *if* α *and* β *are limit ordinals and* $\beta > \alpha$.

PROOF. (i) $\overline{\delta} \leqslant \mathfrak{a}_{\delta}$ implies that

$$\mathfrak{a}_{\alpha}^{\mathfrak{a}_{\delta}} \leqslant \sum_{\xi<\delta+1} \mathfrak{a}_{\alpha}^{\mathfrak{a}_{\xi}} \leqslant \mathfrak{a}_{\alpha}^{\mathfrak{a}_{\delta}} \cdot \overline{\delta} = \mathfrak{a}_{\alpha}^{\mathfrak{a}_{\delta}}.$$

(ii) By definition,

$$s_{\gamma+1,\beta} = \sum_{\xi<\beta} 2^{\mathfrak{a}_{\gamma}\cdot\mathfrak{a}_{\xi}} = \sum_{\xi<\beta} 2^{\mathfrak{a}_{\gamma}} = \sum_{\xi<\beta} \mathfrak{a}_{\gamma+1} = \overline{\beta}\cdot\mathfrak{a}_{\gamma+1} = \mathfrak{a}_{\gamma+1}.$$

(iii) Similarly we have

$$s_{\gamma+1,\beta} = \mathfrak{a}_{\gamma+1} + \sum_{\gamma+1<\xi<\beta} \mathfrak{a}_{\xi+1} = \mathfrak{a}_{\beta}.$$

(iv) From Theorem 2 we obtain

$$s_{\alpha,\beta} = \sum_{\xi<\beta} \mathfrak{a}_{\alpha}^{\mathfrak{a}_{\xi}} = \sum_{\xi<\beta} \mathfrak{a}_{\alpha} = \mathfrak{a}_{\alpha}\cdot\overline{\beta} = \mathfrak{a}_{\alpha}.$$

(v) Similarly,

$$s_{\alpha,\beta} = \mathfrak{a}_{\alpha} + \sum_{cf(\alpha)\leqslant\xi<\beta} \mathfrak{a}_{\alpha}^{\mathfrak{a}_{\xi}} = \mathfrak{a}_{\alpha} + \overline{\beta - cf(\alpha)}\cdot\mathfrak{a}_{\alpha+1} = \mathfrak{a}_{\alpha+1}.$$

(vi) From the elementary formula $\mathfrak{a}_{\alpha}^{\mathfrak{a}_{\xi}} = \mathfrak{a}_{\xi+1}$ for $\alpha < \xi$ it follows that

$$s_{\alpha,\beta} \geqslant \sum_{\alpha\leqslant\xi<\beta} \mathfrak{a}_{\alpha}^{\mathfrak{a}_{\xi}} = \sum_{\alpha\leqslant\xi<\beta} \mathfrak{a}_{\xi+1} = \mathfrak{a}_{\beta};$$

on the other hand, it is clear that

$$\sum_{\xi<\beta} \mathfrak{a}_{\alpha}^{\mathfrak{a}_{\xi}} \leqslant \sum_{\xi<\alpha} \mathfrak{a}_{\alpha}^{\mathfrak{a}_{\xi}} + \sum_{\alpha\leqslant\xi<\beta} \mathfrak{a}_{\alpha}^{\mathfrak{a}_{\xi}} \leqslant \overline{\alpha}\cdot\mathfrak{a}_{\alpha+1} + \overline{\beta}\sum_{\xi<\beta} \mathfrak{a}_{\xi+1} \leqslant \mathfrak{a}_{\beta}.$$

The hypothesis (H) was used only to prove (iv) and (v). Using Theorem 2 we can further obtain explicit values for $s_{\alpha,\delta+1}$.

In a similar way we can also calculate the sum $t_{\alpha,\beta} = \sum_{\xi<\alpha} \mathfrak{a}_{\xi}^{\mathfrak{a}_{\beta}}$. We shall give this result without proof.

°THEOREM 4:

(i) $$t_{\gamma+1,\beta} = \mathfrak{a}_{\gamma}^{\mathfrak{a}_{\beta}},$$

(ii) $t_{\alpha,\beta} = \mathfrak{a}_{\beta+1}$, *if* α *is a limit ordinal and* $\beta \geqslant \alpha$.

(iii) $t_{\alpha,\beta} = \mathfrak{a}_{\alpha}$, *if* α *is a limit ordinal and* $\beta < \alpha$.

Formula (i) reduces the evaluation of $t_{\gamma+1,\beta}$ to Theorem 2.

The following theorem shows that by accepting (H) we do not have to distinguish between weakly inaccessible and strongly inaccessible cardinals.

°THEOREM 5: *The hypothesis* (H) *implies that every weakly inaccessible cardinal is strongly inaccessible.*

PROOF. If conditions (i) and (ii) from p. 310 are satisfied, then $\mathfrak{m} = \aleph_\alpha$ where α is a limit ordinal, thus $\mathfrak{n} < \mathfrak{m}$ implies that $\mathfrak{n} = \aleph_\xi$ where $\xi < \alpha$. Consequently, by (H) $2^{\mathfrak{n}} = \aleph_{\xi+1} < \aleph_\alpha = \mathfrak{m}$ and it follows that $\mathfrak{m}$ satisfies condition (iii) from p. 311.

There are many simple properties of cardinal numbers which are equivalent to the hypothesis (H). We shall give several examples[1]):

°THEOREM 6: *The hypothesis* (H) *is equivalent in the axiom system* $\Sigma°$[TR] *to each of the following formulas:*

(1) $$\bigwedge_\alpha (\aleph_{\alpha+1}^{\aleph_\alpha} = \aleph_{\alpha+1}),$$

(2) $$\bigwedge_\alpha (\aleph_{\alpha+1}^{\aleph_\alpha} < \aleph_{\alpha+2}^{\aleph_\alpha}),$$

(3) $$\bigwedge_\alpha (\sum_{\xi\leqslant\alpha} \aleph_{\alpha+1}^{\aleph_\xi} = \aleph_{\alpha+1}).$$

Remark: Formula (3) states that for every set X of power $\aleph_{\alpha+1}$ the family of all subsets $Y \subset X$ which are not equipollent with X has the same power as X. For sets X whose power is an aleph whose index is a limit ordinal such a formula is not true (provided we accept (H); see Theorem 3 (v)).

PROOF. (H) $\equiv$ (1), since

$$\aleph_\alpha < \aleph_{\alpha+1} \leqslant \aleph_{\alpha+1}^{\aleph_\alpha} \leqslant 2^{\aleph_\alpha \cdot \aleph_\alpha} = 2^{\aleph_\alpha}.$$

(H) $\to$ (2), because

$$\aleph_{\alpha+1}^{\aleph_\alpha} = 2^{\aleph_\alpha \cdot \aleph_\alpha} = 2^{\aleph_\alpha} = \aleph_{\alpha+1}$$

[1]) See H. Bachman, *Transfinite Zahlen*, Ergebnisse der Mathematik und ihrer Grenzgebiete, Springer 1955, p. 157. This book contains many other similar equivalences.

and

$$\aleph_{\alpha+2}^{\aleph_\alpha} = (2^{\aleph_{\alpha+1}})^{\aleph_\alpha} = 2^{\aleph_{\alpha+1}} = \aleph_{\alpha+2}.$$

$\neg$(H)$\to\neg$(2). Assume that $\aleph_{\alpha+1} < 2^{\aleph_\alpha}$. Then $\aleph_{\alpha+1} < \aleph_{\alpha+2} \leqslant 2^{\aleph_\alpha}$ and thus

$$2^{\aleph_\alpha} \leqslant \aleph_{\alpha+1}^{\aleph_\alpha} \leqslant \aleph_{\alpha+2}^{\aleph_\alpha} \leqslant (2^{\aleph_\alpha})^{\aleph_\alpha} = 2^{\aleph_\alpha},$$

which implies $\neg$(2).

(H)$\to$(3). Indeed, by (H), $\sum_{\xi\leqslant\alpha} \aleph_{\alpha+1}^{\aleph_\xi} = s_{\alpha+1,\,\alpha+1}$ and by Theorem 3 (i) we easily obtain that $s_{\alpha+1,\,\alpha+1} = \mathfrak{a}_{\alpha+1} = \aleph_{\alpha+1}$.

(3)$\to$(H). Indeed, (3) implies $\aleph_{\alpha+1}^{\aleph_\alpha} \leqslant \aleph_{\alpha+1}$ and thus

$$2^{\aleph_\alpha} \leqslant \aleph_{\alpha+1}^{\aleph_\alpha} \leqslant \aleph_{\alpha+1} \leqslant 2^{\aleph_\alpha},$$

whence $\aleph_{\alpha+1} = 2^{\aleph_\alpha}$.

°THEOREM 7: *The hypothesis* (H) *is equivalent in the system* Σ° [TR] *to the theorem:*

(T) *For every infinite set X, the set 2^X can be represented as the union $\bigcup_{\xi<\alpha} M_\xi$ of a strictly increasing sequence of sets M_ξ equipollent with X.*

PROOF. (H)$\to$(T). Let $\overline{\overline{X}} = \aleph_\gamma$; from (H) it follows that the set 2^X is equipollent with $W(\omega_{\gamma+1}) = \bigcup_{\omega_\gamma<\xi<\omega_{\gamma+1}} W(\omega_\xi)$. Choosing for M_ξ the image of the set $W(\omega_\xi)$ we obtain the desired representation of 2^X.

(T)$\to$(H). Assume that we have a representation of 2^X as described in (T) and let $\overline{\overline{X}} = \aleph_\gamma$. Then $2^{\aleph_\gamma} = \aleph_\gamma \cdot \overline{\alpha}$ and thus $\overline{\alpha} \geqslant \aleph_{\gamma+1}$ and $\alpha \geqslant \omega_{\gamma+1}$.

Let $S = \bigcup_{\xi<\omega_{\gamma+1}} M_\xi$. We shall show that $2^X = S$. Indeed, $\overline{\overline{S}} = \aleph_{\gamma+1}$ by the assumption that $M_\xi \subset M_\eta$, $M_\xi \neq M_\eta$ and that $\overline{\overline{M_\xi}} = \aleph_\gamma$ for $\xi < \eta < \alpha$. If $Y \in 2^X$ then there exists $\eta < \alpha$ such that $Y \in M_\eta$. Because $\overline{\overline{M_\eta}} = \aleph_\gamma$, it follows that the set M_η cannot contain the entire union S and thus there exists $\xi < \omega_{\gamma+1}$ such that $M_\xi - M_\eta \neq 0$; hence $\eta < \xi$ and $\eta < \omega_{\gamma+1}$. Therefore $2^X \subset S$; the opposite inclusion is obvious. From the equation $2^X = S$ we infer that $2^{\aleph_\gamma} = \overline{\overline{S}} = \aleph_{\gamma+1}$. Q.E.D.

In the next section we shall deduce from the hypothesis (H) several theorems in the theory of ordered sets.

The hypothesis (H) and even its particular case $2^{\aleph_0} = \aleph_1$ has many consequences in various areas of mathematics and particularly in the theory of real functions. We shall give only one characteristic example.

#°THEOREM 8[1]): *There exists a non-countable subset Z of the set of real numbers $\mathcal{E}$ such that the intersection of Z with every nowhere-dense subset of $\mathcal{E}$ is countable.*

PROOF. Let $\boldsymbol{R}$ be the family of closed nowhere-dense subsets of $\mathcal{E}$ (see p. 32). Since $\overline{\overline{\boldsymbol{R}}} = \mathfrak{c}$ (see the exercise on p. 196), there exists a sequence F of type Ω whose set of terms coincides with the family $\boldsymbol{R}$.

Let $E_\xi = F_\xi - \bigcup_{\eta<\xi} F_\eta$. There exist uncountably many indices ξ such that $E_\xi \neq 0$; otherwise there would exist an ordinal $\alpha < \Omega$ such that

$$\bigcup_{\eta<\alpha} F_\eta = \bigcup_{\eta<\beta} F_\eta \quad \text{for} \quad \alpha \leqslant \beta < \Omega$$

and then we would have $\bigcup_{\eta<\alpha} F_\eta = \mathcal{E}$ since every one-element set belongs to $\boldsymbol{R}$. But then the set $\mathcal{E}$ would be the countable union of nowhere-dense sets, in contradiction to one of the basic theorems of topology due to Baire[2]).

Let $\boldsymbol{S}$ denote the family of non-empty sets E_ξ. By the axiom of choice there exists a set Z containing exactly one point from each of these sets. Therefore $\overline{\overline{Z}} > \aleph_0$. Let H be a nowhere-dense subset of E. Because the closure $\overline{H}$ of H is also nowhere-dense, it too belongs to $\boldsymbol{R}$ and thus $\overline{H} = F_\xi$ for some $\xi < \Omega$. Since $\overline{\overline{Z \cap F_\xi}} \leqslant \aleph_0$, it follows that $\overline{\overline{Z \cap H}} \leqslant \aleph_0$. #

We conclude this section with the proof of a theorem which implies as an immediate consequence that the axiom of choice follows from the hypothesis (C) (see p. 329).

THEOREM 9[3]): *If $\mathfrak{m}$ is an infinite cardinal and if neither between $\mathfrak{m}$ and $2^{\mathfrak{m}}$ nor between $2^{\mathfrak{m}}$ and $2^{2^{\mathfrak{m}}}$ lies any cardinal, then $\mathfrak{m}$ is an aleph.*

[1]) N. Lusin, Comptes Rendus de l'Académie des Sciences, Paris **158** (1914) 1259.

[2]) See. K. Kuratowski, *Topology I*, p. 414.

[3]) See the paper of E. Specker cited on p. 295.

PROOF. Let us abbreviate the formula $\bigwedge_{\mathfrak{x}} \neg(\mathfrak{m} < \mathfrak{x} < 2^{\mathfrak{m}})$ as $H(\mathfrak{m})$. Using Corollary 10, p. 296 we obtain $\mathfrak{m} \leqslant \mathfrak{m}+1 < 2^{\mathfrak{m}}$, whence $\mathfrak{m} = \mathfrak{m}+1$ by $H(\mathfrak{m})$. From $\mathfrak{m} \leqslant \mathfrak{m}+\mathfrak{m} \leqslant 2^{\mathfrak{m}}\cdot 2 = 2^{\mathfrak{m}+1}$ it follows now $\mathfrak{m} \leqslant 2\mathfrak{m} \leqslant 2^{\mathfrak{m}}$. $H(\mathfrak{m})$ implies that either $\mathfrak{m} = 2\mathfrak{m}$ or $2\mathfrak{m} = 2^{\mathfrak{m}}$. But the second equation is impossible by Theorem 9, p. 295, because $\mathfrak{m}^2 \geqslant 2\mathfrak{m}$.

We prove next that $H(\mathfrak{m})$ implies $\mathfrak{m}^2 = \mathfrak{m}$. For $\mathfrak{m} \leqslant \mathfrak{m}^2 \leqslant 2^{\mathfrak{m}}$. $2^{\mathfrak{m}} = 2^{\mathfrak{m}+\mathfrak{m}} = 2^{\mathfrak{m}}$. The equation $\mathfrak{m}^2 = 2^{\mathfrak{m}}$ is impossible by Theorem 9, p. 295. Thus by $H(\mathfrak{m})$ we have that $\mathfrak{m}^2 = \mathfrak{m}$.

By Theorem 7, p. 278 $2^{\aleph(\mathfrak{m})} \leqslant 2^{2^{\mathfrak{m}}}$ and

$$2^{\mathfrak{m}} \leqslant 2^{\mathfrak{m}} + \aleph(\mathfrak{m}) < 2^{(2^{\mathfrak{m}}+\aleph(\mathfrak{m}))} = 2^{2^{\mathfrak{m}}}\cdot 2^{\aleph(\mathfrak{m})}$$

$$\leqslant 2^{2^{\mathfrak{m}}}\cdot 2^{2^{\mathfrak{m}}} = 2^{2^{\mathfrak{m}}\cdot 2} = 2^{2^{\mathfrak{m}+1}} = 2^{2^{\mathfrak{m}}},$$

thus by $H(2^{\mathfrak{m}})$, $2^{\mathfrak{m}} = 2^{\mathfrak{m}} + \aleph(\mathfrak{m})$ and $\aleph(\mathfrak{m}) \leqslant 2^{\mathfrak{m}}$. From

$$\mathfrak{m} < \mathfrak{m}+\aleph(\mathfrak{m}) \leqslant \mathfrak{m}\cdot\aleph(\mathfrak{m}) \leqslant 2^{\mathfrak{m}}\cdot\aleph(\mathfrak{m}) \leqslant 2^{\mathfrak{m}}\cdot 2^{\mathfrak{m}} = 2^{\mathfrak{m}+1} = 2^{\mathfrak{m}}$$

it follows by $H(\mathfrak{m})$ that $\mathfrak{m}+\aleph(\mathfrak{m}) = \mathfrak{m}\cdot\aleph(\mathfrak{m})$, which implies (see Lemma 4, p. 293) that $\mathfrak{m}$ is an aleph.

COROLLARY: *The hypothesis* (C) *implies the axiom of choice*[1]).

§ 7. η_ξ-sets

In this section we shall show how the continuum hypothesis can be used to solve the following problem in the theory of linear orderings[2]): given a cardinal $\mathfrak{m}$, does there exist a linearly ordered set H of power $\mathfrak{m}$ such that every linearly ordered set of power $\leqslant \mathfrak{m}$ is

[1]) This corollary was proved by Tarski and Lindenbaum. See their paper *Communication sur les recherches de la théorie des ensembles,* Comptes rendus de la Société des Sciences et des Lettres de Varsovie, Classe III **19** (1926) 299–330. Our proof is due to Specker. Another proof was given by W. Sierpiński, *L'hypothèse généralisée du continu et l'axiome du choix*, Fundamenta Mathematicae **34** (1947) 1–5.

[2]) This problem was posed and solved by F. Hausdorff. See his *Grundzüge der Mengenlehre* (Leipzig 1914), p. 181.

The construction given here is due to W. Sierpiński, *Sur une propriété des ensembles ordonnés,* Fundamenta Mathematicae **36** (1949) 56–67.

similar to a subset of H? For the case $\mathfrak{m} = \aleph_0$ we have already discussed this problem and solved it affirmatively (Chapter VI, p. 219).

DEFINITION: A linearly ordered set H (of arbitrary power) is said to be an *η_ξ-set* if $H \neq 0$ and if for every two subsets A, B of power $< \aleph_\xi$ such that

$$(a \in A) \wedge (b \in B) \rightarrow (a < b) \tag{1}$$

there exist $u, v, w \in H$ such that

$$(a \in A) \wedge (b \in B) \rightarrow (u < a < v < b < w).$$

The η_0-sets are simply sets which are densely ordered and have no first and no last element.

°THEOREM 1: *If H is an η_ξ-set and X is a linearly ordered set of power $\leqslant \aleph_\xi$, then X is similar to a subset of H.*

PROOF. Let $\overline{\overline{X}} = \aleph_\alpha, \alpha \leqslant \xi$ and let τ be a one-to-one sequence of type ω_α whose set of terms is equal to X; moreover, let χ be a one-to-one sequence (of type ω_γ) whose set of terms is the set H.

We shall define by transfinite recursion a sequence of elements of H such that the set of terms of the sequence is similar to X. The construction is almost identical to the construction used in the analogous case of sets of type η (p. 219).

For $\varrho < \omega_\alpha$ let

$$\varphi_\varrho = \min_\zeta \bigwedge_{\eta<\varrho} \{(\chi_\zeta \neq \chi_{\varphi(\eta)}) \wedge [(\tau_\varrho \prec_X \tau_\eta) \equiv (\chi_\zeta \prec_H \chi_{\varphi(\eta)})]\},$$

where $\prec_X$ and $\prec_H$ denote the "less than" relation in the set X and in the set H, respectively. The function min is to be understood in such a way that $\min_\zeta A(\zeta) = 0$ in the case where $\neg A(\zeta)$ for all ζ.

We shall prove by induction that $\varphi_\varrho \neq \varphi_\eta$ for $\eta < \varrho < \omega_\alpha$. In fact, let

$$C = \{\varrho < \omega_\alpha : \bigwedge_{\eta<\varrho} (\varphi_\varrho \neq \varphi_\eta)\}$$

and assume that $\varrho < \omega_\alpha$ and $W(\varrho) \subset C$. To show that $\varrho \in C$ it suffices to show that there exists an element $a \in H$ such that for all $\eta < \varrho$,

$$a \neq \chi_{\varphi(\eta)} \quad \text{and} \quad (a \prec_H \chi_{\varphi(\eta)}) \equiv (\tau_\varrho \prec_X \tau_\eta).$$

For this purpose let

$$A = \{\chi_{\varphi(\eta)}\colon (\eta < \varrho) \wedge (\tau_\eta \prec_X \tau_\varrho)\},$$

$$B = \{\chi_{\varphi(\eta)}\colon (\eta < \varrho) \wedge (\tau_\varrho \prec_X \tau_\eta)\}.$$

The sets A and B are of power $\leqslant \overline{\varrho} < \overline{\omega}_\alpha \leqslant \aleph_\xi$ and satisfy (1), thus there exist u, v, w satisfying (2). If $B = 0$ then let $a = w$, if $A = 0$ let $a = u$, and if $A \neq 0 \neq B$ let $a = v$.

Since $\varphi_0 = 0$, it follows from the inequality obtained above that

$$\chi_{\varphi(\varrho)} \prec_H \chi_{\varphi(\eta)} \equiv \tau_\varrho \prec_X \tau_\eta,$$

which completes the proof of the theorem.

We shall construct an η_ξ-set, assuming that ω_ξ is a regular ordinal (see Exercise 3, p. 339).

Let H_ξ be the lexicographically ordered set of those sequences $\varphi \in \{0, 1\}^{W(\omega_\xi)}$ for which there exists a number $\varkappa < \omega_\xi$ such that $\varphi_\varkappa = 1$ and $\varphi_\sigma = 0$ for $\sigma > \varkappa$.

THEOREM 2: *If ω_ξ is a regular ordinal then H_ξ is an η_ξ-set.*

PROOF. Let A and B be subsets of H_ξ of powers $< \aleph_\xi$ and let α and β be one-to-one sequences of the types ω_μ and ω_ν respectively ($\mu < \xi, \nu < \xi$) such that the set of terms of the sequence α is A and the set of terms of β is B. Assume that A and B satisfy condition (1). Denote by $<$ the relation of lexicographical ordering.

For every $\varrho < \omega_\mu$ the term α_ϱ is itself a sequence of type ω_ξ whose terms are either 0 or 1 and there exists an ordinal $\varkappa = \varkappa(\varrho) < \omega_\xi$ such that $\alpha_{\varrho, \varkappa(\varrho)} = 1$ and $\alpha_{\varrho\sigma} = 0$ for $\sigma > \varkappa(\varrho)$. We shall call the ordinal $\varkappa$ "critical" for the sequence α_ϱ and we shall employ similar terminology for the sequences β_ϱ, $\varrho < \omega_\nu$, where by $\lambda(\sigma)$ we denote the critical ordinal of the sequence β_σ.

The regularity of ω_ξ implies that the sequence of critical ordinals for the sequences $\alpha_\varrho, \varrho < \omega_\mu$ is not cofinal with ω_ξ. Thus there exists an ordinal $\zeta < \omega_\xi$ such that $\varkappa(\varrho) < \zeta$ for all $\varrho < \omega_\mu$. Let $\varphi_\gamma = 0$ for $\gamma \neq \zeta$ and let $\varphi_\zeta = 1$. Then $\varphi \in H_\xi$ and $\varphi < \alpha_\varrho$ for all $\varrho < \omega_\mu$. Similarly there exists an ordinal $\zeta' < \omega_\xi$ such that $\lambda(\sigma) < \zeta'$ for all $\sigma < \omega_\nu$. If $\psi_\gamma = 1$ for $\gamma \leqslant \zeta'$ and $\psi_\gamma = 0$ for $\gamma > \zeta'$, then $\psi \in H_\xi$ and $\beta_\sigma < \psi$ for all $\sigma < \omega_\gamma$.

To prove the theorem it remains to construct a sequence $\vartheta \in H_\xi$ such that $\alpha_\varrho < \vartheta < \beta_\sigma$ for all $\varrho < \omega_\mu$ and $\sigma < \omega_\nu$.

First we construct by transfinite induction a sequence ϑ^* of type ω_ξ which does not necessarily belong to H_ξ but is such that

$$\alpha_\varrho \leqslant \vartheta^* \leqslant \beta_\sigma \quad \text{for} \quad \varrho < \omega_\mu,\ \sigma < \omega_\nu.$$

Let τ be an ordinal $\leqslant \omega_\xi$ and let $\varphi \in \{0, 1\}^{W(\tau)}$. For $\gamma < \tau$ we put $F(\varphi, \gamma) = 1$ if there exists an ordinal $\varrho < \omega_\mu$ such that $\varphi|\gamma = \alpha_\varrho|\gamma$ and $\alpha_{\varrho,\gamma} = 1$ and $F(\varphi, \gamma) = 0$ if there is no such ϱ.

From the theorem on transfinite induction it follows that there exists a sequence ϑ^* of type ω_ξ such that

$$\vartheta^*_\gamma = F(\vartheta^*|\gamma, \gamma) \quad \text{for} \quad \gamma < \omega_\xi;$$

thus

$$(\vartheta^*_\gamma = 1) \equiv \bigvee_{\varrho<\omega_\mu} \bigwedge_{\delta<\gamma} [(\alpha_{\varrho\delta} = \vartheta^*_\delta) \wedge (\alpha_{\varrho\gamma} = 1)].$$

Assume that $\alpha_\varrho > \vartheta^*$; then there exists an ordinal $\gamma < \omega_\xi$ such that $\alpha_{\varrho\gamma} = 1, \vartheta^*_\gamma = 0$ and $\alpha_{\varrho\delta} = \vartheta^*_\delta$ for $\delta < \gamma$. By the definition of the sequence ϑ^* it follows that $\vartheta^*_\gamma = 1$, which is impossible. Thus $\alpha_\varrho \leqslant \vartheta^*$ for every $\varrho < \omega_\mu$.

In turn, assume that $\vartheta^* > \beta_\sigma$; thus there exists an ordinal $\gamma < \omega_\xi$ such that $\vartheta^*_\gamma = 1$, $\beta_{\sigma\gamma} = 0$ and $\vartheta^*_\delta = \beta_{\sigma\delta}$ for $\delta < \gamma$. From the definition of the sequence ϑ^* it follows that for some $\varrho < \omega_\mu$

$$\alpha_\varrho|\gamma = \vartheta^*|\gamma \quad \text{and} \quad \alpha_{\varrho\gamma} = 1.$$

Hence $\alpha_\varrho > \beta_\sigma$ contrary to our assumptions.

We now modify the sequence ϑ^* so as to obtain the desired sequence ϑ. We examine two cases:

Case I: *For every* $\gamma_0 < \omega_\xi$ *there exist* $\gamma > \gamma_0$ *such that* $\vartheta^*_\gamma = 1$.

In this case $\vartheta^* \notin H_\xi$ and thus the strict inequality $\alpha_\varrho < \vartheta^* < \beta_\sigma$ holds for arbitrary $\varrho < \omega_\mu$ and $\sigma < \omega_\nu$. Let γ_0 be an ordinal such that $\vartheta^*_{\gamma_0} = 1$. Let $\vartheta_\gamma = \vartheta^*_\gamma$ for $\gamma \leqslant \gamma_0$ and $\vartheta_\gamma = 0$ for $\gamma > \gamma_0$. Clearly for every γ_0 the sequence ϑ belongs to H_ξ. We shall show that we can choose γ_0 in such a way that the sequence ϑ satisfies the desired conditions.

Let $\gamma_0 > \max(\zeta, \zeta')$. From $\vartheta^* < \beta_\sigma$ it follows that there exist ordinals δ such that $\vartheta^*_\delta \neq \beta_{\sigma\delta}$ and the least such ordinal δ_0 satisfies the equations $\vartheta^*_{\delta_0} = 0$ and $\beta_{\sigma,\delta_0} = 1$. Thus $\delta_0 \leqslant \zeta'$ (since $\beta_{\sigma,\delta} = 0$ for $\delta > \zeta'$); hence $\vartheta_{\delta_0} < \beta_{\sigma,\delta_0}$ and $\vartheta_\delta = \beta_{\sigma,\delta}$ for $\delta < \delta_0$. Therefore $\vartheta < \beta_\sigma$.

For $\varrho < \omega_\mu$ there exists an ordinal $\delta_0(\varrho)$ such that $\alpha_{\varrho,\delta_0(\varrho)} = 0$ and $\vartheta^*_{\delta_0(\varrho)} = 1$ and for all $\gamma < \delta_0(\varrho), \alpha_{\varrho,\gamma} = \vartheta^*_\gamma$. Choose $\gamma_0 > \delta_0(\varrho)$ for all $\varrho < \omega_\mu$. The sequence ϑ obtained from ϑ^* by the modification just described satisfies the condition $\alpha_\varrho < \vartheta$ for $\varrho < \omega_\mu$.

Case II. *There exists* $\gamma_0 < \omega_\xi$ *such that* $\vartheta^*_\gamma = 0$ *for* $\gamma > \gamma_0$.

Let $\gamma_1 > \max(\gamma_0, \zeta, \zeta')$ and modify the sequence ϑ^* so that $\vartheta_\gamma = \vartheta^*_\gamma$ for $\gamma \neq \gamma_1$ and $\vartheta^*_{\gamma_1} = 1$. It is easy to check that the sequence obtained in this way belongs to H_ξ and satisfies the condition $\alpha_\varrho < \vartheta < \beta_\sigma$.

°THEOREM 3: $\overline{\overline{H}}_{\alpha+1} = 2^{\aleph_\alpha}$; *if* ξ *is a limit ordinal, then* $\overline{\overline{H}}_\xi = \sum_{\alpha<\xi} 2^{\aleph_\alpha}$.

PROOF. Assume that $\xi = \alpha+1$ and $\gamma_0 < \omega_\xi$. The set Z_{γ_0} of those sequences $\varphi \in \{0,1\}^{W(\omega_\xi)}$ for which $\varphi_{\gamma_0} = 1$ and $\varphi_\gamma = 0$ for $\gamma > \gamma_0$ has a power $\leqslant 2^{\aleph_\alpha}$. Since $H_\xi = \bigcup_{\gamma_0<\omega_\xi} Z_{\gamma_0}$, it follows that

$$\overline{\overline{H}}_\xi \leqslant 2^{\aleph_\alpha}\overline{\omega}_\xi = 2^{\aleph_\alpha}\aleph_{\alpha+1} \leqslant 2^{\aleph_\alpha}2^{\aleph_\alpha} = 2^{\aleph_\alpha}.$$

Since Z_{ω_α} has power $2^{\aleph_\alpha}$ and $Z_{\omega_\alpha} \subset H_\xi$, we conclude that $\overline{\overline{H}}_\xi = 2^{\aleph_\alpha}$.

The proof of the second part of the theorem is similar.

°COROLLARY 4: *If* $\mathfrak{m} = \aleph_\xi$ *is strongly inaccessible then there exists an* η_ξ*-set of power* $\mathfrak{m}$.

PROOF. For such ξ, $\sum_{\alpha<\xi} 2^{\aleph_\alpha} = \aleph_\xi$.

COROLLARY 5: *If* $2^{\aleph_\alpha} = \aleph_{\alpha+1}$, *then there exists an* $\eta_{\alpha+1}$*-set of power* $\aleph_{\alpha+1}$.

This corollary follows immediately from Theorems 2 and 3.

It can be shown that if $2^{\aleph_\alpha} > \aleph_{\alpha+1}$ then no $\eta_{\alpha+1}$-set has power $\aleph_{\alpha+1}$. On the other hand, for ordinals ξ where ω_ξ is not regular, every η_ξ-set has a power $> \aleph_\xi$. This fact follows from the theorem (proved by Hausdorff) which states that every $\eta_{\alpha+1}$-set contains a subset of power $2^{\aleph_\alpha}$ [1]).

[1]) A simple proof can be found in the paper of W. Sierpiński cited on p. 334. Interesting algebraic applications of the η_1-sets are given by P. Erdös, L. Gillman and M. Henriksen, *An isomorphism theorem for real closed fields*, Annals of Mathematics **61** (1955) 542–554.

Applications to logic are given by S. Kochen, *Ultraproducts in the theory of models*, Annals of Mathematics **74** (1961) 221–261.

Exercises

1. Every two η_ξ-sets of power $\aleph_\xi$ are isomorphic. [Hausdorff]

Hint: Use an argument similar to that used in the proof of Theorem 2, p. 217.

2. If H is an η_ξ-set and if H' is a subset of H, dense in H, then H' is also an η_ξ-set.

3. If ω_ξ is a singular ordinal, then every η_ξ-set is also an $\eta_{\xi+1}$-set.

4. If $\overline{R} = \eta$ and I is a non-principal prime ideal in the family 2^N, then the reduced direct product R^N/I is of type η_1. [Kochen]

Hint: Let f_n and g_m $(n, m \in N)$ be elements of R^N such that $\{i: f_n(i) \geqslant g_m(i)\} \in I$ for arbitrary n, m. The essential step in the proof depends upon the construction of a sequence $h \in R^N$ such that the sets $\{i: f_n(i) \geqslant h(i)\}$ and $\{i: h(i) \geqslant g_m(i)\}$ belong to I. If $f_n(i) \leqslant f_{n+1}(i)$ and $g_{m+1}(i) < g_m(i)$ for all $n, m, i \in N$, then let X_j be a decreasing sequence of sets X not belonging to I such that $X_0 = N$ and $\bigcap_j X_j = 0$ and for $i \in X_j - X_{j+1}$ let

$$h(i) = \tfrac{1}{2}[f_{K(j)}(i) + g_{L(j)}(i)].$$

If the sequences f_n and g_m do not satisfy the inequalities above, then they can be modified in such a way as to obtain functions belonging to the same classes mod I and satisfying the desired inequalities. For example, monotonicity can be obtained by letting $f'_0(i) = f_0(i)$, $f'_{n+1}(i) = \max(f'_n(i), f_n(i))$ and similarly for g_m.

CHAPTER X

INTRODUCTION TO THE THEORY OF ANALYTIC AND PROJECTIVE SETS

In this chapter we shall deal with the so-called operation (A) and the projection operation. We shall also treat the family of sets resulting from the application of these operations to sets belonging to a given fixed family, and, in particular, to the family of closed subsets of the space N^N. The results we shall obtain constitute an introduction to what is called *descriptive set theory.*

§ 1. The operation (A)

We define this operation, first introduced by Suslin in his investigation of Borel sets [1]), as follows:

Let H be a function defined on the set of finite sequences of natural numbers which associates with each such sequence a certain set. At times we shall refer to such a function as a *defining system.* For a given defining system H and for an arbitrary sequence $\varphi \in N^N$ we set

$$P_\varphi = \bigcap_{n \in N} H_{\varphi|n},$$

where $\varphi|n$ is, as usual, the sequence of n terms $\varphi_0, \varphi_1, \ldots, \varphi_{n-1}$ obtained from φ by restricting the domain of φ to the set of numbers less than n.

[1]) It was M. Suslin (1894–1919) who first gave an example of a projective, non-Borel set. To construct this example he introduced an operation on families of sets to be called later the *operation* (A). It is interesting that he conceived the idea of this operation after finding an er¯or in a paper of Lebesgue. More information about this topic is provided by W. Sierpiński, *Les ensembles projectifs et analytiques*, Mémorial des Sciences Mathématiques, fasc. CXII (Paris 1950), p. 28.

The union of all P_φ is called the *result of the operation* (A) performed on the defining system H:

$$A(H) = \bigcup_{\varphi \in N^N} P_\varphi = \bigcup_{\varphi} \bigcap_{n} H_{\varphi|n}.$$

Examples

1. Let F be an infinite sequence of sets. We define a defining system by letting

$$H_e = F_{e_0}$$

for $e \in N^{n+1}$, and for the empty sequence $e = 0$ by letting $H_0 = F_0$. Then

$$A(H) = \bigcup_{n} F_n.$$

2. Let $H'_e = F_n$ for $e \in N^{n+1}$ and $H'_0 = F_0$. Then

$$A(H') = \bigcap_{n} F_n.$$

The examples above show that the operation (A) is a generalization of the operations of countable union and intersection.

The operation (A) is *monotone* in the sense that if $H'_e \subset H''_e$ for every finite sequence e of natural numbers, then $A(H') \subset A(H'')$.

We call a defining system H *regular* if for any finite sequence e and for arbitrary $n \in N$ the formula

$$H_e \subset H_{e|n}$$

holds. In other words, if e' is an initial segment of e, then $H_e \subset H_{e'}$.

If H is an arbitrary defining system, then the defining system H' given by the formula

$$H'_e = \bigcap_{j<n} H_{e|j} \quad \text{for} \quad e \in N^n$$

is regular and, as is easily shown, $A(H') = A(H)$.

It follows that in most circumstances we may consider the operation (A) as being performed only on regular defining systems.

By $m;e$ we shall denote the sequence whose first term is m and whose following terms are the terms of the sequence e. More generally, for $e \in N^n$ and $f \in N^m$ we shall denote by $e;f$ the sequence of $(n+m)$ terms whose first n terms coincide with the terms of e, and whose last m terms coincide with those of f, in their original order.

LEMMA: *If the defining system H is regular, then*

(1) $$\bigcup_{\varphi} \bigcap_{n} H_{\varphi|n} = \bigcup_{m} \bigcup_{\psi} \bigcap_{n} H_{m;\psi|n},$$

(2) $$\bigcup_{\varphi} \bigcap_{n} H_{e;\varphi|n} = \bigcup_{k} \bigcup_{\psi} \bigcap_{n} H_{e;(k;\psi|n)}.$$

PROOF. If $x \in \bigcap_{n} H_{\varphi|n}$, then by letting $\psi_n = \varphi_{n'}$ we have $\varphi|n' = \varphi_0; \psi|n$, so that

$$x \in \bigcap_{n} H_{\varphi_0;\psi|n} \subset \bigcup_{m} \bigcup_{\psi} \bigcap_{n} H_{m;\psi|n}.$$

Conversely, if for a fixed m and every $n \in N$ the formula $x \in H_{m;\psi|n}$ holds, then by letting $\varphi_0 = m$, $\varphi_{n'} = \psi_n$ we obtain $x \in H_{\varphi|n'}$ for every n. By the regularity of H it also follows that $x \in H_{\varphi|0}$. Thus $x \in \bigcap_{n} H_{\varphi|n}$ and (1) holds.

Equation (2) follows from (1) by substituting in (1) for the defining system H the system H' where

$$H'_f = H_{e;f}$$

and where f is a finite sequence.

The following theorems are straightforward and deal with the relationship between the operation (A) and the operations of forming cartesian products and projections.

THEOREM 1: *If H and Q are defining systems and if $H_e \subset X$ and $Q_e \subset Y$ for every finite sequence $e \in N^n$, then*

$$A(H) \times A(Q) = A(U),$$

where the defining system U is given by

$$U_e = H_{K'(e)|K(n)} \times Q_{L'(e)|L(n)} \quad \text{for} \quad e \in N^n$$

(see pp. 97–99 for the definitions of the functions K, L, K', L').

PROOF. From the distributivity of union and intersection over cartesian product we obtain

$$A(H)\times A(Q)=\Big(\bigcup_{\varphi}\bigcap_{n} H_{\varphi|n}\Big)\times\Big(\bigcup_{\psi}\bigcap_{m} Q_{\psi|m}\Big)$$

$$=\bigcup_{\varphi\psi}\bigcap_{nm}(H_{\varphi|n}\times Q_{\psi|m}).$$

We replace the double union $\bigcup_{\varphi\psi}$ by $\bigcup_{\vartheta}$ and the double intersection $\bigcap_{nm}$ by $\bigcap_{p}$. In the expression $H_{\varphi|n}$ we replace φ by $K^*(\vartheta)$ and n by $K(p)$; in $Q_{\psi|m}$, ψ by $L^*(\vartheta)$ and m by $L(p)$ (see p. 123–124). Then we obtain $A(H)\times A(Q)=A(U)$ because $K^*(\vartheta)|K(n)=K'(\vartheta|n)|K(n)$, and similarly for the function L.

THEOREM 2: *The set $A(H)$ is the projection onto the X-axis of the set $M=\bigcap_{n} M_n$ in the space $X\times N^N$, where*

$$M_n=\{\langle x,\varphi\rangle:\ x\in H_{\varphi|n}\}.$$

In fact,

$$x\in A(H)\equiv\bigvee_{\varphi}\bigwedge_{n}(x\in H_{\varphi|n})\equiv\bigvee_{\varphi}\Big(\langle x,\varphi\rangle\in\bigcap_{n} M_n\Big)\equiv\bigvee_{\varphi}[\langle x,\varphi\rangle\in M].$$

We shall now examine the iteration of the operation (A). Assume that with every finite sequence e is associated a defining system $G^{(e)}$. Let

$$H_e=A(G^{(e)})=\bigcup_{\varphi}\bigcap_{n} G^{(e)}_{\varphi|n},$$

$$M=A(H)=\bigcup_{\psi}\bigcap_{m} H_{\psi|m}=\bigcup_{\psi}\bigcap_{m}\bigcup_{\varphi}\bigcap_{n} G^{(\psi|m)}_{\varphi|n}.$$

°THEOREM 3: *There exists a defining system S such that $M=A(S)$ and for every e the set S_e is one of the sets $G^{(f')}_{f''}$.*

PROOF. From (11), p. 124 it follows that

(3) $$M=\bigcup_{\vartheta}\bigcap_{p} G^{(K^*(\vartheta)|K(p))}_{L^*(\vartheta)^{(K(p))}|L(p)}.$$

For an arbitrary finite sequence $e\in N^n$, let

$$e^{(m)}=\mathop{F}_{i<t} e_{J(m,i)}$$

where t is the largest natural number such that $J(m,t)\leqslant n$. Note that the sequence $e^{(m)}$ is empty if for every t, $J(m, t) > n$. Denote by $d(e)$ the length of the sequence e and let

$$S_e = G_{L'(e)^{(K(d(e)))}|L(d(e))}^{(K'(e)|K(d(e)))} \tag{4}$$

(see p. 99 for the definition of K' and L'). We shall show that for every $\vartheta \in N^n$

$$S_{\vartheta|p} = G_{L^*(\vartheta)^{(K(p))}|L(p)}^{(K^*(\vartheta)|K(p))}. \tag{5}$$

In fact, letting $e = \vartheta|p$ in (4) and noticing that $d(\vartheta|p) = p$ we see that it suffices to prove the equations

$$K'(\vartheta|p)|K(p) = K^*(\vartheta)|K(p), \tag{6}$$

$$L'(\vartheta|p)^{(K(p))}|L(p) = L^*(\vartheta)^{(K(p))}|L(p). \tag{7}$$

Equation (6) follows from the fact that $K(\vartheta|p)$ is a finite sequence of length p whose terms are $K(\vartheta_i)$, so that both the left and right side of (6) denote the sequence of length $K(p)$ whose terms are $K(\vartheta_i)$. (We appeal, of course, to the fact that $K(p) \leqslant p$, see p. 97.)

For the proof of (7) we observe that $L'(\vartheta|p)^{(K(p))}$ is a finite sequence whose terms are $L(\vartheta_{J(K(p),i)})$ and whose length is t, where t is the largest number such that $J(K(p), t) \leqslant p$. Since $J(K(p), L(p)) = p$, it follows that $t = L(p)$ because the function $J(x, y)$ is increasing. Thus the sequence $L'(\vartheta|p)^{(K(p))}$ is identical with $L^*(\vartheta)^{(K(p))}|L(p)$. Since $L(p) \leqslant p$, it follows that both sides of equation (7) denote the same sequence.

Thus equation (5) is proved. Comparing equations (3) and (5) we conclude that $M = A(S)$. Q.E.D.

§ 2. The family $A(R)$

Let $\boldsymbol{R}$ be an arbitrary family of sets. By $A(\boldsymbol{R})$ we denote the family of all sets of the form $A(H)$ where H is an arbitrary defining system and $H_e \in \boldsymbol{R}$ for every finite sequence e. The sets belonging to $A(\boldsymbol{R})$ are called *A-sets* with respect to $\boldsymbol{R}$.

The family $A(\boldsymbol{R})$ satisfies the formulas (see p. 127):

(i) $\boldsymbol{R} \subset A(\boldsymbol{R})$,

(ii) $\boldsymbol{R}' \subset \boldsymbol{R}'' \rightarrow A(\boldsymbol{R}') \subset A(\boldsymbol{R}'')$.

For if $X \in \boldsymbol{R}$ and if the defining system H satisfies the equation $H_e = X$ for every e, then $A(H) = X$ and thus $X \in A(\boldsymbol{R})$. Formula (ii) is obvious. We shall prove now that formula (iii), p. 127 also holds.

°THEOREM 1: $A(A(\boldsymbol{R})) = A(\boldsymbol{R})$.

PROOF. The inclusion $A(\boldsymbol{R}) \subset A(A(\boldsymbol{R}))$ follows from (i) and (ii). To prove the opposite inclusion, assume that $M \in A(A(\boldsymbol{R}))$, i.e. that $M = A(H)$ where $H_e \in A(\boldsymbol{R})$ for every finite sequence. Therefore for every such e there exists a defining system G such that $G_f \in \boldsymbol{R}$ for every finite sequence f and $H^{(e)} = A(G)$. By the axiom of choice we associate with every e one defining system $G^{(e)}$. Then

$$M = A(H),$$

$$H_e = A(G^{(e)}) \qquad \text{for every } e,$$

$$G_f^{(e)} \in \boldsymbol{R} \qquad \text{for every } e \text{ and } f.$$

By Theorem 3, p. 343 it follows that there exists a defining system S such that $S_e \in \boldsymbol{R}$ for all $e \in N^n$ and $M = A(S)$.

Thus $M \in A(\boldsymbol{R})$. Q.E.D.

Since the operations of countable union and intersection are special cases of the operation (A) (see Examples 1 and 2, p. 341), we obtain the following consequences of Theorem 1.

THEOREM 2: *For an arbitrary family $\boldsymbol{R}$, the family $A(\boldsymbol{R})$ is both σ-additive and σ-multiplicative.*

THEOREM 3: *The family $A(\boldsymbol{R})$ contains the family $B(\boldsymbol{R})$* (see p. 129).

For $B(\boldsymbol{R})$ is the smallest σ-additive and σ-multiplicative family containing $\boldsymbol{R}$.

THEOREM 4: *$A(\boldsymbol{R})$ is the smallest family $\boldsymbol{S}$ closed with respect to the operation (A) (that is, the set resulting from applying the operation (A) to a defining system H, where $H_e \in \boldsymbol{S}$ for all e, is itself a member of $\boldsymbol{S}$).*

PROOF. The family $A(\boldsymbol{R})$ contains $\boldsymbol{R}$ and by Theorem 1 is closed with respect to the operation (A). On the other hand, if $\boldsymbol{S}$ also contains $\boldsymbol{R}$ and is closed with respect to the operation (A), then $\boldsymbol{R} \subset \boldsymbol{S}$ and $A(\boldsymbol{R}) \subset A(\boldsymbol{S}) = \boldsymbol{S}$.

In Section 4 we shall discuss the case where $\boldsymbol{R}$ is the family of closed sets in the space N^N and we shall establish certain criteria for a set belonging to $\boldsymbol{A}(\boldsymbol{R})$ to be Borel. In this section we shall prove a basic theorem applicable to arbitrary families $\boldsymbol{R}$, from which the above mentioned criteria follow easily.

DEFINITION: Let $\boldsymbol{R}$ be a family of subsets of the set X and let A, $B \subset X$. We say that the sets A and B are *$\boldsymbol{R}$-separable* if there exist sets $P, Q \in \boldsymbol{R}$ such that

$$A \subset P, \quad B \subset Q \quad \text{and} \quad P \cap Q = 0.$$

°LEMMA: *If $A = \bigcup_n A_n$ and $B = \bigcup_n B_n$ and if every pair A_m, B_n is $\boldsymbol{R}$-separable, then the sets A and B are $\boldsymbol{R}_{\delta\sigma}$-separable.*

PROOF. Let $A_n \subset P_{n,m}$, $B_m \subset Q_{n,m}$, where $P_{n,m} \in \boldsymbol{R}$, $Q_{n,m} \in \boldsymbol{R}$ and $P_{n,m} \cap Q_{n,m} = 0$. It follows that

$$A \subset \bigcup_n \bigcap_m P_{n,m} \quad \text{and} \quad B \subset \bigcup_m \bigcap_n Q_{n,m}$$

and that

$$\bigcup_n \bigcap_m P_{n,m} \in \boldsymbol{R}_{\delta\sigma}, \quad \bigcup_m \bigcap_n Q_{n,m} \in \boldsymbol{R}_{\delta\sigma}.$$

We now have

$$\bigcup_n \bigcap_m P_{n,m} \cap \bigcup_m \bigcap_n Q_{n,m} = \bigcup_{n,p} \bigcap_{m,q} (P_{n,m} \cap Q_{q,p}) \subset \bigcup_{n,p} (P_{n,p} \cap Q_{n\,p}) = 0,$$

proving the lemma.

Note that the axiom of choice is used in this proof to associate with each pair A_n and B_m the sets $P_{n,m}$ and $Q_{n,m}$.

°THEOREM 5[1]: *If the defining systems H and Q are regular, if $H_e \in \boldsymbol{R}$ and $Q_e \in \boldsymbol{R}$ and if for all sequences φ, $\psi \in N^N$ there exists an n such that $H_{\varphi|n} \cap Q_{\psi|n} = 0$, then the sets $A(H)$ and $A(Q)$ are $\boldsymbol{B}(\boldsymbol{R})$-separable.*

PROOF. Assume that the sets A and B are not $\boldsymbol{B}(\boldsymbol{R})$-separable. Because $\boldsymbol{B}(\boldsymbol{R})_{\delta\sigma} = \boldsymbol{B}(\boldsymbol{R})$ and

$$A = \bigcup_p \bigcup_\varphi \bigcap_n H_{p;\varphi|n}, \quad B = \bigcup_q \bigcup_\psi \bigcap_m Q_{q;\psi|m}$$

[1]) See W. Sierpiński, *Le théorème d'unicité de M. Lusin pour les espaces abstraits*, Fundamenta Mathematicae **21** (1933) 250–275.

(see (1), p. 342), we can use the lemma and infer that there exist numbers p_0 and q_0 such that the sets $\bigcup_{\varphi}\bigcap_{n} H_{p_0;\varphi|n}$ and $\bigcup_{\psi}\bigcap_{m} Q_{q_0;\psi|m}$ are not $\boldsymbol{B}(\boldsymbol{R})$-separable.

We shall define by induction sequences ϱ and σ such that for every k the sets

$$(8) \qquad \bigcup_{\varphi}\bigcap_{n} H_{\varrho|k;\varphi|n} \quad \text{and} \quad \bigcup_{\varphi}\bigcup_{n} Q_{\sigma|k;\varphi|n}$$

are not $\boldsymbol{B}(\boldsymbol{R})$-separable. For this purpose we define for arbitrary finite sequences f and g of natural numbers,

$$\zeta(f,g) = \begin{cases} \text{the least number } p \text{ such that the sets } \bigcup_{\varphi}\bigcap_{n} Q_{g;L(p);\varphi|n} \\ \qquad \text{and } \bigcup_{\varphi}\bigcap_{n} H_{f;K(p);\varphi|n} \text{ are not } \boldsymbol{B}(\boldsymbol{R})\text{-separable,} \\ \text{or } 0 \text{ if such a } p \text{ does not exist.} \end{cases}$$

Then the sequences ϱ and σ defined inductively by

$$\varrho_0 = p_0, \qquad \sigma_0 = q_0,$$

$$\varrho_{k+1} = K\zeta(\varrho|k, \sigma|k), \qquad \sigma_{k+1} = L\zeta(\varrho|k, \sigma|k)$$

satisfy the desired condition (8). Clearly, for $k = 0$ the sets (8) are not $\boldsymbol{B}(\boldsymbol{R})$-separable, by definition of the numbers p_0 and q_0. Assume that for some given k the sets (8) are not $\boldsymbol{B}(\boldsymbol{R})$-separable. By (2) these sets can be represented as unions

$$\bigcup_{m}\bigcup_{\varphi}\bigcap_{n} H_{\varrho|k;m;\varphi|n} \quad \text{and} \quad \bigcup_{h}\bigcup_{\varphi}\bigcap_{n} Q_{\sigma|k;h;\varphi|n}.$$

By the lemma there exist numbers m and h such that the two sets $\bigcup_{\varphi}\bigcap_{n} H_{\varrho|k;m;\varphi|n}$ and $\bigcup_{\varphi}\bigcap_{n} Q_{\sigma|k;h;\varphi|n}$ are not $\boldsymbol{B}(\boldsymbol{R})_{\delta\sigma}$-separable. One such pair of numbers is the pair ϱ_{k+1} and σ_{k+1}. Since $\boldsymbol{B}(\boldsymbol{R})_{\delta\sigma} = \boldsymbol{B}(\boldsymbol{R})$, it follows that the sets obtained from (8) by replacing k by $k+1$ are not $\boldsymbol{B}(\boldsymbol{R})$-separable.

By the regularity of the defining system H it follows that $H_{\varrho|k;\varphi|n} \subset H_{\varrho|k}$, and thus

$$\bigcup_{\varphi}\bigcap_{n} H_{\varrho|k;\varphi|n} \subset H_{\varrho|k} \in \boldsymbol{R}$$

and similarly

$$\bigcup_{\varphi} \bigcap_{n} Q_{\sigma|k;\,\varphi|n} \subset Q_{\sigma|k} \in \boldsymbol{R}.$$

Since the left-hand sides of these inclusions denote sets which are not $\boldsymbol{B}(\boldsymbol{R})$-separable, it follows that $H_{\varrho|k} \cap Q_{\sigma|k} \neq 0$ for all k, in contradiction to the hypothesis of the theorem.

§ 3. Hausdorff operations

In this section we shall consider operations on sequences of sets. These operations will be generalizations of the operation (A).

First of all we note that an operation defined for arbitrary sequences of sets is not in general a function (see p. 72). Thus, for instance, the operation of forming the union of a sequence of sets is an operation defined by the propositional function

$$\bigwedge_{x} [x \in X \equiv \bigvee_{n} (x \in F_n)];$$

similarly the operation (A) is an operation defined by the propositional function

$$\bigwedge_{x} [x \in X \equiv \bigvee_{\varphi} \bigwedge_{n} (x \in H_{\varphi|n})].$$

Hausdorff operations are also defined by propositional functions with the additional property that each such operation depends upon some fixed set $B \subset N^N$, called the *base* of the operation. The propositional function

$$\bigwedge_{x} [x \in X \equiv \bigvee_{\varphi \in B} \bigwedge_{n} (x \in F_{\varphi(n)})]$$

defines the Hausdorff operation of base B, and the set X satisfying this formula is denoted by $H_B(F)$. By definition,

$$H_B(F) = \bigcup_{\varphi \in B} \bigcap_{n} F_{\varphi(n)} \text{ [1]}. \tag{1}$$

[1]) Hausdorff operations (also called in literature the δs-operations) were defined independently by F. Hausdorff und A. N. Kolmogorov in 1927. See L. Kantorovitch and B. Livenson, *Memoir on Analytical Operations and Projective sets,* Fundamenta Mathematicae **18** (1932) 214–279. Newer bibliography can be found in the paper: Ju. S. Oczan, *Teorija operacij nad množestvami,* Uspehi Mat. Nauk **10**, No. **3** (1955) 71–128 (Russian).

Examples

1. If B contains only a single element, the sequence $(0, 1, 2, \ldots)$, then $H_B(F) = \bigcap_n F_n$.

2. If B is the set of all sequences $\varphi \in N^N$ whose range is infinite, then $H_B(F) = \text{Lim sup } F_n$. Indeed, if $x \in H_B(F)$, then there exists a $\varphi \in B$ such that $x \in F_{\varphi(n)}$ for all n; this x belongs to F_k for infinitely many values of k, because the range of φ is infinite. Conversely, suppose that $x \in \text{Lim sup } F_n$; then there exist infinitely many numbers k such that $x \in F_k$. If φ is an infinite sequence whose set of terms coincides with those numbers k, then $x \in \bigcap_n F_{\varphi(n)} \subset H_B(F)$.

3. If B is the set of all constant sequences, then $H_B(F) = \bigcup_n F_n$.

Now we prove a theorem which characterizes Hausdorff operations.

THEOREM 1: *Every Hausdorff operation* $\Phi = H_B$ *has the properties:*

(i) $\Phi(F) \subset \bigcup_n F_n$;

(ii) $(a \in \Phi(F)) \wedge (b \notin \Phi(G)) \rightarrow \bigvee_n [(a \in F_n) \wedge (b \notin G_n)]$.

Conversely, every operation satisfying conditions (i) *and* (ii) *is a Hausdorff operation.*

PROOF: (i) follows directly from the definition of a Hausdorff operation.

If $a \in H_B(F)$ and $b \notin H_B(G)$, then there exists $\varphi_0 \in B$ such that $\bigwedge_n (a \in F_{\varphi_0(n)})$, and on the other hand for every $\varphi \in B$ there exists an n such that $b \notin G_{\varphi(n)}$. In particular, if $\varphi = \varphi_0$, there is an n_0 such that $b \notin G_{\varphi_0(n_0)}$. Thus condition (ii) is satisfied by taking n to be $\varphi_0(n_0)$.

Let Φ be an operation (or equivalently, a propositional function) and assume that Φ satisfies (i) and (ii) for arbitrary sequences of sets F and G. Let $D_k = \{\varphi\colon \bigvee_n (\varphi_n = k)\}$; then D is a sequence of sets contained in N^N and $\Phi(D) \subset N^N$. We shall show that $\Phi = H_B$ where $B = \Phi(D)$.

For assume that there exists an a such that either

$$a \in H_B(F), \quad a \notin \Phi(F), \tag{2}$$

or

(3) $$a \notin H_B(F), \quad a \in \Phi(F).$$

In case (2) there exists φ such that $\varphi \in B$ and

(4) $$a \in \bigcap_p F_{\varphi(p)}.$$

Since $\varphi \in \Phi(D)$ and $a \notin \Phi(F)$, it follows by (ii) that for some n

$$\varphi \in D_n \quad \text{and} \quad a \notin F_n.$$

Thus, for some p, $\varphi(p) = n$ and $a \notin F_{\varphi(p)}$ contradicting (4).

In case (3) we have first by (i) that $a \in \bigcup_n F_n$ and then by the definition of the operation H_B

(5) $$\bigwedge_{\varphi \in B} \bigvee_n (a \notin F_{\varphi(n)}).$$

Let $Z = \{n\colon a \in F_n\}$ and let φ_0 be an infinite sequence with range equal to Z. Thus $\bigwedge_n (a \in F_{\varphi_0(n)})$ and by (5) $\varphi_0 \notin B$ and $\varphi_0 \notin \Phi(D)$. Because at the same time $a \in \Phi(F)$, we conclude applying (ii) that for some p, $\varphi_0 \notin D_p$ and $a \in F_p$. The first of these formulas together with the definition of D_p implies that $p \notin Z$, the second that $p \in Z$, which is a contradiction.

Thus both (2) and (3) lead to a contradiction, and so for all F, $H_B(F) = \Phi(F)$ and $H_B \equiv \Phi$. Q.E.D.

We shall show that in a certain sense the operation (A) is equivalent to a Hausdorff operation.

Let $e \in N^p$ and $f \in N^q$. We shall call the sequence e an *immediate extension* of the sequence f if $p = q+1$ and if $e|q = f$ (equivalently, e results from f by the addition of a single term). Let σ^c be a one-to-one mapping of N onto the set of all finite sequences of natural numbers such that $\sigma^c(0) = 0$ and let

$$B_0 = \{\varphi\colon (\varphi(0) = 0) \wedge \bigwedge_n \sigma^c(\varphi(n+1)) \text{ is an immediate extension of } \sigma^c(\varphi(n))\}.$$

For every defining system Q let $Q'_n = Q_{\sigma^c(n)}$. In this way to each defining system there corresponds in a one-to-one manner a sequence of sets.

THEOREM 2: *For every defining system Q we have*

$$A(Q) = H_{B_0}(Q').$$

PROOF. From the definition of the operation (A) it follows that

$$x \in A(Q) \equiv \bigvee_{\varphi} \bigwedge_{n} (x \in Q_{\varphi|n}) \equiv \bigvee_{\varphi} \bigwedge_{n} (x \in Q'_{\sigma(\varphi|n)}).$$

For every $\varphi \in N^N$ the sequence ψ defined by $\psi_n = \sigma(\varphi|n)$ belongs to B_0, because $\psi(0) = 0$ and $\sigma^c(\psi_{n+1})$ is an immediate extension of $\sigma^c(\psi_n)$. In fact, the first of these sequences is equal to $\varphi|(n+1)$ and the second to $\varphi|n$. It follows that

$$x \in A(Q) \to x \in \bigcup_{\psi \in B_0} \bigcap_{n} Q'_{\psi(n)} \equiv x \in H_{B_0}(Q').$$

Assume now that $x \in H_{B_0}(Q')$, that is, that for some sequence $\psi \in B_0$ we have $x \in \bigcap_n Q'_{\psi(n)}$, that is $x \in \bigcap_n Q_{\sigma^c(\psi(n))}$. From the definition of the set B_0 it follows that for every n the sequence $\sigma^c(\psi(n))$ has exactly n terms. Denote by φ_{n-1} the last term of the sequence $\sigma^c(\psi(n))$. It follows without difficulty that $\sigma^c(\psi(n)) = \varphi|n$, thus $x \in \bigcap_n Q_{\varphi|n}$, which implies that $x \in A(Q)$. Q.E.D.

Exercise

1. Find the set B such that

$$H_B(F) = \operatorname{Lim\,inf} F_n.$$

§ 4. Analytic sets

Let X be a topological space (see p. 26) and $\boldsymbol{F}$ the family of closed subsets of X.

DEFINITION. The family $A(\boldsymbol{F})$ is called the *family of analytic subsets of the space X.*

From the theorems in § 2 we obtain a number of theorems about analytic sets, for instance:

THEOREM 1: *The family $A(\boldsymbol{F})$ is σ-additive and σ-multiplicative.*

THEOREM 2: $B(\boldsymbol{F}) \subset A(\boldsymbol{F})$; *that is, every Borel subset of X is analytic.*

THEOREM 3: *The family $A(F)$ is closed under the operation (A). In particular, the result of applying the operation (A) to a defining system H where H_e is Borel for every e is an analytic set.*

Theorems 1 and 2 result from Theorems 2 and 3, p. 345, Theorem 3 from Theorem 1, p. 343.

THEOREM 4: *The cartesian product of two analytic sets in the spaces X and Y respectively is an analytic set in the space $X \times Y$.*

PROOF. By Theorem 1, p. 342 this product is the result of performing the operation (A) on the defining system U where, for every e, U_e is the cartesian product of a set closed in X and of a set closed in Y. Thus U_e is closed in the space $X \times Y$. Q.E.D.

THEOREM 5: *Every analytic set in the space X is the projection onto the X axis of a set closed in the space $X \times N^N$.*

PROOF. By Theorem 2, p. 343 it suffices to show that the set

$$M_n = \{\langle x, \varphi\rangle : x \in H_{\varphi|n}\}$$

is closed in $X \times N^N$, provided that the sets H_e are closed in X. Assume then that $\langle x_0, \varphi_0\rangle \notin M_n$, that is, $x_0 \notin H_{\varphi_0|n}$. Thus there is a neighborhood U of the point x_0 such that $u \notin H_{\varphi_0|n}$ for every $u \in U$. The set $\{\varphi : \varphi|n = \varphi_0|n\} = V$ is a neighborhood of the point φ_0 in the space N^N. Thus $U \times V$ is a neighborhood of the point $\langle x_0, \varphi_0\rangle$ in the space $X \times N^N$. For $\langle x, \varphi\rangle \in U \times V$ we have $x \notin H_{\varphi|n}$, that is, $\langle x, \varphi\rangle \notin M_n$. Hence the complement of M_n is an open set. Q.E.D.

Deeper theorems concerning analytic sets require additional assumptions regarding the space X. We shall not consider the general theory and limit ourselves to the consideration of the case where $X = (N^N)^k$ $(k = 1, 2, \ldots)$; the basic properties of analytic sets are already apparent in this simple case[1]).

Note that it is possible to limit the discussion to the case where $k = 1$:

[1]) The theory of analytic sets for complete separable spaces (that is, for continuous images of the space N^N) is given by K. Kuratowski, *Topology*, pp. 478–514. 386–421. For more general topological spaces the theory of those sets is given by Z. Frolik, *A contribution to the descriptive theory of sets and spaces*, Proceedings of the symposium on General Topology and its relations to Modern Analysis and Algebra (Praha 1961), pp. 157–173.

theorems proved for the space N^N are automatically translatable into theorems for the space $(N^N)^k$, since N^N and $(N^N)^k$ are homeomorphic: there exists a one-to-one mapping p of the space N^N onto the space $(N^N)^k$ such that both p and p^c are continuous. Such a mapping is given by the formula

$$p(\varphi) = \langle \varphi^{(0)}, \ldots, \varphi^{(k-1)} \rangle,$$

where $\varphi^{(j)}(n) = \varphi(kn+j)$ for $n \in N$ and $j < k$.

We shall prove that p is a homeomorphism in the case $k = 2$.

The function p is one-to-one. Assume that $\varphi \neq \psi$ and

$$p(\varphi) = \langle \varphi^{(0)}, \varphi^{(1)} \rangle, \quad p(\psi) = \langle \psi^{(0)}, \psi^{(1)} \rangle.$$

If $\varphi(2n) \neq \psi(2n)$, then

$$\varphi^{(0)}(n) = \varphi(2n) \neq \psi(2n) = \psi^{(0)}(n);$$

if, on the other hand, $\varphi(2n+1) \neq \psi(2n+1)$, then similarly

$$\varphi^{(1)}(n) = \varphi(2n+1) \neq \psi(2n+1) = \psi^{(1)}(n).$$

Thus in any case $p(\varphi) \neq p(\psi)$.

The function p is continuous. In other words the inverse image of every open set is open (see. p. 77); that is, if U is a neighborhood of the point $p(\varphi) = \langle \varphi^{(0)}, \varphi^{(1)} \rangle$, then $p^{-1}(U)$ contains a neighborhood of φ. Every neighborhood U contains a neighborhood of the form $N_{\varphi^{(0)}|k} \times N_{\varphi^{(1)}|k}$[1]). It is easy to check that $\psi \in N_{\varphi|2k+1}$ implies $p(\psi) \in N_{\varphi^{(0)}|k} \times N_{\varphi^{(1)}|k}$.

The function p^c is continuous. For if $p(\varphi) = \langle \varphi^{(0)}, \varphi^{(1)} \rangle$ and if $N_{\varphi|n}$ is a neighborhood of φ, then $p^1(N_{\varphi|n})$ contains a neighborhood $N_{\varphi^{(0)}|k} \times N_{\varphi^{(1)}|k}$ of the point $p(\varphi)$, where $k > n/2$.

Because the function p is bicontinuous and one-to-one, it follows that $x \to p(x)$ maps the family of open sets in the space N^N onto the family of open sets in the space $(N^N)^k$; similarly for the family of closed sets and the family of analytic sets.

We prove now several theorems concerning the relationship between analytic sets and continuous functions in the space N^N.

THEOREM 6: *If $f\colon N^N \to N^N$ is continnous and if Z is a set closed in N^N, then the set $f^1(Z)$ is analytic.*

[1]) See p. 138 for the definition of the set N_e where e is a finite sequence of natural numbers.

PROOF: Let

$$Q_e = \overline{f^1(N_e \cap Z)} = \text{the closure of the set } f^1(N_e \cap Z).$$

The defining system Q is regular and its values are closed sets. We shall show that

$$f^1(Z) = A(Q).$$

If $\varphi \in Z$, then $\varphi \in N_{\varphi|n} \cap Z$ for every n; thus $f(\varphi) \in f^1(N_{\varphi|n} \cap Z) \subset Q_{\varphi|n}$, which implies that $f(\varphi) \in \bigcap_n Q_{\varphi|n}$ and $f(\varphi) \in A(Q)$. Therefore $f^1(Z) \subset A(Q)$.

Next assume that $\alpha \in A(Q)$, i.e. that there exists a φ such that $\alpha \in \bigcap_n Q_{\varphi|n}$. We shall show that $\alpha = f(\varphi)$. If $\alpha \neq f(\varphi)$, then there exist disjoint neighborhoods N_e and N_d of the points α and $f(\alpha)$: if the first $k-1$ terms of the sequences α and $f(\varphi)$ are identical and differ in the kth term, then let $e = \alpha|(k+1)$ and $d = f(\varphi)|(k+1)$.

Since α belongs to the closure of the set $f^1(N_{\varphi|n} \cap Z)$, it follows that $N_e \cap f^1(N_{\varphi|n} \cap Z) \neq 0$ and thus for every n there exists a point [1] $\psi_n \in N_{\varphi|n} \cap Z$ such that $f(\psi_n) \in N_e$ for every n.

By the continuity of f the set $f^{-1}(N_d)$ contains a neighborhood of the point φ, for instance the neighborhood $N_{\varphi|q}$. Therefore $\psi_q \in f^{-1}(N_d)$ and $f(\psi_q) \in N_d$, so that $f(\psi_q) \notin N_e$. The contradiction thus obtained proves that $\alpha = f(\varphi)$.

It remains to show that $\varphi \in Z$. Otherwise a neighborhood $N_{\varphi|m}$ would be disjoint from Z, contradicting the definition of the point ψ_m. Thus $\varphi \in Z$ and $\alpha = f(\varphi) \in f^1(Z)$.

We prove the converse theorem.

THEOREM 7: *Every analytic set has the form $f^1(Z)$, where Z is a set closed in N^N and f is a continuous map of N^N into N^N* [2].

[1]) The existence of the point ψ_n is a consequence of the inequality $N_e \cap f^1(N_{\varphi|n} \cap Z) \neq 0$; on the other hand, the existence of the sequence ψ is a consequence of the axiom of choice. The use of this axiom in that place could be eliminated for it can be proved on the basis of the axioms Σ alone that there exists a function which associates with each closed non-empty subset of N^N one of its elements.

[2]) It can be proved that each closed subset of N^N is a continuous image of N^N. Thus the family of analytic sets in the space N^N coincides with the family of continuous images of this space. See K. Kuratowski, op. cit., p. 440.

PROOF. By Theorem 5, p. 352 the analytic set A is the projection of the closed set W in the space $N^N \times N^N$: $A = g^1(W)$, where the projection g is a continuous map of the space $N^N \times N^N$ onto N^N. Now apply the mapping p^c (p. 353). The set $Z = p^{-1}(W)$ is closed in N^N; the composition $f = g \circ p$ is a continuous map of the space N^N into itself, and $f^1(Z) = g^1(p^1(Z)) = g^1(W) = A$.

COROLLARY 8: *If* g: $N^N \to N^N$ *is a continuous function and* A *is an analytic set, then the set* $g^1(A)$ *is also analytic.*

PROOF. By Theorem 7 the set A has the form $f^1(Z)$ where f is a continuous map of the space N^N into itself and Z is a closed set. Thus the set $g^1(A)$ is the image $h^1(Z)$ where $h = g \circ f$ is a continuous map of N^N into itself.

Similarly one proves that *if* g: $(N^N)^k \to (N^N)^m$ *and if* g *is continuous, then the image* $g^1(A)$ *of the analytic set* A *in* $(N^N)^k$ *is analytic in* $(N^N)^m$. Thus in particular *the projection of an analytic set is analytic*. We conclude that the converse of Theorem 5 holds for the space N^N.

We prove now an important theorem concerning separation:

° THEOREM 9: (THE FIRST SEPARATION THEOREM.) *Any two disjoint analytic sets in the space* N^N *are separable by Borel sets; that is, there exist Borel sets* P *and* Q *such that* $X \subset P$, $Y \subset Q$ *and* $P \cap Q = 0$[1].

PROOF. Let H be a regular defining system such that for every finite sequence e the set H_e is closed in N^N. Let $H'_e = N_{K'(e)} \cap H_{L'(e)}$.

Clearly, $A(H') \subset A(H)$. We shall show that the opposite inclusion also holds. In fact, if $\psi \in A(H)$, then there exists φ such that for all n $\psi \in H_{\varphi|n}$; since $\psi \in N_{\psi|n}$, we obtain $\psi \in H'_{\vartheta|n}$, where $\vartheta = J^*(\psi, \varphi)$.

Assume that the sets $A = A(H) = A(H')$ and $B = A(Q) = A(Q')$ are analytic in N^N but are not separable by Borel sets. By Theorem 5, p. 346 there exist sequences $\varrho, \sigma \in N^N$ such that the sets $H'_{\varrho|n}$ and $Q'_{\sigma|n}$ are separable for no n. Thus for every n there is a point $\xi^{(n)} \in H'_{\varrho|n} \cap Q'_{\sigma|n}$. By the definition of the defining systems H' and Q' the point $\xi^{(n)}$ is an element of $N_{K'(\varrho|n)} \cap N_{L'(\sigma|n)}$. It follows that the first n terms

[1]) This theorem (and its name) is due to N. Lusin. See his *Leçons sur les ensembles analytiques* (Paris 1930). In the proof of Theorem 9 we appeal to Theorem 5, p. 346, thus, indirectly, to the axiom of choice.

of the sequences $\xi^{(n)}$, $\varrho^* = K^*(\varrho)$ and $\sigma^* = L^*(\sigma)$ are identical. Since n was arbitrary, we conclude that $\varrho^* = \sigma^*$.

We shall show that $\varrho^* \in A \cap B$. For this purpose we choose an arbitrary number $n_0 \in N$ and an arbitrary neighborhood Γ of the point ϱ^*. This neighborhood contains a neighborhood of the form $N_{\varrho^*|n} = N_{K'(\varrho|n)}$ where n is an arbitrary number greater than n_0. Thus Γ contains the point $\xi^{(n)}$ which is an element of $H'_{\varrho|n}$ and thus an element of $H_{\varrho|n} \subset H_{\varrho|n_0}$. Hence $\Gamma \cap H_{\varrho|n_0} \neq 0$, that is, $\varrho^* \in \overline{H}_{\varrho|n_0} = H_{\varrho|n_0}$ since H_e is a closed set for every e. Since n_0 was arbitrary, it follows that $\varrho^* \in \bigcap_n H_{\varrho|n} \subset A$.

In an entirely similar manner we can show that $\sigma^* \in B$, and because $\varrho^* = \sigma^*$ we have proved that every two analytic sets which are not separable by Borel sets are not disjoint. Q.E.D.

°THEOREM 10: *Every analytic subset of N^N whose complement is analytic is Borel*[1]).

For the Borel sets separating X and $N^N - X$ are identical with X and $N^N - X$.

Clearly analogous theorems also hold for the space $(N^N)^k$.

The separation theorem and Theorem 10 proved here for the space $(N^N)^k$ hold for more general spaces as well, for instance, for arbitrary compact spaces and also for complete separable spaces[2]) although not for arbitrary complete spaces and not even for metric locally separable spaces[3]).

Exercises

1. Using Theorem 5, p. 346 prove the separation theorem for compact spaces.

2. If f is a one-to-one continuous mapping from the space N^N into itself, then the image $f^1(A)$ of a Borel set A is itself a Borel set. [Suslin]

Hint: Show that the complement of $f^1(A)$ is analytic. Use the equivalence $\varphi \in f^1(A) \equiv \bigwedge_\alpha [(\varphi = f(\alpha)) \to (\alpha \in A)]$.

[1]) This is a theorem of M. Suslin; see Comptes rendus de l'Académie des Sciences, Paris **164** (1917), p. 89. The converse is also true, because every Borel set is analytic (see p. 351) and in the space $(N^N)^k$ the complement of a Borel set is itself Borel.

[2]) See, for example, K. Kuratowski, *Topology* I, p. 458.

[3]) W. Sierpiński, *Sur un espace complet qui n'admet pas le théorème de Souslin*, Fundamenta Mathematicae **34** (1947) 66–68.

3. If B is analytic in N^N and F a sequence of analytic sets in N^N, then the Hausdorff operation with base B applied to the sequence F gives an analytic set.

4. Let A be a set of points of the plane $\langle x, y\rangle$ where $0 < x < 1$ and $0 < y < 1$. We define as a base for the topology on A the family of all open segments parallel to the X-axis. Show that the continuous image of a closed set in this space is not always analytic. [Sierpiński]

Hint: Let M be a set of power continuum lying in the interval $(0, 1)$ of the X-axis and not analytic, and ψ — a one-to-one map of the interval $(0, 1)$ of the Y-axis onto M. Take as f the function $f(x, y) = \langle\psi(y), 0\rangle$.

§ 5. Projective sets

These sets were first introduced by N. Lusin as a generalization of the analytic sets [1]). In this section we shall consider the basic definitions of the theory of projective sets. We shall formulate them under general assumptions. As a result the relationship between analytic and projective sets will not be apparent in the beginning, but on the other hand, the significance of projective sets for the mathematical theory of definability will become evident [2]).

Let S be a set $\neq 0$. For $X \subset S^q$ and $Y \subset S^r$ let

$$X \oplus Y = \{\langle x_1, \ldots, x_q, y_1, \ldots, y_r\rangle : \langle x_1, \ldots, x_q\rangle \in X \vee \langle y_1, \ldots, y_r\rangle \in Y\},$$

$$X \odot Y = \{\langle x_1, \ldots, x_q, y_1, \ldots, y_r\rangle : \langle x_1, \ldots, x_q\rangle \in X \wedge \langle y_1, \ldots, y_r\rangle \in Y\}.$$

We call these sets the *free union* and the *free intersection*. (We use the notation $\langle u_1, \ldots, u_q\rangle$ for elements of S^q, for $q = 1$ we identify u_1 with $\langle u_1\rangle$.)

If π is a permutation of the set $\{1, \ldots, q\}$ and $X \subset S^q$, then by X_π we denote the set

$$\{\langle x_1, \ldots, x_k\rangle : \langle x_{\pi(1)}, \ldots, x_{\pi(q)}\rangle \in X\}$$

and we say that X_π arises from X *by a permutation of coordinates.*

For $1 \leqslant i < j \leqslant q$ and $X \subset S^q$ let

$$\mathrm{Id}_{ij} X = \{\langle x_1, \ldots, x_{q-1}\rangle : \langle x_1, \ldots, x_{j-1}, x_i, x_{j+1}, \ldots, x_{q-1}\rangle \in X\};$$

[1]) N. Lusin, *Leçons sur les ensembles analytiques*, Coll. Borel (Paris 1930).

[2]) The connection between the theory of projective sets and the notion of definability was established by K. Kuratowski and A. Tarski in the paper *Les opérations logiques et les ensembles projectifs*, Fundamenta Mathematicae 17(1931) 240–248.

we say that $\mathrm{Id}_{ij}X$ arises from X by *identification of the i-th and j-th coordinates.*

Finally for $1 \leqslant r < q$ we denote by $P_r^q(X)$ the set

$$\Big\{\langle x_1, \dots, x_r\rangle : \bigvee_{y_1, \dots, y_{q-r}} \langle x_1, \dots, x_r, y_1, \dots, y_{q-r}\rangle \in X\Big\};$$

$P_r^q(X)$ is the *projection of X onto S^r.*

We note the following elementary laws concerning these operations.

(i) $[P_r^q(X)]_\pi = P_r^q(X_{\pi'})$,

where π' is the permutation of the set $\{1, \dots, q\}$ which is identical with π on the set $\{1, 2, \dots, r\}$ and is equal to the identity permutation on the set $\{r+1, \dots, q\}$.

(ii) $P_r^q(\mathrm{Id}_{ij}(X)) = \mathrm{Id}_{ij}(P_r^q(X))$ *for* $1 \leqslant i < j \leqslant r < q$.

(iii) *If $X \subset S$ and $Y \subset S$, then*

$$\mathrm{Id}_{12}(X \oplus Y) = X \cup Y \quad \text{and} \quad \mathrm{Id}_{12}(X \odot Y) = X \cap Y.$$

More generally, *if $X \subset S^q$ and $Y \subset S^q$, then*

$$\mathrm{Id}_{1,q+1}\mathrm{Id}_{2,q+2} \dots \mathrm{Id}_{q,2q}(X \oplus Y) = X \cup Y,$$

$$\mathrm{Id}_{1,q+1}\mathrm{Id}_{2,q+2} \dots \mathrm{Id}_{q,2q}(X \odot Y) = X \cap Y.$$

(iv) *If $X \subset S^q$, then*

$$(S^q - X)_\pi = S^q - X_\pi.$$

(v) *If $X \subset S^q$ and $1 \leqslant i < j \leqslant q$, then*

$$\mathrm{Id}_{ij}(S^q - X) = S^{q-1} - \mathrm{Id}_{ij}(X).$$

(vi) *If $X \subset S^q$ and $Y \subset S^r$, then*

$$(S^q - X) \oplus (S^r - Y) = S^{q+r} - (X \odot Y),$$

$$(S^q - X) \odot (S^r - Y) = S^{q+r} - (X \oplus Y).$$

(vii) *If Y is a sequence of subsets of S^r and $X \subset S^q$, then*

$$X \oplus \bigcup_n Y_n = \bigcup_n (X \oplus Y_n), \qquad \bigcup_n Y_n \oplus X = \bigcup_n (Y_n \oplus X),$$

$$X \oplus \bigcap_n Y_n = \bigcap_n (X \oplus Y_n), \qquad \bigcap_n (Y_n \oplus X) = \bigcap_n (Y_n \oplus X).$$

(viii) *Under the same assumptions as in* (vii),

$$X \odot \bigcup_n Y_n = \bigcup_n (X \odot Y_n), \qquad \bigcup_n Y_n \odot X = \bigcup_n (Y_n \odot X),$$

$$X \odot \bigcap_n Y_n = \bigcap_n (X \odot Y_n), \qquad \bigcap_n Y_n \odot X = \bigcap_n (Y_n \odot X).$$

We omit the proofs of these propositions which are not difficult.

We give several more definitions and then proceed to the definition of the class of projective sets.

Let $K_0 \subset \bigcup_{q>0} 2^{S^q}$ and denote by K_{0q} the intersection $K_0 \cap 2^{S^q}$. We shall assume that K_0 satisfies the following conditions, where $q, r > 0$ are arbitrary.

(1) $0 \in K_{01}$ *and* $S \in K_{01}$.

(2) K_{0q} *is a field of subsets of* S^q.

(3) *If* $X \in K_{0q}$ *and* $Y \in K_{0r}$, *then* $X \oplus Y \in K_{0,\,q+r}$ *and* $X \odot Y \in K_{0,\,q+r}$.

(4) *If* $X \in K_{0q}$ *and* π *is a permutation of the numbers* $1, 2, \ldots, q$, *then* $X_\pi \in K_{0q}$.

(5) *If* $1 \leqslant i < j \leqslant q$ *and* $X \in K_{0q}$, *then* $\mathrm{Id}_{ij} X \in K_{0,\,q-1}$.

We call a family K_0 satisfying (1)–(5) a *base*.

For an arbitrary family $L \subset \bigcup_{q>0} 2^{S^q}$ we denote by $P(L)$ the family of all projections of sets belonging to L, i.e.

$$P(L) = \{Y: \bigvee_{qr} \bigvee_X [(1 \leqslant r < q) \wedge (X \in L \cap 2^{S^q}) \wedge (Y = P^q_r(X))]\}.$$

We let

$$C(L) = \{Y: \bigvee_q \bigvee_X [(X \in L \cap 2^{S^q}) \wedge (Y = S^q - X)]\};$$

that is, $C(L)$ is the family of complements of sets belonging to L.

Applying to the base K_0 the operations P and C in succession we obtain *classes of projective sets with respect to the base* K_0:

$$K_1 = P(K_0),\ K_2 = C(K_1),\ \ldots,\ K_{2n+1} = P(K_{2n}),\ K_{2n+2} = C(K_{2n+1}),\ \ldots$$

The family K_n is the *n-th projective class with respect to* K_0 and the union $\bigcup_n K_n = K_\infty$ is the *family of all projective sets with respect to* K_0. We define

$$K_{n,q} = K_n \cap 2^{S^q}.$$

THEOREM 1: *For all $n \in N$ and for every base K_0 the class K_n satisfies conditions* (1), (3), (4), (5).

PROOF. Instead writing "the family K_n satisfies condition (i)" we shall write (i_n). Clearly $(1_0) \wedge (3_0) \wedge (4_0) \wedge (5_0)$. Assume that $n \geqslant 0$ and that $(1_n) \wedge (3_n) \wedge (4_n) \wedge (5_n)$. We shall prove the analogous formula for $n+1$.

Case 1: *n even.*

Because $0 \subset S^2$ and $0 \in K_n$ by (1_n), we obtain $0 \in P(K_n) = K_{n+1}$ since $0 = P_1^2(0)$. Similarly, $S = P_1^2(S^2)$ implies $S \in K_{n+1}$. Thus (1_{n+1}) holds.

(4_{n+1}) and (5_{n+1}) follow from (i) and (ii).

To prove (3_{n+1}) assume that $X = P_{q_1}^q(X^*)$ and $Y = P_{r_1}^r(Y^*)$, where $1 \leqslant q_1 < q$ and $1 \leqslant r_1 < r$ and where $X^* \in K_{n,q}$ and $Y^* \in K_{n,r}$. Thus

$$\langle x_1, \ldots, x_{q_1}, y_1, \ldots, y_{r_1}\rangle \in X \oplus Y$$
$$\equiv \bigvee_{u_1 \ldots, u_{q-q_1}, v_1, \ldots, v_{r-r_1}} [\langle x_1, \ldots, x_{q_1}, u_1, \ldots, u_{q-q_1}\rangle \in X^*$$
$$\vee \langle y_1, \ldots, y_{r_1}, v_1, \ldots, v_{r-r_1}\rangle \in Y^*].$$

Applying (1_n), (4_n) and (5_n) we conclude that there exist sets X' and Y' belonging to $K_{n,q+r}$ such that

$$\langle x_1, \ldots, x_{q_1}, y_1, \ldots, y_{r_1}, u_1, \ldots, u_{q-q_1}, v_1, \ldots, v_{r-r_1}\rangle \in X'$$
$$\equiv \langle x_1, \ldots, x_{q_1}, u_1, \ldots, u_{q-q_1}\rangle \in X^*,$$
$$\langle x_1, \ldots, x_{q_1}, y_1, \ldots, y_{r_1}, u_1, \ldots, u_{q-q_1}, v_1, \ldots, v_{r-r_1}\rangle \in Y'$$
$$\equiv \langle y_1, \ldots, y_{r_1}, v_1, \ldots v_{r-r_1}\rangle \in Y^*.$$

The union $X' \cup Y' = Z$ belongs to $K_{n,q+r}$; for the free union of these sets belongs to $K_{n,2(q+r)}$, and we obtain the ordinary union from this free union by iterated application of the operation Id (see (iii)), which by (5_n) does not lead outside of the family K_n. Thus

$$\langle x_1, \ldots, x_{q_1}, y_1, \ldots, y_{r_1}\rangle \in X \oplus Y \equiv$$
$$\bigvee_{u_1, \ldots, u_{q-q_1}, v_1, \ldots, v_{r-r_1}} [\langle x_1, \ldots, x_{q_1}, y_1, \ldots, y_{r_1}, u_1, \ldots, u_{q-q_1}, v_1, \ldots, v_{r-r_1}\rangle \in Z];$$

that is, $X \oplus Y = P_{q_1+r_1}^{q+r}(Z) \in K_{n,q+r}$.

The proof that $X \odot Y \in K_{n,q+r}$ is similar.

Case 2: *n odd.*

(1_{n+1}) follows directly from (1_n). (3_{n+1}) follows from (3_n) by (vi), (4_{n+1}) and (5_{n+1}) follow from (4_n) and (5_n) by (iv) and (v).

THEOREM 2: *If* $q > 0$, *then each of the families* $K_{n,q}$ *is a lattice of sets; the families* $K_\infty \cap 2^{S^q}$ *and* $K_{n,q} \cap K_{n+1,q}$ *are fields of sets.*

PROOF. The free union and free intersection of two sets belonging to $K_n \cap 2^{S^q}$ also belong to the same class. By applying the operation Id we obtain the ordinary union and intersection and the operation Id does not lead outside of the class K_n. Thus $K_n \cap 2^{S^q} = K_{n,q}$ is a lattice of sets. The family $K_\infty \cap 2^{S^q}$ is a field of sets, because $X \in K_n \cap 2^{S^q}$ implies $S^q - X \in K_{n+1} \cap 2^{S^q}$ for n odd, $S^q - X \in K_{n-1} \cap 2^{S^q}$ for positive even n and $S^q - X \in K_0 \cap 2^{S^q}$ for $n = 0$. Finally the family $K_{n,q} \cap K_{n+1,q}$ is a field of sets, because by the first part of the theorem it is a lattice and by the definition of K_n it satisfies the condition $X \in K_{n,q} \cap K_{n+1,q} \to S^q - X \in K_{n,q} \cap K_{n+1,q}$.

THEOREM 3: *The following inclusion relations hold among the families* K_n (where the sign $\to$ stands in place of the inclusion sign $\subset$):

$$\begin{array}{ccccccccc} & & K_1 & \to & K_3 & \to \;\dots & K_{2n-1} & \to & K_{2n+1} \;\dots \\ & \nearrow & & \times & & & & \times & \\ K_0 & & & & & & & & \\ & \searrow & & & & & & & \\ & & K_2 & \to & K_4 & \to \;\dots & K_{2n} & \to & K_{2n+2} \;\dots \end{array}$$

PROOF. Let $X \in K_0 \cap 2^{S^q}$; thus $X \odot S \in K_0 \cap 2^{S^{q+1}}$ and $X = P_1^{q+1}(X \odot S) \in K_1$. Hence $K_0 \subset K_1$ and by taking complements we obtain $K_0 = C(K_0) \subset C(K_1) = K_2$.

Arguing by induction we assume that $K_{2n} \subset K_{2n+2}$ and $K_{2n-1} \subset K_{2n+1}$. From this assumption it follows that

$$K_{2n+1} = P(K_{2n}) \subset P(K_{2n+2}) = K_{2n+3},$$

and thus

$$K_{2n+2} = C(K_{2n+1}) \subset C(K_{2n+3}) = K_{2n+4}.$$

This argument establishes the inclusions in the upper and lower lines of the diagram.

The inclusion $K_{2n} \subset K_{2n+1}$ follows from $K_{2n+1} = P(K_{2n}) \supset K_{2n}$; applying the operation C we obtain $C(K_{2n}) \subset C(K_{2n+1})$, i.e. $K_{2n-1} \subset K_{2n+2}$.

We shall now explain the significance of projective sets for the theory of definability of sets. Let Φ be a propositional function of $q \geqslant 1$ free variables ranging over the set S. The *graph* of Φ in S is the set

$$Z_\Phi = \{\langle x_1, \ldots, x_q\rangle \in S^q\colon\ \Phi(x_1, \ldots, x_q)\}.$$

We say that Φ defines the set Z_Φ. The major problems in the theory of projective sets consist of investigating the projective class of sets definable by various propositional functions.

We say that a *propositional function Φ is projective with respect to the base $\boldsymbol{K}_0$* if $Z_\Phi \in \boldsymbol{K}_\infty$, and we say that Φ is a *propositional function of class n with respect to $\boldsymbol{K}_0$* if $Z_\Phi \in \boldsymbol{K}_n$.

THEOREM 4[1]: *If Φ, Φ_1 and Φ_2 are propositional functions of class n, then*

(a) *$\Phi_1 \vee \Phi_2$ and $\Phi_1 \wedge \Phi_2$ are propositional functions of the same class;*

(b) *$\neg\Phi$ is a propositional function of class $n+1$ if n is odd, of class $n-1$ if n is even, and of class 0 if $n = 0$;*

(c) *$\bigvee\limits_x \Phi$ is a propositional function of class $n+1$ if n is even, and of class n if n is odd;*

(d) *$\bigwedge\limits_x \Phi$ is a propositional function of class n if $n \neq 0$ is even, of class $n+3$ if n is odd, and of class 2 if $n = 0$.*

PROOF. (b) holds because $Z_{\neg\Phi}$ is the complement of Z_Φ.

(c) holds because the graph of $\bigvee\limits_x \Phi$ is the projection of the graph of Φ.

(d) follows from (b) and (c) by de Morgan's laws.

It remains to prove (a). Assume at first that the propositional functions Φ_1 and Φ_2 have no free variables in common. Then the graph of $\Phi_1 \vee \Phi_2$ is $Z_{\Phi_1} \oplus Z_{\Phi_2}$ and the graph of $\Phi_1 \wedge \Phi_2$ is $Z_{\Phi_1} \odot Z_{\Phi_2}$, so both graphs belong to $\boldsymbol{K}_n$. If Φ_1 and Φ_2 have free variables in common, then we can obtain the graphs of $\Phi_1 \vee \Phi_2$ and $\Phi_1 \wedge \Phi_2$ from the free union and from the free product of the sets Z_{Φ_1} and Z_{Φ_2} by identification and permutation of coordinates.

[1]) Theorem 4 is a scheme: for each propositional function we obtain a separate theorem.

Theorem 4 is important because it allows us to estimate by a simple inspection the projective class of a propositional function.

We give examples of bases. The most important example is the family of all Borel sets of finite dimension.

Let S be a topological space; then S^q for positive $q \in N$ is also a topological space with the Tychonoff topology.

Let $\boldsymbol{B}(S^q)$ be the family of Borel sets of the space S^q and let

$$\boldsymbol{B} = \boldsymbol{B}(S) = \bigcup_q \boldsymbol{B}(S^q).$$

THEOREM 5: *If every open set in S is a Borel set in S, then $\boldsymbol{B}$ is a basis* [1]).

PROOF. Condition (1) clearly holds. To prove (2) it suffices to show that the complement of a Borel set is again a Borel set. Thus let $\boldsymbol{R}$ be the family of those sets $Z \subset S^q$ whose complement is a Borel set. By the hypothesis of the theorem it follows that the family of closed subsets is contained in $\boldsymbol{R}$. De Morgan's laws show that the family $\boldsymbol{R}$ is both σ-additive and σ-multiplicative, and thus $\boldsymbol{R}$ contains the family of Borel sets in S^q.

To prove (3) we let, for $X \subset S^q$:

$$\boldsymbol{U}(X) = \{Y \subset S^r\colon X \oplus Y \in \boldsymbol{B}(S^{q+r})\},$$

$$\boldsymbol{V}(X) = \{Y \subset S^r\colon X \odot Y \in \boldsymbol{B}(S^{q+r})\}.$$

It may easily be shown that the free union and the free product of closed sets is closed; hence

$$X \in \boldsymbol{F} \to (\boldsymbol{F} \subset \boldsymbol{U}(X)) \wedge (\boldsymbol{F} \subset \boldsymbol{V}(X)),$$

where $\boldsymbol{F}$ denotes the family of closed sets in the space S^q.

Equations (vii) and (viii) imply that the families $\boldsymbol{U}(X)$ and $\boldsymbol{V}(X)$ are σ-additive and σ-multiplicative, thus

$$X \in \boldsymbol{F} \to (\boldsymbol{B}(S^r) \subset \boldsymbol{U}(X)) \wedge (\boldsymbol{B}(S^r) \subset \boldsymbol{V}(X)).$$

Now we denote by $\boldsymbol{U}$ the family $\{X \subset S^q\colon \boldsymbol{B}(S^r) \subset \boldsymbol{U}(X)\}$ and by $\boldsymbol{V}$

[1]) The assumption of Theorem 5 is satisfied, in particular, for the space N^N, where every open set is the union of all neighborhoods of the form N_e included in it, consequently a union of a countable number of closed sets. The same holds true for the space $(N^N)^k$.

the family $\{X \subset S^q\colon \boldsymbol{B}(S^r) \subset \boldsymbol{V}(X)\}$. Then $\boldsymbol{F} \subset \boldsymbol{U}$ and $\boldsymbol{F} \subset \boldsymbol{V}$. We shall show that the families $\boldsymbol{U}$ and $\boldsymbol{V}$ are σ-additive and σ-multiplicative.

We assume that $X_i \in \boldsymbol{U}$ for $i \in N$; that is, $\boldsymbol{B}(S^r) \subset \boldsymbol{U}(X_i)$ or, in other words, $X_i \oplus Y \in \boldsymbol{B}(S^{q+r})$ for every Borel set $Y \subset S^r$. From (vii) and (viii), p. 358 it follows that $(\bigcup_i X_i) \oplus Y \in \boldsymbol{B}(S^{q+r})$ and $(\bigcap_i X_i) \oplus Y \in \boldsymbol{B}(S^{q+r})$ for every set $Y \in \boldsymbol{B}(S^r)$, thus $\bigcup_i X_i \in \boldsymbol{U}$ and $\bigcap_i X_i \in \boldsymbol{U}$. Hence the family $\boldsymbol{U}$ is both σ-additive and σ-multiplicative. Similarly, we can show that the family $\boldsymbol{V}$ is σ-additive and σ-multiplicative. Since both families contain the family $\boldsymbol{F}$ of closed sets, they also contain the family $\boldsymbol{B}(S^q)$. This means that for arbitrary sets X and Y such that $X \in \boldsymbol{B}(S^q)$ and $Y \in \boldsymbol{B}(S^r)$, $X \oplus Y \in \boldsymbol{B}(S^{q+r})$ and $X \odot Y \in \boldsymbol{B}(S^{q+r})$. Thus condition (3) holds.

The proofs of (4) and (5) run similarly: denoting by $\boldsymbol{W}'$ and $\boldsymbol{W}''$ the families consisting of sets $X \in \boldsymbol{B}(S^q)$ such that $X_\pi \in \boldsymbol{B}(S^q)$ and $\mathrm{Id}_{ij} X \in \boldsymbol{B}(S^{q-1})$, we show that these families contain $\boldsymbol{F}$ and are both σ-additive and σ-multiplicative. Q.E.D.

We shall call the sets projective with respect to $\boldsymbol{B}$ simply *projective classes,* without reference to the base $\boldsymbol{B}$. Ordinarily we shall denote the projective class zero by $\boldsymbol{B}(S)$, the $(2n-1)$st class by $\boldsymbol{P}_n(S)$ and the $2n$th class by $\boldsymbol{C}_n(S)$.

The following corollaries result from Theorem 5.

COROLLARY 6: *The cartesian product of two subsets of S belonging to any of the classes* $\boldsymbol{B}(S), \boldsymbol{P}_n(S), \boldsymbol{C}_n(S)$ $(n \geqslant 1)$ *belongs to the same class.*

In fact, the cartesian product is here identical with the free product.

COROLLARY 7: *If* $f \in (S^p)^{S^q}$ *and if the graph of f (i.e. the set* $W = \{(x,y) \in S^{p+q}\colon f(x) = y\}$*) belongs to the class* $\boldsymbol{P}_n(S)$, *where* $n \geqslant 1$, *then*

$$Y \in \boldsymbol{P}_n(S) \to f^{-1}(Y) \in \boldsymbol{P}_n(S) \quad \text{and} \quad Y \in \boldsymbol{C}_n(S) \to f^{-1}(Y) \in \boldsymbol{C}_n(S).$$

PROOF. From the equivalences

$$x \in f^{-1}(Y) \equiv f(x) \in Y \equiv \bigvee_y [(f(x) = y) \wedge (y \in Y)]$$
$$\equiv \bigvee_y [((x,y) \in W) \wedge (y \in Y)]$$

it follows that the set $f^{-1}(Y)$ is the projection of the set $\{(x,y)\colon$

$((x, y) \in W) \wedge (y \in Y)\}$. This set is in turn obtained from the sets W and Y by the operations of free product and of identification of arguments and thus is an element of the class $\boldsymbol{P}_n(S)$. Since $n \geqslant 1$, it follows that $f^{-1}(Y)$ belongs to $\boldsymbol{P}_n(S)$.

The proof of the second part of the corollary is similar and is based upon the equivalence

$$x \in f^{-1}(Y) \equiv \neg \bigvee_y [(f(x) = y) \wedge (y \notin Y)].$$

°THEOREM: 8 *If* $S = (N^N)^k$, *then the class* $\boldsymbol{P}_1(S)$ *is identical with the class of analytic sets.*

In fact, in this case the projection of a Borel set is analytic and conversely (see p. 355).

REMARK: A theorem analogous to Theorem 8 holds not only for spaces $(N^N)^k$ but more generally for complete separable spaces [1]).

We give now a second example of a base.

We shall call the set $X \subset N^q$ *elementary* if there exist polynomials f and g of q variables and with natural numbers as coefficients such that

$$\langle x_1, \ldots, x_q \rangle \in X \equiv [f(x_1, \ldots, x_q) = g(x_1, \ldots, x_q)].$$

Let $\boldsymbol{D}^q$ be the least field of sets contained in N^q and containing all elementary sets.

THEOREM 9: *The family* $\boldsymbol{D} = \bigcup_q \boldsymbol{D}^q$ *is a base.*

We omit the proof of this theorem.

The projective sets with respect to $\boldsymbol{D}$ constitute the family of *arithmetically definable sets*; they have numerous applications in mathematical logic [2]).

We conclude this section by giving two examples of projective sets.

\# 1. We shall denote by $\boldsymbol{G}$ the family of open sets in the space under consideration.

Let F be a closed set lying in the plane (or more generally

[1]) A detailed discussion of projective sets for such spaces can be found in the monograph of K. Kuratowski, *Topology*, pp. 453–478.

[2]) See S. C. Kleene, *Hierarchies of number theoretic predicates*, Bulletin of the American Mathematical Society **61** (1955) 193–213.

$F \subset \mathcal{E}^n$). We say that a point $p \in F$ is *linearly accessible* if there exists a segment pq which except for the point p has no points in common with F. Denoting by A the set of linearly accessible points of F and by $|p-q|$ the distance between p and q we have

$$A = F \cap \Big\{p: \bigvee_q (q \neq p) \wedge \bigwedge_r [(|p-r|+|r-q| = |p-q|) \wedge (r \neq p) \to \neg (r \in F)]\Big\}$$

$$= F \cap \Big\{p: \bigvee_q \bigwedge_r (q \neq p) \wedge [(|p-r|+|r-q| \neq |p-q|) \vee (r = p) \vee \neg(r \in F)]\Big\}.$$

The set A is projective because each of the propositional functions

$$\Gamma(p, q) \equiv (q = p), \quad \Delta(p, q, r) \equiv [|p-r|+|r-q| = |p-q|] \quad \text{and} \quad \Lambda(r) \equiv (r \in F)$$

is projective (where, of course, p, q and r are variables for the elements of $\mathcal{E}^2$).

From the definition of A we shall evaluate its class; we shall show that A is a set of the first projective class.

Each of the sets

$$\{\langle p, q\rangle: \Gamma(p, q)\}, \quad \{\langle p, q, r\rangle: \Delta(p, q, r)\} \quad \text{and} \quad \{r: \Lambda(r)\}$$

is closed. The set $\{\langle p, q, r\rangle: \Phi(p, q, r)\}$, where

$$\Phi(p, q, r) \equiv (q \neq p) \wedge [(|p-r|+|r-q| \neq |p-q|) \vee (r = p) \vee \neg(r \in F)],$$

is a G_δ set since it is the intersection of an open set with the union of two open sets and one closed set; for

$$\{\langle p, q, r\rangle: \Phi(p, q, r)\} = \{\langle p, q, r\rangle: (q \neq p)\}$$
$$\cap\big(\{\langle p, q, r\rangle: (|p-r|+|r-q| \neq |p-q|)\} \cup \{\langle p, q, r\rangle: (r = p)\} \cup \{\langle p, q, r\rangle: \neg(r \in F)\}\big).$$

The set $\big\{\langle p, q\rangle: \bigwedge_r \Phi(p,q,r)\big\}$ is G_δ[1]), and finally the set

[1]) This follows from the remark that a projection of a closed and bounded set in the space $\mathcal{E}^n$ is a closed set, and consequently, a projection of any closed set is an F_σ-set. For other spaces (for example N^N) this theorem — as we know from § 4 — is false.

$$A = \{p: \bigvee_q \Psi(p,q)\}, \quad \text{where} \quad \Psi(p,q) \equiv \bigwedge_r \Phi(p,q,r),$$

is of the first projective class, as the projection of a $\boldsymbol{G}_\delta$ set [1]).

2. Let a be a double sequence of natural numbers (i.e. $a \in N^{N\times N}$) such that the set $\{\langle m,n,p\rangle: a_{mn} = p\}$ is arithmetically definable. Denote by A the set $\{m: \liminf_{n\to\infty} a_{mn} = +\infty\}$. We shall show that *the set A is arithmetically definable*. For

$$m \in A \equiv \bigwedge_p \bigvee_q \bigwedge_n [n > q \to a_{mn} \geqslant p].$$

Writing $\bigvee_y [x+y = z]$ instead of $x \leqslant y$ we may rewrite the formula above as

$$m \in A \equiv \bigwedge_p \bigvee_q \bigwedge_n \bigvee_{uv} [(n+u = q) \vee (p+v = a_{mn})]$$

$$\equiv \bigwedge_p \bigvee_q \bigwedge_n \bigvee_{uvw} [(w \neq a_{mn}) \vee (n+u = q) \vee (p+v = w)].$$

Since each of the propositional functions $w \neq a_{mn}$, $q+u = n$, $p+v = w$ is projective with respect to $\boldsymbol{D}$, the set A is also projective with respect to $\boldsymbol{D}$. Using Theorem 4 it is easy to see that if the propositional function $w = a_{mn}$ is of the class $\boldsymbol{K}_0$ with respect to $\boldsymbol{D}$, then the set A belongs to the class $\boldsymbol{K}_4$ with respect to $\boldsymbol{D}$.

§ 6. Universal functions

Let S be a set and $\boldsymbol{K}_0$ a base, that is, a family contained in the union $\bigcup_{q>0} 2^{S^q}$ satisfying conditions (1)–(5) on p. 359. As on p. 359 we denote by $\boldsymbol{K}_n$ the nth projective class with respect to $\boldsymbol{K}_0$ and we let $\boldsymbol{K}_{n,q} = 2^{S^q} \cap \boldsymbol{K}_n$.

DEFINITION 1: For an arbitrary family $\boldsymbol{R}$ of subsets of $\bigcup_{q\in N} S^q$, f is

[1]) The arguments above do not imply that our estimate is sharp, i.e. that we cannot lower the class in this estimate. However, in our case the estimate is sharp, because there exists a closed set $F \subset \mathcal{E}^3$ for which the set A is non-Borel (this was proved by O. Nikodym, Fundamenta Mathematicae **7** (1925) 250 and by P. Urysohn, Proceedings K. Akademie van Wetenschappen **28** (1925) 984).

a *universal function for R* if the domain of f is S and the range of f is R.

DEFINITION 2: A sequence F of functions is a *normal sequence of universal functions for R* if

(1) F_q is a universal function for the family $R \cap 2^{S^q}$ ($q \in N, q > 0$);

(2)   for $q > 0$ the set $\Gamma_q = \{\langle x, s \rangle : x \in F_q(s)\}$ belongs to $R \cap 2^{S^{q+1}}$.

THEOREM 1: *If F is a normal sequence of universal functions for the n-th projective class K_n, then the set*

$$M_q = \{\langle x_0, \ldots, x_{q-2}, s \rangle : \langle x_0, \ldots, x_{q-2}, s \rangle \notin F_q(s)\}$$

belongs to $K_{n+1,q} - K_{n,q}$ if n is odd and to $K_{n-1,q} - K_{n,q}$ if n is even.

PROOF. If $M_q \in K_{n,q}$, then for some $s_0 \in S$

$$\langle x_0, \ldots, x_{q-2}, x_{q-1} \rangle \in M_q \equiv \langle x_0, \ldots, x_{q-1} \rangle \in F_q(s_0)$$

for arbitrary $x_0, \ldots, x_{q-1} \in S$. By the definition of M_q we have

$$\langle x_0, \ldots, x_{q-2}, x_{q-1} \rangle \notin F_q(x_{q-1}) \equiv \langle x_0, \ldots, x_{q-2}, x_{q-1} \rangle \in F_q(s_0).$$

Letting $x_{q-1} = s_0$ we obtain a contradiction. Thus $M_q \notin K_{n,q}$.

The set M_q arises from Γ_q by identifying the qth and $(q+1)$st coordinates and then by complementation. The first operation leads from a set belonging to $K_{n,q+1}$ to a set belonging to $K_{n,q}$ (see Theorem 1, p. 360), the second operation leads from a set belonging to $K_{n,q}$ to a set belonging $K_{n+1,q}$ or to $K_{n-1,q}$ depending upon whether n is odd or even (see p. 362). Thus Theorem 1 is proved.

COROLLARY 2: *If for every $n \geqslant 1$ there exists a normal sequence of universal functions for the class K_n, then all inclusions in the diagram* (see p. 361)

$$
\begin{array}{ccccccccc}
& & K_1 \rightarrow K_3 \rightarrow & \cdots & \rightarrow K_{2n-1} \rightarrow & K_{2n+1} \rightarrow & \cdots \\
K_0 & & & & & & \\
& & K_2 \rightarrow K_4 \rightarrow & \cdots & \rightarrow K_{2n} \rightarrow & K_{2n+2} \rightarrow & \cdots
\end{array}
$$

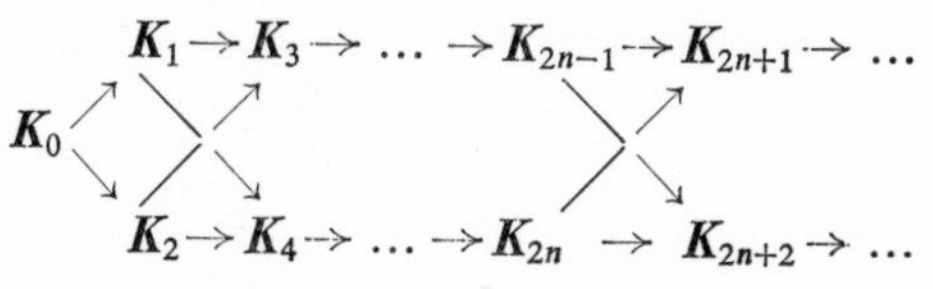

are strict. Moreover,

$$K_{2n+1} - K_{2n+2} \neq 0 \neq K_{2n+2} - K_{2n+1} \quad \text{for} \quad n \geqslant 0.$$

PROOF. From Theorem 1 it follows that

$$K_{2n+1}-K_{2n+2} \neq 0 \neq K_{2n+2}-K_{2n+1} \tag{3}$$

for every $n \geqslant 0$.

If $K_{2n-1} = K_{2n+1}$, then by the diagram above

$$K_{2n+2} \subset K_{2n-1} = K_{2n+1}$$

contradicting (3); similarly, if $K_{2n} = K_{2n+2}$, then

$$K_{2n+1} \subset K_{2n} = K_{2n+2}$$

also contradicting (3). Moreover, $K_{2n-1} = K_{2n+2}$ implies $K_{2n+2} \subset K_{2n+1}$, and $K_{2n} = K_{2n+1}$ implies $K_{2n+1} \subset K_{2n+2}$.

Analogously we show that $K_0 \neq K_1$ and $K_0 \neq K_2$.

Corollary 2 shows that if for every $n \geqslant 1$ there is a normal sequence of universal functions for K_n, then for arbitrary $n \geqslant 1$ there exist sets belonging exactly to the nth projective class. Thus in this case the classification of projective sets cannot be reduced to a smaller number of classes.

We shall prove that the hypothesis of Corollary 2 is satisfied when $S = N^N, n > 0$ and the base K_0 is the family $B = B(N^N)$ of Borel sets. The construction of the desired sequence of universal functions proceeds in several steps. Firt we let G_q be the family of open sets of the space $(N^N)^q$ and let $G = \bigcup_{q>0} G_q$.

LEMMA 3: *There exists a normal sequence of universal functions for the family* G.

PROOF. Every open set $X \in G_q$ is the union of the neighborhoods it contains, that is, of the cartesian products

$$N_{e_0} \times N_{e_1} \times \ldots \times N_{e_{q-1}} = \prod_{j<q} N_{e_j},$$

where e is a finite sequence of natural numbers. Using the one-to-one function σ^c introduced on page 98 to map N onto the set of finite sequences of natural numbers, we can represent every neighborhood in the form $\prod_{j<q} N_{\sigma^c(a_j)}$ where $a_j \in N$ for $j < q$. Let $\zeta_q = \tau^c_{q-1}$ (see p. 98) map N onto N^q. Then $\zeta_q(n)$ is a sequence of q terms $\zeta_q(n, 0), \zeta_q(n, 1), \ldots,$

$\zeta_q(n, q-1)$. Thus an arbitrary neighborhood in $(N^N)^q$ can be represented in the form

$$O(n) = \prod_{j<q} N_{\sigma^c \zeta_q(n,j)},$$

where $n \in N$. Let

$$H_q(\varphi) = \bigcup_{m \in N} O(\varphi(m)).$$

The function H_q is universal for the family $\boldsymbol{G}_q$. In fact, for every φ the set $H_q(\varphi)$ is open because it is a union of neighborhoods. If $X \in \boldsymbol{G}_q$ and φ is the sequence of all natural numbers m such that $O(m) \subset X$, then $X = H_q(\varphi)$. Thus the range of H_q is $\boldsymbol{G}_q$.

It remains to show that the set $\Gamma_q = \{\langle x, \varphi\rangle : x \in H_q(\varphi)\}$ is open. This set is the union $\bigcup_{m \in N} \Gamma_{q,m}$, where $\Gamma_{q,m} = \{\langle x, \varphi\rangle : x \in O(\varphi(m))\}$; it suffices to show that each set $\Gamma_{q,m}$ is open. For this purpose assume that $\langle x, \varphi\rangle = \langle \varphi_0, \ldots, \varphi_{q-1}, \varphi\rangle \in \Gamma_{q,m}$, i.e.

$$\langle \varphi_0, \ldots, \varphi_{q-1}\rangle \in O(\varphi(m)) = \prod_{j<q} N_{\sigma^c \zeta_q(\varphi(m),j)},$$

or

$$\varphi_j \in N_{\sigma^c \zeta_q(\varphi(m),j)} \quad \text{for} \quad j < q.$$

Let $O' = \prod_{j<q} N_{\sigma^c \zeta_q(\varphi(m),j)} \times N_{\varphi|m+1}$; O' is a neighborhood of the point $\langle \varphi_0, \ldots, \varphi_{q-1}, \varphi\rangle$ in the space $(N^N)^{q+1}$. We shall show that $O' \subset \Gamma_{q,m}$. In fact, if $\langle \varphi_0', \ldots, \varphi_{q-1}', \varphi'\rangle \in O'$, then $\varphi'|(m+1) = \varphi|(m+1)$ and

$$\varphi_j' \in N_{\sigma^c \zeta_q(\varphi(m),j)} \quad \text{for } j < q.$$

It follows that $\varphi'(m) = \varphi(m)$ and thus

$$\varphi_j' \in N_{\sigma^c \zeta_q(\varphi'(m),j)} \quad \text{for} \quad j < q.$$

This shows that $\langle \varphi_0', \ldots, \varphi_{q-1}'\rangle \in O(\varphi'(m))$, whence

$$\langle \varphi_0', \ldots, \varphi_{q-1}', \varphi'\rangle \in \Gamma_{q,m}. \quad \text{Q.E.D.}$$

LEMMA 4: *There exists a normal sequence of universal functions for the family $\boldsymbol{P}_1(N^N)$ of analytic sets.*

PROOF. Let

$$F_{1q}(\varphi) = (N^N)^q \cap \{x : \bigvee_{\psi} \langle x, \psi\rangle \notin H_{q+1}(\varphi)\}$$
$$= (N^N)^q \cap \{x : \bigvee_{\psi} (\langle x, \psi, \varphi\rangle \notin \Gamma_{q+1})\}.$$

Since the set Γ_{q+1} is open, it follows that $F_{1q}(\varphi)$ as the projection of a closed set is analytic. If X is an analytic subset of the space $(N^N)^q$, then X is the projection (say with respect to the qth axis) of a closed set Y in the space $(N^N)^{q+1}$ (p. 352). Thus, for some φ, $Y=(N^N)^{q+1}-H_{q+1}(\varphi)$ and it follows that $X=F_{1q}(\varphi)$. Finally the set $\{\langle x,\varphi\rangle: x\in F_{1q}(\varphi)\}$ is analytic, because

$$x\in F_{1q}(\varphi)\equiv x\in(N^N)^q\wedge\bigvee_{\psi}[\langle x,\psi,\varphi\rangle\notin\Gamma_{q+1}];$$

hence this set is the projection of a set closed in $(N^N)^{q+1}$.

Lemma 4 shows that for the family of projective sets the hypothesis of Corollary 2 holds in the case $n=1$. In order to extend this result to higher projective classes we shall make use of a mapping which will allow us to replace a finite number of projections by one projection.

Let h be a fixed positive integer; for $j<h$, and for arbitrary $\varphi\in N^N$, let (see p. 353) $\varphi^{(j)}=\underset{n\in N}{F}[\varphi(hn+j)]$. It is easy to check that if $q>0$, then the function

$$f_{q,h}\colon \langle\varphi_0,\ldots,\varphi_{q-1},\varphi\rangle\to\langle\varphi_0,\ldots,\varphi_{q-1},\varphi^{(0)},\ldots,\varphi^{(h-1)}\rangle$$

maps the space $(N^N)^{q+1}$ onto the space $(N^N)^{q+h}$.

LEMMA 5: *If $n\geqslant 1$ and B belongs to one of the projective classes $\boldsymbol{P}_n(N^N)$ or $\boldsymbol{C}_n(N^N)$ and if $B\subset(N^N)^{q+h}$, then the set $f_{q+h}^{-1}(B)$ belongs to the same projective class and is a subset of $(N^N)^{q+1}$.*

PROOF. The invariance of the projective class follows from Corollary 7, p. 364 and from the remark that the set $W=\{(x,y): f_{q,h}(x)=y\}$ is closed. In order to establish the validity of this remark we assume that

$$(x,y)\notin W \quad\text{and}\quad x=\langle\varphi_0,\ldots,\varphi_{q-1},\varphi\rangle \quad\text{and}$$
$$y=\langle\psi_0,\ldots,\psi_{q-1},\vartheta_0,\ldots,\vartheta_{h-1}\rangle.$$

From the inequality $y\neq f_{qh}(x)$ it follows that either $\varphi_i\neq\psi_i$ or $\varphi^{(j)}\neq\vartheta_j$ for at least one $i<q$, $j<h$. If for instance $\varphi_i(n)\neq\psi_i(n)$ then, taking as a neighborhood U of the point (x,y) all those points

$$(x',y')=(\varphi_0',\ldots,\varphi_{q-1}',\varphi',\psi_0',\ldots,\psi_{q-1}',\vartheta_0',\ldots,\vartheta_{h-1}')$$

for which the equations $\varphi_j(n)=\varphi_j'(n)$ and $\psi_j(n)=\psi_j'(n)$ hold for $j<q$,

we infer that the sets U and W are disjoint. Similarly, one shows that if $\varphi^{(j)} \neq \vartheta_j$, then there exists a neighborhood of the point (x, y) which is disjoint from W. Thus the complement of W is open and W itself is closed.

THEOREM 6: *For each of the projective classes* $\boldsymbol{P}_n(N^N)$ *and* $\boldsymbol{C}_n(N^N)$, $n \geqslant 1$, *there exists a normal sequence* $F^{(n)}$, $F'^{(n)}$ *of universal functions.*

PROOF. The existence of the sequence $F^{(1)}$ was proved in Lemma 4. Thus it suffices to prove that

(I) the existence of $F^{(n)}$ implies the existence of $F'^{(n)}$ and

(II) the existence of $F'^{(n)}$ implies the existence of $F^{(n+1)}$.

(I). Letting $F_q'^{(n)}(\varphi) = (N^N)^q - F_q^{(n)}(\varphi)$ we obtain, as can easily be checked, the desired sequence of universal functions.

(II). For this case, let

$$F_q^{(n+1)}(\varphi) = (N^N)^q \cap \{x: \bigvee_{\psi} \langle x, \psi\rangle \in F_{q+1}'^{(n)}(\varphi)\}.$$

The set $\{\langle x, \varphi\rangle: x \in F_q^{(n+1)}(\varphi)\}$ is the projection of a set of the class $\boldsymbol{C}_n(N^N)$, because

$$x \in F_q^{(n+1)}(\varphi) \equiv \bigvee_{\psi} [\langle x, \psi\rangle \in F_{q+1}'^{(n)}(\varphi)].$$

Therefore this set belongs to the class $\boldsymbol{P}_{n+1}(N^N)$.

For every φ, $F_q^{(n+1)}(\varphi) \in \boldsymbol{P}_{n+1}(N^N)$. It remains to show that every X of the class $\boldsymbol{P}_{n+1}(N^N)$ can be represented in the form $F_q^{(n+1)}(\varphi)$ for some φ_0. If $X \subset (N^N)^q$ then X arises from a set $B \in \boldsymbol{C}_n(N^N)$ by finitely many projections. If h is the number of projections, then $B \subset (N^N)^{q+h}$.

Since permutation of coordinates does not change the projective class of X we may assume that

$$x \in X \equiv \bigvee_{\psi_0 \ldots \psi_{h-1}} [\langle x, \psi_0, \ldots, \psi_{h-1}\rangle \in B].$$

This condition is equivalent to

$$\bigvee_{\varphi} [\langle x, \varphi^{(0)}, \ldots, \varphi^{(h-1)}\rangle \in B],$$

that is,

$$\bigvee_{\varphi} [\langle x, \varphi\rangle \in f_{q,h}^{-1}(B)].$$

The set $f_{q,h}^{-1}(B)$ belongs to $\boldsymbol{P}_{n+1}(N^N)$ (Lemma 5); it follows that for some φ_0, $f_{q,h}^{-1}(B) = F_{q+1}^{\prime(n)}(\varphi_0)$, which implies that

$$x \in X \equiv \bigvee_{\varphi} [\langle x, \varphi\rangle \in F_{q+1}^{\prime(n)}(\varphi_0)] \equiv x \in F_q^{(n+1)}(\varphi_0). \qquad \text{Q.E.D.}$$

Theorem 6 implies, in particular, that in the space N^N for every n there are sets which belong to the nth projective class but not to any lower class.

We conclude this section by giving examples of families for which there exists no normal sequence of universal functions.

THEOREM 7: *There does not exist a normal sequence of universal functions either for the family $\boldsymbol{B}$ of Borel sets in the space N^N or for the family $\boldsymbol{K}_\infty$ of all projective subsets of N^N.*

PROOF. Assume that Φ is a universal function for the family $\boldsymbol{B} \cap 2^{(N^N)}$ (or for $\boldsymbol{K}_\infty \cap 2^{(N^N)}$). It suffices to show that the set $\{\langle\psi, \varphi\rangle\colon \psi \in \Phi(\varphi)\}$ is not Borel (or projective). Supposing that it were Borel (projective) then the set $\{\varphi\colon \varphi \in \Phi(\varphi)\}$, and thus the set $\{\varphi\colon \varphi \notin \Phi(\varphi)\}$, would also be Borel (projective), since the operations of identification of coordinates and of complementation do not lead outside of the classes $\boldsymbol{B}$ and $\boldsymbol{K}_\infty$. From the assumption of the existence of a normal sequence of universal functions it then follows that for some φ_0, $\{\varphi\colon \varphi \notin \Phi(\varphi)\} = \Phi(\varphi_0)$, that is, $\varphi \notin \Phi(\varphi) \equiv \varphi \in \Phi(\varphi_0)$. Substituting φ_0 for φ we obtain a contradiction. Q.E.D.

In § 11 we shall use the following theorem, which can be proved without difficulty by applying the methods obtained above.

° THEOREM 8: *For arbitrary n and for $k \geqslant 1$ the classes*

$$\boldsymbol{B}(N^N) \cap (N^N)^k, \quad \boldsymbol{P}_n(N^N) \cap (N^N)^k \quad \textit{and} \quad \boldsymbol{C}_n(N^N) \cap (N^N)^k$$

are σ-additive and σ-multiplicative.

PROOF. The theorem holds for the zero projective class, because this class coincides with the family of Borel sets. If the theorem holds for the $(2n+1)$st class (i.e. for $\boldsymbol{P}_n(N^N)$), then it holds for the $(2n+2)$nd class (i.e. for $\boldsymbol{C}_n(N^N)$), because sets belonging to this class are just complements of sets belonging to the $(2n+1)$st class. Thus it suffices to prove the theorem for the class $\boldsymbol{P}_{n+1}(N^N)$ assuming that it holds for the class $C_n(N^N)$. (If $n=0$ then we replace $C_n(N^N)$ by the class of Borel sets.)

Therefore, we assume that $X_i \in P_{n+1}(N^N)$ and $X_i \subset (N^N)^k$ for $i \in N$. By Lemma 5 it follows that there exists a set $Y_i \subset (N^N)^{k+1}$ such that $Y_i \in C_n(N^N)$, and

$$x \in X_i \equiv \bigvee_{\vartheta} [\langle x, \vartheta\rangle \in Y_i] \quad \text{for} \quad i \in N.$$

Thus

$$x \in \bigcup_i X_i \equiv \bigvee_{\vartheta} [\langle x, \vartheta\rangle \in \bigcup_i Y_i],$$

which implies that $\bigcup_i X_i \in P_{n+1}(N^N)$, because by the inductive assumption $\bigcup_i Y_i \in C_n(N^N)$.

To prove that $\bigcap_i X_i \in P_{n+1}(N^N)$ we apply (10) from p. 123 and obtain

$$x \in \bigcap_i X_i \equiv \bigwedge_i \bigvee_{\vartheta} (\langle x, \vartheta\rangle \in Y_i) \equiv \bigvee_{\vartheta} \bigwedge_m (\langle x, \vartheta^{(m)}\rangle \in Y_m),$$

where $\vartheta^{(m)}$ is defined as on p. 99.

It remains to show that the set $\{\langle x, \vartheta\rangle : \langle x, \vartheta^{(m)}\rangle \in Y_m\}$ belongs to class $C_n(N^N)$. But this set is equal to the set $f^{-1}(Y_m \times N^N)$, where f is the function defined by the equation $f(x, \vartheta) = \langle x, \vartheta^{(m)}\rangle$. Because the graph of this function is Borel, applying Corollary 7, p. 364 we obtain the desired result.

Exercises

1. Prove that the classes $P_n(N^N)$ are closed under the operation (A) for $n \geqslant 1$.

2. Prove that there exists a normal sequence of universal functions for the families F_σ, G_δ, $F_{\sigma\delta}$, $G_{\delta\sigma}$, etc. in the spaces N^N, $(N^N)^2$, ... and derive as a corollary a statement about the inclusion relations which hold between these families.

3. The pair $\langle U, V\rangle$, where U and V are subsets of the space $(N^N)^2$, is a universal pair for a family K of subsets of N^N if and only if for arbitrary sets $A, B \in K$ there exists $\varphi \in N^N$ such that $A = \{\psi : \langle\varphi, \psi\rangle \in U\}$ and $B = \{\psi : \langle\varphi, \psi\rangle \in V\}$. Prove that if F is a normal sequence of universal functions for the n-th projective class $P_n(N^N)$ or $C_n(N^N)$, then the pair $\langle U, V\rangle$ where $U = \{\langle\varphi, \psi\rangle : \psi \in F_1(K^*(\varphi))\}$ and $V = \{\langle\varphi, \psi\rangle : \psi \in F_1(L^*(\varphi))\}$ is universal for the family $P_n(N^N) \cap N^N$ or $C_n(N^N) \cap N^N$ and that U and V both belong to $P_n(N^N)$ or to $C_n(N^N)$. [Lusin]

§ 7. Sieves

In §§ 7–11 we shall use the theory of ordinal numbers to investigate the projective sets of the space $(N^N)^k$. We shall denote this space by X, where k is an arbitrary fixed natural number (without loss of generality we may let $k = 1$; see p. 353).

The applications which we have in mind make use of a special ordering of the set $\mathcal{S} = \bigcup_n N^{n+1}$, that is, of the set of all non-empty finite sequences of natural numbers. σ will denote the one-to-one mapping of $\mathcal{S} \cup \{0\}$ (the set of all finite sequences of natural numbers) onto N which satisfies the condition $\sigma(0) = 0$ (see p. 98).

For arbitrary sequences $e \in N^n$, $f \in N^m$ $(n > 0, m > 0)$, let

$$e \prec_1 f \equiv \bigvee_{k<\min(n,m)} [(e_k < f_k) \wedge (\bigwedge_{p<k} (e_p = f_p))],$$

$$e \prec_2 f \equiv \bigvee_{k<m} (f = e|k),$$

$$e \preceq f \equiv [(e = f) \vee (e \prec_1 f) \vee (e \prec_2 f)].$$

The relation $e \prec_2 f$ holds exactly when f is a proper initial segment of e. The meaning of the relation $\prec_1$ is illustrated by the following examples:

$$\langle 2, 10\rangle \prec_1 \langle 3, 10\rangle, \qquad \langle 1\rangle \prec_1 \langle 5\rangle, \qquad \langle 4, 1, 5\rangle \prec_1 \langle 4, 2, 8, 2\rangle.$$

THEOREM 1: *The relation $\preceq$ orders the set $\mathcal{S}$ into type η.*

PROOF. The reflexivity of $\preceq$ is obvious.

Antisymmetry. Assume that $e \preceq f$ and $f \preceq e$. If neither e is a proper initial segment of f nor f is a proper initial segment of e, then either $e = f$, or there exists a least $k < \min(n, m)$ such that $e_k \neq f_k$. In the latter case it follows by the assumption that $e \prec f$ and $f \prec e$; but $e \prec f$ contradicts the inequality $f_k < e_k$ and $f \prec e$ contradicts $f_k > e_k$. Thus the only remaining possibility is $e = f$.

Connectedness. Assume $e \neq f$ and e non $\prec f$. If f is a proper initial segment of e, then $e \prec_2 f$ and thus $e \prec f$. Otherwise there exists a least $k < \min(n, m)$ such that $e_k \neq f_k$; and by the assumption that e non $\prec f$, we have $e_k > f_k$ and thus $f \prec e$.

Transitivity. Clearly $e \succ_2 f \succ_2 g \rightarrow e \succ_2 g$.

If $e \succsim_1 f \succsim_2 g$ and k is the least number such that $e_k \neq f_k$, then $e_k > f_k$ and $e_k > g_k$ because f is a proper initial segment of g. Moreover, $e_p = f_p = g_p$ for $p < k$. Thus $e \succsim_1 f \succsim_2 g \to e \succsim_1 g$.

If $e \succsim_2 f \succsim_1 g$ and k is the least number such that $f_k \neq g_k$, then $f_k > g_k$ and $f_p = g_p$ for $p < k$. If the length of e is greater than k, then it follows that $e_k = f_k > g_k$ and $e_p = g_p$ for $p < k$, and thus $e \succsim_1 g$. On the other hand, if the length of e is less than k, then $e \succsim_2 g$, because $e_j = f_j = g_j$ for all terms of the sequence e. Thus $e \succsim_1 f \succsim_2 g \to e \succsim g$.

Finally assume that $e \succsim_1 f \succsim_1 g$ and let k and h satisfy the conditions

$$e_k > f_k, \quad p < k \to e_p = f_p,$$

$$f_h > g_h, \quad q < h \to f_q = g_q.$$

If $k \leqslant h$, then $e_k > g_k$ and $p < k \to e_p = g_p$; if $k > h$, then $e_h < g_h$ and $q < h \to e_q = g_q$. Thus $e \succsim_1 f \succsim_1 g \to e \succsim_1 g$.

The four cases above exhaust all possibilities, and thus the transitivity of the relation $\precsim$ is proved.

The set $\mathcal{S}$ has neither the first nor the last element. For if $n > 0$ and $e = \langle e_0, e_1, \ldots, e_{n-1}\rangle$, then

$$\langle e_0+1, e_1, \ldots, e_{n-1}\rangle \succsim e \succsim \langle e_0, e_1, \ldots, e_{n-1}, 0\rangle.$$

The set $\mathcal{S}$ is dense. Assume first that $e \succsim_2 f$ and let $e = \langle f_0, \ldots, f_{k-1}\rangle$ and $f = \langle f_0, \ldots, f_{k-1}, f_k, \ldots, f_m\rangle$, where $k \leqslant m$. Then the sequence $\langle f_0, f_1, \ldots, f_{k-1}, f_k+1\rangle$ lies between e and f.

Assume next that $e \succsim_1 f$ and that k is the least number such that $e_k \neq f_k$. Then $e_k > f_k$. If the length of f is $> k+1$, then

$$e \succsim_1 \langle e_0, \ldots, e_{k-1}, f_k, f_{k+1}+1\rangle = \langle f_0, \ldots, f_{k-1}, f_k, f_{k+1}+1\rangle \succsim_1 f;$$

if, on the other hand, the length of f is $k+1$, then

$$e \succsim_2 \langle e_0, \ldots, e_{k-1}, e_k, 0\rangle = \langle f_0, \ldots, f_{k-1}, e_k, 0\rangle \succsim_1 f.$$

The set $\mathcal{S}$ is, therefore, densely ordered without first or last element, thus the order type of $\mathcal{S}$ is η (see p. 219).

We can prove Theorem 1 differently. Let R_0 be the set of rational numbers $(2m+1)/2^n$ contained in the open interval $(0, 1)$. Every number $r \in R_0$ can be represented in the form $\sum_{k=1}^{n} 2^{-c_k}$, where

$n>0$ and $0<c_1<c_2 \ldots <c_n$. Associating the number r with the sequence $e(r)=\langle c_1-1, c_2-c_1-1, \ldots, c_n-c_{n-1}-1\rangle$ we obtain a one-to-one mapping of R_0 onto $\mathcal{S}$ such that $r_1 \geqslant r_2 \equiv e(r_1) \precsim e(r_2)$. #

THEOREM 2: *If* $\varphi \in N^N_i$, *then* $\varphi|n \succ \varphi|(n+1)$ *for* $n>0$.

PROOF. The sequence $\varphi|n$ is a proper segment of the sequence $\varphi|n+1$.

THEOREM 3: *Let* $e^{(n)} \in N^{k_n}$ *for* $n \in N$ *and* $k_n>0$. *Assume that* $e^{(n)} \succ e^{(n+1)}$ *for* $n \in N$. *Then there exists an increasing sequence of natural numbers* p_n *such that* $k_{p_n} \geqslant n+1$ *and such that the sequence* $e^{(p_n)}|(n+1)$ *is a proper initial segment of the sequence* $e^{(p_{n+1})}|(n+2)$ *for every* $n \in N$.

PROOF. If $e^{(n)} \succ_1 e^{(n+1)}$, then $e_0^{(n)} \geqslant e_0^{(n+1)}$; on the other hand, if $e^{(n)} \succ_2 e^{(n+1)}$, then $e_0^{(n)} = e_0^{(n+1)}$. Thus the sequence $e_0^{(n)}$ is non-increasing. Because there exists no infinite decreasing sequence of natural numbers, it follows that, from a value of n on all the terms $e_0^{(n)}$ are equal. Let p_0 be the first number such that

$$e_0^{(n)} = e_0^{(p_0)} \quad \text{for} \quad n \geqslant p_0 .$$

Then $k_{p_0} \geqslant 1$ and $e^{(n)}|1 = e^{(p_0)}|1$ for $n \geqslant p_0$.

Assume that $s>0$ and that the numbers p_j for $j<s$ satisfy the conditions

$$p_0 < p_1 < \ldots < p_{s-1}, \qquad k_{p_j} \geqslant j+1,$$

$$n \geqslant p_j \rightarrow (k_n \geqslant j+1) \wedge (e^{(n)}|(j+1) = e^{(p_j)}|(j+1)).$$

We consider now the sequence of numbers $e_s^{(n)}$ for $n \geqslant p_{s-1}$. Since $e^{(n)}|s = e^{(p_{s-1})}|s$, it follows that for $n \geqslant p_{s-1}$ the sequence $e^{(n)}$ has length $\geqslant s$ and that the equations $e_j^{(n)} = e_j^{(n+1)}$ hold for all $j<s$.

If $e^{(p_{s-1})} \succ_2 e^{(n)}$, then the sequence $e^{(n)}$ has at least $s+1$ terms. If $e^{(p_{s-1})} \succ_1 e^{(n)}$ then there exists $h<\min(k_{p_{s-1}}, k_n)$ such that $e_h^{(p_{s-1})} > e_h^{(n)}$. Thus $h \geqslant s$ and again $k_n \geqslant s+1$. It follows that all the sequences $e^{(n)}$ for $n \geqslant p_{s-1}$ have length at least $s+1$ and that the term $e_s^{(n)}$ is defined.

For $n \geqslant p_{s-1}$ the numbers $e_s^{(n)}$ form a non-increasing sequence. Thus there exists a least number $p_s > p_{s-1}$ such that $e_s^{(n)} = e_s^{(p_s)}$ for all

$n \geqslant p_s$. It follows that

$$k_{p_s} \geqslant s+1 \quad \text{and} \quad n > p_s \to (k_n \geqslant s+1) \wedge (e^{(n)}|(s+1) = e^{(p_s)}|(s+1)).$$

The sequence of numbers p_n defined in this way by induction satisfies the assertion of Theorem 3.

COROLLARY 4: *If the hypotheses of Theorem 3 are satisfied, then there exists an infinite sequence $\varphi \in N^N$ such that for some infinite increasing sequence of natural numbers p_n*

$$\varphi|n = e^{(p_n)}|(n+1) \quad \textit{for} \quad n \in N.$$

PROOF. We may take for φ the sequence defined by the formula $\varphi_n = e_n^{(p_n)}$, where p_n is the nth term of the sequence defined in Theorem 3.

We introduce the notion of sieve[1]).

A function $L \in (2^X)^{\mathcal{S}}$, that is, a function with domain $\mathcal{S}$ such that L_e is a subset of X for every $e \in \mathcal{S}$, is called a *sieve*. The sieve L is called *open* (*closed*, *Borel*, *analytic*, etc.) if for every $e \in \mathcal{S}$ the set L_e is open (closed, Borel, etc.).

For any sieve L and for $x \in X$ we let

$$I_L(x) = \{e \in \mathcal{S}\colon\ x \in L_e\}.$$

Thus for every x the set $I_L(x)$ is a subset of $\mathcal{S}$.

Denote by $R(L)$ the set of $x \in X$ for which there exists an infinite sequence $e^{(n)}$ of elements of $I_L(x)$ such that $e^{(n)} \succcurlyeq e^{(n+1)}$ for $n \in N$. Then

$$x \in R = \{\text{the set } I_L(x) \text{ is not well-ordered}\}.$$

We say that the set $R(L)$ is *sifted* through the sieve L.

We can picture the function L as a subset of the plane, where $\mathcal{S}$ is the vertical axis, X the horizontal axis and L_e as a horizontal segment with ordinate e. For $e_1 \preccurlyeq e_2$ we can interpret e_2 as lying higher than e_1 on the vertical axis. The set $I_L(x)$ then consists of those e that the vertical line through x intersects L_e. The sifted set $R(L)$ consists of points x such that the intersection of the vertical line through x and

[1]) The notion of sieve is due to N. Lusin; see his paper, *Sur les ensembles analytiques*, Fundamenta Mathematicae **10** (1927) 1–95. In a particular case this notion was considered by Lebesgue in 1905. See H. Lebesgue, *Sur les fonctions représentables analytiquement*, Journal de Math., 1905, pp. 213–214.

the sets L_e is not a well-ordered set (the intersection contains an infinite decreasing sequence).

°THEOREM 5: *The set sifted through an analytic sieve is analytic.*

PROOF. By definition, $x \in R(L)$ if and only if there exists an infinite sequence of elements of $\mathcal{S}$ such that

$$e^{(n)} \succ e^{(n+1)} \quad \text{and} \quad x \in L_{e^{(n)}} \quad \text{for all } n \in N.$$

Letting $\varphi_n = \sigma(e^{(n)})$ we have

$$\varphi_n \neq 0, \quad \sigma^c(\varphi_n) \succ \sigma^c(\varphi_{n+1}) \quad \text{and} \quad x \in L_{\sigma^c(\varphi_n)}$$

for all $n \in N$. Thus

$$x \in R(L) \equiv \bigvee_{\varphi} \bigwedge_{n} [(\varphi_n \neq 0) \wedge (\sigma^c(\varphi_n) \succ \sigma^c(\varphi_{n+1})) \wedge (x \in L_{\sigma^c(\varphi_n)})].$$

Clearly the set Q'_n of those pairs $\langle \varphi, x \rangle$ for which $\varphi_n \neq 0$ is Borel. The set Q''_n of those pairs $\langle \varphi, x \rangle$ for which $x \in L_{\sigma^c(\varphi_n)}$ is analytic. In fact,

$$\langle \varphi, x \rangle \in Q''_n \equiv \bigvee_{q \in N} \bigvee_{e \in \mathcal{S}} [(x \in L_e) \wedge (\varphi_n = q) \wedge (\sigma(e) = q)],$$

and thus

$$Q''_n = \bigcup_{q \in N} \bigcup_{e \in \mathcal{S}} [(N^N \times L_e) \cap (\{\varphi\colon \varphi_n = q\} \times X) \cap Z_{eq}],$$

where $Z_{eq} = 0$ or $Z_{eq} = N^N \times X$ depending on whether $\sigma(e) \neq q$, or $\sigma(e) = q$. Since the set $N^N \times L_e$ is analytic, it follows that the set Q''_n is analytic.

Similarly one proves that the set Q'''_n which consists of those pairs $\langle \varphi, x \rangle$ for which $\sigma^c(\varphi_n) \succ \sigma^c(\varphi_{n+1})$ is a Borel set. Thus

$$x \in R(L) \equiv \bigvee_{\varphi} [\langle \varphi, x \rangle \in \bigcap_{n} (Q'_n \cap Q''_n \cap Q'''_n)],$$

and the set $R(L)$ is therefore the projection of an analytic set and, as such, is itself analytic (see p. 355).

THEOREM 6: *Every analytic set can be obtained by applying the function R to a closed sieve.*

PROOF. Let $M = \bigcup_{\varphi} \bigcap_{n} H_{\varphi|n}$, where H is a regular defining system such that for every $e \in \mathcal{S}$ the set H_e is closed. For simplicity we may assume that $H_0 = X$.

Let $L_e = H_e$ for $e \in \mathcal{S}$; the function L is then a closed sieve. We shall show that $M = R(L)$.

First we suppose that $x \in M$, i.e. that there exists a sequence $\varphi \in N^N$ such that $x \in \bigcap_n H_{\varphi|n} = \bigcap_n L_{\varphi|n}$. Then $\varphi|n \in I_L(x)$ for all $n > 0$ and thus the set $I_L(x)$ is not well-ordered, because for every $n > 0$, $\varphi|n \succ \varphi|(n+1)$. Hence $x \in R(L)$ and $M \subset R(L)$.

Next we suppose that $x \in R(L)$, i.e. that there exists a sequence of elements of $\mathcal{S}$ such that

$$e^{(n)} \in I_L(x), \qquad x \in L_{e^{(n)}} = H_{e^{(n)}}$$

and $e^{(n)} \succ e^{(n+1)}$ for all $n \in N$. By Corollary 4, p. 378 there exists a sequence $\varphi \in N^N$ such that for some infinite sequence of natural numbers p_n, we have $e^{(p_n)}|n = \varphi|n$. From the regularity of H it follows that $x \in H_{e^{(p_n)}} \subset H_{e^{(p_n)}|_n} = H_{\varphi|n}$ and thus $x \in \bigcup_\varphi \bigcap_n H_{\varphi|n}$. Q.E.D.

Theorem 6 does not imply that there is a one-to-one correspondence between analytic sets and closed sieves: in fact different sieves can determine the same sets. Let V be a segment of $\mathcal{S}$ such that $\overline{V} = \eta$ and let f be an order-preserving map of $\mathcal{S}$ onto V. For any sieve L, let

$$L'_e = L_{f^c(e)} \quad \text{if} \quad e \in V,$$
$$L'_e = 0 \quad \text{if} \quad e \notin V.$$

It follows from definition that

$$(e \in V) \to [(e \in I_{L'}(x)) \equiv (f^c(e) \in I_L(x))].$$

Thus for arbitrary $e \in \mathcal{S}$ we have $f(e) \in I_{L'}(x) \equiv e \in I_L(x)$; that is, $I_{L'}(x) = f^1(I_L(x))$. Clearly the sets $I_L(x)$ and $I_{L'}(x)$ are similar, thus $R(L) = R(L')$ although the sieves L and L' are in general distinct.

Now let v be an element of $\mathcal{S}$ greater than all the elements of V and let L'' differ from L' only in that $L''_v = X$. Clearly $I_{L''}(x) = I_{L'}(x) \cup \{v\}$, and thus $R(L'') = R(L')$. We have proved the following theorem:

THEOREM 7: *For every analytic set M there exists a closed sieve L such that $M = R(L)$ and such that the set $I_L(x)$, for every x, has a largest element.*

Similarly, replacing v by a sequence of type ω all of whose terms are greater than those of V we obtain the following

THEOREM 8: *For every analytic set M there exists a closed sieve such that $M = R(L)$ and for no $x \in X$ the set $I_L(x)$ has a largest element.*

§ 8. Constituents

We shall use sieves to analyze sets of the class C_1, that is, sets which are complements of analytic sets.

For a given sieve L and a given ordinal $\alpha < \Omega$ we let

$$C_\alpha(L) = \{x\colon \overline{I_L(x)} = \alpha\}.$$

We call this set the *α-th constituent determined by the sieve L.*

THEOREM 1: $X - R(L) = \bigcup_{\alpha<\Omega} C_\alpha(L)$.

For $x \in X - R(L)$ if and only if there exists an ordinal α which is the order type of the set $I_L(x)$; it follows that $\alpha < \Omega$ and thus $x \in C_\alpha(L)$.

We shall show that under certain assumptions all constituents are Borel sets. For this purpose we need several auxiliary theorems.

For arbitrary sieves L and L', let

$$T = T(L, L') = \{\langle x, x'\rangle\colon \text{the set } I_L(x) \text{ is similar to a part of } I_{L'}(x')\},$$

$$T^* = T^*(L, L') = \{\langle x, x'\rangle\colon \text{there is an } e \text{ in } I_{L'}(x') \text{ such that } I_L(x) \text{ is similar to a part of the segment } O(e) \text{ of } I_{L'}(x')\}.$$

LEMMA 2: *If the sieves L and L′ are Borel, then the sets T and T* are analytic.*

PROOF. The condition

$$\langle x, x'\rangle \in T \tag{1}$$

is equivalent to the existence of a one-to-one order preserving function which maps the set $I_L(x)$ into $I_{L'}(x')$. Because the sets $I_L(x)$ and $I_{L'}(x')$ are countable, we may restate the condition above in the following form: there exist two infinite sequences

$$e^{(0)}, e^{(1)}, \ldots, \qquad f^{(0)}, f^{(1)}, \ldots$$

of elements of $\mathcal{S}$ such that $I_L(x)$ is the set of terms of the first sequence, $I_{L'}(x')$ contains the set of terms of the second sequence and

$e^{(i)} \precsim e^{(j)} \equiv f^{(i)} \precsim f^{(j)}$ for all $i, j \in N$. Using the mapping σ (see p. 98) we can reformulate this condition as follows: there exist sequences $\varphi, \psi \in N^N$ such that

(2) $$\bigwedge_n [(\varphi_n \neq 0) \wedge (\psi_n \neq 0)],$$

(3) $$\bigwedge_n \{(\sigma^c(\varphi_n) \in I_L(x)) \wedge [(\sigma^c(n) \in I_L(x)) \rightarrow \bigvee_p (n = \varphi_p)]\},$$

(4) $$\bigwedge_n (\sigma^c(\psi_n) \in I_{L'}(x')),$$

(5) $$\bigwedge_{ij} [(\sigma^c(\varphi_i) \precsim \sigma^c(\varphi_j)) \equiv (\sigma^c(\psi_i) \precsim \sigma^c(\psi_j))].$$

Let H_i $(i = 2, 3, 4, 5)$ be the set of quadruples $\langle \varphi, \psi, x, x' \rangle \in N^N \times N^N \times X \times X$ which satisfy condition (i) for $i = 2, 3, 4, 5$.

It is obvious that H_2 is Borel,

The set H_5 is also Borel, because

$$\langle \varphi, \psi, x, x' \rangle \in H_5 \equiv \bigwedge_{ij} \bigvee_{pqrs} \{(\varphi_i = p) \wedge (\psi_i = q) \wedge (\varphi_j = r) \wedge (\psi_j = s) \wedge [(\sigma^c(p) \precsim \sigma^c(r)) \equiv (\sigma^c(q) \precsim \sigma^c(s))]\};$$

thus H_5 is equal to

$$\bigcap_{ij} \bigcup_{pqrs} (A_{ip} \cap A_{jr} \cap B_{iq} \cap B_{js} \cap Z_{pqrs}),$$

where

$$A_{mn} = \{\langle \varphi, \psi, x, x' \rangle : \varphi_m = n\}, \qquad B_{mn} = \{\langle \varphi, \psi, x, x' \rangle : \psi_m = n\}$$

and

$$Z_{pqrs} = 0 \quad \text{or} \quad Z_{pqrs} = N^N \times N^N \times X \times X$$

depending on whether the sentence

$$(\sigma^c(p) \precsim \sigma^c(r)) \equiv (\sigma^c(q) \precsim \sigma^c(s))$$

is false or true.

Since the sets A_{mn}, B_{mn} and Z_{pqrs} are Borel, it follows that H_5 is also Borel.

The sets H_3 and H_4 are Borel. We shall prove only that H_3 is Borel, because the proof for H_4 is similar. From the definition of the set $I_L(x)$ we have

$$\langle \varphi, \psi, x, x' \rangle \in H_3 \equiv \bigwedge_n \bigvee_q \{(\varphi_n = q) \wedge (x \in L_{\sigma^c(q)}) \wedge [(x \notin L_{\sigma^c(n)}) \vee \bigvee_p (\varphi_p = n)]\},$$

thus

$$H_3 = \bigcap_n \bigcup_q \bigcup_p (A_{nq} \cap (N^N \times N^N \times L_{\sigma^c(q)} \times X)) \\ \cap [(N^N \times N^N \times (X - L_{\sigma^c(q)}) \times X) \cup A_{pn}],$$

and it follows that H_3 is Borel since the class of Borel sets is closed with respect to the operations of union, intersection, complementation (see pp. 363–364) and cartesian product.

Condition (1) is thus equivalent to

$$\bigvee_{\varphi\psi} [\langle \varphi, \psi, x, x' \rangle \in H_2 \cap H_3 \cap H_4 \cap H_5],$$

and thus the set T is the projection of a Borel set and as such is analytic.

The proof that T^* is analytic is similar except that we replace condition (4) by

$$\bigvee_k \bigwedge_n [(\sigma^c(k) \in I_{L'}(x')) \wedge (\sigma^c(\psi_n) \prec \sigma^c(k)) \wedge (\sigma^c(\psi_n) \in I_{L'}(x'))].$$

The set H_4^* of quadruples satisfying this condition is Borel. Since T^* is a projection of the set $H_2 \cap H_3 \cap H_4^* \cap H_5$, it is analytic.

°THEOREM 3: *If L is a Borel sieve, then every constituent $C_\alpha(L)$ belongs to the class $\mathbf{P}_1 \cap \mathbf{C}_1$; that is, every constituent is analytic and has analytic complement.*

PROOF. We may assume that the constituent $C_\alpha(L) = C_\alpha$ is non-empty. Let $x_0 \in C_\alpha$ and let $T = T(L, L)$. Clearly,

$$(x \in C_\alpha) \to (\langle x, x_0 \rangle \in T) \wedge (\langle x_0, x \rangle \in T).$$

Conversely, suppose that $\langle x, x_0 \rangle \in T$ and $\langle x_0, x \rangle \in T$. The first condition implies that the set $I_L(x)$ is similar to a subset of $I_L(x_0)$. This set is of type α, thus $I_L(x)$ is well-ordered and its type is $\leqslant \alpha$. Similarly, the second condition implies that the type of $I_L(x)$ is $\geqslant \alpha$. Thus the type of $I_L(x)$ is exactly α. In this way we have shown that

$$C_\alpha = \{x: (\langle x, x_0 \rangle \in T) \wedge (\langle x_0, x \rangle \in T)\},$$

which proves that the constituent C_α is analytic.

The complement of C_α consists of those x which satisfy one of the following conditions:

the set $I_L(x)$ is not well-ordered;
the set $I_L(x)$ is well-ordered and its type is $<\alpha$;
the set $I_L(x)$ is well-ordered and its type is $>\alpha$.

The set of x satisfying the first condition is analytic because it is equal to $R(L)$. The set of x satisfying the second condition is equal to the set $\{x:\langle x, x_0\rangle \in T^*\}$, and the set of x satisfying the third condition is equal to $[X-R(L)] \cap \{x: \langle x_0, x\rangle \in T^*\}$. Thus

$$X-C_\alpha = R(L) \cup \{x: \langle x, x_0\rangle \in T^*\} \cup \{x: \langle x_0, x\rangle \in T^*\},$$

and the set $X-C_\alpha$ is analytic.

°COROLLARY 4: *Every constituent is Borel.*

PROOF. The family $\boldsymbol{P}_1 \cap \boldsymbol{C}_1$ is identical with the family $\boldsymbol{B}_0$ (see p. 356).

°COROLLARY 5: *Every set $M \in \boldsymbol{C}_1$ is the union of $\aleph_1$ Borel sets.*

For every such set is equal to $X-R(L)$, where L is a Borel sieve. Thus M is the union of $\aleph_1$ constituents, all of which are Borel.

Exercises

1. Deduce from Corollary 4 that every set belonging to $\boldsymbol{P}_2$ is the union of $\aleph_1$ analytic sets and thus the union of $\aleph_1$ Borel sets.

2. Let H be a defining system such that the sets H_e are Borel. Let

$$H_e^0 = H_e, \quad H_e^{\alpha+1} = H_e^\alpha \cap \bigcup_k H_{e;k}^\alpha$$

and

$$H_e^\lambda = \bigcap_{\xi<\lambda} H_e^\xi \text{ for limit ordinals } \lambda$$

(the expression $e;k$ denotes the sequence obtained from e by adding k as the last term). Prove that

$$X-\bigcup_\varphi \bigcap_n H_{\varphi|n} = \bigcup_{\alpha<\Omega} E^\alpha, \quad \text{where} \quad E^\alpha = \bigcup_{e\subset N} H_e^\alpha$$

(union indexed by sequences of one term)[1]). [Sierpiński]

[1]) This statement shows that it is possible to decompose an analytic complement into the union of $\aleph_1$ Borel sets without using the notion of sieve. See W. Sierpiński, *Sur une propriété des ensembles (A)*, Fundamenta Mathematicae **8** (1926) 362.

§ 9. Universal sieve and the function t

With each point φ of the space N^N we associate the order type $t(\varphi)$ of the set

$$\{\sigma^c(\varphi_0), \sigma^c(\varphi_1), \ldots, \sigma^c(\varphi_n), \ldots\} - \{0\} \subset \mathcal{S}$$

ordered by the relation $\preceq$.

By Theorem 1, p. 375 and by the universality of the type η (p. 219), for every countable order type τ there exists a $\varphi \in N^N$ such that $t(\varphi) = \tau$. For if τ is the order type of a non-empty set $E \subset \mathcal{S}$ and if $e_0, e_1, \ldots$ is an infinite sequence (possibly with repetitions) whose terms constitute the set E, then it suffices to take for φ the sequence $\varphi_n = \sigma(e_n)$. If $E = 0$, then it suffices to take for φ the sequence all of whose terms are 0.

By Q we shall denote the set of all φ for which $t(\varphi)$ is an ordinal number.

THEOREM 1: *The set $N^N - Q$ is analytic; there exists a Borel sieve U (all of whose values are F_σ-sets) such that $N^N - Q = R(U)$ and such that for every $\alpha < \Omega$ the constituent $C_\alpha(U)$ consists of those φ for which $t(\varphi) = \alpha$.*

PROOF. For e in $\mathcal{S}$ let $U_e = \{\varphi : \bigvee_n (\sigma^c(\varphi_n) = e)\}$. The set U_e belongs to the class F_σ, because

$$\varphi \in U_e \equiv \bigvee_{nq} [(\varphi_n = q) \wedge (q \neq 0) \wedge (\sigma^c(q) = e)],$$

and the set $\{\varphi : \varphi_n = q\} = A_{nq}$ is closed. The set $I_U(\varphi)$ consists of all non-empty sequences of the form $\sigma^c(\varphi_n)$ and thus $\overline{I_U(\varphi)} = t(\varphi)$, which proves the theorem.

We call the sieve U *universal*; this name is justified by the fact that among the sets $I_U(\varphi)$ occur ordered sets of all possible countable order types. In particular, the constituents $C_\alpha(U)$ are non-empty for all $\alpha < \Omega$[1].

Using the set Q and the constituents $C_\alpha(U)$ we can introduce a *ge-*

[1]) Neglecting non-essential differences, the set Q and the sieve U were defined already by Lebesgue. See his paper cited on p. 378.

ometrization of the cardinal numbers $< \Omega$ [1]). This geometrization relies upon the fact that every relation $R(\alpha, \beta, \gamma, \ldots)$ among ordinal numbers $< \Omega$ can be replaced by a relation R' among elements of N^N which holds for the points $\varphi, \psi, \vartheta, \ldots$ exactly when $R(t(\varphi), t(\psi), \ldots)$.

We shall not examine the details of this geometrization here and shall only define two operations which we shall use later in § 11.

For $\varphi \in N^N$ and $q \in N-\{0\}$ we denote by $\varepsilon(\varphi, q)$ the sequence defined by the following formulas:

$$\psi_n = \begin{cases} \varphi_n & \text{if} \quad \sigma^c(\varphi_n) \precsim \sigma^c(q) \ \text{or} \ \varphi_n = 0, \\ 0 & \text{if} \quad \sigma^c(\varphi_n) \underline{\succ} \sigma^c(q); \end{cases}$$

in addition we let $\varepsilon(\varphi, 0) = \varphi$.

THEOREM 2: *For every $\varphi \in N^N$ and $q \in N-\{0\}$ the set $I_U(\varepsilon(\varphi, q))$ consists of those elements of the set $I_U(\varphi)$ which are $\precsim \sigma^c(q)$; moreover, for every q the set $\{\langle\varphi, \psi\rangle : \psi = \varepsilon(\varphi, q)\}$ is Borel.*

The first part of the theorem follows from the fact that $I_U(\varphi)$ consists of all finite non-empty sequences of the form $\sigma^c(\varphi_n)$ and that $I_U(\varepsilon(\varphi, q))$ consists of those $\sigma^c(\varphi_n)$ which are $\precsim \sigma^c(q)$. The second part of the theorem follows from the formula

$$\begin{aligned}[\psi = \varepsilon(\varphi, q)] \equiv \bigwedge_n \Big(\{(\psi_n = \varphi_n) \wedge [(\varphi_n = 0) \vee (\sigma^c(\varphi_n) \precsim \sigma^c(q))]\} \\ \vee [(\psi_n = 0) \wedge (\sigma^c(q) \underline{\precsim} \sigma^c(\varphi_n))]\Big) \\ \equiv \bigwedge_n \bigvee_p \Big((\varphi_n = p) \wedge \big(\{(\psi_n = p) \wedge [(p = 0) \vee (\sigma^c(p) \precsim \sigma^c(q))]\} \\ \vee [(\psi_n = 0) \wedge (\sigma^c(q) \underline{\precsim} \sigma^c(p))]\big)\Big).\end{aligned}$$

THEOREM 3: *If $q \neq 0$, then the set*

$$\{\varphi : \sigma^c(q) \text{ is the last element of the set } I_U(\varphi)\}$$

is Borel.

PROOF. This set is equal to

$$\Big\{\varphi : \bigvee_n \bigwedge_m \{(\varphi_n = q) \wedge [(\varphi_m = 0) \vee (\sigma^c(\varphi_m) \underline{\precsim} \sigma^c(q))]\}\Big\}.$$

[1]) This method of investigation of ordinal numbers is due to K. Kuratowski. Detailed information on geometrization of ordinal numbers can be found in his *Topology*, pp. 503–508.

We prove now two important theorems about C_1-sets. The first of them (Theorem 4) will show that in a certain sense the set Q is universal. The second (Theorem 7) will give necessary and sufficient conditions for a set to be Borel.

THEOREM 4: *For every set $M \subset X$ belonging to the class C_1 there exists a function $f \in (N^N)^X$ whose graph $\{\langle x, \varphi\rangle : \varphi = f(x)\}$ is Borel and such that $M = f^{-1}(Q)$.*

In other words, *every set of the class C_1 is the Borel inverse image of the set Q.*

PROOF. Let $e_0, e_1, \ldots$ be a sequence such that $\mathcal{S}$ is the set of ist terms.

Assume that $X - M = R(L)$ where L is a closed sieve and let $f(x)$ be the sequence φ defined by the formula

$$\varphi_n = \begin{cases} 0 & \text{if} \quad e_n \notin I_L(x) \ \text{(i.e. } x \notin L_{e_n}), \\ \sigma(e_n) & \text{if} \quad e_n \in I_L(x) \ \text{(i.e. } x \in L_{e_n}). \end{cases}$$

The graph of f is Borel, because

$$(f(x) = \varphi) \equiv \bigwedge_n \{[(x \notin L_{e_n}) \wedge (\varphi_n = 0)] \vee [(x \in L_{e_n}) \wedge (\varphi_n = \sigma(e_n))]\}$$

and the sets L_{e_n} are Borel by assumption.

Let $x \in X$ and let $\varphi = f(x)$. By definition it follows that $I_U(\varphi) = I_L(x)$, and hence $t(\varphi) = \overline{I_L(x)}$. Thus $t(\varphi)$ is an ordinal number if and only if the set $I_L(x)$ is well-ordered. Hence

$$(x \in M) \equiv (x \in X - R(L)) \equiv \{t(\varphi) \text{ is an ordinal number}\}$$
$$\equiv (\varphi \in Q) \equiv (f(x) \in Q),$$

which implies that $M = f^{-1}(Q)$.

°COROLLARY 5: *The set Q is not Borel*[1]).

PROOF. Let $M \in C_1$ be a non-Borel set in the space N^N (see p. 373). By Theorem 4, $M = f^{-1}(Q)$ and thus

$$(\psi \in M) \equiv (f(\psi) \in Q) \equiv \bigvee_\varphi [(f(\psi) = \varphi) \wedge (\varphi \in Q)],$$

$$(\psi \in M) \equiv \bigwedge_\varphi [(f(\psi) = \varphi) \to (\varphi \in Q)] \equiv \neg \bigvee_\varphi [(f(\psi) = \varphi) \wedge (\varphi \notin Q)].$$

[1]) This is a theorem of Lusin and Sierpiński; see their paper: *Sur un ensemble non mesurable (B)*, Journal de Mathématique, 1923, p. 68.

If Q were Borel, then the formulas above would imply that M belongs to the class $\boldsymbol{P}_1 \cap \boldsymbol{C}_1$, and would be Borel since in the space N^N the intersection $\boldsymbol{P}_1 \cap \boldsymbol{C}_1$ coincides with the class of all Borel sets (p. 356).

° COROLLARY 6: *The notion of well-ordering for subsets of N is not definable in terms of the operations of the propositional calculus and quantification limited to elements of N*[1]).

PROOF. Assume that

$$\{R \text{ is a well-ordering relation for a subset of } N\} \equiv \Phi(R),$$

where Φ is a propositional function constructed from expressions of the form xRy, $x=y$, by means of the operations of the propositional calculus and quantification over elements of N.

For $\varphi \in N^N$, let

$$R_\varphi = \{\langle m, n\rangle :\ (\varphi_m \neq 0) \wedge (\varphi_n \neq 0) \wedge (\sigma^c(\varphi_n) \precsim \sigma^c(\varphi_m))\}.$$

The set $\{\varphi:\ mR_\varphi n\}$ is Borel. It follows that, for every propositional function Φ of the kind under consideration, the set $\{\varphi: \Phi(R_\varphi)\}$ is Borel. Thus the set

$$\{\varphi:\ R_\varphi \text{ is a well-ordering}\}$$

s Borel, which is impossible since

$$\{R_\varphi \text{ is a well-ordering}\} \equiv \{\text{the set } I_U(\varphi) \text{ is well ordered}\}$$
$$\equiv \varphi \in Q.$$

° THEOREM 7: *Let M be an arbitrary subset of the space X. The following three conditions are equivalent*:

(i) *$M \in \boldsymbol{P}_1$ and for every Borel sieve L, $M = R(L)$ implies that there exists $\alpha_0 < \Omega$ such that all constituents $C_\alpha(L)$ for $\alpha > \alpha_0$ are empty.*

(ii) *There exist a Borel sieve L and $\alpha_0 < \Omega$ such that $M = R(L)$ and $C_\alpha(L) = 0$ for $\alpha > \alpha_0$.*

(iii) *$M \in \boldsymbol{P}_1 \cap \boldsymbol{C}_1$.*

[1]) This is a theorem of A. Tarski, *Grundzüge des Systemenkalküls II*, Fundamenta Mathematicae **26** (1936) 301. The proof given here is due to K. Kuratowski, *Les types d'ordres définissables et les ensembles boreliens*, Fundamenta Mathematicae **29** (1937) 97–100.

PROOF. (i) → (ii). $M \in \boldsymbol{P}_1$ implies that $M = R(L)$ for some Borel sieve L. By (i) for every such L there exists $\alpha_0 < \Omega$ such that all constituents with indices $> \alpha_0$ are empty.

(ii) → (iii). By (ii), $X - M = \bigcup_{\alpha<\Omega} C_\alpha(L) = \bigcup_{\alpha<\alpha_0} C_\alpha(L)$. Every constituent $C_\alpha(L)$ is Borel and thus the union of countably many $C_\alpha(L)$ is also Borel. Thus the sets $X - M$ and M belong to the class $\boldsymbol{P}_1 \cap \boldsymbol{C}_1$.

(iii) → (i). Let M belong to $\boldsymbol{P}_1 \cap \boldsymbol{C}_1$ and let L be a Borel sieve such that $M = R(L)$. Assume that there exist non-empty constituents $C_\alpha(L)$ for arbitrarily large countable α.

Let $T = T(U, L)$; we shall show that

$$(1) \qquad (\varphi \in Q) \equiv \bigvee_{x \notin M} (\langle \varphi, x \rangle \in T).$$

For if $x \notin M$ and $\langle \varphi, x \rangle \in T$, then the set $I_U(\varphi)$ is similar to a subset of $I_L(x)$ and thus is similar to a subset of a well-ordered set. Thus $I_U(\varphi)$ is well ordered, that is, $\varphi \in Q$.

Conversely, if $\varphi \in Q$ and $\overline{\overline{I_U(\varphi)}} = \alpha$, then by assumption there exists an x which does not belong to M such that $\overline{\overline{I_L(x)}} > \alpha$, and thus $\langle \varphi, x \rangle \in T$.

Formula (1) has been proved. Since the complement of M is analytic and since the set T is also analytic (see Lemma 2, p. 381), it follows by (1) that Q is also analytic. Since $Q \in \boldsymbol{C}_1$, we have that $Q \in \boldsymbol{P}_1 \cap \boldsymbol{C}_1$, which implies that Q is Borel.

Thus the assumption that there exist non-empty constituents $C_\alpha(L)$ for α arbitrarily large leads to a contradiction.

°COROLLARY 8[1]: *A set $M \subset X$ is Borel if and only if it satisfies one of the conditions* (i), (ii) *or* (iii) *of Theorem* 7.

Exercises

1. Let M be Borel and α_0 an ordinal $< \Omega$. Construct a sieve L such that $R(L) = M$ and $C_{\alpha_0}(L) \neq 0$.

2. Prove that if L is a Borel sieve in N^N and E is an analytic set contained in

[1]) This corollary is due to N. Lusin. See his paper *Sur les ensembles analytiques*, Fundamenta Mathematicae **10** (1927) 71.

$X-R(L)$, then there exists an ordinal $\alpha_0 < \Omega$ such that $E \subset \bigcup_{\alpha<\alpha_0} C_\alpha(L)$. [Lusin]

Hint: Use an argument similar to that used in the proof of Corollary 8.

3. Prove that if L is a Borel sieve, then the sets $\{x: \overline{I_L(x)} = \eta\}$ and $\{x: I_L(x) = \omega^*\}$ are Borel [1]).

§ 10. The reduction theorem and the second separation theorem

Let $\boldsymbol{K}$ be an arbitrary family of sets. We say that $\boldsymbol{K}$ has the *reduction property* if for arbitrary M_1 and M_2 belonging to $\boldsymbol{K}$ the union $M_1 \cup M_2$ can be represented as the disjoint union $Z_1 \cup Z_2$ of two sets Z_1 and Z_2 belonging to $\boldsymbol{K}$ and contained in M_1 and M_2 respectively:

(1) $Z_1 \cup Z_2 = M_1 \cup M_2, \quad Z_1 \cap Z_2 = 0, \quad Z_i \subset M_i$ for $i = 1, 2$.

°THEOREM 1: *The family $\boldsymbol{C}_1 = \boldsymbol{C}_1(N^N)$ of complements of analytic sets has the reduction property* [2]).

PROOF. Let $X - M_i = R(L_i)$, $i = 1, 2$, where the Borel sieves L_1, L_2 are chosen in such a way that for every $x \in X$ the set $I_{L_1}(x)$ has a last element and such that for no $x \in X$ the set $I_{L_2}(x)$ has a last element (see p. 380–381).

Let

$$Z_1 = \{x: \langle x, x\rangle \notin T(L_2, L_1)\} \cap M_1,$$

$$Z_2 = \{x: \langle x, x\rangle \notin T(L_1, L_2)\} \cap M_2.$$

The sets Z_i belong to the class $\boldsymbol{C}_1$ (see Lemma 2, p. 381), and $Z_i \subset M_i$ for $i = 1, 2$. Moreover,

$x \in Z_1 \equiv (x \in M_1) \wedge$ [the set $I_{L_2}(x)$ is not similar to any part of $I_{L_1}(x)$],

$x \in Z_2 \equiv (x \in M_2) \wedge$ [the set $I_{L_1}(x)$ is not similar to any part of $I_{L_2}(x)$].

Clearly, the sets Z_1 and Z_2 are disjoint. For $x \in Z_1 \cap Z_2$ implies

[1]) See S. Hartman, *Zur Geometrisierung der abzählbaren Ordnungstypen*, Fundamenta Mathematicae **29** (1937) 209–214. D. Scott has proved that for every order type τ the set $\{x: \overline{I_U(x)} = \tau\}$ is Borel. See his paper *Invariant Borel sets*, Fund. Math. **56** (1964) 117–128. See also C. Ryll-Nardzewski, *On Borel measurability of orbits*, ibidem, 129–130.

[2]) See K. Kuratowski, *Sur les théorèmes de séparation dans la théorie des ensembles*, Fundamenta Mathematicae **26** (1936) 183–191.

that both of the sets $I_{L_1}(x)$ and $I_{L_2}(x)$ are well ordered and none is similar to any part of the other, which is a contradiction (see p. 231).

It remains to be shown that $M_1 \cup M_2 \subset Z_1 \cup Z_2$. Assume that $x \in M_1 - Z_1$, then $I_{L_1}(x)$ is well ordered and $I_{L_2}(x)$ is similar to a part of the set $I_{L_1}(x)$. It follows that $x \in M_2$ and that the set $I_{L_1}(x)$ is not similar to any part of the set $I_{L_2}(x)$, since by assumption the types of the sets $I_{L_1}(x)$ and $I_{L_2}(x)$ are distinct.

Thus $x \in Z_2$ and $M_1 - Z_1 \subset Z_2$. Similarly, $M_2 - Z_2 \subset Z_1$ and hence $M_i \subset Z_1 \cup Z_2$ for $i = 1, 2$. Q.E.D.

The reduction property is closely associated with the second separation principle. We say that the *second separation principle* holds for the family $\boldsymbol{K}$ if for arbitrary sets H_1 and H_2 belonging to $\boldsymbol{K}$ there exist sets D_1 and D_2 such that

$$H_1 - H_2 \subset D_2, \qquad H_2 - H_1 \subset D_1,$$
$$D_1 \cap D_2 = 0 \quad \text{and} \quad X - D_i \in \boldsymbol{K}, \quad i = 1, 2.$$

°COROLLARY 2: *The second separation principle holds for the family* $\boldsymbol{P}_1$[1].

PROOF. Applying the reduction theorem to the sets $X - H_i$ we obtain sets D_i belonging to $\boldsymbol{C}_1$ such that

$$(X - H_1) \cup (X - H_2) = D_1 \cup D_2 \quad \text{and} \quad D_i \subset X - H_i \quad \text{for} \quad i = 1, 2.$$

It follows that $H_i \cap D_i = 0$ for $i = 1, 2$, and thus

$$H_2 - H_1 = H_2 \cap [(X - H_1) \cup (X - H_2)] = H_2 \cap (D_1 \cup D_2) = H_2 \cap D_1 \subset D_1$$

and similarly $H_1 - H_2 \subset D_2$.

It was shown by Novikov that if $X = N^N$ (or, more generally, if X is a complete separable space), then the reduction property holds for the family $\boldsymbol{P}_2$ and the second separation principle holds for $\boldsymbol{C}_2$[2]. It is likely that the reduction property and the second separation principle for other projective classes are independent from the axioms of set theory. On the other hand, it has been shown that the reduction prop-

[1]) See N. Lusin, *Leçons sur les ensembles analytiques* (Paris 1930), p. 210.

[2]) P. Novikov, *Sur la séparabilité des ensembles projectifs de seconde classe*, Fundamenta Mathematicae **25** (1935) 459–466.

erty for the classes $\boldsymbol{P}_n$ $(n \geqslant 2)$ and the second separation principle for the classes $\boldsymbol{C}_n$ $(n \geqslant 2)$ are not contradictory with the axioms [1]).

Exercises

1. Show that if the reduction property holds for the family $\boldsymbol{K}$, then the second separation principle holds for the family $C(\boldsymbol{K})$ consisting of all complements of sets belonging to $\boldsymbol{K}$.

2. We say that the *first separation principle* holds for the family $\boldsymbol{K}$, if for arbitrary disjoint sets M_1 and M_2 belonging to $\boldsymbol{K}$ there is a set $E \in \boldsymbol{K} \cap C(\boldsymbol{K})$ such that $M_1 \subset E$ and $E \cap M_2 = 0$. Show that if the family $\boldsymbol{K}$ has the reduction property, then the first separation principle holds for $C(\boldsymbol{K})$.

3. Using Exercise 2 above and Theorem 1, p. 390 prove Theorem 6, p. 355.

4. Neither the first nor the second separation principle holds for the family $\boldsymbol{C}_1$ in the space N^N.

Hint: Let $\langle U, V\rangle$ be a universal pair for the family $\boldsymbol{C}_1$, where the sets U and V are complements of analytic sets (see Exercise 3, p. 374). By virtue of reduction property there exist sets $U_1 \subset U$ and $V_1 \subset V$ such that $U \cup V = U_1 \cup V_1$. If the sets U_1 and V_1 could be separated by a Borel set W, then the function $F(\varphi) = \{\psi: \langle\varphi, \psi\rangle \in W\}$ would be universal for the family of Borel subsets of N^N and the set $\{\langle\varphi, \psi\rangle: \psi \in F(\varphi)\}$ would be Borel, which is impossible (see p. 373). Note, moreover, that the second separation principle for $\boldsymbol{C}_1$ implies the first.

§ 11. The problem of projectivity for sets defined by transfinite induction

Let H be a function which assigns to every set $M \subset (N^N)^k = X$ a set $H(M) \subset X$. By the theorem on inductive definitions, for every $Z \subset X$ there exists a sequence of type Ω of subsets of X such that

$$D_0 = Z, \quad D_{\xi+1} = H(D_\xi), \quad D_\lambda = \bigcup_{\xi<\lambda} D_\xi \text{ for } \lambda \text{ a limit ordinal.}$$

Let $E = \bigcup_{\xi<\Omega} D_\xi$. The problem which we shall deal with in this section concerns the projectivity of the set E[2]).

Applying the general idea of geometrization of ordinal numbers, we let

$$D' = \{\langle\varphi, x\rangle: (\varphi \in Q) \wedge (x \in D_{t(\varphi)})\}.$$

[1]) J. W. Addison, *Separation principles in the hierarchies of classical and effective descriptive set theory*, Fundamenta Mathematicae **46** (1959) 123–135.

[2]) This problem (in a more general setting) was solved by K. Kuratowski, *Les ensembles projectifs et l'induction transfinie*, Fundamenta Mathematicae **27** (1936) 269–276.

Clearly $x \in E \equiv \bigvee_{\varphi} [\langle \varphi, x \rangle \in D']$; thus, in order to evaluate the projective class of the set E, it suffices to consider the same problem for the set D'.

We shall use the following notation. If $A \subset N^N \times Y$ where Y is an arbitrary space, then $A^{(\varphi)}$ will denote the set $\{y: \langle \varphi, y \rangle \in A\}$ we call it the crossection of A through φ. We shall denote the projective classes $\boldsymbol{P}_n(N^N) \cap (N^N)^k$ and $\boldsymbol{C}_n(N^N) \cap (N^N)^k$ by $\boldsymbol{P}_{n,k}$ and $\boldsymbol{C}_{n,k}$, or by $\boldsymbol{P}_n$ and $\boldsymbol{C}_n$ if k is fixed and if no confusion can occur.

DEFINITION: A function $H \in (2^X)^{2^X}$ is *projective of class* $\boldsymbol{P}_n$ (or $\boldsymbol{C}_n$) if for every set $A \in \boldsymbol{P}_{n,k+2}$ (or $A \in \boldsymbol{C}_{n,k+2}$) the set $\{\langle \varphi, \psi, x \rangle: x \in A^{(\varphi)(\psi)}\}$ belongs to the class $\boldsymbol{P}_{n,k+2}$ (or to the class $\boldsymbol{C}_{n,k+2}$).

In the sequel we shall restrict our attention to functions of class $\boldsymbol{P}_n$, but all arguments can be shown to hold for functions of class $\boldsymbol{C}_n$.

LEMMA 1: *If H is a function of class $\boldsymbol{P}_n$ ($n \geqslant 1$), then*

$$(M \subset X) \cap (M \in \boldsymbol{P}_n) \rightarrow H(M) \in \boldsymbol{P}_n.$$

PROOF. If $M \in \boldsymbol{P}_n$ then the set $A = N^N \times N^N \times M$ belongs to the class $\boldsymbol{P}_{n,k+2}$, and thus the set

$$B = \{\langle \varphi, \psi, x \rangle: x \in H(A^{(\varphi)(\psi)})\} = \{\langle \varphi, \psi, x \rangle: x \in H(M)\}$$

belongs to the class $\boldsymbol{P}_{n,k+2}$. It follows that $H(M)$ is the projection of the set B:

$$x \in H(M) \equiv \bigvee_{\varphi, \psi} [\langle \varphi, \psi, x \rangle \in B];$$

thus, $H(M) \in \boldsymbol{P}_n$ since $n \geqslant 1$.

LEMMA 2: *If $Z \in \boldsymbol{P}_{n,k}$ and H is a projective function of class $\boldsymbol{P}_n$ ($n \geqslant 1$), then $D_\xi \in \boldsymbol{P}_{n,k}$ for all $\xi < \Omega$.*

PROOF. Let $K = \{\xi < \Omega: D_\xi \in \boldsymbol{P}_n\}$ and let $W(\alpha) \subset K$; by the induction principle it suffices to show that $\alpha \in K$. This is clear for $\alpha = 0$ because $D_0 = Z \in \boldsymbol{P}_n$. If α is a limit ordinal, then D_α is the countable union of sets belonging to the class $\boldsymbol{P}_n$ and thus $D_\alpha \in \boldsymbol{P}_n$ (see p. 373). Finally, if $\alpha = \beta + 1$ then $D_\beta \in \boldsymbol{P}_n$ by hypothesis and thus $D_\alpha = H(D_\beta) \in \boldsymbol{P}_n$ by Lemma 1.

LEMMA 3: *Under the same hypotheses as in Lemma 2, the union* $\bigcup_{\xi<\alpha}(C_\xi(U)\times D_\xi)$ *belongs to the class* $\boldsymbol{P}_{n,k+1}$.

PROOF. Each constituent $C_\xi(U)$ is Borel and the class $\boldsymbol{P}_n$ is closed with respect to the operations of countable union and of cartesian product.

In the following lemma we use the notation

$$K_q = \{\varphi\colon \sigma^e(q) \text{ is the last element of the set } I_U(\varphi)\}.$$

The set K_q is Borel as was proved in Theorem 3 on p. 386. We shall use T to denote the set $T(U, U)$ (see p. 381). For $\varphi, \psi \in Q$ the condition $t(\varphi) \leqslant t(\psi)$ is equivalent to $\langle\varphi, \psi\rangle \in T$.

LEMMA 4: *If* $Z \in \boldsymbol{P}_n$, *H is a function of class* $\boldsymbol{P}_n$ $(n \geqslant 1)$ *and if* $\langle\varphi, x\rangle \in D'$, *then there exists a set* $A \subset N^N \times X$ *having the following properties*:

(1) $\langle\varphi, x\rangle \in A$;

(2) $\psi \in C_0(U) \rightarrow A^{(\psi)} = Z$;

(3) $(\psi \in Q) \wedge (\langle\psi, \varphi\rangle \in T) \wedge (\psi \in K_q) \wedge (q \neq 0) \rightarrow \big(A^{(\psi)} = H(A^{(\varepsilon(\psi, q))})\big)$;

(4) $(\psi \in Q) \wedge (\langle\psi, \varphi\rangle \in T) \wedge \bigwedge_{q\neq 0} (\psi \notin K_q) \rightarrow \big(A^{(\psi)} = \bigcup_{q\neq 0} A^{(\varepsilon(\psi, q))}\big)$;

(5) $A \in \boldsymbol{P}_{n,k+1}$.

Conversely, if there exists a set A satisfying (1)–(5) *where* $\varphi \in Q$, *then* $\langle\varphi, x\rangle \in D'$.

PROOF. The first part of the lemma follows from the fact that the set

$$A = \bigcup_{\xi \leqslant t(\varphi)} (C_\xi(U) \times D_\xi)$$

satisfies conditions (1)–(5).

To prove the second part we assume that A satisfies (1)–(5) and that $\varphi \in Q$. Let $\alpha = t(\varphi)$. We shall show by induction on β that if $\beta \leqslant \alpha$, then

(6) $$t(\psi) = \beta \rightarrow A^{(\psi)} = D_\beta.$$

Let Y be the set consisting of all countable ordinals $> \alpha$ and of ordinals $\leqslant \alpha$ which satisfy (6). Assume that $W(\beta) \subset Y$. It suffices to show that $\beta \in Y$. Clearly we may also assume that $\beta \leqslant \alpha$. If $\beta = 0$

then β satisfies (6), since $t(\psi) = 0$ implies that $\psi \in C_0(U)$ and thus by (2), $A^{(\psi)} = Z = D_0$.

If $\beta = \gamma + 1$ and $t(\psi) = \beta$ then $\overline{I_U(\psi)} = \gamma + 1 \leqslant \alpha$, and thus $\langle \psi, \varphi \rangle \in T$, $\psi \in Q$ and there exists a $q \neq 0$ such that $\sigma^c(q)$ is the last element of the set $I_U(\psi)$, that is, $\psi \in K_q$. From (3) it then follows that $A^{(\psi)} = H(A^{(\varepsilon(\psi,q))})$, and because (see p. 386) $t(\varepsilon(\psi, q)) = \gamma \in Y$, we have $A^{(\varepsilon(\psi,q))} = D_\gamma$ and $A^{(\psi)} = H(D_\gamma) = D_{\gamma+1} = D_\beta$.

If β is a limit ordinal and $t(\psi) = \beta$, then $\overline{I_U(\psi)} \leqslant \alpha$, thus $\psi \in Q$ and $\langle \psi, \varphi \rangle \in T$; moreover, $\psi \notin K_q$ for all natural numbers $q \neq 0$. From (4) it follows that $A^{(\psi)} = \bigcup_{q \neq 0} A^{(\varepsilon(\psi, q))}$. On the other hand, for every q, $t(\varepsilon(\psi, q)) < t(\psi) = \beta$, and every ordinal $\gamma < \beta$ can be represented in the form $t(\varepsilon(\psi, q))$ where q is a natural number $\neq 0$. Since $t(\varepsilon(\psi, q)) \in Y$, we have

$$A^{(\psi)} = \bigcup_{q \neq 0} D_{t(\varepsilon(\psi, q))} = \bigcup_{\gamma < \beta} D_\gamma = D_\beta .$$

Thus formula (6) holds. Substituting in (6) $\beta = t(\varphi)$ and $\psi = \varphi$, we obtain $A^{(\varphi)} = D_{t(\varphi)}$, and thus by (1)

$$\langle \varphi, x \rangle \in C_{t(\varphi)}(U) \times D_{t(\varphi)} \subset D'. \qquad \text{Q.E.D.}$$

Now let F be a universal function for the class $\boldsymbol{P}_{n,k+1}$ such that the set

$$W = \{\langle \vartheta, x \rangle : \; x \in F(\vartheta)\}$$

belongs to class $\boldsymbol{P}_{n,k+2}$. The existence of such a function was proved on p. 372. Notice that

$$W^{(\vartheta)} = F(\vartheta)$$

according to the definition.

Every set $A \in \boldsymbol{P}_{n,k+1}$ can be represented in the form $F(\vartheta)$, that is in the form $W^{(\vartheta)}$ and $W^{(\vartheta)} \in \boldsymbol{P}_{n,k+1}$ for every ϑ. Hence substituting $A = W^{(\vartheta)}$ in Lemma 4 we obtain the following statement:

LEMMA 5: *If $Z \in \boldsymbol{P}_{n,k}$ and H is a function of class $\boldsymbol{P}_n$, then the formula $\langle \varphi, x \rangle \in D'$ is equivalent to the existence of a point $\vartheta \in N^N$ such that for all ψ:*

(7) $$(\langle \vartheta, \varphi, x \rangle \in W) \wedge (\varphi \in Q);$$

(8) $$\psi \in C_0(U) \rightarrow (W^{(\vartheta)(\psi)} = Z);$$

$$(9)\quad \bigwedge_{q\neq 0}(\psi\in Q)\wedge(\langle\psi,\varphi\rangle\in T)\wedge(\psi\in K_q)\to\big(W^{(\vartheta)(\psi)}=H(W^{(\vartheta)(\varepsilon(\psi,q))})\big);$$

$$(10)\quad (\psi\in Q)\wedge(\langle\psi,\varphi\rangle\in T)\wedge\bigwedge_{q\neq 0}(\psi\notin K_q)\to\big(W^{(\vartheta)(\psi)}=\bigcup_{q\neq 0}W^{(\vartheta)(\varepsilon(\psi,q))}\big).$$

The lemma above allows us to solve the problem of projectivity of the set D'. Namely, by Lemma 5 we have the equivalence

$$\langle\varphi,x\rangle\in D'\equiv\bigvee_{\vartheta}\bigwedge_{\psi}[\Phi_1\wedge\Phi_2\wedge\Phi_3\wedge\Phi_4],$$

where Φ_1–Φ_4 are the propositional functions (7)–(10).

Let $H_i=\{\langle\varphi,x,\vartheta,\psi\rangle\colon\ \Phi_i\}$ for $i=1,2,3,4$. Then

$$(11)\qquad \langle\varphi,x\rangle\in D'\equiv\bigvee_{\vartheta}\bigwedge_{\psi}[\langle\varphi,x,\vartheta,\psi\rangle\in H_1\cap H_2\cap H_3\cap H_4].$$

LEMMA 6: *If $n\geqslant 1$ then the sets H_i belong to class $\boldsymbol{C}_{n+1,k+3}$ for $i=1,2,3,4$.*

PROOF. The set H_1 can be obtained from the set $[W\times N^N]\cap[N^N\times\times N^N\times Q\times X]$ by permutation and identification of coordinates. Therefore H_1 belongs to class $\boldsymbol{P}_{n,k+3}$ since $W\in\boldsymbol{P}_{n,k+2}$ and $Q\in\boldsymbol{C}_{1,1}\subset\boldsymbol{P}_{n,1}$. Thus $H_1\in\boldsymbol{C}_{n+1,k+3}$.

The set H_2 can be defined by the equivalence

$$\begin{aligned}
&\langle\varphi,x,\vartheta,\psi\rangle\in H_2\\
&\quad\equiv\{(\psi\notin C_0(U))\vee\bigwedge_{y}[(y\in W^{(\vartheta)(\psi)})\equiv(y\in Z)\}\\
&\quad\equiv\bigwedge_{y}\{(\psi\notin C_0(U))\vee[(\langle\vartheta,\psi,y\rangle\in W)\wedge(y\in Z)]\\
&\qquad\qquad\vee[(\langle\vartheta,\psi,y\rangle\notin W)\wedge(y\notin Z)]\}\\
&\quad\equiv\neg\bigvee_{y}\{[\psi\in C_0(U)]\wedge[(\langle\vartheta,\psi,y\rangle\notin W)\vee(y\notin Z)]\\
&\qquad\qquad\wedge[(\langle\vartheta,\psi,y\rangle\in W)\vee(y\in Z)]\}.
\end{aligned}$$

The propositional function Θ written inside the brackets $\{\,\}$ defines a set which is the intersection of a Borel set (the first component of Θ in square brackets [ ]), a set of class $\boldsymbol{C}_n$ (the second component in [ ]), and a set of class $\boldsymbol{P}_n$ (the third component in [ ]). Thus Θ belongs to class $\boldsymbol{P}_{n+1}$. Prefixing with the existential quantifier $\bigvee_y$ the propositional function Θ we do not change the projective class of the set defined by Θ, since the class $\boldsymbol{P}_{n+1}$ is closed with respect to projections. Thus the propositional function $\neg \bigvee_y \Theta$ determines a set of class $\boldsymbol{C}_{n+1}$.

The argument for the sets H_3 and H_4 is similar. We can define H_3 equivalently by

$$
\begin{aligned}
(12)\qquad & \langle \varphi, x, \vartheta, \psi\rangle \in H_3 \\
& \equiv \bigwedge_{q\neq 0} \{\Theta_q(\varphi,\psi) \vee \bigwedge_y [(y \in W^{(\vartheta)(\psi)}) \equiv (y \in H(W^{(\vartheta)(\varepsilon(\psi,q))})]\} \\
& \equiv \bigwedge_y \bigwedge_{q\neq 0} \{\Theta_q(\varphi,\psi) \vee [(\langle \vartheta,\psi,y\rangle \in W) \wedge (y \in H(W^{(\vartheta)(\varepsilon(\psi,q))}))] \\
& \qquad \vee [(\langle \vartheta,\psi,y\rangle \notin W) \wedge (y \notin H(W^{(\vartheta)(\varepsilon(\psi,q))}))]\},
\end{aligned}
$$

where Θ_q is the propositional function

$$\neg [(\psi \in Q) \wedge (\langle \psi, \varphi\rangle \in T) \wedge (\psi \in K_q)].$$

Clearly Θ_q determines a set of class $\boldsymbol{P}_2$ since Q belongs to $\boldsymbol{C}_1$, T is analytic, and K_q is Borel.

The propositional function $\langle \vartheta, \psi, y\rangle \in W$ defines a set of class $\boldsymbol{P}_n$ since $W \in \boldsymbol{P}_n$. On the other hand, the propositional function $y \in H(W^{(\vartheta)(\varepsilon(\psi,q))})$ also defines a set of class $\boldsymbol{P}_n$ by the assumption that H is a function of class $\boldsymbol{P}_n$. Thus the propositional function

$$(\langle \vartheta, \psi, y\rangle \in W) \wedge (y \in H(W^{((\vartheta)(\varepsilon(\psi,q))}))$$

determines a set of class $\boldsymbol{P}_n$. It can be shown similarly that the propositional function written in the last square brackets on the right-hand side of equivalence (12) determines a set of class $\boldsymbol{C}_n$. It follows, similarly as for the set H_2, that $H_3 \in \boldsymbol{C}_{n+1,k+3}$.

The proof that $H_4 \in \boldsymbol{C}_{k+1,k+3}$ follows in an analogous manner from the equivalence

$$
\begin{aligned}
\langle \varphi, x, \vartheta, \psi\rangle \in H_4 \equiv \bigwedge_y \bigvee_{q\neq 0} \{ & \Theta_q^* \vee [(\langle \vartheta,\psi,y\rangle \in W) \\
& \wedge \bigvee_{q\neq 0} (\langle \vartheta, \varepsilon(\psi,q), y\rangle \in W)] \vee [(\langle \vartheta,\psi,y\rangle \notin W) \\
& \qquad \wedge \bigwedge_{q\neq 0} (\langle \vartheta, \varepsilon(\psi,q), y\rangle \notin W)]\},
\end{aligned}
$$

where Θ^* is the propositional function

$$(\psi \in Q) \wedge (\langle\psi, \varphi\rangle \in T) \wedge (\psi \notin K_q).$$

From formula (11) and Lemma 6 we obtain the desired result:

THEOREM 1: *If* $Z \in \boldsymbol{P}_{n,k}$ *and* H *is a projective function of class* $\boldsymbol{P}_n$ $(n \geqslant 1)$, *then the sets* D' *and* E *are projective of class* $\boldsymbol{P}_{n+2}$.

PROOF. From (11) it follows that

$$\langle\varphi, x\rangle \in D' \equiv \bigvee_{\vartheta} \neg \bigvee_{\psi} (\langle\varphi, x, \vartheta, \psi\rangle \notin H_1 \cap H_2 \cap H_3 \cap H_4).$$

The complement of the set $H_1 \cap H_2 \cap H_3 \cap H_4$ belongs to $\boldsymbol{P}_{n+1}$. Application of the quantifier $\bigvee_{\psi}$ corresponds to the operation of projection and thus yields a set of the same class, $\boldsymbol{P}_{n+1}$; application of negation yields a propositional function which determines a set of class $\boldsymbol{C}_{n+1}$ and the projection corresponding to the application of the quantifier $\bigvee_{\vartheta}$ gives a set of class $\boldsymbol{P}_{n+2}$.

From the above it follows by the equivalence $x \in E \equiv \bigvee_{\varphi} (\langle\varphi, x\rangle \in D')$ that the theorem holds for the set E.

It can be shown by an analogous argument that if $Z \in \boldsymbol{C}_{n,k}$ and if H is a projective function of class $\boldsymbol{C}_n$ $(n \geqslant 1)$, then the sets D' and E both belong to $\boldsymbol{P}_{n+2}$.

In general, deciding whether the function H is projective and evaluating its class presents no difficulty if the formula $x \in H(M)$ is defined by an equivalence of the form

$$x \in H(M) \equiv \Phi(x, M),$$

where Φ is a propositional function whose bound variables range over the sets N and N^N. For example, if all quantifiers occurring in Φ bind only variables which range over the set of natural numbers, then H is a Borel function.

LIST OF IMPORTANT SYMBOLS

$p \wedge q$	conjunction (logical product) of the sentences p and q 1
$p \vee q$	disjunction (logical sum) of p and q 1
$p \rightarrow q$	implication "if p then q" 2
$p \equiv q$	equivalence of p and q 2
$\neg p$	negation of the sentence p 2
$\mathfrak{Z}(x)$	"x is a set" 5
$x \in y$	"x is an element of y" 5
$x \notin y$ or $\neg(x \in y)$	"x is not an element of y" 5
$x \, \mathrm{TR} \, y$	"x is the relational type of y" 5
$A \cup B$	sum of the sets A and B 6
$A - B$	difference of the sets A and B 6
$A \cap B$	intersection of the sets A and B 7
$A \dot{-} B$	symmetric difference of A and B 7, 14
$\subset$	inclusion relation 7
0	empty set 9
$A \doteq B \pmod{I}$	"the sets A and B are congruent modulo the ideal I" 17
1	space (universe) 18
A^c, $-A$	complement of the set A 18
$\bar{A}$, A^-	closure of the set A 26, 28
$\mathrm{Int}(A)$	interior of the set A 28
$\mathrm{Fr}(A)$	boundary of the set A 31
A'	derivative of the set A 32
$a \vee b$	sum of elements of a Boolean algebra 33
$a - b$	difference of elements of a Boolean algebra 33
$a \triangle b$	symmetric difference of elements of a Boolean algebra 33
$a \wedge b$	product of elements of a Boolean algebra 33
o	zero element of a Boolean algebra 33

$f_K(a_1, a_2, \dots)$	value of the Boolean polynomial f 34
$f \sim g$	"Boolean polynomial f is immediately transformable into the polynomial g" 35
$a \leqslant b$	order relation in a Boolean algebra 37
i	unit of a Boolean algebra 37
$a \stackrel{*}{-} b$	pseudo-difference of elements of a Brouwerian lattice 43
$\stackrel{*}{-} b$	pseudo-complement of an element of a Brouwerian lattice 43
$\bigwedge$	universal quantifier 45, 46
$\bigvee$	existential quantifier 45, 46
$\mathfrak{K}$	class of propositional functions of general set theory 50
$\mathfrak{K}[P, Q, \dots]$	class of propositional functions of general set theory extended by the primitive terms P, Q, ... 51
$S(A)$, $\bigcup_{X \in A} X$	union of sets belonging to the family A 52
2^A	power set of the set A 52
$\{x \in A: \Phi(x)\}$	the set of x which belong to A and for which $\Phi(x)$ 54
$\{\Phi\}$"A	image of the set A obtained by the transformation Φ 55
Σ°	infinite system of axioms of set theory 55
Σ	system of axioms which does not contain the axiom of choice 55
$\{a, b\}$	unordered pair of the elements a and b 59
$\langle a, b\rangle$	ordered pair of the elements a and b 59
$P(A)$, $\bigcap_{X \in A} X$	intersection of sets belonging to the family A 61
$X \times Y$	cartesian product of the sets X and Y 63
$\mathcal{E}$	the set of real number 63
$\langle a, b\rangle \in R$, $a R b$	"a is in the relation R to b" or: "the relation R holds between a and b" 64
D_l	left domain of a relation 64
D_r	right domain (range, counter-domain) of a relation 64
$D_l(f)$	domain of the function f 69
$D_r(f)$	range of the function f 69
$F(R)$	field of the relation R 64
R^c	inverse of the relation R 65

$R \circ S$	composition of the relations R and S 65
x/R	equivalence class containing the element x 68
C/R	quotient class of the set C with respect to the relation R 68
Y^X	set of all mappings of X into Y 70
$f: X \to Y$, $X \underset{f}{\to} Y$	"f maps X into Y" 70
$f(x)$	value of the function f at x 70
$g\|A$	restriction f of g for which $D_1(f) = A$ 72
$\underset{x \in A}{\boldsymbol{F}} [\ldots x \ldots]$	function defined by the propositional function ... x ... 73
$R^1(X)$	image of the set X under the relation R 74
$f^1(X)$	set of values of the function f on the set X 74
$R^{-1}(Y)$	inverse image of the set Y under the relation R 75
$f^{-1}(Y)$	inverse image of the set Y under the function f 75
K/I	factor Boolean algebra 79
$\bigvee_{t \in T} f_t$	least upper bound of a set 82
$\bigwedge_{t \in T} f_t$	greatest lower bound of a set 82
0_A, 0	zero element of an ordered set 82
1_A, 1	unit element of an ordered set 83
$\langle A, R_0, R_1, \ldots, R_{k-1} \rangle$	relational system of characteristic $(p_0, p_1, \ldots, p_{k-1})$ 84
$\langle A, R \rangle$	relational system of characteristic (2) 84
$\langle A, R \rangle \approx \langle B, S \rangle$, $R \approx S$	isomorphism of the relational systems $\langle A, R \rangle$ and $\langle B, S \rangle$ 84
X'	successor of the set X 88
$a^{n \rfloor}$	nth iteration of the function a 93
$\|X\| = n$	"the set X has n elements" 100
$[X]_2$	complete graph with the field X 107
$S(W) = \bigcup_t F_t$	union of the sets F_t belonging to the family W being the range of F 111
$P(W) = \bigcap_t F_t$	intersection of the sets belonging to the family W being the range of F 111
$\operatorname{Lim\,sup}_{n=\infty} F_n$	limit superior of the sequence $F_0, F_1, \ldots$ 121

$\underset{n=\infty}{\operatorname{Lim\,inf}} F_n$ limit inferior of the sequence $F_0, F_1, \ldots$ 121

$\underset{n=\infty}{\operatorname{Lim}} F_n$ limit of the sequence $F_0, F_1, \ldots$ 122

R_s least family of sets containing the family R and closed under the union of sets 127

R_d least family containing the family R and closed under the intersection of sets 127

R_σ family of sets of the form $\bigcup_n H_n$, where $H \in R^N$ 129

R_δ family of sets of the form $\bigcap_n H_n$, where $H \in R^N$ 129

$B(R)$ least σ-additive and σ-multiplicative family containing R 129

$\prod_{t \in T} F_t$ cartesian product of sets 131

Y^T cartesian power of the set Y 132

C Cantor set 137

C_T the generalized Cantor set 137

$\sim I$ equivalence relation modulo the ideal I 142

$\left. \begin{array}{c} F_\infty \\ \underleftarrow{\operatorname{Lim}}\, U \\ \underset{t_0 < t_1}{\operatorname{Lim}} (F_t, f_{t_0 t_1}) \end{array} \right\}$ inverse limit of the inverse system $U = (X, T, F, f)$ 147

$\langle X, Y \rangle$ cut in an ordered set 159

$\leqslant$ order relation between cuts 159

$\mathfrak{P}$ family of all cuts of an ordered set 159

$A \sim B$ "the set A is equipollent to the set B" 169

$\bar{\bar{A}}$ cardinal number or power of the set A 174

$\mathfrak{a}$ cardinal number of infinite countable sets 174

$X \sim_{\text{fin}} Y$ "the sets X and Y are equivalent by finite decomposition" 191

$\mathfrak{c}$ power of the continuum 193

$\bar{A}$ order type of the relational system $\langle A, R \rangle$ 206

$\left. \begin{array}{c} x <_R y \\ x \prec y \end{array} \right\}$ the element x precedes y under the relation R 209

$O_R(x)$ initial segment defined by the element x under the ordering relation R 209

ω, η, λ	order types of sets 216, 217, 219
α^*	inverse of the order type α 222
$\lim\limits_{\gamma<\lambda} \varphi(\gamma)$	limit of the λ-sequence $\varphi(\gamma)$ for $\gamma < \lambda$ 235
$\Pi(\Phi)$	"the propositional function Φ defines an operation" 238
$R(\Phi)$	"the operation defined by the propositional function Φ is increasing" 238
$\operatorname{Lim}\limits_{\xi<\lambda} \{\Phi\}$	limit of the operation defined by the propositional function Φ 238
$\operatorname{Cont}\{\Phi\}$	"the operation defined by the propositional function Φ is continuous" 238
$\bigvee\limits_{y}!$	"there exists exactly one y" 238
$\min\limits_{\mu} (\dots \mu \dots)$	"the least ordinal number μ which satisfies the condition ... μ ..." 238
$M(\Phi)$	"φ is the inductive sequence for Φ of type $\alpha+1$" 244
$\operatorname{Ind}\{\Phi\}$	formalization of a definition by means of transfinite induction 244
R_α	family of sets of rank at most α 246
π^α	αth power of the ordinal number π 246
$\alpha(+)\beta$	natural sum of the ordinal numbers α and β 260
$\alpha(\cdot)\beta$	natural product of the ordinal numbers α and β 260
VN ordinal	ordinal number in the sense of von Neumann 269
$\bar{\xi}$	cardinal number of the ordinal ξ 274
Ω	smallest uncountable ordinal number 274
$\aleph_1$	power (cardinal number) of the ordinal number Ω 274
$\aleph(\mathfrak{m})$	Hartog's aleph function 278
ω_0, ω_1	initial ordinals of the powers $\mathfrak{a}$ and $\aleph_1$ 279
$P(\varphi)$	set of all initial ordinals $\psi < \varphi$ 280
$\iota(\varphi)$	index of the initial ordinal φ 280
ω_α	initial ordinal whose index is equal to α 281
$cf(\alpha)$	the least number ξ such that the limit ordinal α is cofinal with ω_ξ 282
$\aleph_\alpha$	power of an initial number whose index is equal to α 282
$\mathfrak{a}_\xi$	ξth term of the exponential hierarchy of cardinals 297

$\mathrm{In}(\alpha)$	$\aleph_\alpha$ is strongly inaccessible 326
$m; e$	sequence whose first term is m and whose following terms are the terms of the sequence e 341
$e; f$	sequence of $(n+m)$ terms whose first n terms coincide with the terms of the sequence e, and whose last m terms coincide with those of f in their original order 342
$\boldsymbol{A}(\boldsymbol{R})$	family of A-sets with respect to the family $\boldsymbol{R}$ 344
$\boldsymbol{A}(\boldsymbol{F})$	family of analytic subsets of a topological space 351
$X \oplus Y$	free union of the sets X and Y 357
$X \odot Y$	free intersection of the sets X and Y 357
X_π	the set which arises from the set X by permutation of coordinates 357
$\mathrm{Id}_{ij}X$	the set which arises from the set X by identification of the ith and jth coordinates 358
$P^q_r(X)$	projection of the set X onto the set S^r 358
$P(\boldsymbol{L})$	family of all projections of sets belonging to the family $\boldsymbol{L}$ 359
$C(\boldsymbol{L})$	family of complements of sets belonging to the family $\boldsymbol{L}$ 359
$\mathcal{S}$	set of all non-empty finite sequences of natural numbers 375
L	sieve 373
$C_\alpha(L)$	αth constituent determined by the sieve L 381

AUTHOR INDEX

SUBJECT INDEX